THE
MACHINIST DICTIONARY

OTHER BOOKS BY FRED H. COLVIN

The Machinist Dictionary

by FRED H. COLVIN

The authoritative handbook of terms,
definitions, and accepted standards
of the machinist craft and industry

SIMMONS-BOARDMAN PUBLISHING CORPORATION

NEW YORK

PREFACE

In a lifetime spent among the various branches of machine manufacturing, I have been impressed again and again with the loss of time and money due to misunderstandings as to the meanings of names and terms used in different plants, and especially in different parts of the country. This confusion includes the designation of materials and processes as well as the machines and tools used.

Lack of understanding of many terms used in machine manufacturing often means costly delays in ordering materials and tools and in directing machine operations. It causes mistakes in giving and in interpreting directions on blue prints or in giving instructions, either oral or printed. Such common terms as "pitch," "quill" and "back-face" can be differently interpreted in plants within the same locality.

Add to these common terms the hundreds of new terms which have come into use during the past twenty years, and the opportunities for honest differences of opinions and costly errors multiply. The use of surface quality measuring methods, for example, has introduced new terms and almost a new language. The same is true of the growing use of optical flats, lightwave bands, cutting-tool angles, sintered metals, sine bars, jig-borers and other machines and methods.

Many tools and elements which are vital to machine manufacturing have been standardized by representatives of the American Society of Mechanical Engineers, the National Machine Tool Builders Association, the Metal Cutting Institute and others. These standards have been adopted by the American Standards Association. A knowledge of these standards is necessary for successful economical production of machine products. It saves time and money to incorporate these standards in new designs and to use them in ordering materials and tools for various machining operations.

A knowledge of the terms used at present and in the past, plus a knowledge of the standards which have been adopted, is necessary for economical design and manufacture. This volume has been prepared to supply this information in convenient form. Cross-references have been included to enable the user to find both the old and new terms for the same thing. In many cases a brief definition has been deemed sufficient, while in others it has seemed more desirable to give detailed data. Some of the new standards are given to save the time necessary to consult other sources.

There are included illustrations in cases where a few sketched lines save

v

many words of explanation. It is sometimes difficult to paint a word picture even of comparatively simple tools or devices that cannot be misunderstood, especially by those not familiar with the subject.

Considering the present confusion in terminology, I believe that practically everyone connected with machine building or repair will find much of value and interest in this volume. Designers, operation planners, purchasing agents and other executives should find this a helpful reference on many subjects. Teachers and their students in apprentice schools and trade schools, and those in shop-training in connection with engineering courses also will be benefited.

Knowing the right name saves time and costly mistakes. It is for this purpose that this volume has been prepared.

FRED H. COLVIN.

December, 1955

THE MACHINIST DICTIONARY

A

ABC SCREW THREADS—Standard screw threads adopted by America, Britain and Canada. See *Screw Threads.*

ABRASIVE—Hard material used in grinding or abrading metal surfaces. There are many kinds and many trade names for similar materials. Artificial abrasives are most widely used. They are graded from "coarse" with 16 to 24 grains per inch to "fine" with from 120 to 600 grains per inch. See *Grinding.*

ABRASIVE(S), ALUMINUM OXIDE—These are not as hard as silicon abrasives but the crystals are tougher, the grains not being as easily broken. They have greater resistance to the impact of striking the work and are suggested for grinding carbon steels, alloy steels, high-speed steel, annealed malleable iron, wrought iron and hard bronze.

ABRASIVE GRAIN SCALE—This is based on the size of the mesh or opening through which the grains will pass. Grains which will pass through a screen having 8 openings per inch are No. 8. The Carborundum Co. gives the following grain sizes from coarse to fine range. Beginning with No. 280 they are usually known as Flour Sizes:

Coarse Range		Medium Range		Fine Range	
6	14	30	60	120	280 or F
8	16	36	70	150	320 or FF
10	20	40	80	180	400
12	24	50	90	220	500 or FFF
			100	240	600

ABRASIVE GRINDING WHEEL—See *Grinding Wheel.*

ABRASIVE POINTS for grinding—These "points" or small grinding wheels are made in a variety of shapes. The amount these points overhang the bearings is important. They should be properly mounted. See *Grinding Points.*

ABRASIVE(S), SILICATE CARBIDE—These are hard abrasives which break readily into particles with sharp corners or edges. They are considered best for hard materials, and for some others, such as gray or chilled iron, sintered carbides, brass and soft bronze, aluminum and copper, marble and other stones, rubber and leather.

ABRASIVE TRADE NAMES—Makers of abrasives and grinding wheels use trade names to distinguish their products; wheels similar in both abrasives and bonds may be sold under different names. Aloxite and Alundum, for example, are both aluminum oxide; Carborundum and Crystolon are both silicon carbide. Bond names are, however, now standardized in six groups. See *Bonds for Abrasive Wheels.* The most prominent trade names for abrasives are:

Aloxite	Aluminum Oxide
Alowalt	Aluminum Oxide
Alumina	Aluminum Oxide
Aluminox	Aluminum Oxide
Alundum	Aluminum Oxide
Borite	Aluminum Oxide
Boro	Aluminum Oxide
Borolon	Aluminum Oxide
Carbolite	Silicate Carbide
Carbolox	Silicate Carbide
Carbonoid	Silicate Carbide
Carbora	Silicate Carbide
Carborite	Silicate Carbide
Carborundum	Silicate Carbide
Carbowalt	Silicate Carbide
Corex	Silicate Carbide
Corundum	Aluminum Oxide
Crystolon	Silicate Carbide
Electrolon	Silicate Carbide
Excelite	Aluminum Oxide
Green Grit	Silicate Carbide
Hy-Tens	Aluminum Oxide
Litan	Special Alum. Oxide
Lo-Tens	Silicate Carbide

(List continued on next page.)

1

ABRASIVE TRADE NAMES (Continued)

Minalox	Aluminum Oxide
Natalite	Aluminum Oxide
Natalon	Silicate Carbide
Onalite	Aluminum Oxide
Onalon	Silicate Carbide
Oxaluma	Aluminum Oxide
Oxylum	Aluminum Oxide
Rex	Aluminum Oxide
Sil-Cut	Silicate Carbide
Silexon	Silicate Carbide
Silox	Silicate Carbide
Staralon	Silicate Carbide
Staralox	Aluminum Oxide
Sterbon	Silicate Carbide
Sterlith	Aluminum Oxide
Westaluma	Aluminum Oxide
Westcarbo	Silicon Carbide

ABRASIVE WHEEL BONDS—See *Bonds for Abrasive Wheels.*

ABSCISSA—In charts made on cross-sectioned paper, the horizontal lines are the abscissa and the vertical lines the ordinates.

ACCELERATED DEPRECIATION—Depreciation of machinery or other equipment at a faster rate than normal because of special conditions. Obsolescence, due to development of more efficient machinery for the same work, may be one of the causes for accelerated depreciation.

ACCELERATION—Increase in velocity in a measured unit of time.

ACCUMULATOR—A reservoir in which air pressure or any fluid is accumulated to be used as needed. This provides for a supply in excess of the normal output of the pump which supplies it. In Great Britain the same term is used for electricity in what we call storage batteries.

ACETYLENE GAS—A gas known as C_2H_2 made from water in contact with calcium carbide. It is largely used in connection with oxygen for cutting and welding metals. It is also used in portable lighting apparatus.

ACID BRITTLENESS—Brittleness in steel due to hydrogen being absorbed in pickling or in electroplating.

ACID STEEL—Steel made in a furnace in which the lining (such as sand or rocks containing silicon) has an acid reaction. This does not mean that the steel is acid.

ACME THREAD—See *Screw Threads Acme.*

ACORN NUT—See *Nut, Acorn* or *Crown.*

ACRE—43,560 square feet. A square of 208.71 feet equals one acre. A square of 147.561 feet equals one-half acre. A square of 104.355 feet equals one-quarter acre. A lot 100 by 435.6 feet equals one acre. A circle 235.5 feet in diameter equals one acre.

ACTION—The parts of any mechanism which produce motion, such as the "bolt action" of some types of rifles. The actuating mechanism of a watch.

ACTIVE SALT BATHS—Baths which impregnate the surface of steel with carbon and nitrogen to increase surface hardness, as with cyanide baths.

ADAPTER—Any device which makes it possible to utilize parts not primarily designed to fit together. A plug fitting the 3.5-inch taper of a modern milling machine spindle and having a tapered hole to receive a smaller tapered arbor, is an adapter. They frequently have both internal and external screw threads.

Adapter to hold chucks from larger spindles.

ADMIRALTY METAL—A mixture of 70 parts copper, 29 parts zinc and 1 part tin.

AERO-THREAD—See *Screw Threads, Aero.*

AERONAUTICAL SCREW THREADS—See *Screw Threads, Aeronautical.*

AGING—Change in structure of metals after they have been cast or forged. Strains due to heating sometimes release themselves by ageing. They are also released by proper heat treatment and by vibration, such as light hammer blows.

AIR-BEND DIES—See *Dies, Air-Bend.*

AIRCRAFT METAL FORMING—See *Metal Forming, Aircraft.*

AIR GAGE—See *Gage, Air.*

AIR GAGING—See *Gaging, Air.*

AIR HAMMER—See *Hammer, Air.*

AIR HARDENING—Hardening by cooling in open air rather than by dipping in water or any cooling solution. An air blast under pressure is generally used to insure rapid cooling.

AIR HOIST—A hoisting device using compressed air in a cylinder, acting against a piston, with suitable outside connections, such as a hook.

AIR POWERED SPRAY GUN — See *Spray Gun, Air Powered.*

AIR TOOLS—This generally refers to portable tools such as air-driven drills, chipping hammers, riveters, sand rammers in foundry work, and small grinding heads.

ALBATA—A name sometimes given to a white alloy used in the making of cutlery.

ALCUMITE—An aluminum bronze alloy with a copper base and some iron, manganese and nickel.

AL-FIN PROCESS—A method of bonding aluminum and steel with a ferric-aluminum bond that is stronger than the aluminum. It was developed by the Fairchild Engine & Airplane Co. for bonding an aluminum muff with cooling fins to a steel cylinder. The bond is about 0.004 inch thick.

ALIGN (ALINE)—To arrange parts of mechanisms in proper alignment (alinement).

ALLOWANCE—The amount "allowed" for clearance between mating parts. Should not be confused with tolerance. See *Tolerance.*

ALLOWANCE, NEGATIVE—The amount by which the two parts of a fit interfere. This is used in shrink, expansion, or press fit.

ALLOYS—Any combination of basic metals. Common brass is an alloy of copper and zinc, in varying proportions, to secure the desired quality in the brass which is produced. Chromium, nickel, manganese, tungsten, and other metals are alloyed with carbon steel to give it desired qualities.

Symbols of Metals Used as Alloys

Aluminum	Al
Barium	Ba
Beryllium	Be
Carbon	C
Cadmium	Cd
Chromium	Cr
Cobalt	Co
Copper	Cu
Iridium	Ir
Iron	Fe

(List continued next column)

Symbols of Metals Used as Alloys
(Continued.)

Lead	Pb
Magnesium	Mg
Manganese	Mn
Molybdenum	Mo
Nickel	Ni
Phosphorus	P
Silicon	Si
Sulphur	S
Titanium	Ti
Tin	Si
Tungsten	W
Vanadium	V
Zinc	Zn

ALLOYS, BRASS, FOR DIFFERENT USES—Brass is an alloy of copper and zinc in varying proportions. More than 75 per cent of all wrought brass contains about 65 per cent copper and 35 per cent zinc. Hardness of sheet brass is obtained by rolling cold after the last annealing and is known as "temper." Hardness is denoted by number. If the thickness is reduced one number, by the B & S gage, as from No. 18 to No. 19, or from 0.040 to 0.036 inch, the sheet is known as one-quarter hard. Reducing the thickness two numbers makes it one-half hard; three numbers makes it three-quarters hard, and four numbers makes it *hard*. Other designations are deep-drawing, drawing and light annealed, and sometimes dead soft, soft and light annealed. Descriptions of various brasses follow:

Cartridge Brass—This alloy is made up of 70 per cent of copper and 30 per cent of zinc, the highest grade of zinc being used, containing practically no lead. Its high quality makes it a good drawing metal, and it derives its name from its use in making deep-drawn cartridge shells.

Clock Brass—This brass contains 62 per cent of copper, 36 per cent of zinc and 2 per cent of lead. It can be cut and blanked with clean sharp edges, and is especially adapted for such parts as clock gears. It will withstand only slight forming and cupping.

Commercial Bronze—This alloy derives its name from its bronze color, but it is a true brass. It contains 90 per cent of copper and 10 per cent of zinc. Sometimes it is made up, however, with 88 per cent of copper, 11½ per cent of zinc and ½ per cent of tin.

Gilding Metal—This alloy contains 95 to 97 per cent of copper and 5 to 3 per cent of zinc. It has a reddish gold color, and is used for the manufacture of jewelry. It is also used in making such articles as bullet jackets and primers.

High Brass—This is the most common commercial sheet brass and contains 65 per cent of copper and 35 per cent of zinc. When annealed it is used for general cupping and forming and in hard tempers it is employed for parts made by blanking, bending and forming. It is also used for spinning.

Leaded High Brass—This alloy contains approximately 65 per cent copper, from ½ to 1½ per cent of lead, and the remainder zinc. It is easier to machine than high brass but is less ductile. It does not foul the threading and cutting tools, and is used especially for cut, drawn and formed parts on which a clean thread must be cut. This property of free cutting is gained at the expense of its drawing capacity.

Low Brass—An alloy containing 80 per cent of copper and 20 per cent of zinc. It has a fine yellow color, and is used for decorative work.

Low Brass, Rich—An alloy containing 85 per cent of copper and 15 per cent of zinc. The color is reddish, and it is generally used for hardware.

Muntz Metal—This is the name applying to the group of brasses containing approximately 60 per cent of copper and 40 per cent of zinc. They can be hot rolled as well as cold rolled. Muntz metal sheet is used for ship sheathing and for very large sheets.

Naval Brass—This brass is sometimes erroneously called Naval Bronze. It contains 60 per cent copper, 39¼ per cent of zinc and ¾ per cent of tin. It is used for articles requiring corrosion resistance properties, and can be worked both hot and cold.

Yellow Brass—A brass made with 60 to 70 parts copper and the rest zinc. It is a very common mixture, but is not good for bearings.

ALLOYS, CERRO—A series of low melting alloys, marketed by the Cerro de Pasco Copper Corp., which are widely used in industry.

There are five of these alloys. See *Cerro Metals*.

Properties of Cerro Alloys

Name	Melting Temp. °F.	Freezing Range, °F.	Wt. per cu. in., lb.	% Elong. in 2 in.	Tensile Strength	Bhn.
Cerrobase	255	255-255	0.371	60-70	6400	10.2
Cerrobend	158	158-158	0.339	200	5990	9.2
Cerrosafe	165	194-158	0.341	220	5400	9.2
Cerromatrix	248	440-218	0.343	1	13,000	19.0
Cerrotru	281	281-290	0.315	—	8000	22.0

Bhn = Brinell hardness number.

ALLOYS, COINAGE—Alloys of gold, silver, copper and other metals which have been used in making coins. Copper is used in both gold and silver coins. The British standard for gold is given as: Gold, 91.66 parts; copper, 8.33 parts. The American and Latin Union standard is: Gold, 90 parts; copper, 10 parts. The British standard for silver coins is given as: Silver, 92.5 parts; copper, 7.5 parts.

ALLOYS, EFFECT OF ON STEEL—Steel is greatly affected by different alloys. The effect of 21 alloys is shown by the following summary.

Properties Given to Steel by Alloying Elements

Application of elements to iron to produce steels of varying qualities strikingly similar to the application of drugs in medicine. Each element has separate and often powerful effects with frequently other effects in combination with additional elements. Like drugs, they may be beneficial in tiny quantities, but ruinous in great quantities unless neutralized or checked by supplemental elements.

An understanding of the chief characteristics given to steel by the elements is an aid to a better selection and use of steels, especially in tool use.

Aluminum — Deoxidizer. Restricts grain growth by forming dispersed nitrides and oxides. Forms hard nitrides when heated in contact with nitrogen, making extremely hard steel. Small amounts increase strength, but large amounts embrittle steel. From 2 to 5 per cent gives heat resistance and oxidation resistance. The term "austinitic" refers to hardness and toughness.

Carbon—Hardener, by forming Fe₃C under

heat-treatment. Increases strength rapidly up to saturation point of 0.85 per cent, above which the steel becomes increasingly brittle unless there are other elements besides iron to take up the carbon. Forms hard carbides with iron, chromium, vanadium, increasing strength and wear resistance. Even slight additions decrease the ductility.

Chromium—Forms hard carbides. Gives very deep hardening and great wear resistance. Small amounts toughen steel, increasing strength and impact resistance. Decreases machinability. Decreases hardening range unless balanced with nickel. Retains hardness at more elevated temperatures than iron carbide. Gives slight red hardness.

Cobalt—Adds red hardness. Retains hard carbides at high temperatures, but tends to decarbonize steel in heat-treatment. Increases hardness and tenacity, but considerable amounts decrease impact resistance. Increases residual magnetism and coercive magnetic force of steels for magnets.

Columbium—Used to minimize intergranular corrosion in stainless steels. Has carbide-forming properties increasing strength and hardness, but not used generally for the purpose. Softening effect shortens time of annealing of high-chromium steels.

Lead—Forms minute strings and finely divided particles. Minute quantites give free machining without imparting the weakening effect of sulphur.

Lithium—Combines easily with oxygen, hydrogen, sulphur, to form low-melting-point compounds which pass off as gases. Powerful deoxidizer and degasifier. Lithium treatment increases elastic limit of carbon steels. Increases fluidity of stainless steel to produce dense casting with high yield point.

Manganese—Deoxidizer and desulphurizer. Even minute amounts increase hardness, wear resistance, and strength. Raises solubility of the carbon. Lowers critical point and widens hardening range, thus permitting a less drastic treatment in oil. Air hardening begins at about 1.5 per cent. Makes steel austenitic at about 12 per cent. High-manganese steel work hardens and is nonmagnetic. Increases coefficient of expansion. Small amounts increase depth of hardening and speed of hardening. Decreases tendency to distort under heat-treatment. Inter-

mediate amounts produce brittleness unless other elements are present.

Molybdenum—Adds red hardness. Increases strength and impact resistance at high temperatures, but hardens and embrittles at low temperatures. Retards grain growth. Gives deep hardening and widens hardening range. Increases creep resistance and resistance to deformation at moderate temperatures. Goes into solid solution, but when other elements are present forms hard carbides. In aluminum steels small amounts reduce temper brittleness. Increases machinability of carbon steels. Increases corrosion resistance of stainless steels at high temperatures.

Nickel—Increases hardness, strength, ductility, and impact resistance. Narrows hardening range, but lowers critical point, reducing danger of warpage and cracking. Refines structure. Retards grain growth. Decreases machinability. Makes chromium steels austenitic. Balances the intensive deep-hardening effect of chromium. Large amounts gives resistance to oxidation at high temperatures.

Nitrogen — Normally undesirable. Hardens slightly and reduces ductility. Small amounts refine grain and increase strength of high-chromium steels. Forms hard nitrides with aluminum and, introduced externally into balanced aluminum-bearing steels, inhibits grain growth at high temperatures.

Phosphorous — Promotes cold-shortness. Small amounts increase strength slightly and increase resistance to corrosion. Slight amounts decrease tendency of steel sheets to stick together.

Silicon — Deoxidizer. Graphitizer. Throws carbon out of solution. Small amounts increase impact resistance, and up to 1.75 per cent increases elastic limit, but needs assistance of other carbide-forming elements. Strengthens low-alloy steels. Medium amounts increase magnetic permeability and decrease hysteresis loss. Forms hard iron silicides, and large amounts give great hardness, wear resistance, and acid resistance, but cause brittleness. Has wide range of utility if used with expert technique, especially in alloy steels.

Sulphur—Forms salt and weak sulphides which weaken the steel and promote hot-shortness. Minute quantities advantageous to aid machinability.

• *Tantalum*—Used in some special steels to give increased resistance to scaling at high temperatures.

Tellurium — Small amounts form sulphide which aids machining without making the steel hot short.

Titanium — Deoxidizes and denitrogenizes. Increases strength and hardness. Fixes carbon inert particles. Minimizes intergranular corrosion in high-chromium steels.

Tungsten—Adds red hardness and stability of the hard carbides at high heats. Widens hardening range, and gives deep hardening. Increases strength and wear resistance. Small quantities produce fine grain structure, but large quantities embrittle the steel. Produces both a hard carbide and an iron tungstide. Large quantities to produce full red hardness, must be supplemented by other carbide-forming elements. Forms hard abrasive-resistant particles in high-carbon steels. Adds acid resistance and corrosion resistance. Gives increased residual magnetism and greater coercive force in steel for magnets.

Uranium — Increases elastic limit and strength of steels. Is power deoxidizer and denitrogenizer. Has carbide-forming qualities. Because of expense used only in some tool steels.

Vanadium—Powerful deoxidizer. Toughens and strengthens steels. Forms hard carbides. Refines the grain. Widens hardening range. Retains hardness at higher temperatures than carbon steel. Reduces grain growth. Increases fatigue resistance and shock resistance. Forms double carbide with chromium, giving hard "keen-edge" quality to steel.

Zirconium—Powerful deoxidizer and desulphurizer. Steels can be made without manganese by use of zirconium. Carries off nitrogen. Makes uniformity of grain and produces ductility and shock resistance. Small amount of residual zirconium form zirconium sulphide which aids machinability and rolling. Reduces aging fatigue in steel.

ALLOYS FOR NON-FERROUS FORGINGS
—See *Forgings, Alloys, Non-Ferrous.*

ALLOYS IN STEEL—Some of the various alloys used in making steel for special purposes,

and the way in which they affect the steel, are as follows:

Ingredient	Its Effect
Aluminum	Kills or deoxidizes steel.
Carbon	The determinative.
Chromium	For resisting shocks.
Iron	The basis of all steel.
Manganese	Adds strength.
Molybdenum	Hardener and heat resister.
Nickel	Adds strength and toughness.
Oxygen	A strength destroyer.
Phosphorus	The weak link.
Silicon	Impurity and hardener.
Sulphur	The strength sapper.
Titanium	Removes nitrogen and oxygen.
Tungsten	Hardener and heat resister.
Vanadium	Purifier and fatigue resister.

ALLOYS, R. W. M. A.—A group of copper-base alloys recommended by the Resistance Welding Manufacturers Association for use in resistance welding. Group A is a copper base alloy, while Group B includes copper-tungsten alloys.

ALL-THREAD BOLT—See *Bolt, All-Thread.*

ALODINE—A chemical process for protecting aluminum against salt spray or salt water.

ALPACA—A white tableware alloy used by the British, consisting of 65 parts copper, 20 parts zinc, 13 parts nickel and 2 parts silver.

ALUMINUM—A basic metal obtained from some kinds of clay, such as bauxite. It is about one-third the weight of steel and about one-third as strong. It weighs 168.5 pounds per cubic foot, and melts at about 1,200 deg. F. Alloyed with copper and manganese it becomes duralumin. In England it is called "aluminium." It is nonmagnetic. Its specific gravity is 2.70.

ALUMINUM ALLOYS—Aluminum is alloyed with brass, bronze, chromium, magnesium, managanese and nickel to secure different qualities.

ALUMINUM BRASS—Brass with a small amount of aluminum which changes its characteristics. One per cent added to brass of 60-40 mixture increases its strength 30 per cent and its hardness 25 per cent. See *Revalon.*

ALUMINUM BRONZE—A copper aluminum alloy, with about 10 per cent of aluminum, which has excellent qualities.

ALUMINUM OXIDE—An artificial corundum which is sold under a variety of trade names such as Alozite and Alundum.

ALUMINUM OXIDE ABRASIVES — See *Abrasives, Aluminum Oxide.*

ALUMINUM STEEL—Steel alloyed with aluminum.

ALUNDUM—An artificial abrasive of aluminum oxide. See *Abrasive Trade Names.*

ALUNDUM, NO. 32.—A type of abrasive invented by R. R. Ridgeway of the Norton Co. The process gives crystals of the desired size which do not have to be crushed to size.

AMALGAM—A combination of mercury with another metal. Used by dentists, and for filling holes in castings.

AMOLA STEEL—A steel alloy developed by the late C. Harold Wills to approximate or duplicate the properties of chrome-vanadium steel at a lower cost. It contains molybdenum, manganese and silicon.

AMMETER, or AMPERE METER—A device for measuring the number of amperes being delivered to any device using electrical current.

AMMONIUM CHLORIDE—Also known as sal ammoniac. Used as a flux in soldering and as an electrolyte primary in wet batteries.

AMORPHOUS—As applied to metals, this means that they are not made up of crystals.

AMPERE — The unit of electric current strength. It is the amount of current that will pass through a wire having a resistance of one ohm with a pressure of one volt.

AMPCO METAL—A bronze alloy with hard particles held in a softer matrix to give long wear resistance. It is centrifugally cast, and used for bearing and wearing surfaces.

ANCHOR BOLTS—See *Bolt, Anchor.*

ANDEROMETER—An instrument for determining the quality of ball bearings by checking irregularities in the movement between the inner and outer races caused by waviness in the bearing surfaces. It is calibrated in terms of micro-inches so that permissible tolerances

can be given by purchasers and tested by the makers.

ANGLE—The difference between the axes of two parts which do not lie in the same plane. An acute angle is less than 90 degrees. A right angle is just 90 degrees. An obtuse angle is more than 90 degrees. See also *Clearance Angle, Cutting Angle, Angle of Approach,* and *Pressure Angle* under *Gearing Nomenclature.*

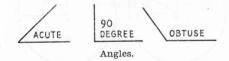

Angles.

ANGLE, ACUTE—Any angle of less than 90 degrees. See *Angle, Obtuse.*

ANGLE OF APPROACH—The angle at which one part, such as a cutting tool point, approaches the work.

ANGLE BLOCKS—Blocks for holding work at an angle to a cutting tool. They are made both with a fixed angle and so they can be adjusted for a variety of work.

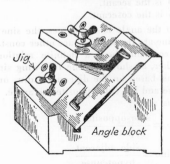

Angle block.

ANGLE, CLEARANCE—See *Cutting Tools, such as Milling Cutters.*

ANGLE, COMPOUND—An angle made by cutting a rectangular solid at an angle to two of its surfaces.

ANGLE CONSTANTS—The term angle constants refers to the fixed relations between the radius of a circle and the various angles formed by lines which contact it. Each constant has a name which always refers to the angle on one side of the center line and not to the included angle. Referring to the figure, lines AE and AH are called radii of the circle, which is always considered as *one unit* of

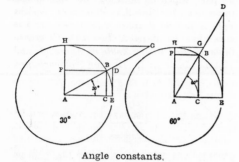

Angle constants.

measurement, usually one inch. The other lines are:

AC is the cosine of the angle.
FB is always the same as the consine.
CE is the versed sine.
FH is the conversed sine.
CB is the sine.
ED is the tangent.
HG is the cotangent.
AD is the secant.
AG is the cosecant.

When the angle is 45 degrees, the sine and the cosine are the same, as are other constants. These constants bear a definite relation to each other, as shown by the following simple formulas, based on the diagonal radius or hypotenuse and the side opposite the angle. The formulas are:

1. $\text{Sine} = \dfrac{\text{side opposite}}{\text{hypotenuse}}$

2. $\text{Cosine} = \dfrac{\text{side adjacent}}{\text{hypotenuse}}$

3. $\text{Tangent} = \dfrac{\text{side opposite}}{\text{side adjacent}}$

4. $\text{Cotangent} = \dfrac{\text{side adjacent}}{\text{side opposite}}$

5. $\text{Hypotenuse} = \dfrac{\text{side opposite}}{\text{sine}}$

6. Side opposite = hypotenuse $\times$ sine

7. Side adjacent = hypotenuse $\times$ cosine

8. Side opposite = side adjacent $\times$ tangent

9. Side adjacent = cotangent $\times$ side opposite.

10. $\text{Hypotenuse} = \dfrac{\text{side adjacent}}{\text{cosine}}$

The side adjacent is opposite the hypotenuse. The hypotenuse is the line making the angle with the base, which is considered as horizontal.

ANGLE GEAR—See *Gear, Bevel.*

ANGLE IRONS or PLATES—Rolled steel strips with the sides forming angles with each other, usually a 90-degree angle. They are also rolled in U shape and with Z sections. Angle irons are also made of cast iron or steel for holding work at desired angles to cutting tools. They may be used on the face plates of a lathe or on the bed of any machine such as drill press, a planer or a boring mill.

ANGLE MILLING CUTTERS—See *Milling Cutters, Single and Double Angle,* page 272.

ANGLE, OBLIQUE—Any angle that is not a right angle. It may be either acute or obtuse.

ANGLE, OBTUSE—Any angle of more than 90 degrees but not exceeding 180 degrees. See *Angle, Acute.*

ANGLE OF REPOSE, or FRICTION ANGLE —See *Friction, Angle of.*

ANGLE PLATE, COMPOUND—A surface plate which can be adjusted to angles in two or more directions.

ANGLE PLATE, LATHE—An angle plate used on the face plate of a lathe to hold work that cannot be held conveniently in a chuck.

Lathe angle plate.

ANGLE PLATE, SINE—An angle plate having surfaces from which the sines of angles can be accurately measured. Illus. page 9.

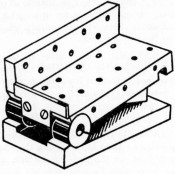

Sine angle plate.

ANGLE-PLATE WORK—The use of angle plates in addition to face plates. See *Angle Plate, Lathe.*

ANGULAR DEPTH—The length of the angular side of a screw thread or similar piece. In a sharp V-thread this equals the pitch of the thread, while the depth of the thread is only 0.866 of the pitch.

ANGULAR GEARS—Name sometimes applied to bevel gears. See *Gear, Bevel.*

ANGULAR MEASUREMENT—Measuring the angle included between two lines which meet at a point. Usually expressed in degrees. Each degree is 1/360th part of a complete circle drawn from the point where the lines forming the sides of the angle meet.

ANGULAR VELOCITY—The number of degrees through which a given point passes in a unit of time, usually one minute. The angular velocity of a pulley will be no greater at the rim than at the hub, as both move through 360 degrees in the same time.

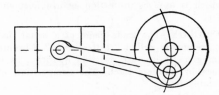

Angularity of connecting rods.

ANGULARITY OF CONNECTING RODS— The angle assumed when one end revolves and the other has a reciprocating motion. During the outer half-stroke the crank pin travels more than half a revolution, as shown in the illustration.

ANNEALING—Heating slightly above the critical range and holding this temperature for a definite period, followed by cooling. This leaves the metal in a relatively soft condition for machining. Different metals require different special treatment.

ANNEALING, BRIGHT—Annealing steel in a closed container with a reducing atmosphere to prevent oxidization.

ANNEALING, FULL CYCLE—When metal is heated above its critical point and definite cooling rates are used for the various critical ranges, it is known as full cycle annealing. It is used to obtain specific types of annealed structures and requires good equipment and careful handling.

ANNEALING, FULL GENERAL — Heating iron base alloys above the critical range and holding them above that range for a proper period, followed by a slow cooling.

ANNEALING, WATER—A makeshift method of softening some grades of steel by heating and quenching when it has cooled to a certain temperature. Sometimes resorted to when the time of regular annealing would be too great. Not always dependable.

ANTHRACITE — Commonly called "hard coal."

ANTI-FRICTION BEARINGS—An erroneous designation of bearings in which balls or rollers are interposed between the moving parts and its stationary support, as in shafting of various kinds. Friction-reducing bearings would be a more correct term. See *Bearing.*

ANTIOCH CASTING PROCESS—A method of producing intricate aluminum castings in plaster molds developed by the Allison-Bedford Foundry at Bedford, Ind. The molds are a mixture of gypsum and sand in proper proportions to give enough porosity for the escape of gases and yet maintain a surface which gives the smoothness necessary in the castings. The aluminum alloy must also be of just the right consistency to secure the desired results. The molds and cores require special treatment. While an expensive process, it permits the making of intricate shapes at much less cost than any other known method. It should not be confused with the lost wax process.

ANTIMONY—A hard, bluish white metal used almost entirely as an alloy in copper and lead mixtures. Specific gravity is 6.62; melting point 824 deg. F.

ANVIL—Block of cast iron or steel on which metals are hammered or forged. If of cast iron they usually have a steel face. A small square hole is usually provided at the back end for holding hardies, fuller block or chisels. In shop terms, any part which receives a pressure or blow may be called an anvil. The fixed point in a micrometer is known as the anvil.

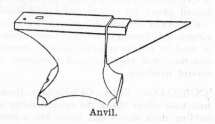

Anvil.

APPROACH OF MILLING CUTTERS—The distance the machine table must move from the end of its stroke before it begins to cut. It also includes the distance from the point where the cutter teeth leave the work until it clears so as to permit removal from the machine. This is time lost in cutting, but must be calculated in estimating the time necessary to mill a piece of work.

APRON—Any protecting or covering plate that encloses any mechanism, such as the apron of a lathe carriage.

AQUA FORTIS—See *Nitric Acid.*

ARBOR—A shaft or bar for holding and driving cutting tools. It often has a tapered shank fitting the spindle of a machine. The term was formerly used interchangeably with "mandrel," on which work is held. See *Mandrels.*

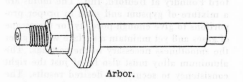

Arbor.

ARC—Part of a circle, usually less than 90 degrees. Refers to the curved surface or outside, not to area between the surface and center.

ARC OF CONTACT—The length of contact between curved surfaces, as with gear teeth. The distance between the points where the contact begins and ends.

ARC, ELECTRIC— The flame produced between two points, or electrodes, one from the positive and the other from the negative pole of a generator. Originally produced between carbon rods for street lighting, its use is now largely confined to electric welding.

ARC, LENGTH OF CIRCULAR—The length of a portion of a circle. Knowing the chord, or distance between the ends of the arc, and the height from this line to the arc itself, the formula is:

$$L = \frac{4 \sqrt{C^2 + 4H^2} - C}{3}$$

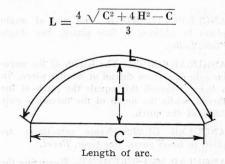

Length of arc.

ARC MACHINING—Cutting or disintegrating metal by an arc formed between an electrode and the metal to be cut. Holes can be cut and threaded in hard materials such as carbide by using a threaded brass tube, rotating it and also advancing it at the proper rate to match the pitch of the thread to be cut. For bottomed holes the core is broken off at the bottom.

ARC WELDING—See *Welding, Arc.*

ASBESTOS—A variety of fibrous mineral which is used as protection against heat and fire.

ASCOLOY—The trade name of a metal that is frequently called "rustless iron." Chromium gives it its rust resisting qualities, as it does in stainless steel. The composition of ascoloy is:

Carbon,	under 0.12 per cent
Manganese,	” 0.5 ” ”
Sulphur	” 0.025 ” ”
Phosphorus,	” 0.025 ” ”
Chromium,	” 12 to 16 per cent
Silicon,	” 0.5 per cent
Nickel	” 0.5 ” ”

Its elastic limit is from 40,000 to 50,000 pounds, and it elongates considerably before breaking at 72,000 to 85,000 pounds. Its Brinell hardness runs from 140 to 170.

ASSEMBLY DRAWING—Shows a combination of the parts necessary to make a complete mechanism from which the machine or unit can be constructed.

ASSOCIATION THREAD—See *Screw Thread, British Association.*

ATOM—Formerly thought to be the smallest particle of which all matter was formed. Now still smaller particles are known and are utilized in producing heat and explosive bombs.

ATOMIC HEAT—See *Heat, Atomic.*

ATOMIC NUMBER—This represents the net, positive charge on the nucleus of an atom of the element in question.

ATOMIC VOLUME—Atomic weight divided by specific gravity.

ATOMIC WEIGHT—The weight of a substance based on 16 as the weight for oxygen.

AUSTEMPERING — A heat-treating process (patented) in which iron based alloys are quenched from a temperature above the transformation range in a bath which extracts the heat rapidly. It sustains a uniform temperature in the metal until the transformation is completed, at a lower heat than formation of pearlite and above that of martensite.

AUSTENSIC S T E E L S — Steels containing enough alloying elements, such as nickel and chromium, to lower the transformation temperatures below that of ordinary steel.

AUTOGENOUS JOINING or WELDING—The fusing of two metals by use of a hydrogen flame.

AUTOMATIC CYCLE MACHINES — Machines which perform a series or cycle of operations on work placed in or fastened to the machine by hand. They include many types of machines such as those used in drilling, turning, milling, boring, and grinding. They are semi-automatic machines.

AUTOMATIC MACHINES — Machines in which all the operations of feeding the stock, machining the work, and discharging it, are done automatically. They only require putting new bar or other stock into the machine by hand. Many so-called automatic machines are only semi-automatic, as the work is put in the machine by hand.

AUTOMATION—A term coined by the automotive industry to describe any automatic handling of work.

AXIAL ADVANCE—The amount of advance of a screw, bolt, etc., along its axis in one turn. With a 10-pitch thread, the axial advance is 1/10 inch for each revolution of the screw.

AXIAL LEAD—The distance a nut moves on a screw in one turn. In a single-start screw both pitch and lead are the same, but with multiple threads the lead is as many times the pitch as there are "starts" or threads.

AXIAL PITCH—In a screw thread the distance, in inches, between the threads of a screw. See *Screw Threads.*

AXIAL PLANE—In screw threads and helical gearing axial plane refers to the axis of the helix, or the center line around which the helix is wrapped. Helical angles of threads are calculated at 90 degrees from the axis.

AXIAL RAKE—The rake of the cutting tooth with reference to the axis. See *Milling Cutters.*

B

BABBITT— One of the original bearing metals. The original formula is said to have been 4 parts copper, 12 parts tin, 8 parts antimony and an additional 12 parts of tin added after melting. It melts at 462 deg. F. A general name for white bearing metals.

BABBITTING BEARINGS—The surfacing of the bearing that will contact the shaft with babbitt or other bearing mixture by practically soldering it to the bearing shell. The inner surface of the shell is coated with tin or solder and the bearing heated before the babbitt is poured into place, around a dummy shaft. Most modern plain bearings have a bearing shell which is placed in the retaining bearing without heat.

BACK FACE—Facing or finishing a surface around a hole on the *inside* of a casting or forging. A bar is put through the hole and the facing cutter put on the bar (or through it where a flat cutter is used), and the surface faced by pulling *back* on the cutter as it revolves. This gives it the name of back facing.

BACK PLATE—The back of a lathe chuck containing the screw thread by which it is fastened to the lathe spindle. Also called a face plate.

BACK REST— A rest for supporting work against the pressure of a tool or grinding wheel, or for other similar uses. When the rest follows the cutting tool it is called a follower rest, or follow rest. These differ from a steady rest, which surrounds the work near the tool.

BACKING-OFF—Removing metal behind the cutting edge of a tool to lessen the friction in cutting, as in drills, taps, reamers or milling cutters. This may also be called "relief." It should not be confused with "clearance."

BACKING-OFF ATTACHMENT or LATHE —A device or machine for removing the metal back of the cutting edge of such tools as milling cutters. See *Backing-Off*.

BACKLASH—Lost motion in moving parts, such as the end movement between a bolt and its nut, or between the mating teeth of gears.

BAFFLE—A plate or shield which diverts or deflects heat, flame or air for any purpose. See *Muffle*.

BALANCE, DYNAMIC or RUNNING—The distribution of weight so that shafts or pulleys will run without vibration.

BALANCE, STATIC or STANDING — Distributing the weight of pulleys, shafts or other revolving bodies so that, when placed on knife-edge ways, they will stand in any position. If unbalanced, the heavy side rolls to the bottom. Parts which are perfectly symmetrical and of uniform density throughout which are in static balance should also be in dynamic balance.

BALANCE WHEEL—A wheel which balances or compensates for irregular forces in any driving mechanism. In steam or gas engines it stores up energy so that irregular impulses at different points of the piston stroke are transformed into a steady rotation of the main shaft. They are usually called "flywheels" and are used on many machine tools, such as milling machines, to maintain a uniform speed of the cutting spindle when the resistance to the cutter may vary. This adds to the life of the cutter and also produces better work.

Olsen static-dynamic balancing machine.

BALANCING MACHINE—A machine for determining whether rotating bodies, such as motor armatures or engine crankshafts will run with a minimum of vibration. The machine

12

illustrated shows both the static, or standing, balance, and the dynamic, or running, balance. Balancing is especially important at high speeds as any unbalance at 1000 r p m is multiplied *four* times at 2000 r p m. The machine shows the amount of metal necessary to be removed to secure balance, and its location on the revolving part. Unbalance is considered in "ounce-inches" and refers to the weight in ounces and the distance, in inches, from the center of rotation. See *Ounce-Inches.*

BALANCING WAYS—Level strips or sharp-edged disks for testing shafts or pulleys for static or standing balance. The disks are usually mounted on ball bearings.

Balancing ways.

BALATA—A non-elastic rubber.

BALING PRESS—See *Press, Cabbaging.*

BALL AND ROLLER BEARINGS—Devices for reducing friction in bearings by the use of balls or rollers. The figure shows single ball, plain and taper rollers, small diameter or "needle" bearings, and a ball end or thrust bearing. The balls or rollers revolve between inner and outer "races," one being stationary and the other revolving with the shaft. They vary widely in design and application. They are frequently called "anti-friction" bearings, which is incorrect, as all bearings have some friction. See page 15.

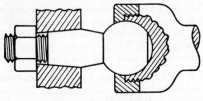

Ball and socket joint.

BALL AND SOCKET JOINT—A joint in which a rod with a ball shaped end fits into a similarly shaped part to permit free movement between the parts while they are still so united as to be one unit.

BALL BEARING LATHE CENTER—A center having a ball bearing head which rotates with the work. See *Center, Ball Bearing.*

BALL BURNISHING—The use of steel balls in wood lined tumbling barrels for producing a burnished surface on the work. The surface is not abraded but is rubbed down, or burnished, by the combined rolling and rubbing action. About twice the volume of balls as of work, and a soapy water lubricant, is recommended by the Abbot Ball Co.

BALL MILL—A mechanism for grinding material by a crushing action from balls which roll over the material as the outer casing revolves.

BALSA WOOD—A very light wood found in Mexico and Ecuador. It weighs only 10 to 12 pounds per cubic foot, as compared with 52 pounds for oak and 76 for ebony.

BAND SAW—An endless or continuous saw blade running on and driven by pulleys. Originally used only on wood, it is now a regular machine shop tool for metal. For inside work the saw is broken, the ends put through a drilled hole and the ends welded in a special welder on the machine. In some cases band saws are used in cutting by friction rather than by the teeth in the saw.

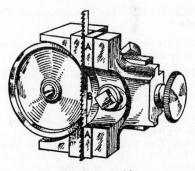

Band saw guide.

BAND SAW GUIDE—A device for supporting a band saw against the pressure of the work, and also guiding it as to alignment. Jaws AA keep the saw aligned and the wheel rim B supports it against the pressure.

BAR—The third stage in making ingots into shapes and sizes for commercial use. See *Ingot.* Also used interchangeably with rod.

BARIUM—A metallic alkaline element used as a bath in heat treating. Sp. gr. 3.78. Melts at 1,562 deg. F.

BARK—The decarbonized surface below the scale of a piece of metal that has been heated.

BARREL CAM—See *Cam, Barrel.*

BARREL NUT—See *Nut, Barrel.*

BARTH KEY—See *Key, Barth.*

BASIC HOLE SYSTEM OF FITS—A system in which the hole is kept as near basic as possible and fit variations are made in the shaft. See *Fits.*

BASIC RACK—See *Gearing.*

BASIC SHAFT SYSTEM—A system in which the shaft is kept as near basic as possible and fit variations made in the hole. See *Fits.*

BASIC SIZE—See *Size, Basic.*

BASIC STEEL—Steel melted in a furnace in which the bottom and lining have a basic reaction. Basic materials are burnt dolomite, magnesite or basic slag. Nearly all American steel is basic.

BASTARD—Not regular. The term is used in referring to odd sizes or shapes. Its most general shop use is in connection with the teeth of files, or the shape or pitch of threads.

BASTARD SIZE—Any size not considered as standard.

BASTARD THREAD—Any thread which does not have a standard form or pitch.

BATH METAL—A little known mixture said to contain between 4 and 5 ounces of zinc to one pound of copper.

BATHS, QUENCHING—Baths prepared for rapid cooling or quenching of steels in heat treating. They may be either water or oil and may be kept at given temperatures by rapid circulation so as to cool the heated work rapidly and evenly. There are many variations in the compositions used.

BATWING CHUCK—See *Chuck, Batwing or Box.*

BAUXITE—An aluminum hydroxide, either white or red, from which aluminum metal is made. It is also used to line furnaces and places where there is intense heat.

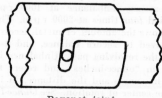
Bayonet joint.

BAYONET JOINT—A method of holding two parts together, in which one part has a projecting pin which slides into a slot in the other part and is held by turning it slightly into a small notch at right angles to the first. Originated with the bayonet on military rifles and is widely used in many other lines.

BEAM CALIPER—See *Caliper, Slide.*

BEAM DIVIDERS—See *Trammels.*

BEAM STRENGTH OF GEAR TOOTH—The strength of a gear tooth considered as a beam supported at one end.

BEARING—The support for a revolving or sliding part. It may be a plain surface or have balls or rollers between the moving parts. See *Ball and Roller Bearings* and *Anti-Friction Bearings.*

BEARING METALS — Includes babbitt or white metals, bronzes and cast iron. Many of the steels do not make good bearings.

BEARING, STEP—The bearing at the bottom of a vertical shaft. There are numerous types of step bearings—plain, ball, roller and "wedge," by which a "wedge" of lubricant is forced under the bearing plates. See *Ball and Roller Bearings.*

BELL CENTER PUNCH—See *Center Punch, Bell.*

BELL METAL—An alloy of copper and tin which is varied to some extent. It approximates 75 per cent copper and 25 per cent tin. The bells on Big Ben in London are said to be 76.5 per cent copper and 23.5 per cent tin.

BELT CLAMP—Clamps for holding the ends of belting while it is being laced. They are also used for drawing the ends of the belt together. Other belt clamps hold the beveled ends while they are being cemented and press the lap together. Lacing is almost obsolete.

BELT, COG—A type of V-belt with projections on the inner surface. These enable the belt to bend easily around pulleys of smaller diameter than belts made without these cogs, or projections. They are only used where the power is greater than could be transmitted with a regular belt of small cross-section generally used on small pulleys.

BELT DRESSING—Mixtures of materials which make a belt more pliable and improve its driving capacity. Sometimes somewhat sticky substances are used to secure adhesion to pulleys, but they are of doubtful value except in emergencies.

BELT, ENDLESS—A continuous belt made either by weaving without a joint, or a leather belt with the ends cemented together to avoid the joint of a laced belt. They are particularly desirable at high speeds. On some work the action of a joint on the pulley affects the quality of the operation being done.

BELT LACE—Strips of rawhide or partly tanned leather for fastening the ends of flat belts. See *Lacing Belts.*

BELT, LINK—Really a chain made of flat links fastened together in groups, with rivets

which act as bearings on which the links can turn to conform to the pulley or gear on which it runs. Construction varies from having a series of solid blocks fastened by side links that go outside the gear or sprocket teeth, to having all thin links with projections on one

Link belt.

side which fit between specially shaped gear teeth. Some of these are called "silent" chains.

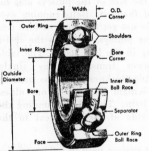

In ball bearings, weight of load is transmitted through tough steel balls

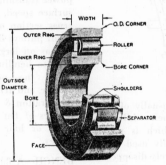

Steel rollers carry the weight from inner to outer ring of roller bearing

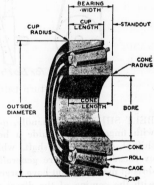

Rolls with different end diameters are used in tapered roller bearings

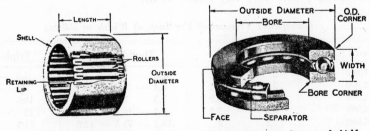

Needle bearings are roller bearings with high ratio of roller length to diameter

Sealed ball bearings have metal shield between inner and outer rings of assembly

Ball bearing and roller bearing assemblies. Lower right is a step bearing.

BELT, QUARTER-TURN — An arrangement of pulleys and belting for driving shafts at 90 degrees from each other. This can be with shafts at right angles in the same plane or with one shaft horizontal and the other vertical. It requires guide pulleys properly located to guide the belt from one plane to the other. Reversing the direction of the driving shaft will throw the belt off the pulleys.

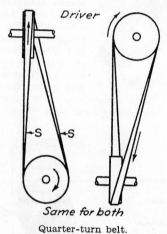

Quarter-turn belt.

BELT SHIFTER — A handle, usually of wood with fingers which guide a belt while it is shifted on a countershaft, which is usually overhead. These were generally used on all sorts of machines, but have largely disappeared with the coming of the direct motor drive.

BELT, V — A belt of triangular shape which runs on pulleys having a groove of similar shape and which has a wedging action that gives great pulling power. They vary some-

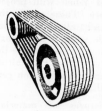

Multiple-V-belt.

what in cross section, according to the ideas of the makers. They are usually endless to avoid the use of fastenings of any kind. They have almost completely replaced the old round belt.

BELT WEB — A belt made of fabric woven to the proper width, used to replace leather or rubber. The term is usually applied to flat belts only, although many V-belts and some round belts are made in this way. Many web belts are woven in one piece, or endless, so as to avoid joints. These were devised for grinding machines where belts with a joint are apt to affect the quality of the work. V-belts are now often used in grinding, as elsewhere.

BELTING, POWER TRANSMITTED — The power transmitted by any belt depends on the surface speed, the size of the pulleys and the cross section of the belt. Belts running over small pulleys do not get the same surface contact as on larger pulleys, owing to the resistance to bending in the belt itself. The table shows the power transmitted by single, double and triple thickness belts, as used by the Gratton & Knight Co., one of our oldest makers of flat belts. The advise running the *grain* or hair side of the belt next to the pulley.

BENCH — A flat surface used to hold work for inspection, laying-out or while being worked on in various ways. Designated as inspection, lay-out and work benches. Some are made with casters or wheels and can be moved easily.

Horsepower Transmited Per Inch of Width of Belting

Speed f.p.m.	Single belt		Double belt			Triple belt	
1,000	2	2.2	2.8 —	3.2 —	4.3	7.5 —	4.4
2,000	3.8	4.2	5.4 —	6 —	6.7	7.5 —	8.4
3,000	5.3	5.9	7.5 —	8.5 —	9.4	10.6 —	11.8
4,000	6.5	7.2	9.2 —	10.4 —	11.5	13 —	14.4
5,000	7.2	8	10.2 —	11.5 —	12.8	14.4 —	16
6,000	7.3	8.1	10.4 —	11.6 —	13	14.6 —	16.2
Pulley size	3-in. —	5-in.	7-in. —	10-in. —	13-in.	22-in. —	30-in.

BENCH PLATE—Another name for a surface plate, especially when used for laying out or inspecting work, rather than for accuracy of a flat surface.

BENCH, WORK—Any bench on which work is done. Benches for machinists, and for many other kinds of work, have a vise and usually one or more drawers. Most modern

Work bench.

benches have steel legs and wooden tops. Some bench tops are of hard wood laid on edge. Others use planking for the top. For small work the bench top is often covered with heavy linoleum to present a smooth surface. While most benches are stationary, some have wheels or casters to permit moving from place to place.

BENDING DIES, COMPOUND—Dies that bend material in two or more directions.

BENDING DIES, PLAIN—Any dies that simply bend material in one direction.

BENDING ROLLS—Machines having three rollers on shafts with adjustable centers so that rings or curves of varying radii can be rolled between them. The rolls shown are for use on angle iron, one roll being grooved to receive one leg of the angle, as well as to help guide the work.

BENT SHANK TAPS—Taps used for continuous threading of nuts in nut tapping machines.

BERYLLIUM—A light weight, hard metallic element sometimes called glucinum. Alloyed with copper and used in springs. Will cut glass. Sp. Gr. 1.84. Melts at 2,345 deg. F.

BERYLLIUM BRONZE—An alloy of 3 per cent or less of beryllium with copper Sometimes called beryllium copper.

BESSEMER STEEL—Steel made by blowing air through molten metal. Developed by Sir Henry Bessemer about 1860.

BESSEMER STEEL CONVERTER—A device for making steel by forcing air through melted pig iron, steel scrap and limestone, through the trunnions of the converter. The air oxidizes the impurities. A "blow" takes about 18 minutes. Some converters hold 30 tons. Steel is poured out by tilting converter on its trunnions. (See illus., p. 18.)

Bending rolls.

BEST WIRE SIZES—See *Screw Thread Measurement.*

BETA-RAY THICKNESS GAGE—A device developed by the General Electric Co. to measure the thickness of thin metallic foils while they are being rolled at high speed. See *Betatron.*

BETATRON—An electron accelerator for testing materials in much the same way as the radiograph, or X-ray photograph. One has been built up to 100,000,000 volts capacity. This permits examination of thicker sections of steel, bronze and other metals.

BEVEL—Any surface not at right angles to the rest of the piece. When at 45 degrees it is often called a Miter. Sometimes called a chamfer. When it is simply to remove the sharp corner it is called "breaking the edge."

It is also the name of a tool to measure or lay out angles. When combined with a scale of degrees it is a bevel protractor.

BEVEL GEAR PLANER OR SHAPER—A machine especially for planing the teeth of bevel gears. See *Gear Cutting Machines.*

BEVEL GEARS—See *Gears, Bevel.*

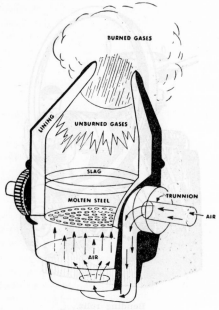

Bessemer furnace.
(See definition, p. 17.)

BICKERN—The point or horn of an anvil.

BILLET—The second stage in forming ingots into shape for further processing. See *Ingot.*

BINDING HEAD SCREWS—See *Screws, Binding Head.*

BIRMINGHAM WIRE GAGE—See *Gages, Wire or Sheet.*

BISMUTH—A soft white metal generally used as an alloy. Sp. Gr. 8.75. Melts at 518 deg. F.

BITUMINOUS COAL—Commonly called soft coal, to distinguish it from anthracite, or "hard" coal

BLACK ANNEALING—A process used in making tin plate, which gives steel sheets a black oxide color before they are coated with tin.

BLACKFISH OIL—An oil obtained from blackfish, or pilot whales, and used for lubricating fine machine and instrument bearings.

BLANCHARD LATHE—See *Lathe, Blanchard.*

BLANKING DIE—See *Die, Blanking.*

BLASTED DIES—See *Dies, Blasted.*

BLIND FASTENERS—Devices for fastening sheets or similar parts together without the aid of screws or rivets. After being placed through the holes and turned, a spring contacts the under side of the sheet.

BLIND HOLE—Any hole which does not go all the way through any object.

BLISTER STEEL—Steel formed from wrought iron by cementation and so called because of the blisters on the surface. See *Cementation.*

BLOCK AND TACKLE—Arrangements of fixed and movable pulleys with ropes to convert movement into power. As with levers, power is never increased or gained, only used to better advantage by applying it through a greater distance. A single fixed pulley has no advantage except to change the direction of power application. A single movable pulley makes it possible for the same weight to be moved with half the force moved through twice the distance. See *Block, Hoisting.* Multiplying the number of movable pulley decreases the force necessary, but increases the distance through which it must be moved.

BLOCK CHAIN SPROCKETS—See under *Sprockets.*

BLOCK GAGING—See *Gaging, Measuring.*

BLOCKS, HOISTING—Any combination of pulleys, ropes or chains for lifting weights. They are usually hand operated, but may employ electric or air motors. Differential, planetary or worm gearing may be used. Frequently called pulley-blocks.

BLOCKS, MEASURING—Blocks of hardened steel made to very close dimensions for measuring accurate work. They are often used in setting or checking other measuring instruments, or may be used directly in inspection work or in laying out. Their origin has been usually credited to Carl Johannsson of Sweden, but is also claimed by descendents of Tjalmar Ellstrom, also of Sweden. They have been known as "Jo" blocks in the shops. Similar blocks are also made by Brown & Sharpe, (who now make the Johannsson blocks), Pratt & Whitney (Hoke), Van Keuren, and Webber. They are made in a series of sizes so that various combinations to five decimal places can be made. A complete set of 81 blocks gives 120,000 combinations in steps of only 0.0001 inch.

BLOOM—The first stage in forming ingots into blooms, billets and bars. A billet whose cross section exceeds 36 square inches. See *Ingot.*

BLOOMERY—A forge and furnace where steel blooms are made.

BLOW HOLE—A hole in a casting formed by air pocket when the casting was poured.

BLOW PIPE—A device for mixing a jet of air with a flame both to direct it and to increase the heat. Small ones are used with an alcohol lamp and blown by the mouth. Large blowpipes use gas and compressed air, as shown.

BLOW TORCH—A portable device using compressed air to blow a gasoline flame for securing intense local heat. Used by plumbers and for similar work.

BLUE ANNEALING—A method of annealing steel sheets after they are rolled. They are allowed to cool slowly after hot rolling and passed through an open furnace which gives them a blue-black appearance.

BLUING—Any material which produces a blue surface on metal to assist in laying out work on it. The bluing makes a dark background so that lines made by a scriber are plainly seen. There are various materials, one being copper sulphate. Prepared bluing liquids are also on the market.

Bluing is also a process of coating metal as a rust preventative. It was formerly used largely by gun makers, who now use a browning finish or one of the patented coatings, such as Parkerizing.

BLUING OF STEEL—A process used in firearms and similar small parts for producing a blue surface which tends to resist rust. A mixture of nitre (saltpeter) and black oxide of manganese in a 10 to 1 proportion, by weight, is used in many places. The parts are heated to 800 to 850 deg. F. in cast iron pots for from 10 to 15 minutes.

BOARD FEET—A basis for estimating or measuring the volume of boards and planks, based on a board being one inch thick. It is the size of the board in square feet multiplied by the thickness in inches. A board one-half inch thick has only half the "board feet" of a board of the same size one inch thick.

BODY BOLT—See *Bolt, Body.*

BOG ORE—A type of soft iron ore found in swamps or bogs.

BOILER PATCH BOLT—See *Bolt, Boiler Patch.*

BOILER PLUGS—Threaded plugs screwed into boiler shells below the safe water line. They have a fusible metal center which will melt if the water gets below the safe level. Sometimes called "fusible plugs."

BOLSTER—A block sometimes called a die-block used for holding a die in a punch press. It is usually attached to the bed of the press by bolts.

BOLT—A metal rod, usually with a head at one end, a screw thread at the other. A threaded nut on the threaded end produces pressure to holds parts together. There are many kinds of bolts, frequently designed for special purposes. Those most frequently used are illustrated on page 20.

BOLT(S) AND NUTS—There are so many kinds and so many makers of bolts and nuts that uniformity could not be expected except through such an organization as the American Institute of Bolt, Nut & Rivet Manufacturers, which is now known as the Industrial Fasteners Institute. In most cases, the names adopted are self-explanatory to anyone at all familiar with machine work. Standard abbreviations have also been adopted and these, too, are likely to be understood by those using them. In the same way a compilation has been made of materials used as well as types of finish.

Complete lists can be secured from the Industrial Fasteners Institute, Cleveland 5, Ohio. The more common types of bolts and nuts are shown.

BOLT(S) AND SCREWS, DISCARDED TERMS—The following terms have been *discarded* by a Committee on Standardizing Terms for Mechanical Fasteners:

Askew head bolt—stove bolt (machine screw with a nut).

Boiler rivet—cone head rivet.

Flat fillister head screw—oval fillister screw.

Flat top binding screw—truss head screw.

Hull and tank rivets—cone head rivets.

Lentil head screw—oval head screw.

Oval binding head screw—truss head screw.

Oven head screw—truss head screw.

Plumbers' head screw—round head screw.

Stove head screw—truss head screw.

Stripper bolt—socket head shoulder screw.

Stud bolt—stud.

Tap rivet—patch bolt.

BOLT, AGRICULTURAL—The body has helical ridges to prevent it from turning when used to hold parts of wood. Designed for use in agricultural implements.

BOLT, ALL THREAD—A bolt threaded the whole length. Not a commonly used term. Same as *Tap Bolt*.

BOLT, ANCHOR—A bolt with a large plate or anchor under the head, to be submerged in concrete to hold machines on their foundations. See *Bolt, Foundation*.

BOLT, BODY—A bolt that is finished smoothly so as to be a good fit in the part in which it is used. When so used it holds the parts from side movement.

BOLT, BOILER PATCH—Designed for fastening patches on steam boilers. The patch is countersunk for the coned head. An undercut below the square head makes it easy to knock this off when bolt is tight in place.

BOLT, CONNECTING ROD—A body bolt which fits the holes in the ears of connecting rods and has a special shaped head to conform to the design of the rod.

BOLT CUTTER—A machine for machining and threading bolts. Many are automatic with the blanks fed into the machine and the finished bolt dropped out after threading. Also called *Bolt Threader*.

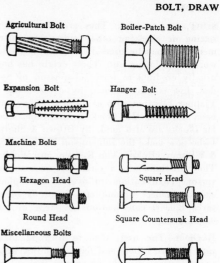

Agricultural Bolt

Boiler-Patch Bolt

Expansion Bolt

Hanger Bolt

Machine Bolts

Hexagon Head

Square Head

Round Head

Square Countersunk Head

Miscellaneous Bolts

Tire

Loom or Carriage

Oval T-Head

Joint

Step

Eye

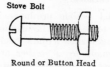

Deck

Bridge or Roof

Sink

Track

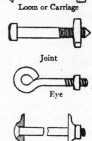

U

Hook

Stove Bolt

Tap Bolt

Round or Button Head

Hexagon Head Tap Bolt

Types of bolts.

BOLT, DOUBLE END—A name sometimes used for a stud, or bolt which is threaded on both ends.

BOLT, DRAW—See *Draw Bolt*.

20

BOLT, EYE—A bolt having a ring or eye formed on the end instead of the usual square or hexagon shaped head.

BOLT, EXPANSION—A bolt having a split sleeve in place of a nut. The sleeve goes into a hole drilled in masonry and is expanded into the hole when the bolt is screwed in place.

BOLT, FITTING-UP—A bolt with a modified thread form of less than standard depth, used largely in temporary assembling of structural steel beams.

BOLT, FORELOCK—A bolt having a hole or slot in the end instead of screw threads. A pin or key is used instead of a nut. Not in common use.

BOLT, FOUNDATION—A bolt designed to hold machines solidly to the floor. They are made in various ways, some being very simple. The one shown is by the Giddings & Lewis Co., and includes a screw at the top of the bolt for levelling the machine after it is in place. These are used in concrete foundations in which a 2-inch pipe has been set, as shown. Minimum dimensions are shown.

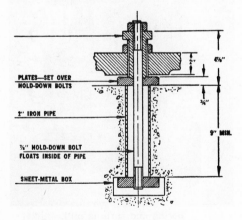

PLATES—SET OVER HOLD-DOWN BOLTS

2" IRON PIPE

⅞" HOLD-DOWN BOLT FLOATS INSIDE OF PIPE

SHEET-METAL BOX

2"   4⅛"

¾"

9" MIN.

Foundation bolt.

BOLT, FOX—A seldom used bolt having the end split to be opened out by a wedge. Sometimes used as an anchor bolt.

BOLT, HANGER—A bolt used in fastening hangers or other parts to wood work. One end is threaded like a wood or lag screw, the other for a regular nut.

BOLT, JAG—Any bolt with a notched or barbed shank for gripping concrete when used as a foundation bolt.

BOLT, LOCK—Any bolt which locks two parts of a mechanism together. Sometimes has special devices for preventing movement.

BOLT, MACHINE—Bolts used in fastening various parts of machinery together. The usual types have square, hexagonal, round or countersunk heads. There are also many types of bolts for special purposes, some of which are shown.

BOLT, PLOW—Ten types of bolts used in agricultural machinery are: Large round head; square head; round head, square shank; round head; key head; tee head; button head; concave head; reverse head; large key head.

BOLT, RING—An eye bolt having a ring put through the eye.

BOLT, ROLLED THREAD—Rolled thread bolts are usually made from stock the same as the pitch diameter of the thread. This leaves the shank above the thread of smaller diameter than the thread. Where this is objectionable both head and body may be upset or the threaded section may be extruded of the proper diameter. Rolling enlarges the thread to the body diameter. Bolts with a cut thread have a pointed or rounded end. Rolled thread bolts are not rounded but the first thread is usually of somewhat smaller diameter which aids in assembling. Rolled threads were orginally used only on bolts and screws where fit was not important but this is no longer the case. Bolts threaded the whole length are the same by both methods, except for the point.

BOLT, SOCKET—A bolt having a recessed head for receiving a wrench. It can also be turned with a flat screw driver.

BOLT, STOVE—Made primarily for assembling stoves. Sizes vary from ⅛ to ⅜ inch in diameter. Common types of heads are round, button and flat, and countersunk. They are National Coarse threads and are frequently rolled.

BOLT, STRIPPER—Bolts used in connection with punch press work strippers, operated either by springs or positive action.

BOLT, T FOR CLAMPING WORK—Bolt
made with T-head which fits standard slots in machine tool tables, as shown. A washer and nut should be used. See *T-Bolt*.

BOLT, TAP—Tap
bolts are threaded full length. These were formerly not machined before threading. They have square or hexagonal heads. Same as all-thread bolt.

BOLT TERMS—
Boiler patch bolt—the patch is countersunk at the same angle as the cone head of the bolt and the square head is knocked or cut off after assembly.

Bolt or screw points—See *Screws, Set*.

Driver head—designed for such tools as screw drivers but not wrenches.

Full-size body—body equal to major diameter of thread.

Hanger bolt—a headed bolt with a lag screw thread for use in wood work.

Length of bolt, screw or rivet—measured from under the head to largest diameter at end.

Rolled point—point made by cupping of threads at end due to rolling the thread.

Track bolt—has oval under the head which fits holes in fish plates to prevent turning. *See illustrations of all bolts.*

Under size body—body approximating the pitch diameter of thread, as in some bolts with rolled threads.

Washer face—a circular face under the head. Either a shoulder or a face made by chamfering the corners.

BOLT HEAD, PLACE TYPE—A
bolt head with a cavity in the center which provides a spring element when bolt is tightened. They also save weight.

BOLT, WIRED-HEAD—Bolt
heads drilled for locking wires as shown.

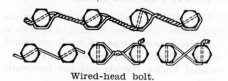

Wired-head bolt.

BOND—Material used in uniting two or more parts, usually by brazing, soldering or welding. Electrical bonds or connections are sometimes made simply by forcible contacts without heat or other materials. Cements, glues or other materials used for joining two or more parts are also called bonds.

BONDS FOR ABRASIVE WHEELS — The names of materials used as bonds for holding grains of abrasives together in wheels or blocks have been standardized by the Grinding Wheel Institute, as follows: 1—Vitrified bond (clay or glasses); 2—resinoid bond (synthetic resins); 3—rubber bond (vulcanite or vulcanized products); 4—shellac bond (elastic products); 5—silicate bond (silicate of soda); 6—oxychloride or magnesite.

BONDERIZING—A process of treating metal to prevent corrosion and to make paint, enamel or other finishes last longer. In the same class as Parkerizing.

BONE SCREW—See *Screw, Bone*.

BORING AND TURNING MILL—Usually called a boring mill or vertical mill. A machine with a rotating table which holds the work and one or more tool heads which per-

Boring and turning mill.
(Bullard.)

form various turning and boring operations. Many now have a tool carrying side head in addition to two tool heads on the cross-rail. Sometimes called a vertical lathe. Tools are held in a sliding saddle which provides the feed. In some cases the saddle can be swiveled to bore or turn at an angle. The one shown is a Bullard. Boring machines with a horizontal

Floor-type, large-table horizontal boring machine. (Lucas.)

spindle are not usually called "mills," but boring machines.

BORING BAR—Extension bar fitted with radial cutters for boring large pieces.

BORING BAR CUTTER GAGE—See *Gage, Boring Bar Cutter.*

BORING HEADS, PACKED BIT—A large drill or boring head with the portion between the cutters packed, or lagged, to steady the head in the hole being bored. The packing was formerly of a close grained wood but later practice in some arsenals is to use babbitt metal instead.

BORING MACHINE, HORIZONTAL—Sometimes known as the bar type machine. It is really a boring and milling machine and is very versatile; it can be used on many kinds of work in either small or large lots. The boring bar or milling spindle head moves vertically on the column and the bar feeds horizontally. Work is positioned by moving the table either across the bed or lengthwise, which also provides the feed for boring. For milling both feeds are used.

BORING MILLS, VERTICAL—See *Boring and Turning Mill.*

BORING TOOL HOLDER—A block for holding boring tools in a tool post or on the lathe carriage.

BORON—A metal which resembles silicon. Sp. Gr. 1.73. Melts at 4,172 deg. F. in an oxidizing atmosphere.

Small, horizontal precision boring machine. (Heald.)

23

BORON CARBIDE—A very hard, black crystalline powder used as an abrasive. Pressed and sintered into solids it is used as contacts for gages. Sp. Gr. 2.52. Melts at 4,440 deg. F.

BOSS—A raised portion of a casting or forging generally used to provide a seating surface above the main surface of the piece. In Britain this is usually called a "spigot." The term also applies to the foreman or head of a shop.

BOTTOMING DIES—See *Dies, Bottoming.*

BOWER-BARFF FINISH—A finish obtained on iron and steel by heating the metal red-hot in a muffle furnace and passing steam into the furnace. This produces a black oxide on the surface. The heat required prevents its being used on some classes of work.

BOX CHUCK—See *Chuck, Box or Batwing.*

BOX TOOLS—Tools for screw machines which are held in frames or boxes, which also support the work while it is being machined. In some the tools are radial and in others the tools are held in a tangential position. See *Screw Machine Tools.*

BRAKE—A device for retarding motion of any kind, such as car wheel brakes on railroads, or band brakes on automobiles.

Press brake.

A machine for bending sheet metals, sometimes called a press brake. It resembles a machine for shearing metals but has no cutting tools.

BRASS—See *Alloys, Brass.*

BRASS DIE CASTING—See *Die Casting, Brass.*

BRASTIL—Trade name of a brass die casting by Doehler with tensile strengths of about 90,000 pounds per square inch.

BRAZING—Joining of metals by use of a copper alloy and a flux, usually some form of borax. This is frequently called hard soldering, although there are regular solders made with different degrees of hardness. Brazing is now done in furnaces with controlled atmospheres of oxygen or hydrogen.

BRAZING, DIP—Brazing by dipping the joints to be brazed into a heated bath of the brazing material. Other parts of the articles are covered so that the brazing metal will not adhere to them.

BRAZING METAL—A brass high in copper for parts to be brazed. A federal specification is 80 to 84 per cent copper, the rest zinc. Some specifications give 75 and 25. This is sometimes used for brazing rods.

BRAZING, SILVER—A brazing process in which silver solder is used. It melts at from 1,250 deg. F. to 1,600 deg. F., depending on whether it is in strip, sheet or granular form. The melting point averages about 1,400 deg. F. The silver solder has about 50 per cent silver, the rest copper and zinc. Increasing the zinc content lowers the melting point. It makes a strong joint and requires little finishing. Borax makes a good flux.

BREECH BLOCK THREAD—See *Screw Thread, Jump.*

BRIDLE—A strap used to hold work against a lathe center in the headstock while the outer end is supported in a steady rest.

BRIGGS PIPE THREAD—Named for Robert Briggs, who formulated the standard for pipe threads some time before 1882. It constitutes the basis for our present pipe thread standards, but has of course been modified to conform to modern practice. The diagrams under the heading *Screw Threads, Pipe,* show the different parts of the thread and how they are measured. The taper is 1 inch in 16 or ¾ inch per foot. The thread is the National Standard as to angle and form. Pitches vary with the diameter of the pipe, starting with 27 threads per inch for ⅛-inch pipe; 18 threads per inch for ¼-inch and ⅜-inch; 14 threads per inch for ½-inch and ¾-inch pipe, 11½ threads per inch for 1- to 2-inch pipe, inclusive, and 8 threads per inch for all larger sizes. See *Screw Thread, Pipe.*

BRIGHT ANNEALING—Annealing in a furnace with a controlled atmosphere which reduces oxidization to a minimum, leaving the work fairly bright. See *Annealing.*

BRIGHT CHARCOAL TINPLATE—See *Tinplate.*

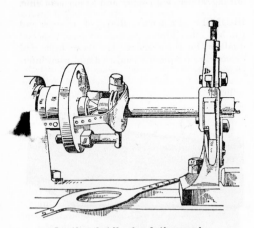

Leather bridle for lathe work.

BRINELL HARDNESS TESTING MACHINE —A machine which tests hardness of metals by forcing a steel ball into the surface at a given pressure. Different balls and different pressures are used for different materials. In practice the hardness is designated as BHN or Brinell Hardness Number. These numbers are based on the diameter of the impression left

by the ball in the metal or other materials, at a given pressure. See *Hardness.*

BRITISH ASSOCIATION SCREW THREADS —See *Screw Threads, British Association.*

BRITISH PIPE THREADS — British pipe threads are usually somewhat finer pitch than American, beginning with 28 threads per inch for 1/8-inch pipe and not using 8 threads per inch until the 11-inch pipe. This is because the pipe used in Great Britain has a thinner wall than ours and the finer threads leave more strength in the pipe ends. They use 19 threads per inch for 1/4- and 3/8-inch pipe; 14 threads per inch up to 7/8-inch; 11 threads from 1 to 6 inches, inclusive, 10 threads from 7 to 10 inches, inclusive, and then 8 threads up to 18 inches, which is their largest regular size. Unless they increase the wall thickness of their pipe they are not likely to adopt our threads. See *Screw Threads, Pipe.*

BRITISH THERMAL UNIT (B. T. U.)—The standard unit of heat in English speaking countries. It means the heat necessary to raise one pound of water 1 deg. F., and is quite accurate between 32 deg. and 212 deg. F. Above 212 deg. F. there is an error which increases with the temperature.

BRITTANIA METAL—An alloy containing 1.46 parts copper, 90.62 parts tin, and 7.81 parts antimony. Proportions are approximate.

BROACH—A tool which is practically a series of small cutting edges or chisels. These are made for either internal or external work. They are pulled or pushed past the work surfaces to be machined. Each tooth takes a light cut. They frequently change a round hole into a square hole with cutting edges properly dis-

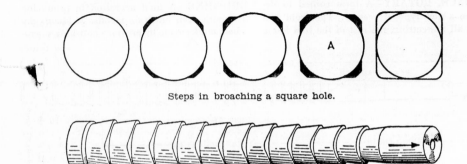

Steps in broaching a square hole.

Broach for square hole.

tributed to give the shape desired. One of the largest broaches to date cuts the teeth of a 44-tooth involute spline in ring gears for truck rear axles. It is 9-3/16-inch outside diameter, 84¾-inches long and weighs half a ton. A small hand reamer used by jewelers is also called a broach.

BROACH, PULL—A broach that is pulled through or past the work.

BROACH, PUSH—A broach that is pushed through the work. They are short broaches generally used on internal work.

BROACHING—Machining parts to desired shapes with the use of broaches. It has become a standard practice for many holes, even round holes in some cases. Flat surfaces, such as the tops and bottoms of cylinder blocks are also machined by broaching. Broaching machines are made in horizontal, vertical and rotary forms, and produce many irregular shapes economically.

BROACHING CAPACITY—Pressure in tons which the machine can exert.

BROACHING MACHINES—Types of machine tools designed to pull or push broaches through or against surfaces to be machined by this method. Broaching machines are designed for many classes of work from finishing round holes already bored or machining them to any desired shape to machining outside surfaces such as tops and sides of cylinder blocks. They are mostly used on comparatively small work, such as finishing the jaws of wrenches. A typical broaching machine is shown.

BROACH, ROTARY—A term coined to describe a new type of reamer. The front end does all the cutting, the rest of the tool being

cylindrical and acting as a burnishing tool behind the cutting edge. It cuts due to end pressure as it rotates in the work. Also a broach for cutting helical grooves or splines.

BRONZE—A copper and tin mixture in various proportions; 80 parts copper, 20 parts tin, is a strong mixture. Weighs 0.315 lb. per cu. in. Melts at 1,868 deg. F.

BRONZE, COMMERCIAL—A mixture containing 90 per cent copper and 10 per cent zinc.

BRONZES—Primarily alloys of copper and tin, but other alloys are used to secure special qualities for certain uses. The terms brass and bronze are frequently confused and used interchangeably.

La Pointe horizontal broaching machine.

BRUSH HYPERSONIC ANALYZER—Similar in operation to the supersonic inspection method, but especially adapted for use on thin materials. See *Inspection, Supersonic*.

BRUSHING—A final operation in producing a smooth even finish on metals. It blends the wheel marks made by previous polishing opera-

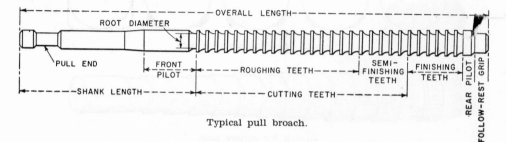

Typical pull broach.

tions. A hair-brush wheel with an emery paste makes a satin finish on brass. Pumice and oil makes a finer finish. Wire brushes produce a peening action similar to a sand blast, but finer. Heavy wires and slower speed gives a matte finish.

BUFFING—The polishing of metals, usually non-ferrous, with rag or similar wheels and polishing material such as rouge. This is an abrasive operation done with wheels coated with fine abrasives, or canvas belts also coated with the same material. Both buffing and polishing machinery should be equipped with exhaust fans to take away the material as it is removed. Logically buffing should be the operation preceding polishing, now generally known as finishing.

BUFFING, COMPRESSED WHEEL FOR—These have steel centers and are made with leather, canvas or linen, compressed to present a solid surface. They are safer and more economical than wooden wheels, are strong and easily kept in balance. They are largely used in cutlery work.

BUGS—Defects in any mechanism. Usually little maladjustments that prevent proper functioning.

Also a shop name for tractors used in moving material from one department to another.

BULL BLOCKS—Blocks containing dies through which wire is drawn to reduce its diameter.

BULL CENTER— See *Center, Bull.*

BULLDOZER—A heavy forming machine for bending or shaping iron or steel, in which the dies usually move horizontally. Similar to a forging press, except that this does not forge hot metal. Name is also now applied to large earth working machines.

Bulldozer.

BULL WHEEL—A term used in several ways. Most common is the large gear which drives the table of a metal planing machine. It is also a wheel or drum around which a rope is wound, as in a windlass.

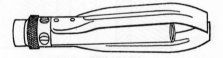

Bunsen burner.

BUNSEN BURNER—A method of securing a hot flame from ordinary illuminating gas by mixing air with the gas in a space below the burner tip. A typical shop burner is shown, which gives a flat flame.

Bur.

BUR—A small milling cutter with very fine teeth used by hand in a small motor driven head or by a flexible shaft. Frequently called a rotary file. The teeth are usually ground after the blank is hardened. The same term applies to rough or sharp edges raised by a cutting tool or by otherwise deforming metal, such as pounding on the end of a cold chisel.

Burs

Teeth Per Inch

Dia. of Hd. In.	Coarse cut	Std. cut	Fine cut
⅛	25	32	36
³⁄₁₆	20	25	36
¼	16	25	32
⁵⁄₁₆	16	20	32
⅜	13	20	25
⁷⁄₁₆	13	20	25
½	11	16	25
⁹⁄₁₆	11	16	25
⅝	11	16	25
¾	9	13	20
⅞	9	13	20
1	8	13	20
1⅛	8	11	20
1¼	8	11	20

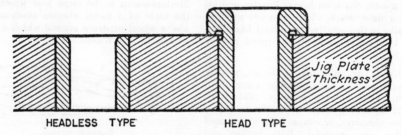

Press fit bushings—headless type and head type.

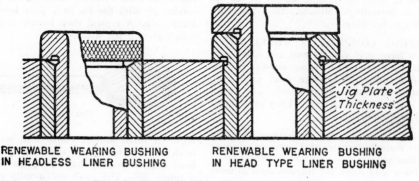

Liner bushings—headless type and head type.

BURETTE—A small glass tube with fine gradations used in drawing off samples of pickling and other solutions. Used in testing the solutions used.

BURNISHERS—Tools of hardened and polished steel, or other hard materials, for finishing softer metals by friction. They are held in contact with the revolving work and secure a high polish by compressing the outer layer of metal.

BURNISHING—Polishing metal or other substances by contact with hardened surfaces called burnishers. Formerly used largely by railroad shops for finishing axle bearings, crankpins and piston rods. Used to some extent for finishing gear teeth before hardening by rolling in contact with hardened master gears. Burnishing is also done in tumbling barrels using steel balls or other objects to contact the work.

BUSHING—A tube or shell supported by other material, as a drill bushing in a drilling

BUSHINGS.

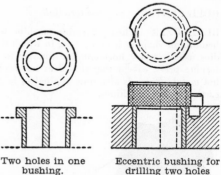

Two holes in one bushing.

Eccentric bushing for drilling two holes close together.

jig. Frequently used as replaceable bearings, as with valve guides in internal combustion engines.

BUTADIENE—A colorless gas used in making synthetic or artificial rubber.

BUTT JOINT—A joint in which the parts being joined butt against each other instead of overlapping each other. See *Plate Joints.*

BUTTON DIE—An adjustable die held in a collet and adjusted by a cone pointed screw. See *Dies, Button; Screw Machine Tools.*

BUTTONS—Usually small round pieces of hardened steel used for locating or supporting work in a fixture of some kind. As used in jigs and fixtures, they are usually screwed into the base. Tool-makers' buttons are hardened steel disks with a hole in the center to permit fastening them to a face plate or other surface. They are used as reference locations in laying out accurately spaced holes in jigs and fixtures, frequently using gage blocks to insure accurate measurements.

BUTT WELD—A welded joint in which the two parts butt against each other and are welded along the edges. See *Welds and Welded Joints.*

BUTTRESS THREAD—See *Screw Threads.*

C

C. E. L. THREADS — See *Screw Threads, British Cycle.*

C. G. (CENTER OF GRAVITY)—The point in a body at which the weight is equally distributed on all sides. In any regular figure of uniform thickness, the C. G. will be in the center, as with a circle or square; but with unequal distribution of weight the C. G. may be at any point. In automobiles or railway trains a low C. G. means that most of the weight is below the center.

C-WASHER—See *Washer, Slip.*

CADMIUM—A heavy silvery metal used in soft solders and for electroplating against rust. Sp. gr. 8.6. Melts at 608 deg. F.

CADMIUM LIGHT—A light-based on the use of cadmium, which has a definite wave length of 39,450.3 to the standard inch. This is now used as a standard as well as measuring blocks. It is a monochromatic light, meaning that it is of one color, or wave length. The lamp is a gas filled tube, similar to those used in neon signs, operated by a 5,000-volt transformer with a 110-volt, 60-cycle circuit. The light emitted has a value of 11.6 millionths of an inch per dark band. These bands are clearly visible when the separation of the surfaces being tested is as much as 0.005 inch. See *Optical Flats.*

CALCIUM—A silver white metal which oxydizes rapidly in air. Much harder than sodium. Used in some lead-base bearing alloys. Behaves something like lithium and stands between sodium and magnesium.

CALCIUM CARBIDE—A crystalline substance used to produce acetylene gas for welding or lighting.

CALESCENCE—One of the critical points in the heating of steel. A pyrometer will show that, as the heat increases to a certain point, the indicating needle suddenly stops, wavers and then drops several degrees, although the heat is increasing. Then the needle suddenly starts to go up. The place where the needle stops is the point of calescence, or the calescence point. See *Recalescence.*

CALIBRATION—The marking of any instrument for measuring or weighing into desired units. It is also the testing or checking of instruments already in use to see that their marking are correct or to note discrepancies.

CALIPER—Tool for measuring outside or inside diameters. They are made in many forms, from plain sheet metal tool to delicate micrometers for measuring to tens of thousandths of an inch. See the various types which follow:

CALIPER, FIRM-JOINT—A plain caliper made from sheet-steel and having a large, firm joint in place of the older style which lacked this refinement. They are made for both inside and outside measurements. Outside calipers have legs which bow out. Inside calipers have straight legs.

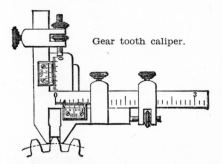

Gear tooth caliper.

CALIPER, GEAR-TOOTH—A caliper with two beams at right angles, as shown. The vertical beam gives tooth depth to the pitch line and the other beam the thickness at the pitch line. Both beams have verniers. They are used in accurate measurement of gear teeth.

CALIPER, HERMAPHRODITE—A combination of one caliper leg with a leg from a divid-

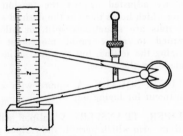

Setting an inside caliper.

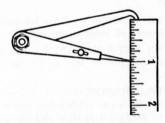

Hermaphrodite caliper.

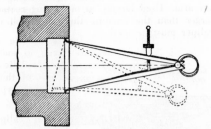

Measuring with inside caliper.

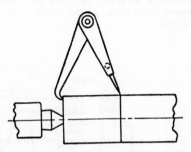

Measuring with hermaphrodite caliper
to locate a shoulder.

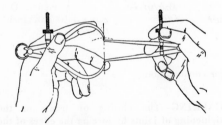

Transferring a measurement from an inside
caliper to an outside caliper.

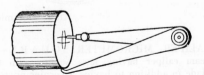

Centering with hermaphrodite calipers.

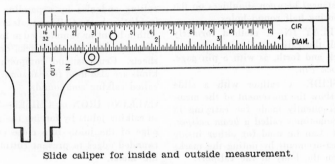

Slide caliper for inside and outside measurement.

er. It is used in testing centered work and in laying off distances from the edge of a piece of work.

CALIPER, INSIDE—A caliper for measuring bores instead of outer diameters.

CALIPER, KEY-HOLE—This has one straight leg and one curved leg, as in an outside caliper.

CALIPER, MICROMETER—A measuring instrument with a fine pitch screw and a barrel or sleeve graduated to show definite parts of a turn of the screw. They usually have a thread of 40 to the inch and the barrel is divided into 25 parts, so that one division shows 1/1,000th of an inch. They are also made to measure 1/10,000th of an inch. See also page 266.

CALIPER, SPRING—A caliper in which the legs are adjusted against the tension of a spring which holds them at the desired setting. The nuts are sometimes split, or otherwise designed to allow rapid movement when changing the setting, but the final adjustment is made by the screw.

CALIPER, SQUARE—A square with caliper adjustment for laying out work.

CALIPER, TRANSFER—A caliper with an auxiliary arm which permits the caliper points to be set to a given diameter, then moved to avoid interference with the work, and reset to the desired dimension by means of the auxiliary arm. Used largely in measuring recesses larger than the opening through which the caliper must be used.

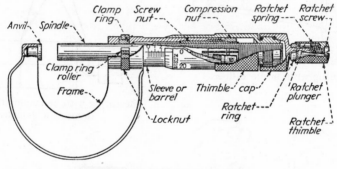

Details of micrometer construction.

CALIPER, MICROMETER SQUARE—A beam caliper having jaws square with the blade in addition to having a vernier micrometer adjustment for accurate measurements.

CALIPER, ODD-LEG—A caliper having both legs pointing in the same direction. Used in measuring distances between shoulders on flat work or in boring half round holes.

CALIPERS, PLAY IN—A method formerly used in which the caliper points are rocked or swung back and forth, as with a pin gage. See *Gage, Rock Pin*.

CALIPER, SLIDE—A caliper with a slide graduated to show the movement of the measuring jaw. Frequently made for carrying in the pocket. Sometimes called a *beam caliper*. (Illus. p. 31.) Can be used for either inside or outside measurements by noting the marks IN and OUT on the body of the calipers.

CALKING—The closing of seams or the tightening of joints by forcing the edges of the material together with a blunt instrument. The seams made in boilers by the lapping of plates are sometimes calked. Tubes in a boiler are always calked into the tube sheet, usually by rolling and also by expanding the tube just inside the sheet. Calking tools are really chisels with a blunt or rounded edge to prevent chipping or making sharp cracks or marks in the sheets. Cements and compounds of various kinds are also used to seal some joints and are called calking compounds.

CALKING IRON or CHISEL—The tool used in calking joints by forcing the metal near the edge of the joints into close contact. It has rounded edges to prevent cutting or chipping the metal.

CALORIMETER—An instrument for measuring the amount of heat generated in an electrical conductor, by friction, combustion or by chemical change.

CALORIZING—Coating steel or other metals with an aluminum-iron alloy to prevent oxidization and scaling at high temperatures. The outer layer is rich in aluminum with a layer of iron underneath. The depth of penetration of the aluminum is given as 0.003 to 0.04 inch. The articles to be coated are packed in a drum in a mixture of powdered aluminum oxide with a little ammonium chloride. The drum is rotated slowly for about 5 hours at about 1,740 deg. F., with a reducing atmosphere, usually of hydrogen. Brass and copper can also be calorized, but at a lower temperature.

CAM—Usually, revolving parts of special design which impart motion to arms or levers which contact them. Their operation depends largely on the way in which they move and how contact is made with other members of the mechanism. Flat plates with special or irregular contours are also used to impart motion to arms or levers. They can be stationary and contact moving parts, or move to control movements of other parts. They may control motion radially, laterally or in straight lines. They also have different names in some sections, as the Scotch yoke and yoke cam. Various kinds are illustrated.

CAM, CYLINDER—A cam cut on the outside of a cylinder. It may either be cut below the surface or raised above it. It produces a motion parallel to its axis. Same as Drum Cam.

CAM, DRUM OR BARREL—A cam with the path for the roll or follower cut around the outside of a drum or cylinder. A roller in the groove imparts motion to a slide or lever in a plane parallel with the axis of the cam. In automatic screw machines the cams are frequently built up with plates fastened to the outside of the drum.

CAM, EDGE OR RADIAL—A cam formed on the edge of a disk. It gives positive action to followers in one direction only, the roller being held against the cam edge by gravity or by a spring. In the cam shown the parts are named. (Illus. p. 34.)

CAM, FACE—Face cams have a groove cut in the side or face of the disk in which a roller or follower operates and imparts motion to a slide or lever, usually the latter. As in the roll cam, the follower is positively guided in both directions. Also called a plate cam as in illustration.

CAM, FLAT—A flat piece of metal having projections of varying height which actuate other parts of a mechanism such as levers or rollers. It may also be a plate with a curved or irregu-

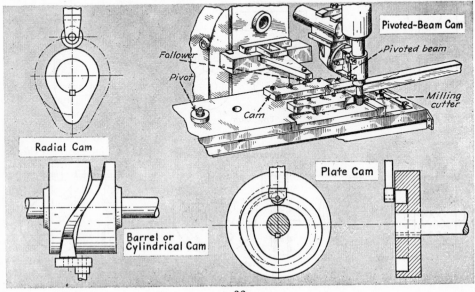

Radial Cam

Follower

Pivot

Cam

Pivoted-Beam Cam

Pivoted beam

Milling cutter

Barrel or Cylindrical Cam

Plate Cam

lar slot which controls the movement of some other part of the mechanism.

CAM LOCK—A patented method of holding end milling cutters in the adapter which drives them. As the taper shank enters the adapter it compresses a spring which helps eject the

shank when the cam is released. This is a Brown & Sharpe patent and is shown on page 35.

CAM, SCOTCH YOKE—A method of securing a reciprocating motion without use of a crank. The cam is a running fit inside the yoke and

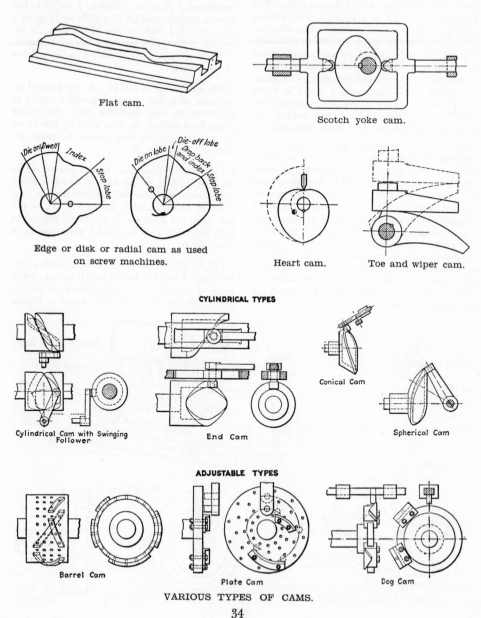

Flat cam.

Scotch yoke cam.

Edge or disk or radial cam as used on screw machines.

Heart cam.

Toe and wiper cam.

CYLINDRICAL TYPES

Cylindrical Cam with Swinging Follower

End Cam

Conical Cam

Spherical Cam

ADJUSTABLE TYPES

Barrel Cam

Plate Cam

Dog Cam

VARIOUS TYPES OF CAMS.

moves it back and forth as the cam revolves. It probably originated in Scotland and was used for driving piston pumps. It eliminates the use of a connecting rod, crank pin and wrist or cross-head pin. Only used in special cases at present.

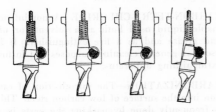

Cam lock: (Left to right) Start, grip, lock, release.

CAMBER—A slight upward bend in an otherwise flat surface.

CAMMING — A term generally applied to preparation and application of cams for automatic screw machines or other mechanisms.

CANNON DRILL—A single-point drill with the cutting edge at the center. See *Drills*.

CANTILEVER—A beam or truss supported only at one end.

CAPILLARY ATTRACTION—A natural attraction between some liquids and some solids. It makes the kerosense used in lamps feed itself up the fabric wick to the flame. The illustration shows the attraction between kerosene and the sharp point of a surface gage and indicates the instant the point touches the liquid. When the liquid is not attracted but is repelled it is called capillary repulsion.

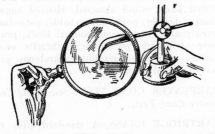

Capillary attraction. Testing level of oil in ways with a surface gage.

CAPILLARY REPULSION—The reverse of capillary attraction.

CAPSTAN LATHE—A British name for a turret lathe.

CARBIDE—A compound of carbon with a metal. Used in making cutting tips for machine tools.

CARBIDE BALLS—Balls made of carbide for use in Brinell and other hardness testing machines using a ball for making the indentation in the metal being tested. Being much harder than steel, they have a longer life.

CARBIDE EXTRUSIONS—Extruded bars or sticks of carbide in rounds, tubes, flats, and special shapes, for various uses. The Kennametal Co. lists them in diameters from $\frac{1}{32}$ inch to $\frac{1}{2}$ inch and up to 10 inches long. They are used for feed fingers, rollers, laps, scribers, engraving tool points, punches and other work. They vary from 0.010 to 0.015 inch oversize.

CARBIDE FILES—See *Files, Carbide*.

CARBIDE INSERTS—Molded sintered carbide pieces to be clamped to tool holders or shanks, for performing various machining operations. They are made in several shapes, such as round, triangular, square and with five sides. Round tools are rotated in the holder to present new cutting edges while the other shapes have three, four or five cutting points. They are not removed for grinding until all the surfaces are dull. See *Carbide Extrusions*.

CARBIDE INSERT and TOOL STANDARDS —The Carbide Industry Standardization Institute Committee has developed standards for tools of different kinds. The standards for brazed tool inserts are shown, these being adopted by the whole industry so that tips will interchange. Complete dimensions can be secured from any maker. Shapes and terminology passes. (Illus. p. 37.)

Tolerances.

+0.015 —0.000 on all tip dimensions up to ⅜ in.

+0.020 —0.000 on all tip dimensions over ⅜ in. through 1 in.

+0.040 —0.000 on all tip dimensions over 1 in. through 2 in.

Extra grinding stock on width to permit grinding on both sides.

Extra grinding stock on length to permit grinding on both ends.

Terminology for Standard Brazed Tools

General Specifications:

Unless otherwise specified by purchaser, the following tolerances apply to all standard and special carbide tipped cutting tools:

Tip:

End Cutting Edge Angle . . Plus or minus 1°
Side Cutting Edge Angle . Plus or minus 1°
Side Relief . . . . Plus or minus 1°
Front Relief . . . . Plus or minus 1°
Back Rake . . . . Plus or minus 2°
Side Rake . . . . Plus or minus 2°
Nose Radius . . . . Maximum 1/32″
Point Location . . . . Plus or minus 1/64″
Tip Thickness—T . . . . . . Plus or minus 1/64″
Tip Width—W . . . . Plus or minus 1/64″
Tip Length—L . . . . Plus or minus 1/64″

Shank:

Front clearance . . . . Plus or minus 1°
Side Clearance . . . . Plus or minus 1°

Shank—Thickness—X

1″ or less . . . . + .000 —.010
Over 1″ . . . . . + .000 —.015

Shank Width—Y

1″ or less . . . . + .000 —.010
Over 1″ . . . . . + .000 —.015

Shank Length—Z

Up to 1″ square &
1″ x 1¼″ . . . ± ⅛″
Over 1″ square &
Over 1″ x 1¼″ . . . ± ¼″

CARBIDE TIPS—Small pieces of sintered carbide molded into different shapes to be brazed or clamped to tool holding shanks for use in various metal cutting machines.

CARBIDE TOOLS—Tools with cutting points of tungsten, tantalum or other alloys of sintered carbides. Carbide tips are brazed to high grade steel shanks or are held by mechanical means in the newer tools.

CARBON—A non-metallic element present in all organic vegetable matter. Dissolves easily in molten iron, turning it into steel.

CARBON ARC WELDING—See *Welding, Arc.*

CARBON STEEL—Any steel made by combining carbon with iron.

CARBON-TETRA-CHLORIDE—A non-inflammable liquid used both as a solvent for oil and grease and as a fire extinguisher. It is used for general cleaning purposes and in fire extinguishing apparatus.

CARBONIZATION—The introduction of carbon into the surface of low carbon steel. This is frequently done by packing the parts in a container or metal box, with carbonizing material, such as charcoal, ground bone, or other suitable substances, and heating for several hours at about 2,000 deg. F., then cooling slowly. The part can then be hardened by heating and quenching.

CARBONIZING or CARBURIZING—A heat treatment of steel which imparts carbon into the outer surfaces so that they can be hardened. The carbon is absorbed from the carburizing material used. This may be done by subjecting the steel to carbon carrying gases or by packing it with carburizing material. In both cases the steel is heated sufficiently to absorb the carbon. The latter method is known as pack-hardening.

CARBORUNDUM—A compound of carbon and silicon which makes a very hard material used as an abrasive. An artificial abrasive made by the Carborundum Co.

CARBURIZING MATERIAL—Any material containing an appreciable amount of carbon can be used in carburizing or case hardening. Among such materials are: powdered or granulated bone, wood charcoal, charred sugar, charred leather, potassium cyanide, potassium ferrocyanide, bichromate, animal black, prussiate of potash, potassium, anthracite coal, barium carbonate, graphite, petroleum gas, acetylene and horn.

CARPENTER CONE TEST—See *Steel, Carpenter Cone Test.*

CARTRIDGE BRASS—A standard alloy of 70 per cent copper and 30 per cent zinc. Weights 0.31 lbs. per cu. in. See *Alloys, Brass.*

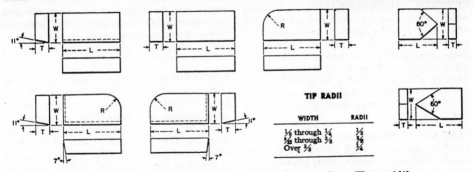

TIP RADII	
WIDTH	**RADII**
1/8 through 1/4	1/8
5/16 through 3/8	3/16
Over 3/8	1/4

Carbide inserts. L = length. T = thickness. R = radius. W = width.

CASE—In heat-treating or carburizing work, the hard outer surface produced by steel's absorption of carbon and the resulting hardened surface when the steel is heated and quenched. Some gears used in automotive work are hardened to a depth of 0.050 inch, this depth being called a "case."

CASE-HARDENING—The forming of a hard *case* or outer layer on iron or soft steels. This is now known as carburizing or carbonizing.

CASE-HARDENING COLORS—The colors produced by the combination of heat and the materials used in carbonizing or carburizing. The process usually gives a mottled appearance with gray, brown and blue tones.

CASE-HARDENING MATERIAL—Any substance from which carbon can be added to the surface of iron or low carbon steel. See *Carburizing Material.*

CASTELLATED—A term generally used in connection with nuts which are slotted across the outer end to permit cotter pins to be inserted in the slots and through the bolt to prevent turning due to vibration. The term comes from the resemblance to the turrets of a castle. See *Nuts.*

CAST IRON—Iron with from 2 to 6 per cent carbon. There are two such irons, white and gray. Sp. Gr. 7.50 for white and 7.10 for gray. Weighs 0.28 lb. per cu. in. Melts at 2,460 deg. F.

CAST STEEL—The term was originally applied to tool steel cast from crucibles. Its present use refers to casting, made from steel instead of from cast iron or other metals.

CASTER TRAILERS—A shop name for flat platforms, floats or pallets mounted on wheels for easy movement or for towing by shop tractors. Sometimes called trucks.

CATALYST—Any material that accelerates chemical action without combining with the other materials.

CATCHING THE THREAD—Re-engaging the lead screw so that the threading tool will coincide with the thread already being cut. Where the thread being cut is a multiple of the pitch of the lead screw, the lead screw may be engaged at any point. Where it is not it is necessary to engage the lead screw at exactly the right point.

CATGUT—Strings made from the intestines of sheep.

CATHEAD CHUCK—Local shop term for an adapter which screws on the spindle nose of a lathe or other machine and holds special work by means of set screws. See also *Chuck, Cathead.*

CAUSTIC—Any substance that causes rapid corrosion.

CAVALIER PROJECTION—See *Projection, Cavalier.*

CELLULOSE—The solid portion forming the structure of plants. When ground it forms a white amorphous powder which dissolves in sulphuric acid but not in water or alcohol. There are two kinds, cellulose-acetate and cellulose-nitrate. Both are used in plastics.

CEMENTS, COLD SETTING—Cements which do not require heat for use, nor much pressure. They are not safe at temperatures over 120 deg. F. The bond strength varies from 300 to 700 lb. per square inch. They resist oil and water.

CEMENTS, THERMOPLASTIC — Cements which become soft with heat and are not used where heat is to be applied afterwards. They require up to 450 deg. F. before being fused. Some require little or no pressure in bonding, while others need up to 2,000 lb. pressure. They should not be used at temperatures over 200 deg. F. Bond strength varies from 1,500 to 3,500 lb. per square inch. They resist oil and water.

CEMENTS, THERMOSETTING — Cements which become set, or hard, after heating. They remain hard, as do thermosetting plastics, after being heated. The cements require from 250 to 400 deg. F. heat and up to 500 lb. pressure per square inch to secure the greatest bond. They should not be subjected to more than 250 deg. F. after being used, some about half this. The bond strength is about 3,000 lb. per square inch. They resist oil and water.

CEMENTATION—The act of causing a chemical combination below the fusion point of the materials. Steel was formerly made by surrounding iron with carbon and heating below the fusion point, this being known as *cemented* steel. It was also called blister steel. This is very much like the sintering process, used in making carbide tips and other tools. These were formerly known as cemented carbide. See *Sintering*.

CEMENTED CARBIDE TOOLS — A name formerly given to all kinds of carbide tools. The term is incorrect, as the pulverized particles which make up the tools or tool tips are not cemented but are sintered. See *Sintering*.

CENTER, BALL BEARING—A center for lathe and similar work in which the dead, or tailstock, center contains a ball bearing. Instead of the work revolving on the sharp pointed center the center revolves with the work.

CENTER, BULL—A supplementary lathe center which fits over the regular dead center and supports a hollow piece of work, as a pipe.

CENTER, CROSS—A lathe center for tailstock with a V at right angles to the lathe. It is useful in holding round work while drilling holes through the diameter of the bar.

CENTER, DEAD—In lathe or similar machine work, the center which does not revolve with the work. In mechanisms involving a crank and a connecting rod, the term "dead center"

means that the center of the crank pin and the center of the axle are in line with the center of the source of power, so that no turning action can take place due to end pressure on the connecting rod.

CENTER GAGE—A sheet metal gage used in setting thread chasing tools in lathe work. It has a 60-degree angular point and two 60-degree notches, as shown. The end notch is sometimes used at the tailstock to set the threading tool by the angularity of the dead center as at lower left. The side is also used as shown at upper left. For internal threading the gage is used as at right.

CENTER, LIVE—The center in the revolving spindle of a lathe or other machine. It is important that all live centers run true to avoid rotating the work in an eccentric path.

CENTER OF GRAVITY—See *C. G.*

CENTER, PIPE—A lathe center having an enlarged cone which revolves on a central spindle and supports a piece of pipe while it is being machined. The center can have a ball bearing if desired.

CENTER PUNCH—A punch for making a round mark on metal to show the location in which a hole is to be drilled or otherwise machined. Frequently called a prick punch.

CENTER PUNCH, AUTOMATIC — A tool with a spring loaded hammer in the handle. Placing the point where desired and pressing on the handle releases the spring which actuates the hammer and marks the work.

CENTER PUNCH, BELL—A center punch which has a hollow coned sleeve through which it slides. When the cone or bell is placed over the end of a round bar square with the axis, it automatically locates the center of the bar with the punch. Centering machines have largely replaced the locating of centers by this and other methods.

CENTER PUNCH, LOCATING or SPACING —Name given to a center punch with a second point that is adjustable. The second point, usually mounted on a spring, is placed in the first punch mark and locates the desired space between the marks to be made.

CENTER REAMER—A cone pointed reamer for preparing work to run on lathe centers.

CENTER REST—Same as *Steady Rest*.

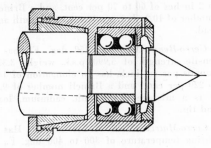

Ball bearing center.

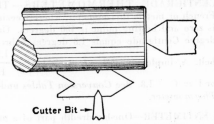

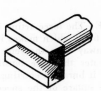

Center gage: Cutter bit set square with work for cutting external screw threads.

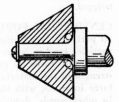

Cross center.

Center for pipe or hollow work.

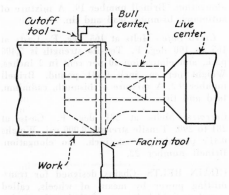

Bull center grips end of stock for cutting collars from tube.

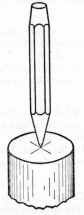

Center punch.

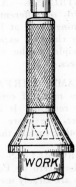

Bell center punch.

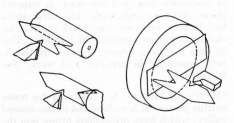

Center gage: Using center gage for setting threading tool.

CENTER SQUARE—A tool having a head with a 90-degree opening and a scale which bisects this angle. Placed against a round bar, it shows the center line. Scribing lines at right angles across the face shows the center.

CENTERING MACHINES—Machines for locating, drilling and reaming center holes on which the work is to run while being machined.

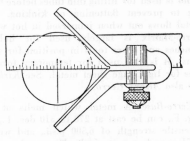

Center square.

CENTIGRADE THERMOMETERS—The French or metric thermometer, where freezing is zero and boiling point is 100 degrees. One degree Centigrade equals 1.8 degrees Fahrenheit. A simple conversion formula is $C = \dfrac{1.8}{F}$ or $F = C \times 1.8$. See *Conversion Tables* under *Thermometer*.

CENTIMETER—One-hundredth part of a meter, or 0.3937 inches. See *Metric System*.

CENTRIFUGAL CLUTCH—See *Clutch, Centrifugal*.

CENTRIFUGAL FORCE—The force acting in all parts of a revolving body which makes its particles tend to move away from the center. When this force is greater than the tensile strength of the material, it bursts. Centrifugal force increases with the square of the speed. In other words, doubling the speed increases the centrifugal force four times, as shown by the diagram. Tripling the speed increases the centrifugal force nine times, as shown in the diagram.

CENTRIFUGE—A device which separates liquids of different densities by rotating or spinning them at high speed. It is used in many chemical experiments and is similar in principle to the cream separators used by farmers.

CERAMIC SURFACE PLATES—Surface plates made of ceramic materials which are wear resisting. It is claimed that they wear longer, are more nearly flat, and have a smoother surface than metal surface plates.

CERRO METALS—Low melting alloys made by the Cerro de Pasco Copper Co. as listed. They are largely used by the airplane industry in forming aluminum sheets for various purposes, sometimes in small quantities. Cerro-Bend is used for filling thin tubes before bending to prevent flattening or kinking. The metal flows out when immersed in hot water. Cerro-Matrix is largely used for holding punches and other tools in position for short runs. It is also used for temporary forming dies for light gage sheet metal. See *Kirksite*. See also *Alloys, Cerro*.

Cerro-Base—A metal which melts at 255 deg. F., can be cast at 270 to 310 deg. F., has a tensile strength of 6,500 p.s.i., and weighs 0.371 pounds per cu. inch. Has an elongation in 2 inches of 60 to 70 per cent, and a Brinell number of 10.2. It is a mixture of bismuth and lead.

Cerro-Bend—Melts at 158 deg. F., has a tensile strength of 5,990 p.s.i., weighs 3.339 pounds per cu. inch, has an elongation of 140 to 220 per cent, and a Brinell number of 9.2. It is a mixture of bismuth, cadmium, lead and tin.

Cerro-Matrix—Melts at 248 deg. F. Has a casting temperature of 300 to 400 deg. F., a tensile strength of 13,000 p.s.i., and weighs 0.343 pounds per cu. inch. Has almost no elongation. Brinell number 19. A mixture of antimony, bismuth, lead and tin.

Cerro Safe—Melts at 165 deg. F. Casts at 165 to 190 deg. F. Tensile strength is 5,400 p.s.i., and elongation 40 per cent in 2 inches. Weight per cu. inch 0.341 pound. Brinell number 9.2. A mixture of bismuth, cadmium, lead and tin.

Cerrotru—Melts at 281 deg. F. Casts at 281 to 290. Tensile strength 8,000 psi. Weighs 0.315 pounds per cu. inch. No elongation. Brinell number 22.

CHAIN BELTS—Chains designed for transmitting power by means of wheels, called sprockets, which have teeth fitting the chains used. Four kinds of chains are used: Block, link, roller and silent. Link chains are usually of malleable iron and are used in exposed places and for rough work. The silent chain has largely replaced the block and roller chain for use on machines in factories. This in turn has been largely replaced by the V-belt, especially in machine tool work. See *Belts, Link*.

CHAIN, GEARING—A chain used for transmitting power. It is endless and passes around pulleys which have projections fitting into the openings in the chain links, or depressions which receive projections on the chain, as with silent chain drive.

CHAIN PULLEY—See *Pulley, Chain*.

CHAIN SLINGS—Chains used in hoisting and handling heavy materials or machines with a crane. See *Crane Slings* for details.

CHAIN TONGS—See *Tongs, Chain*.

CHAMBER—An enlarged space, usually but not always at one end of a hole, as the cartridge chamber in a rifle. Also called a recess.

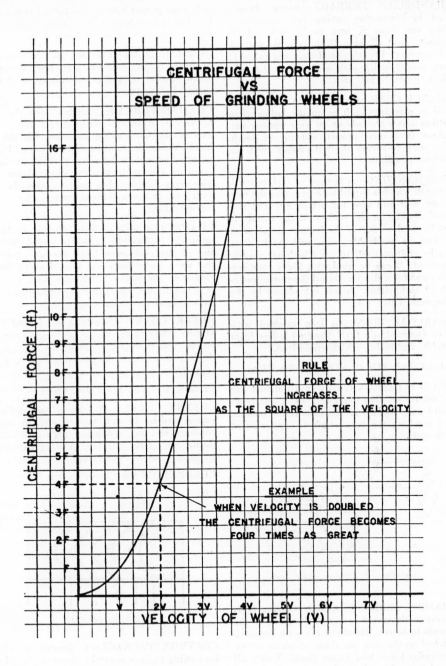

CENTRIFUGAL FORCE
VS
SPEED OF GRINDING WHEELS

RULE
CENTRIFUGAL FORCE OF WHEEL
INCREASES
AS THE SQUARE OF THE VELOCITY

EXAMPLE
WHEN VELOCITY IS DOUBLED
THE CENTRIFUGAL FORCE BECOMES
FOUR TIMES AS GREAT

CENTRIFUGAL FORCE (F)

VELOCITY OF WHEEL (V)

41

CHANDELIER THREADS — Screw threads used in connecting tubing for chandeliers. They run from ¼ inch to ¾ inch outside diameter and all have 27 threads per inch in this country. French chandeliers use tubes 11 mm. (0.433 inch) with a thread of 1.3 mm. pitch, about 20 per inch.

CHANGE GEAR—Gears used to give desired feed to machines such as engine lathes when cutting screw threads or in gear cutting machines to secure proper spacing of teeth. Also used to secure desired cutting feeds on various machines.

CHAPMANIZING—A method of surface hardening in which a liquid bath provides the necessary heat and also the active nitrogen material directly to the surface of the metal. It can be used on any of the ferrous metals such as cast or malleable iron, and steel. Case depths of from 0.002 to 0.035 inch are readily obtained. It can be used with lower temperatures and for a shorter period than some methods of carburizing. It was introduced by the Chapman Valve Co.

CHARCOAL IRON—An iron smelted with wood charcoal as a fuel. The fuel is free from sulphur and makes a high grade iron.

CHARCOAL TIN PLATE—See *Tin Plate.*

CHARPY TEST—A test using a notched bar to determine the toughness of a material. There are standard measurements for making and notching the bar, which is supported at both ends.

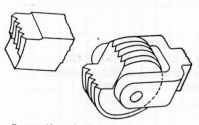

Screw thread chasers—two forms.

CHASERS, SCREW THREAD—Cutting tools having teeth spaced to match the pitch of the threads to be cut. Hand chasers, with the teeth notched on the end, are about obsolete, as few men today know how to use them. Nearly all dies for machine threading have chasers inserted in a die head. As die heads are now

fed at the proper rate for the thread being cut, bearing surface behind the cutting edges is no longer necessary. Also see *Die Heads.*

CHASING DIAL—A device on the carriage of thread cutting lathes to show when the lead screw can be engaged in position to catch the thread being cut.

CHASING THREADS—Cutting screw threads by moving a properly shaped tool along the axis of the work to be threaded. Except in hand chasing the tool usually has but a single point which is fed along the work by the lead screw to secure the desired pitch of thread. The term distinguishes between threads cut with a tap or dies and those produced by screw cutting lathes.

CHATTER—Rough or unsatisfactory surfaces on work. It is usually caused by a slight jumping of the tool away from the work or of the work away from the tool, leaving little ridges on the work. Where the work is thin it is usually the latter, due to vibration in the thin wall of the work.

CHECK CHART—Usually a condensed list of data referring to specific processes or operations, (for example, symptoms or failures in drilling holes), and the probable reason, with suggestions for overcoming the defects.

CHECK VALVE—See *Valve, Check.*

CHERRY CUTTER—A type of end milling cutter used in die sinking machines. It has a rounded end for producing cavities of that form. See *Cutter, Milling.* The operation is frequently called "cherrying."

CHERRYING—See *Cherry Cutter.*

CHERRY RIVET—See *Rivet, Blind.*

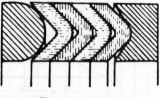

Chevron packing.

CHEVRON PACKING—A flexible packing for sealing passage around piston rods or other moving parts, having a section similar to the chevrons used to designate rank on military uniforms. The V-sections expand against both rod and the gland box in which it is confined. When used on landing gear struts on airplanes they are usually made of synthetic rubber materials so as not to be affected by oils.

CHILL—A metal piece placed in a mold and forming part of the contour so that the hot metal will cool rapidly, or chill, from contact with this piece, or chill. In railroad car wheels the chill is a ring which hardens the whole outer surface, or tread. The term is sometimes applied to the process of chilling parts used in making expansion fits. The parts are chilled with dry ice or by other means which reduces their size so they can be inserted in holes of somewhat smaller dimensions. When they resume room temperature they expand and make a tight fit, the reverse of a shrink fit.

CHIP—The metal removed by a tool. In turning with a single point tool, chips sometimes make continuous curls many feet long and become a menace. Chip-breakers of various kinds are used to make the chip break into short pieces. Chip usually refers to the thickness removed by the tool, which depends on the feed. It seldom refers to depth of cut but to the feed per revolution, in turning, and the feed per tooth in milling.

CHIP BREAKER — A device for breaking chips made by turning metal into small pieces, instead of letting the chip come off in long curls. The usual method is to grind a recess on top of the cutting tool just back of the cutting edge. This recess or groove is so shaped as to bend the chip as soon as it comes

off the work and so break it. In some cases, the chip breaker is a separate piece clamped to the top of the tool but which acts in the same manner. Kennametal suggests the three types shown.

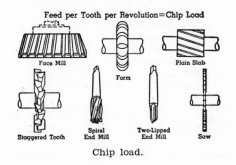

Chip load.

CHIP LOAD—The term used to give the feed per tooth in milling and similar cutters. It is the feed per tooth for each revolution of the cutter or boring bar. The fewer the number of teeth the more the chip load for the same feed per minute. Chip loads for cutters of various kinds, recommended by Kearney & Trecker Co., are tabulated on the next page.

CHIPPING—The cutting of metal with a cold chisel and hammer. It is also used to describe the breaking away, or chipping, of small pieces of metal from any cause.

CHISEL(S)—Tools with sharpened edges for cutting wood or metal. Those for metal are called "cold chisels," and are made in various shapes for special kinds of work. Some of the various kinds are shown on the next page.

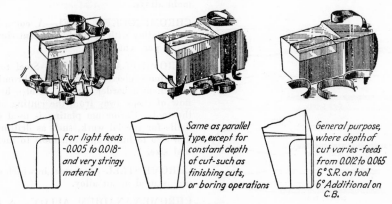

For light feeds -0.005 to 0.018- and very stringy material

Same as parallel type, except for constant depth of cut-such as finishing cuts, or boring operations

General purpose, where depth of cut varies -feeds from 0.012 to 0.065 6° S.R. on tool 6° Additional on C.B.

Chip breaker.

Recommended Chip Load Tables

Type of Cutter	In Cast Iron	In Steel	In Brass Bronze Aluminum
Face Mill, H. S.	.010 to .025	Less 40%	Plus 50%
Slab Mill, H. S.	.010 to .015	Less 40%	Plus 50%
Slotting Cutter, H. S.	.006 to .012	Less 40%	Plus 50%
Form Mill, H. S.	.004 to .006	Less 40%	Plus 50%
End Mill, H. S.	.002 to .010	Less 40%	Plus 50%
Saw, H. S.	.001 to .003	Less 40%	Plus 50%
Cemented Carbide Face Mill	.008 to .012	.004 to .008	.010 to .016

In general, select the proper SPEED for work material and cutter; and then determine the feed, within the above limits, according to the cut and the power available or the finish required.

CHISEL, CAPE—A cold chisel with a narrow point or blade, for cutting grooves such as keyways in shafting or elsewhere.

CHISEL, COLD—Any chisel for cutting cold metal. The name is usually applied to plain flat chisels of various widths.

CHISEL, DIAMOND OR LOZENGE—Similar to a cape chisel, but with the cutting end square in shape and cutting on one corner.

CHISEL, DRAW—A round-nosed chisel used in chipping out one side of the coned hole made by a drill which has started a little to one side of the intended point.

CHISEL, FLOGGING—A heavy chisel used for chipping ingots or heavy castings. A short handled, heavy hammer is generally used with it.

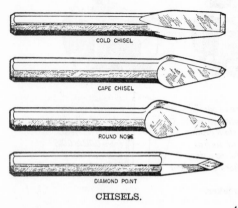

COLD CHISEL

CAPE CHISEL

ROUND NOSE

DIAMOND POINT

CHISELS.

CHISEL, ROUND—A round-ended chisel with the cutting edge ground back to give a good cutting edge. Used for cutting round bottom grooves.

CHOCK—Usually a wedge-shaped block used to prevent round pieces from rolling. Some use the term for shims or wedges used in leveling machinery.

CHORDAL PITCH—The distance between the center of one gear tooth and the next, on the chord, or straight line, between the two at the pitch line. See *Gearing*, page 164.

CHROME CAST—Cast iron with chromium as the main alloy.

CHROME-MOLYBDENUM STEEL—Steel in which chromium and molybdenum are the main alloys.

CHROME-NICKEL STEEL—A corrosion resisting alloy with about 18 per cent chromium and 8 per cent nickel.

CHROME PLATED TOOLS—Steel tools are sometimes electro-plated with chromium to give them a harder surface. It also helps the flow of chips away from the cutting edges of the tools. Chromium plating is used on new drills for special work, such as drilling slate, and also to build up worn tools to their original size.

CHROME STEEL—Any steel in which chromium is used as an alloy.

CHROME-VANADIUM ALLOY — A chrome alloy steel with some vanadium.

CHROMIUM—A metal used in stainless steel and for electro-plating. It is very hard and resists corrosion. Sp. Gr. 6.92. Melts at 2,750 deg. F.

CHROMIUM COPPER—A copper alloy with chromium.

CHROMIZING—A process of impregnating the surfaces of a steel piece with chromium. It converts the surface into a rich chromium alloy.

CHUCK—Device for holding work in machine tools of various kinds. There are many types of chucks, some of which are illustrated here.

CHUCK, BOX OR BATWING—A lathe chuck having a rectangular body, instead of the usual round shape. They save weight but are more dangerous to use and are now seldom seen.

CHUCK, CAT-HEAD — A collar or sleeve which fits closely over a shaft and is fastened to it by set screws. Frequently used over rough work to present a smooth surface for the steady rest jaws. Tool carrying heads for boring bars are also known as cat-heads in some sections.

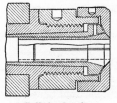

Collet chuck.

CHUCK, COLLET—A chuck for holding finished work of a given diameter. The same chuck can hold various sizes of collets made to fit different diameters.

CHUCK, COLLET, MECHANISMS—There are three types of collet chuck mechanisms in use in turret lathe work. These are known as the stationary, drawback and pushout types. The stationary type provides the more accurate endwise location, as the others have a slight end movement when the collet is tightened. Collets of the stationary type do not move endwise, but may not be as accurate in concentricity. The pushout type closes the collet by forcing the plunger A against the back end. (Illus. p. 46.)

This action is reversed in the drawback type, as can be seen.

CHUCK, DRAW—A chuck in which the jaws are operated by drawing them longitudinally in a tapered bearing. They are frequently called collets, and are used in the more accurate kinds of work.

CHUCK, EXPANDING—Any chuck which expands and grips hollow work on the inside.

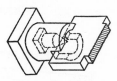

Flat driving chuck.

CHUCK, FLAT DRIVING—A piece which screws on the spindle nose and has a slot across the front end for driving flat cutters or other work to be turned. The slot must permit the centered end of the cutter to reach the live center of the lathe so as to insure the piece being correctly located.

CHUCK, INDEPENDENT—A chuck in which the jaws do not move in unison but can be

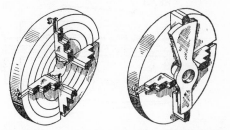

Stepped independent jaws for lathe chucks.

adjusted separately. For many classes of work these have real advantages. In the illustration two of the jaws have been reversed so that the steps act as a base for supporting the odd-shaped piece of work which is held at four points. They are usually made with either three or four jaws.

CHUCK, MAGNETIC—A device for holding iron or steel parts while they are being machined. These chucks are usually for grinding flat surfaces, but are also made for use in lathes. They are made with both permanent

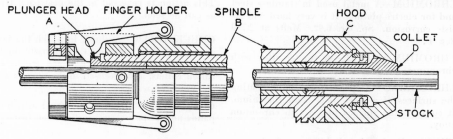

Collet chuck mechanism, pushout type.

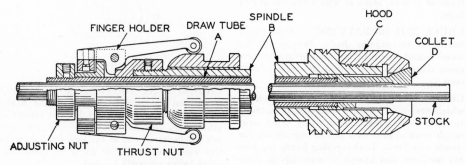

Collet chuck mechanism, drawback type.

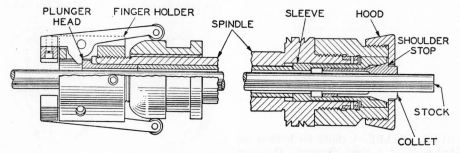

Collet chuck mechanism, stationary type.

magnets and electro-magnets. Probably originated with O. S. Walker of Worcester, Mass.

CHUCK, MASTER—Local shop name for a piece which screws on the spindle nose of a lathe or other machine and which has threads on its outer end to hold chucks or fixtures. It is really a threaded "adapter."

CHUCK OVAL—A special form of lathe chuck that moved the work toward and also away from the tool so as to make the part oval. The positions of the long and short diam-

eters could be varied. It was designed for oval dinner pails which were used by shop men at one time, but it is doubtful if any are still in use.

CHUCK, PERMANENT MAGNET—A chuck with permanent magnets instead of electro-magnets which require connection to an outside supply of electric current. It is made in a variety of sizes and forms to suit different work. The operation of the magnetic flux in both active and neutral positions is shown on p. 47.

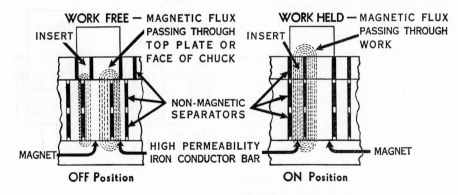

WORK FREE — MAGNETIC FLUX PASSING THROUGH TOP PLATE OR FACE OF CHUCK

WORK HELD — MAGNETIC FLUX PASSING THROUGH WORK

INSERT

NON-MAGNETIC SEPARATORS

MAGNET

HIGH PERMEABILITY IRON CONDUCTOR BAR

MAGNET

OFF Position

ON Position

Permanent magnet chuck.

CHUCK, POT—A chuck bored to fit certain classes of work which cannot be held conveniently in regular chucks. It is a casting or "pot" threaded to fit the lathe spindle and bored to receive the work, as shown. The work is held against turning by a set screw in most cases. The outer end should be supported by a steady rest. Only used where a number of pieces of the same size are to be turned, usually at infrequent intervals.

Pot chuck.

CHUCK, SCREW—The term is usually applied to chucks for holding threaded work by screwing it into the chuck itself. It can also be applied to any chuck in which the pressure is put on the work by means of one or more screws.

CHUCK SCROLL—A type of chuck where the jaws are moved simultaneously by the scroll ring shown. The ring is turned by small bevel gears shown.

CHUCK, STEP—A seldom-used type of chuck in which the work fits into a recess and is held by friction due to the work being a snug fit in the chuck opening. Used only in special types of work, usually on comparatively thin pieces of material.

Step chuck.

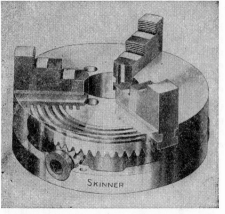

Skinner 3-jaw universal chuck with scroll.

CHUCK, UNIVERSAL—A chuck in which the jaws all move at the same time and at the same rate. This is done either by the use of a scroll or plate with a helix cut in it that operates the jaws, as shown, or small bevel pinions on each screw mesh with a ring gear so that all screws in the jaws move together. The scroll type will usually stand more pressure in tightening the work. They are usually made with either three or four jaws.

CHUCK, VACUUM—A device for holding flat or formed sheet metal work for machining without the use of mechanical clamps of any kind. The fixture has a work surface which has a multitude of holes on which the work is laid in close contact. The fixture has a

47

vacuum pump which exhausts the air from the fixture and holds the work firmly in place.

CIRCULAR FORMING TOOL—See *Forming Tools.*

CIRCULAR PITCH—The distance between two teeth of a gear as measured on the curve of the pitch line. See *Gearing*, page 164.

CLACK BOX—Really a valve in which the valve is a flat piece, usually pivoted at the top, which drops into place when any flow takes place in the wrong direction. It frequently makes a noise, which gives it the name.

CLAD MATERIALS—In metals this means the combination of two or more metals in sheet form. In jewelry and silverware it is sometimes known as "rolled plate." England's "Sheffield plate," originating well over 200 years ago, was made by pressing silver and copper sheets together until they bonded, or became one sheet. Various metals are combined. Light alloys are "clad" with pure aluminum, copper kettles are clad with stainless steel and many other combinations are in use. Steel bars are sometimes "clad" with brass or copper to protect against corrosion.

CLAMP—A device for temporarily holding parts together. They are made in many forms. Screw clamps are most common but clamps are also actuated by cams and levers.

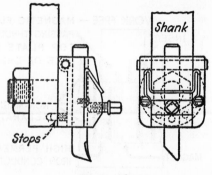

Clapper box.

CLARK RIVETS—Rivets made by the Clark Co., which have standardized flat, button, countersunk, truss and cone heads. These are similar to standard rivets and the name is likely to drop out of use.

CLAW COUPLING—Another name for a jaw clutch or coupling.

CLEARANCE — The space between mating parts to allow freedom of movement or to prevent interference.

CLEARANCE DROP ON CUTTERS AND REAMERS—See *Milling Cutters.*

CLEARANCE FIT—See *Fits.*

CLICK—Another name for a pawl or detent. See *Pawl.*

CLIMB CUTTING—In milling where the feed allows the cutter teeth to climb, or cut down into the work. Sometimes called *down* or *in* cutting. The latter may be adopted as the standard designation for this type of feeding, which has many advantages. See *Milling*, page 279.

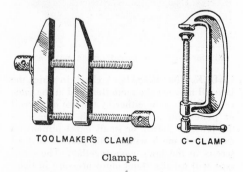

TOOLMAKER'S CLAMP   C-CLAMP

Clamps.

CLAPPER or **CLAPPER BOX**—The hinged piece used on a planer, shaper or similar machine to hold the cutting tool. Being hinged, it permits the tool to raise itself on the return stroke. This is sometimes mounted in a swiveling head, as on some planers. This swiveling head is called a "harp" in some sections of the mid-west, but is usually known as a swivel.

CLINCH NUTS—See *Nuts, Clinch.*

CLOCKWISE—Moving in the same direction as the hands of a clock or other timepiece.

CLOSE NIPPLE—A short connection used in piping work. It is twice as long as the standard length of pipe thread but has no shoulder between the threads on each end.

CLOUDBURST HARDENING—See *Hardening, Cloudburst.*

CLUTCH, CENTRIFUGAL—A clutch with expanding, self-energizing shoes which grip harder as the speed increases. Used with an electric motor, it permits the motor to attain part of its normal speed before the clutch begins to act.

CLUTCH, FLUID—A device in which liquid, usually oil, is forced through restricted passages in the stationary member until the pressure caused by increased speed of flow forces the stationary member to turn. When the driven member is up to speed there is very little slippage. This is being used increasingly in automobile transmissions and also in large and heavy duty machinery, as it gives a very gradual starting of the driven member without mechanical wear of parts involved, as with metal or other friction surfaces.

CLUTCH, FRICTION—A device for engaging a stationary shaft to one that is already in motion. Slippage occurs from the instant the friction surfaces are engaged until the speed of the two shafts is the same. As this means wear of the friction surfaces it is desirable to have as little slippage as possible. Various friction surfaces are used, from leather or plastic to powdered metal, the latter now being impregnated with lubricant to reduce wear. The fluid drive, or clutch, is really a slipping clutch until the parts move in unison, as the oil flows between the two members until both parts move at the same speed.

CLUTCH HEAD SCREW—See *Screw, Clutch Head.*

CLUTCH, JAW—A clutch which has on both members, jaws that engage to provide a positive drive.

CLUTCH, MAGNETIC—A clutch in which the contacting surfaces are drawn together by magnetism, usually by electro-magnets rather than by permanent magnets.

CLUTCH, MERCURY—A fluid clutch in which mercury is used instead of oil. Centrifugal action forces the fluid away from the center and engages the clutch.

COAL OIL—See *Kerosene.*

COBALT—A metal resembling nickel and used as an alloy in steel. Sp. Gr. 8.756. Melts at about 3,000 deg. F.

COBALT STEELS—Steels containing cobalt as an alloy, such as high speed steels.

COEFFICIENT OF EXPANSION—The expansion or contraction which takes place in the metals named for each inch in diameter and each degree change of temperature, Fahrenheit scale. This is necessary to know what allowance to make for shrink and expansion fits. The coefficients are:

Aluminum 0.0000128
Brass, cast and rolled...0.0000104 and 0.0000107
Bronze 0.0000094
Copper 0.0000923
Iron, pure 0.0000065
Steel, soft 0.0000063
        hard 0.0000056
Nickel silver 0.0000102

COG—Formerly used to refer to a gear tooth, but now seldom used. Belongs more to the wooden gear era when gears were called cogwheels.

COG BELT—See *Belt, Cog.*

COGGING—Converting a tool sheet ingot into a billet by hammering, rolling or pressing. The Carpenter Steel Co. reduces the ingot to a billet about 9 inches square.

COIL SPRINGS—See *Springs, Helical or Coil.*

COINAGE ALLOYS—See *Alloys, Coinage.*

COLD FORGING—Forging cold or unheated metals.

COLD HEADING—Producing a head or "upset" of larger diameter than the stock used, by pressure on cold metal.

COLD PRESSURE WELDING—See *Welding, Cold Pressure.*

COLD ROLLED STEEL—A low carbon steel that is rolled into strips, sheets or bars while cold. See *Steel, Cold Rolled.*

COLD SHUT—A spot or area where metals which have been worked hot have not welded or united into a solid mass.

COLD SOLDER—See *Solder, Cold.*

COLLAR PIN—See *Pin, Collar.*

COLLET CHUCK—See *Chuck, Collet.*

COLLIMATOR—A device used for mechanical alignment. Light from a source just below the eye-piece is reflected from a half-silvered mirror and is focused on a glass plate scribed with cross-hairs. The image of the hairs is beamed down through a telescope lens that forms the light into a straight beam of parallel light which then reflects from a mirror and is reflected straight up. A target mirror is mounted on a steel disk with a bottom surface lapped exactly parallel to the mirror. With graduated cross-hairs any non-parallelism can be measured. Used in England and Canada during the war, it checked bomb door alignments on Lancaster bombers within .01 inch in a length of 50 feet.

COLOR CODE—Any system of designating machines, materials, pipes, wires, etc., by using special colors to distinguish different names. See *Pipe Line Colors*.

COLOR IN THE SHOP—Instead of painting machine tools and other equipment a solid dark color, modern management finds that more pleasing colors add to efficiency of men and also tend to prevent accidents. As an example of the modern trend, the colors used in the repair shops of the Chesapeake & Ohio Railway at Huntington, W. Va., are given:

Air lines.....................Black
Ceiling ....Blue White
Cranes ....Yellow
Dado ....Light Gray
End walls (east and west
    ends of the building......Sun-tan Yellow
Fire-fighting equipment .....Red
Gas lines ....Red
Handwheels, levers ....Yellow
Machine bases ....Green
Operating parts (Flywheels,
    slides) ....Ivory
Steam lines ....Buff
Switch boxes, control boxes...Orange
Tool bins, racks, vises.......Tile Red
Trucks......................Maroon
Walls ....Light Blue

Basic green is applied to non-moving machine parts with bright colors showing up rotating and reciprocating members and controls in this large locomotive-repair plant.

COLUMBIUM—A metal with a melting point of 3,200 to 3,300 deg. F. It is somewhat heavier than steel, a cubic inch weighing 0.309 pounds, a cubic foot 534 pounds.

COMBINATION DRILL—Now usually called center drills. See *Drill, Combination*, page 87.

COMBINED CARBON—The carbon present in iron or steel which is not present in the form of carbon.

COMMERCIAL BRASS—See *Alloys, Brass, Commercial*.

COMMERCIAL BRONZE—See *Bronze, Commercial*.

COMMERCIAL TOLERANCES — See *Tolerances, Commercial*.

COMMON BRASS—See *High Brass*.

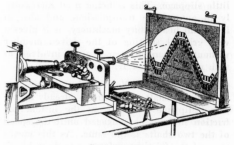

Comparator.

COMPARATOR—A device designed by James Hartness for inspecting screw threads and outlines by comparing them with a greatly enlarged standard chart. As shown, the bolt is laid on supports so that the light from the projector will show its form against the standard chart. If the outline of the screw being tested comes between the outlines on the chart the screw is within the prescribed tolerance. The magnification shown is 50 times. Similar devices are now made by others.

COMPLEMENTARY ANGLES—Two angles which together measure 90 degrees. Each is complementary to the other.

COMPONENT—A single part of any mechanism. Components are usually first put together in sub-assemblies and these put together to form the completed machine.

COMPOSITION BRASS—An alloy about midway between brass and bronze.

COMPOUND ANGLE — See *Angle, Compound*.

COMPOUND DIE—See *Die, Compound*.

COMPOUND FITS—See *Fits, Compound*.

COMPOUND INDEXING—See *Indexing, Compound*.

COMPOUND LEVERS—See *Levers, Compound.*

COMPOUND REST—A tool carrying device on an engine lathe which permits the slide carrying the tool to be fed at any desired angle across the bed. Similar mechanisms are used on other machines as well. See *Slide Rest.*

COMPOUND SCREW—See *Screw, Compound.*

COMPRESSED WHEELS FOR BUFFING—See *Buffing, Compressed Wheels.*

COMPRESSION STRENGTH— See *Strength of Materials.*

CONE—A solid circular or oval mass of material, the diameter of which varies from a sharp point at one end to a round or oval base. If the small end is not a point but is simply of smaller diameter than the base, it is a "truncated cone." The variation in diameters between the two ends is, in either case, regular, which means that the sides of the mass are regular; not jagged or broken. In shop language, a cone is also a pulley having two or more different diameters, forming a series of steps. They were formerly used to drive machines and machine feeds at different rates, from a constant speed line shaft. It is also used in connection with pulleys of varying diameters with grooves for a V-belt. As most machine tools are now motor driven, cone, or stepped pulleys are not commonly used except on smaller and less expensive machines.

CONE, AREA OF—The area of the convex surface of a cone is equal to the circumference of the base multiplied by one-half the height.

CONE DRIVE COUNTERSHAFT—An old device for securing variable speeds. It consisted of two conical drums with an endless belt pinched between them, as shown. When the belt was moved from one end to the other it varied the speed of the driven drum so that an almost infinite variety of speeds could be obtained by the driven machine. It was very useful in some fields but was never very widely used. Known as the Evans drive.

CONE WORM—See *Gear, Hour-glass worm.*

CONIFLEX GEAR TOOTH—A gear tooth slightly thicker at its center than at the end to insure bearing away from the ends of the tooth. Devised by the Gleason Works for bevel gears. See *Gearing.*

CONJU-GAGE GEAR MEASUREMENT—A method devised by engineers in the Eastman Kodak Co. for checking precision gears. It uses a narrow section part of a worm for making contact with the teeth of the gear. These sections are accurately conjugated to *spur or helical gears of any helix angle or any diameter* as long as they have the same normal pitch and pressure angle. These worm sections are made to tolerances almost impossible to attain in circular master gears, especially in the finer pitches. They can be used to check taper and crown as well runout, base pitch errors, tooth thickness variations, profile error, lateral runout and lead errors in helical gears.

CONN ROD—A shop term for connecting rods for any machanism.

CONNECTING ROD BOLT—See *Bolt, Connecting Rod.*

CONSTANTS—Numbers which bear a fixed relation to values of such elements as screw threads, angles or other measurements. They save much time in making calculations, as they usually require only simple multiplication. See *Screw Threads* as an example. Here the values given are subtracted from the outside diameter.

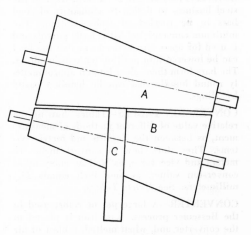

Cone drive countershaft: (A) Driving pulley. (B) Driver pulley. (C) Belt which varies speed of driver as it is moved.

CONSTANTS FOR SCREW THREADS—See *Screw Threads, Constants for Pitch and Root Diameter.*

CONTACT PRESSURE IN GAGING—In making fine measurements by mechanical means, a standard or constant pressure of the instrument on the part being measured is necessary. These contact pressures vary from 2 to 16 ounces, but should be constant where comparative measurements are being made.

CONTINENTAL DIES—See *Dies, Continental.*

CONTINUOUS FILING—Filing with small sections of files attached to a steel band, resembling a band saw. This has largely replaced the older filing machine method in which the file reciprocated vertically through a hole in the work table.

CONTRACT SHOP—A shop which contracts to manufacture parts or complete machines for other concerns. Called a job shop by some.

CONTROL GEAR—See *Gear, Control.*

CONTROL MASTER—A tool used to fabricate or duplicate a tool master, in whole or in part. The control master fits into the master jig and checks mating points.

CONTOUR GROUND—Grinding of milling cutter teeth on the contour instead of on the face. See *Milling Cutters, Contour Ground.*

CONVENTIONAL LIFT—A term used in the steel business to designate a quantity of steel bars to be carried in transportation. The minimum conventional lift is 6,000 pounds and is used for open cars or trucks so that the load can be lowered into position without handling. The bars form themselves into an approximately round bundle that can be handled easily by slings.

CONVERSION TABLES—Tables showing the relative value of different methods of measurement, as between the English and metric systems. They show how to convert inches to meters and vice versa, as well as many other conversion values, as, one inch equals 25.4 millimeters. See *Metric Tables.*

CONVERTER—A large pot or retort used in the Bessemer process. Cast iron is placed in the converter and, when melted, a blast of air is forced through the mass which burns out the surplus carbon, making the iron into steel. See *Bessemer Steel.*

CONVOLUTE—Parts rolled or wound together with one part on another, as the mainspring of a clock or watch. A spiral, it has a constantly increasing diameter.

COOLANTS—Liquids or fluids used to cool work being machined. Some coolants also lubricate the tool to some extent. Air jets are also used to cool work and tool in some cases.

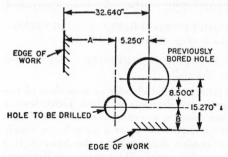

Coordinates for jig boring. Example of vernier scale calculation.

COORDINATES FOR JIG BORERS—Constants for locating the proper spacing of holes by movements of the machine table in two directions, 90 degrees from each other. They show the distance the table must be moved in each direction to locate the holes at the desired points. Tables are prepared to show the movement of the machine table in each direction to lay out different numbers of holes spaced around a circle.

COPING MACHINE—A shear for cutting the flanges and corners of beams of various kinds. It can also bend the ends to desired shapes.

COPPER—A common and very useful metal. Sp. Gr. 8.91. Weight 0.381 lb. per cu. in. Melts at about 1,980 deg. F.

COPPER ALLOYS, NAVY—See *Alloys, Brass.*

COPPER-BASE ALLOYS, CAST, CLASSIFICATION OF—(Based on A.S.T.M. Standard B119-40T).

Copper

Copper—Not over 2 per cent total of arsenic, zinc, cadmium, silicon, chromium, silver, or other elements. Conductivity copper castings, pure copper, deoxidized copper and slightly alloyed copper. Some of these alloys can be precipitation hardened by proper heat-treatment.

BRASS

Red Brass—Zinc, 2 to 8 per cent. Tin less than zinc. Lead less than 0.5 per cent. Alloys in this class without lead seldom used in foundry work.

Leaded Red Brass—Zinc, 2 to 8 per cent. Tin less than 6 per cent, usually less than zinc. Lead *over* 0.5 per cent. May be further modified by addition of nickel. Commonly used foundry alloys. Have good founding and machining characteristics. Used for intricate castings, small gears, pipe fittings, valves and pumps.

Semi-Red Brass—Zinc, 8 to 17 per cent. Tin less than 6 per cent. Lead less than 0.5 per cent. Alloys in this class without lead seldom used in foundry work. Used in the automotive industry for fittings for water pipes which are to be brazed.

Leaded Semi-Red Brass—Zinc, 8 to 17 per cent. Tin less than 6 per cent. Lead over 0.5 per cent. May be further modified by addition of nickel. Commonly used foundry alloys. Inexpensive alloys suitable for low-pressure valves, plumbing fixtures, ornamental castings, hardware fittings and air valves.

Yellow Brass—Zinc, over 17 per cent. Tin less than 6 per cent. Under 2 per cent total aluminum, manganese, nickel, iron or silicon. Lead less than 0.5 per cent. Commonly used for foundry alloys. Used by plumbing industry for valves and fittings, and for making small gears and machine parts in other industries.

Leaded Yellow Brass—Zinc, over 17 per cent. Tin less than 6 per cent. Under 2 per cent total aluminum, manganese, nickel or iron. Lead over 0.5 per cent. Commonly used foundry alloys. Free machining alloys. Used for battery terminals, ship trimmings, valves and fittings, radiator parts and ornamental castings.

High-Strength Yellow Brass—Zinc, over 17 per cent. Tin less than 6 per cent. Over 2 per cent total aluminum, manganese, tin, nickel and iron. Silicon under 0.5 per cent. Lead *under* 0.5 per cent. Commonly used foundry alloys under name of "Manganese Bronze" and various trade names. Have high strength and are resistant to sea water corrosion.

Leaded High-Strength Yellow Brass—Zinc, over 17 per cent. Tin less than 6 per cent. Over 2 per cent total aluminum, manganese, tin, nickel and iron. Lead *over* 0.5 per cent.

Commonly used foundry alloys. Lead content improves machinability at expense of physical properties. Difficult to cast because of aluminum reaction with lead.

Silicon Brass—Over 0.5 per cent silicon. Over 3 per cent zinc. Commonly used foundry alloys. Fair resistance to corrosion and good resistance to season cracking. Should not be used for bearings, nor in contact with steam.

Tin Brass—Over 6 per cent tin. Zinc more than tin. Alloys in this class seldom used in foundry work.

Tin-Nickel Brass—Over 6 per cent tin. Over 4 per cent nickel. Zinc more than tin. Alloys in this class seldom used in foundry work.

Nickel Brass—Over 10 per cent zinc. Nickel in amounts sufficient to give white color. Lead *under* 0.5 per cent. Commonly used foundry alloys. Sometimes called "Nickel Silver" or "German Silver." Has white color and moderate corrosion resistance. Machines easily.

Leaded Nickel Brass—Over 10 per cent zinc. Nickel in amount sufficient to give white color. Lead *over* 0.5 per cent. Commonly used foundry alloys. Sometimes called "Leaded Nickel Silver" or "German Silver." Used for pump parts, marine hardware and fixtures.

BRONZE

Tin Bronze—Tin, 2 to 20 per cent. Zinc less than tin. Lead *under* 0.5 per cent. May be further modified by addition of some nickel or phosphorous, or both. Commonly used foundry alloys. Non-leaded tin bronzes have relatively poor machinability. Castings used for valves and steam fittings, worm gears, and for highly loaded, low speed bearings.

Leaded Tin Bronze—Tin, up to 20 per cent. Zinc less than tin. Lead *over* 0.5 per cent *under* 6 per cent. May be further modified by addition of some nickel or phosphorous, or both. Commonly used foundry alloys. Addition of lead improves machinability, hydraulic pressure tightness and bearing qualities. Used for valves, gears, carburetors, oil pumps and high-duty bearings used at low speeds.

High-Leaded Tin Bronze—Tin, up to 20 per cent. Zinc less than tin. Lead *over* 6 per cent. May be further modified by addition of some nickel or phosphorous, or both. Commonly used foundry alloys. Better suited for high speed bearings than tin bronzes with lower lead content. These alloys machine easily.

Lead Bronze—Lead over 30 per cent. Tin under 10 per cent. Zinc less than tin. Used for special bearing applications. Suitable for bearings where lubrication is intermittent. Do not have sufficient strength for high compressive loads. Some of these alloys used for metallic packing in steam engines.

Nickel Bronze—Nickel over 10 per cent. Zinc less than nickel. Tin under 10 per cent. Lead *under* 0.5 per cent. Commonly used foundry alloys. Sometimes called "Leaded Nickel Silver" or "German Silver." Better machinability than non-leaded alloys. Used for valves and valve seats, marine castings, dairy equipment and hardware.

Aluminum Bronze—Aluminum, 5 to 15 per cent. Up to 10 per cent iron, with or without manganese or nickel. Less than 0.5 per cent silicon. May be further modified by addition of tin. Commonly used foundry alloys. Some may be heat-treated. Have high strength, hardness, toughness and resistance to attack by some corrosive acids. Most of these alloys retain properties at temperatures up to about 500 deg. F.

Silicon Bronze—Silicon over 0.5 per cent. Not over 3 per cent zinc. Not over 98 per cent copper. Commonly used foundry alloys. Some are readily heat-treated. Sand castings are tough, strong and corrosion resistant. Used for marine hardware, gears, chemical process equipment and some munitions.

Beryllium Bronze—Over 2 per cent beryllium plus metals other than copper. Most of these alloys are heat-treatable. Used for welding dies and for making non-sparking safety tools. Also known to industry as "beryllium copper."

The above classification, based on the "Tentative Classification of Cast Copper-Base Alloys" (A. S. T. M. Designation: B119-40T) developed by A. S. T. M. Committee B-5 on Copper and Copper Alloys, Cast and Wrought, includes in the term "copper" all alloys containing 98 per cent or more of copper, includes in the term "brass" all copper-base alloys containing an appreciable amount of zinc, and includes in the term "bronze" all copper-base alloys containing alloying elements other than zinc and in sufficient amounts to be predominant over the zinc in the alloy.

COPPER SILICON ALLOY—Copper alloyed with some silicon and occasionally a little manganese.

COPPER-STEEL—Steel alloyed with 0.25 per cent copper to aid in resisting corrosion.

COPPER SULPHATE—A crystal soluble in water. It is used to paint or coat metals to make it easy to see markings on the surface. Sometimes called bluestone or blue vitriol.

CORE OILS—Binders for sand cores in foundry work. American Foundry Association specifications are 50 per cent raw linseed oil, 25 per cent high grade rosin, 25 per cent water white kerosene.

CORNER ANGLE OF CUTTING TEETH—The angle of the corner with the axis of the cutter. See *Milling Cutters.*

CORROSION-RESISTANT CASTINGS—Castings containing nickel, chromium, carbon, molybdenum and a few other metals which resist both heat and corrosion. The Alloy Casting Institute issues the accompanying list of mixtures which resist corrosion. See page 56.

CORUNDUM—A hard, crystalline mineral abrasive. A natural aluminum oxide.

COSECANT—See *Angle Constants.*

COSINE—See *Angle Constants.*

COTANGENT—See *Angle Constants.*

COTTER—Some consider this a wedge shaped piece driven into a suitable slot for drawing and holding pieces of work together. As usually applied, however, it is a split pin, made from half round stock, so that when formed together the ends go into a drilled hole. The ends may then be spread apart to prevent working out of the hole. While many cotter pins are made with square ends they are easier to use with the ends tapered, and where one leg is slightly longer than the other. Sometimes called cotter keys.

COUNTERBORE—A tool for enlarging a hole for a short distance. It has a pilot which centers it in the hole. Counterbores are made for fillister screw heads and for other purposes. They sometimes have different diameters, as shown.

Counterbore.

COTTERS AND DRILLED BOLTS

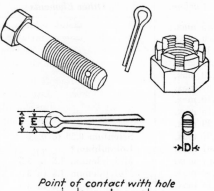

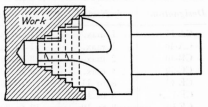

Stepped counterbore.

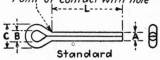

Point of contact with hole

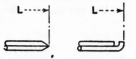

Standard

Miter End   Extended Prong
              Miter End Square Cut

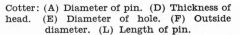

Bevel Point   Hammer Lock

Cotter: (A) Diameter of pin. (D) Thickness of head. (E) Diameter of hole. (F) Outside diameter. (L) Length of pin.

COUNTERBORE, STEPPED— A counterboring tool with various diameters of cutting edges.

COUNTERCLOCKWISE—Turning in the direction *opposite* to the hands of a clock.

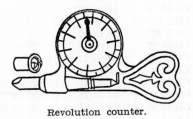

Revolution counter.

COUNTERS—Two kinds of counters are used in manufacturing plants; a revolution counter for checking the number of revolutions per minute of shafting of various kinds, and counters for recording the number of strokes of a press or other machine. The revolution counter is a continuous operating device. The other counter adds the number of motions on a series of dials properly geared together.

Standard Cotter Pins

(Dimensions in Inches)   *General Motors Company*

D—Nominal dia.	³⁄₆₄	¹⁄₁₆	³⁄₃₂	⅛	⁵⁄₃₂	³⁄₁₆	⁷⁄₃₂	¼	⁵⁄₁₆
Actual dia. min.	.042	.058	.086	.118	.146	.172	.202	.220	.275
Actual dia. max.	.045	.061	.090	.122	.150	.176	.207	.225	.280
E—Inside dia., of eye	¹⁄₁₆	³⁄₃₂	⅛	⁵⁄₃₂	⁵⁄₃₂	³⁄₁₆	⁷⁄₃₂	¼	⁵⁄₁₆
F—Outside dia., of eye (approx.)	⁷⁄₆₄	⁵⁄₃₂	⁷⁄₃₂	⁹⁄₃₂	⁵⁄₁₆	⅜	⁷⁄₁₆	½	⅝
Drill dia.	No. 52 (.0635)	No. 48 (.076)	No. 36 (.1065)	No. 28 (.1405)	No. 17 (.173)	No. 7 (.201)	B (.238)	⁹⁄₃₂	¹¹⁄₃₂

Tolerance—plus or minus 0.010 inch.

Designation	% Nickel	% Chromium	% Carbon	% Other Elements
CA-15	1 max.	11 to 14	.15 max.	—
CA-40	1 max.	11 to 14	.20 to .40	—
CB-30	2 max.	18 to 22	.30 max	—
CC-50	4 max.	26 to 30	.50 max.	—
CE-30	8 to 11	26 to 30	.30 max.	—
CF-7	8 to 10	18 to 20	.07 max.	—
CF-10	8 to 10	18 to 20	.10 max.	—
CF-16	8 to 10	18 to 20	.16 max.	—
CF-20	8 to 10	18 to 20	.20 max.	—
CF-7Se	8 to 10	18 to 20	.07 max.	Selenium 0.20 to 0.35
CF-7C	8 to 10	18 to 20	.07 max.	Columbium*
CF-7 M	8 to 10	18 to 20	.07 max.	Molybdenum 1.5 to 3.5
CF-10M	8 to 10	18 to 20	.10 max.	Molybdenum 1.5 to 3.5
CF-16 M	8 to 10	18 to 20	.16 max.	Molybdenum 1.5 to 3.5
CG-7	10 to 12	20 to 22	.07 max.	—
CG-10	10 to 12	20 to 22	.10 max.	—
CG-16	10 to 12	20 to 22	.16 max.	—
CG-16 Se	10 to 12	20 to 22	.16 max.	Selenium 0.20 to 0.35
CG-7 C	10 to 12	20 to 22	.07 max.	Columbium*
CG-7 M	10 to 12	20 to 22	.07 max.	Molybdenum 1.5 to 3.5
CG-10 M	10 to 12	20 to 22	.10 max.	Molybdenum 1.5 to 3.5
CG-16 M	10 to 12	20 to 22	.16 max.	Molybdenum 1.5 to 3.5
CH-10	12 to 15	22 to 26	.10 max.	—
CH-20	12 to 15	22 to 26	.20 max.	—
CH-10 C	12 to 15	22 to 26	.10 max.	Columbium*
CH-10 M	12 to 15	22 to 26	.10 max.	Molybdenum 1.5 to 3.5
CK-25	19 to 22	23 to 27	.25 max.	—
CM-25	19 to 22	8 to 11	.25 max.	—
CN-7	20 to 30	18 to 22	.07 max.	(May contain other elements)
CT-7	34 to 37	13 to 17	.07 max.	(May contain other elements)
HB	2 max.	18 to 22	—	—
HC	4 max.	26 to 30	—	—
HD	3 to 6	26 to 30	—	—
HE	8 to 11	26 to 30	—	—
HF	8 to 11	18 to 23	—	—
HH	11 to 14	23 to 27	—	—
HI	14 to 17	26 to 30	—	—
HK	19 to 22	23 to 27	—	—
HL	19 to 22	28 to 32	—	—
HN	23 to 26	18 to 22	—	—
HP	29 to 31	28 to 32	—	—
HS	29 to 32	8 to 12	—	—
HT	33 to 37	13 to 17	—	—
HU	37 to 41	17 to 21	—	—
HW	58 to 62	10 to 14	—	—
HX	64 to 68	15 to 19	—	—

*Columbium: 8 x Carbon—1.00% max.
Designations with the initial letter "C" indicate alloys generally used to resist corrosive attack at temperatures less than 1200° F. Designations with the initial letter "H" indicate alloys generally used under conditions where the metal temperature is in excess of 1200° F.
All of the above designations apply to type compositions and no attempt is made to cover elements such as manganese, silicon and, in the case of heat-resistant alloys, carbon.

COUNTERSHAFT—An intermediate or auxiliary shaft between the main drive and the final spindle or shaft. Before machines were driven by individual electric motors, a counter-

CONVERSED SINE—See *Angle Constants.*

CRAB—A name sometimes applied to a winch or windlass.

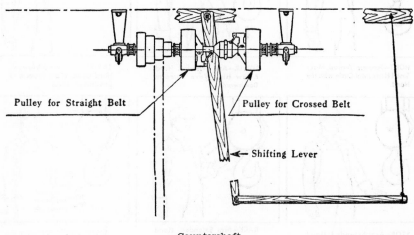

Countershaft.

Pulley for Straight Belt

Pulley for Crossed Belt

← Shifting Lever

shaft was necessary between the line shaft and the machine itself for stopping, starting and reversing the motion of the machine.

COUPLINGS—Devices for fastening two parts together. Line shafts may be made up of several lengths of shafting held together by couplings of various kinds. The usual types of couplings are:

Clamp couplings, made in two or more parts which clamp around the shaft and are held by friction or with the aid of keys and keyways.

Compression couplings, which grip the shaft by compressing tapered bushings on the shaft as shown, or where the bolts parallel to the shaft draw the parts together, by compressing the inner sleeve on the shaft.

Friction couplings, which depend entirely on friction to hold the shafts, as in compression coupling.

Jaw couplings, where projecting parts of each half interlock with its mate. These are generally used as a clutch to engage or disengage two parts of a shaft. See *Clutch, Jaw.*

CRACKLE FINISH—A kind of painted surface which reflects light from many small surfaces to avoid a smooth surface which would show up very small unevenness.

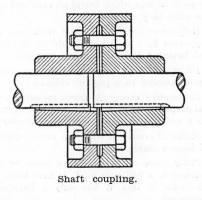

Shaft coupling.

CRANE—A mechanism which lifts and moves parts of machinery or other objects. They are made in many ways, each having its particular field. They are:

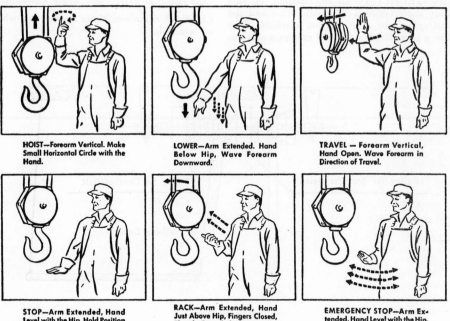

HOIST—Forearm Vertical. Make Small Horizontal Circle with the Hand.

LOWER—Arm Extended. Hand Below Hip, Wave Forearm Downward.

TRAVEL — Forearm Vertical, Hand Open. Wave Forearm in Direction of Travel.

STOP—Arm Extended, Hand Level with the Hip, Hold Position Rigidly.

RACK—Arm Extended, Hand Just Above Hip, Fingers Closed, Thumb Extended Horizontally. Jerk Hand in Direction of Racking.

EMERGENCY STOP—Arm Extended, Hand Level with the Hip, Wave Hand Quickly to Right and Left.

Crane signals. CAUTION—Crane operators are also instructed to observe signals only from persons duly authorized for crane service, and under no circumstances to move a load until the signal is received from the proper man.

Gantry crane—A traveling crane mounted on posts or legs which travel on rails and span the parts they are to lift.

Half-gantry crane—A crane with one end supported by a wall on a building, the other end having a leg and running on rails.

Jib crane—A crane with a swinging arm or boom fastened to a post or column.

Locomotive crane—A crane mounted on a self-propelled platform and running on rails. They are also made on caterpillar tractors.

Monorail crane—A traveling crane suspended from a single rail.

Pillar crane—A crane with a boom or arm fastened to a pillar or post. Differs from the jib crane in that it has only a horizontal movement.

Portable crane—A motor driven unit having a crane arm. Usually small for use inside plants.

Post crane—Same as pillar crane.

Traveling crane—A crane running on two rails which span the shop or room. It has a bridge or cross beam with wheels at each end and a truck which moves on the cross beam. This truck carries the hoisting drum or drums for lifting the work. Each movement has its own motors and is controlled from a central point, usually at the end of the bridge itself.

Wall crane—A movable crane supported by rails along one wall. They are almost obsolete now.

CRANE SIGNALS—Six standard signals have been adopted for use when loads are being handled by cranes. These must be thoroughly understood both by men on the floor and by the crane operator.

CRANK THROW—The distance from the center of the crank shaft to the center of the crank pin. It is one-half the distance traveled, commonly called the "travel" of the piston or ram connected to the crank.

58

CRATERING—The forming of a depression or crater on the top of a cutting tool behind the cutting edge. This occurs mostly in turning at high speeds, due to the abrasive action of the metal chip as it leaves the work and slides across the top of the tool.

CRAZING—The creation of many small cracks in the surface of steel or carbide by suddenly raising the temperature, as in grinding a tool too rapidly.

CRIMPING—Term usually applied to fluting, corrugating or compressing a metal ring to reduce its diameter.

CRITICAL POINTS—Temperatures where transformation occurs in hot steel as it passes through its critical range, with either rising or falling temperatures.

CRITICAL SPEED—The speed of any moving objects where any increase becomes dangerous.
In grinding wheels, the critical speed is affected by the diameter of both the wheel and its spindle and the distance from the wheel to the point of support of the spindle. Unbalance in any revolving body also affects the critical speed.

CROCUS CLOTH—Cloth with powdered oxide of iron glued to its surface. It is used in polishing metals of different kinds.

CROSS BAR—Another name for a pinch, or crow bar. Also a bar, usually horizontal, which connects two parts of a machine or other mechanism.

CROSS-CENTER—See *Center, Cross.*

CROSS-CUT FILE—See *Files, Cross-cut.*

CROSS-RAIL—A part of a machine, such as a planer or boring mill, on which the tool heads or slides move to contact different parts of the work.

CROSSED THREADS—See *Screw Threads, Crossed.*

CROSSING FILE—See *File, Crossing.*

CROW BAR—A steel bar with a chisel shaped end which can be forced under heavy objects to be moved. Sometimes called a pinch bar.

CROWN—The enlarged portion of the face of a pulley or other machine part. The crown may be curved or angular, meeting in the middle. For flat belts, the standard crown for a pulley is ⅛ inch per foot. Too much crown stretches the belt in the center and shortens its life. The enlarged diameter is to keep the belt in the center of the pulley.

CROWN BRASS—The bearing by which locomotive frames are supported on the driving wheel axles. It only contacts the upper side of the axle, as all the weight is on the top. It is held in the driving box which slides vertically, between jaws in the locomotive frame. These jaws are usually known as pedestals.

CROWN NUT—See *Nut, Crown.*

CROWN SAW—See *Saw, Crown.*

CRUSHED WHEEL GRINDING—The grinding of screw threads or other special forms. The grinding wheels are *crushed* to the desired form by contact with a hardened steel roll turned to the form to be ground. The roll has gashes along its axis which help break away the particles of the abrasive. These gashes are sometimes parallel but are frequently at an angle, as with helical milling centers. See *Grinding, Crush Dressing.*

CRYSTOLON—A silicon carbide made in an electric furnace of the resistance type, using coke and sand with sawdust or salt to make a porous mixture and to help the reaction. It is largely used as an abrasive and for furnace linings.

CUBAGE—Cubic content, usually in cubic feet.

CUBE OF A NUMBER—Multiplying a number by itself twice gives the cube, or third power, of that number. This makes 8 the cube, or third power of 2.

CUBE ROOT OF A NUMBER—The number which, mutiplied by itself *twice*, will give the number in the problem. It is the reverse of "cubing a number" or raising it to its third power. This is used in solving many mechanical problems.

CUP LEATHER—A leather packing used in packing pumps and other hydraulic mechanisms. The leather is moulded into a cup shape so that the pressure holds it against the piston rod and the chamber and prevents leakage.

CUPOLA—A furnace for melting iron or other metals, usually in quite large quantities. Iron, limestone and other materials are put in at the top and drawn out at the bottom when melted sufficiently to flow into the molds.

CUPRO-NICKEL—An alloy of copper and nickel.

CURLING DIES—See *Dies, Curling.*

CURVILINEAR — Describes any surface bounded by curved lines.

CUT-OFF BLADES, STRAIGHT — Straight cut-off blades are tools used in lathes and screw machines for cutting off work from a bar after it has been turned or otherwise machined. Standard sizes are given in the table, as are optional shapes. Many provide a bevel of 5 degrees both top and bottom, known as the "clamping bevel," to assist in holding the blades firmly in their holders.

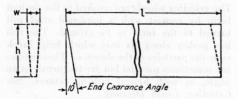

Straight cut-off blades.

CUTTER—A general term for any tools which cut metal in various ways. They are usually designated by the particular type of work they are to perform. Probably the greatest variety of cutters is found in connection with milling machine work and gear cutting. One example of other cutters is a *flue sheet*

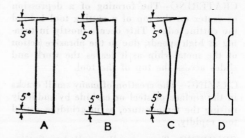

Optional shapes for cut-off blade stock: (A) Without side clearance. (B) With straight side clearance. (C) With concaved side clearance. (D) With channeled sides (heavy duty) made only 1 in. height or greater.

cutter—a special cutter for making holes for flues in sheets used in making boilers.

CUTTER, FLY—A single point revolving cutter used in boring and milling. The term is sometimes used for two or more point cutters as well, where the tools stand out away from the cutter body, but this is incorrect. The single point cutter will generally produce a more accurate surface than one with multiple cutting edges.

CUTTER, MILLING—See *Milling Cutters.*

CUTTING ALLOYS—Non-ferrous alloys, not alloy steel. They include alloys of cobalt, nickel, chromium, tungsten and titanium.

Dimensions of Straight Cut-Off Blades

Width (W)	Height (h) $\times$ Length (l)				
$\frac{1}{16}$	$\frac{1}{2} \times 4\frac{1}{2}$*	$\frac{11}{16} \times 5$	$\frac{13}{16} \times 6$	—	—	—
$\frac{5}{64}$	$\frac{1}{2} \times 4\frac{1}{2}$				
$\frac{3}{32}$	$\frac{1}{2} \times 4\frac{1}{2}$*	$\frac{11}{16} \times 5$	$\frac{13}{16} \times 6$		$1\frac{1}{8} \times 6\frac{1}{2}$*	
$\frac{1}{8}$	$\frac{1}{2} \times 4\frac{1}{2}$*	$\frac{11}{16} \times 5$*	$\frac{13}{16} \times 6$		$1\frac{1}{8} \times 6\frac{1}{2}$*	
$\frac{5}{32}$	—	$\frac{11}{16} \times 5$*	$\frac{13}{16} \times 6$			
$\frac{3}{16}$	—	$\frac{11}{16} \times 5$*	$\frac{13}{16} \times 6$	$\frac{7}{8} \times 6$*	$1 \times 6\frac{1}{2}$	$1 \times 6\frac{1}{2}$
$\frac{1}{4}$	—	—	$\frac{13}{16} \times 6$	$\frac{7}{8} \times 6$*	$1 \times 6\frac{1}{2}$	$1 \times 6\frac{1}{2}$

All dimensions are given in inches.

Cross-sectional shapes and dimensional limits shall be in accordance with the manufacturer's standards.

Height dimensions are nominal.

* Preferred blade sizes for future designs and development. These should not be construed as indicating that other listed sizes are special, non-procurable, or subject to special prices.

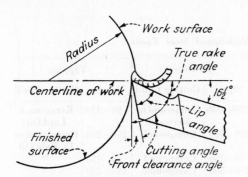

Cutting angles for single-point tools.

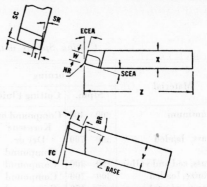

Cutting tool tip elements.

CUTTING ANGLES OF SINGLE POINT TOOLS—To insure uniformity in designating cutting angles of single point tools these angles have been standardized, as shown. See also *Single-Point Tool.*

CUTTING FLUID—Any substance applied to a cutting tool or to the work being cut, to assist in the cutting operation either by cooling or by lubrication. It might also help by washing chips away from the cutting edges, by helping to break up the chips, by reducing power consumption or by improving the quality of the machine surface. It includes a blast of air or gas at a low temperature, aqueous solutions, water emulsions, pastes or oils of any kind. See *Coolants.*

CUTTING OILS—Any oils used to aid in the cutting of metals, either as a lubricant or coolant, or both. They differ from mixtures which are only coolants, these being thin solutions used mainly to keep work and tools cool.

CUTTING SPEEDS WITH HIGH SPEED TOOLS—A general guide for cutting speeds for high speed tools for turning, drilling and tapping is given by the South Bend Lathe Works. In most cases of *turning* these speeds can be doubled with carbide tools. Suitable coolants are also suggested for the different operations. [Sfpm. is surface feet per minute.] (See table on page 62.)

CUTTING TOOLS, SINGLE-POINT ELEMENTS—One form of these can be seen in the illustration above.

CUTTING TOOL TIP NOMENCLATURE—The names of parts of a single point carbide

tool, as given by the Kennametal Corp., are described below:

T—Tip Thickness
W—Tip Width
L—Tip Lenth
NR—Nose Radius
ECEA—End Cutting Edge Angle
SCEA—Side Cutting Edge Angle
SC—Side Clearance
FC—Front Clearance
BR—Back Rake
SR—Side Rake
X—Shank Width
Y—Shank Height
Z—Shank Length

CYANIDE—The common name for cyanide of potassium, which is a very poisonous material, usually found in lump or powder form. It was formerly largely used in casehardening small pieces of low carbon steel. Used in extracting gold and silver from ores, in electroplating and for other purposes.

CYANIDING—A method of introducing carbon into steel by use of cyanide, either in the form of crystals or of gas. In gas carbonizing the normal temperarture is 1,450 deg. F., which gives a case, or hard surface, 4 to 8 thousandths of an inch thick.

CYANIDING, DRY—A process in which parts to be treated are subjected to a vapor instead of being immersed in a bath of salts. A low temperature is used, which greatly reduces distortion. Case depths of 0.025 inch can be secured, with a tough core.

CYCLE THREADS, BRITISH — See *Screw Threads, British Cycle.*

61

Cutting Speeds with High-Speed Steel Tools

Material	Turning		Drilling		Tapping	
	Sfpm.	Cutting Fluid	Sfpm.	Cutting Fluid	Sfpm.	Cutting Fluid
Aluminum	300—400	Compound or Kerosene	200—330	Compound or Kerosene	90—110	Kerosene & Lard Oil
Brass, leaded	300—700	Dry or Compound	200—500	Compound	150—250	Compound or Lt. Base Oil
Brass, red and yellow	150—300	Compound	75—250	Compound	60—150	"
Bronze, leaded	300—700	Compound	200—500	Compound	150—250	"
Bronze, phosphor	75—150	Compound	50—125	Compound	30—60	"
Cast Iron	50—110	Dry	100—165	Dry	70—90	Dry or Comp.
Cast Steel	45—90	Compound	35—45	Compound	20—35	Sul. Base Oil
Copper, leaded	300—700	Compound	200—500	Compound	150—250	Lt. Base Oil
Copper, electro	75—150	Compound	50—125	Compound	30—60	"
Chrome Steel	65—115	Compound	50—65	Compound	20—35	Sul. Base Oil
Die Castings	225—350	Compound	200—300	Compound	60—80	Kerosene & Lard Oil
Duralumin	275—400	Compound	250—375	Compound	90—110	Comp. or Ker. and Lard Oil
Fiber	200—300	Dry	175—275	Dry	80—100	Dry
Machine Steel	115—225	Compound	80—120	Compound	40—70	Comp. Sul. Base Oil or Kero. & Para.
Malleable Iron	80—130	Dry or Comp.	80—100	Dry or Comp.	35—70	Compound or Sul. Base Oil
Manganese Bronze	150—300	Compound	75—250	Compound	60—150	Lt. Base Oil
Manganese Steel	20—40	Compound	15—25	Compound	10—20	Comp. or Sul. Base Oil or Ker. & Par.
Molybdenum Steel	100—120	Compound	50—65	Compound	20—35	Sul. Base Oil
Monel Metal	100—125	Compound or Sul. Base	40—55	Sul. Base	20—30	Sul. Base or Kero. and Lard Oil
Nickel Silver, 18%	75—150	Compound	50—125	Compound	30—60	"
Nickel Silver, leaded	150—300	Compound	75—250	Compound	60—150	"
Nickel Steel	85—110	Dry or Comp. Sul. Base	40—65	Sul. Base Oil	25—40	Sul. Base Oil
Plastics, hot-molded	200—600	Dry	75—300	Dry	40—54	Dry or Water
Rubber, Hard	200—300	Dry	175—275	Dry	80—100	Dry
Stainless Steel	100—150	Sul. Base	30—45	Sul. Base	15—30	Sul. Base
Tool Steel	70—130	Compound	50—65	Compound	25—40	Sul. Base or Kero. and Lard Oil
Tungsten Steel	70—130	Compound	50—65	Compound	20—35	Sul. Base
Vanadium Steel	85—120	Compound	45—65	Sul. Base	25—40	Sul. Base

Note: Cutting speeds are given in surface feet per minute.

CYCLOGRAPH — An apparatus for giving magnetic analysis at a single frequency or within limited frequency range. It is built to operate at frequencies from 2,000 to 200,000 cycles per second for testing both ferrous and nonferrous materials. It consists of a two-stage oscillator with a test coil which is part of the tuned circuit and controls the operating frequency of the oscillator. The output is viewed on a cathode-ray tube screen. It does not reveal cracks or surface defects.

CYCLOID — A curve formed by any point of a circle when it is rolled along a straight line. It was formerly used as a shape for gear teeth but has given way to the involute curve in most cases. See *Gear Teeth, Cycloidal Curve.*

CYLINDER IRON — Close grained iron mixed especially for engine cylinders. Alloys are now being used to secure close grain and long wear.

CYLINDROMETER — An instrument for measuring large diameters by use of tangents rather than radius or diameter. It is based on the fact that the diameter of an object can be found by measuring the tangent corresponding to a definite central angle. The length of the tangent will be in constant ratio to the diameter. If this ratio is known the diameter is found by simple multiplication of the tangent. This is read directly on the cylindrometer. It is credited to Prof. Dr. Ing. N. N. Sawin.

D

DAMASCENING—An inlaying of one metal in another. By using different metals it was possible to produce very handsome and intricate patterns for sword hilts and for decorative jewelry. Seldom used now.

DAMASCUS IRON OR STEEL—Metal made up of small wires welded together which produce a pattern, sometimes quite decorative. Gun makers formerly made shot gun barrels from metal made up in this way and secured fancy designs. Damascus steel was of somewhat unknown quality, but had the reputation of being very hard and was used for swords and other weapons.

DAMASKEENING — A decorative finish on metals done with specially shaped diamond tools, operated by mechanical devices to give the desired pattern.

DARDELAT THREAD—See *Screw Threads*.

DASH-POT—A cylinder in which a piston uses air to cushion its movement, or to give it a rapid motion. The old Corliss steam engines had dashpots connected to their valves which created a vacuum as the valves were opened and accelerated the closing of the valve when they were released.

DEAD-CENTER—See *Center, Dead*.

DEAD LEVEL—A shop term describing precise leveling of a machine or other work. It is also applied to surface plates.

DEAD LOAD—A constant load, due either to weight or pressure, resting on a given point or surface.

DEAD-SMOOTH—A term applied to the finest file made. See *Files*.

DECALESCENCE — The property of steel whereby it absorbs heat owing to internal molecular action when it is heated through its critical range of temperature.

DECALESCENCE POINT—The temperature at which steel continues to absorb heat without an appreciable rise in temperature.

DECARBURIZATION — Removal of carbon from the surface of forgings due to mill operations, usually done to secure good metal for the piece to be machined. The machining allowance for decarburization at the steel mill is shown below. The removal of the amounts given should leave steel in good condition for use.

Machining Allowance for Mill Carburization

Diameter or Thickness	Remove from Surface
Up to and including ½ in.	$\frac{1}{64}$ (0.016)
½ to 2 in.	$\frac{1}{32}$ (0.032)
2 to 3 in.	$\frac{1}{16}$ (0.062)
3 to 4¾ in.	$\frac{1}{8}$ (0.125)
4¾ to 8 in.	$\frac{3}{16}$ (0.1875)

Note: Flat sections where the width is two or more times the thickness, only one-half the allowance shown on the above table is required on the width. The tolerance on the thickness should be the same as shown in the table.

DECIMAL EQUIVALENTS OF FRACTIONS OF AN INCH—The growing use of decimals in measurements of all kinds makes it convenient to have tables which save all calculations. The accompanying table gives equivalents by fractions down to sixty-fourths.

DEEP DRAW—When sheet metal or metal blanks are drawn into cups or cylinders in which the length exceeds the diameter. This is an arbitrary definition but seems to cover most cases. In the drawing of cartridge cases the length is several times the diameter. It usually requires several annealings of the blank before the final length is secured, as the metal "work hardens" during the operation.

DEEP-FREEZING — The application of extreme cold to hardened cutting tools is claimed to increase their life. They are frozen at 120 deg. below zero F. for several hours, and then returned slowly to room temperature. Cooling of metal parts to be inserted in machine elements, such as the rings which form the valve

64

Fractions of One Inch and Decimal and Metric Equivalents

Fractions of an Inch	Decimals of an Inch	Milli-meters	Fractions of an Inch	Decimals of an Inch	Milli-meters
1/64	.0156	0.397	33/64	.5156	13.097
1/32	.0313	0.794	17/32	.5313	13.494
3/64	.0469	1.191	35/64	.5469	13.891
1/16	.0625	1.588	9/16	.5625	14.287
5/64	.0781	1.985	37/64	.5781	14.684
3/32	.0938	2.381	19/32	.5938	15.081
7/64	.1094	2.778	39/64	.6094	15.478
1/8	.1250	3.175	5/8	.6250	15.875
9/64	.1406	3.572	41/64	.6406	16.272
5/32	.1563	3.969	21/32	.6563	16.688
11/64	.1719	4.366	43/64	.6719	17.085
3/16	.1875	4.762	11/16	.6875	17.462
13/64	.2031	5.159	45/64	.7031	17.859
7/32	.2188	5.556	23/32	.7188	18.256
15/64	.2344	5.953	47/64	.7344	18.653
1/4	.2500	6.350	3/4	.7500	19.050
17/64	.2656	6.747	49/64	.7656	19.447
9/32	.2813	7.144	25/32	.7813	19.843
19/64	.2969	7.541	51/64	.7969	20.240
5/16	.3135	7.937	13/16	.8125	20.637
21/64	.3281	8.334	53/64	.8281	21.034
11/32	.3438	8.731	27/32	.8438	21.430
23/64	.3594	9.128	55/64	.8594	21.827
3/8	.3750	9.525	7/8	.8750	22.224
25/64	.3906	9.922	57/64	.8906	22.621
13/32	.4063	10.319	29/32	.9063	23.018
27/64	.4219	10.716	59/64	.9219	23.415
7/16	.4375	11.112	15/16	.9375	23.812
29/64	.4531	11.509	61/64	.9531	24.209
15/32	.4688	11.906	31/32	.9688	24.606
31/64	.4844	12.303	63/64	.9844	25.003
1/2	.5000	12.700	1	1.0000	25.400

seats in automotive engines, are shrunk into place in the same way. Made slightly larger than the cavity which receives them, they are reduced in diameter by freezing and dropped into place. On warming up to room temperature they are a tight fit. This is also known as expansion fitting.

DEGREE—A term applied to both temperature and angles. Temperature is measured by two methods at present, Centigrade and Fahrenheit. The first has 100 divisions, or degrees, between freezing and boiling; the latter 180 degrees. In angles, one degree is 1/360th of a complete circle. Degrees of arc are also divided into minutes and seconds, the same as clocks and other time-keeping instruments. The term is also used in other ways which do not refer to direct measurements.

DENDRITE—A form of crystal which occurs during the cooling or solidifying of steel. It has many branches and forms a pattern resembling a tree. They are sometimes called pine- or fir-tree crystals.

DERMATITIS—A skin disease sometimes caused by various cooling and cutting fluids used in a shop. Modern shops do their utmost to guard against this by frequent cleansing of the cooling fluid used.

DERRICK—A type of lifting apparatus which has an upright, frequently supported by guy wires, and an arm or boom, hinged near the bottom. Ropes or chains running over pulley blocks at the outer end of the arm enable the lifting of heavy weights. Raising or lowering the arms moves the load toward or away from the upright, while turning the upright gives the derrick a wide coverage around its base. Practically the same as a crane.

DESAGATIZED STEEL—A high speed steel made by the Latrobe Electric Steel Co. which is claimed to reduce segregation and produce a very uniform steel structure.

DETAIL—Sometimes used the same as component, but more often in referring to such items as screws, pins and other parts which are common to all mechanisms. Some designate a detail as a manufactured part as differing from purchased parts, such as screws and pins. Sometimes referred to as an "item."

DETAILER—A draftsman whose work is to draw the details after a general design has been decided upon.

DETENT—See *Pawl*.

DETERGENTS—Cleaning materials that act like soap, such as cleansing powders.

DIAL FEED—A device in which a dial or disk is used to feed work into a machine. Its general application is in punch press work.

DIAL INDICATOR OR GAGE—An indicator with a dial resembling a clock or watch and a hand which indicates the movement of an anvil which contacts the work. These indicators are used in many ways, as shown.

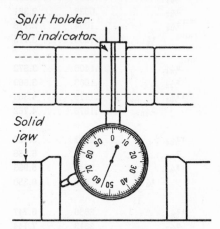

Dial gage aligning vise with indicator.

DIAMETRAL PITCH—See *Gear*, page 164.

DIAMONDS—Very hard crystals of nearly pure carbon. Industrial diamonds are culls from gem stones, or a dark color variety known as bort. Sp. Gr. 3.521. See *Tools, Diamond*.

DIAMOND BORING—The term originated when diamonds were used exclusively to bore very accurate holes. While diamonds are still used in some cases, carbide tools have almost entirely replaced the diamond as a cutting tool. The term now means precision boring. See *Single Point Boring*.

DIAMOND CORE DRILL FITTINGS—Fittings for the pipe used in deep hole drilling in oil exploration work. The bits have diamond bort inserts for cutting through hard rock encountered.

DIAMOND GRINDING WHEELS—See *Grinding Wheels, Diamond*.

DIAMOND HAND TOOL—A tool formerly used in dressing abrasive wheels by hand. This has largely given place to diamond tools held in special devices which secure much better results.

DIAMOND-POINT TOOL—See *Lathe Tools.*

DIAMOND POWDER, GRADES OF—Commercial grades of diamond powder are shown in the accompanying table. The grain size is given in microns, which are millionths of a meter. A micron is 0.000039375 inch.

Grades of Diamond Powder

Grade designation[1]	Grain size (microns)		Sieve number (through)[2]
	Minimum	Maximum	
1........	0	2	. . .
2........	1	3	. . .
3........	1	5	. . .
3X.......	0	6	. . .
6........	4	8	. . .
8........	6	10	. . .
8X.....	4	12	. . .
14.......	8	20	. . .
25.......	13	37	. . .
40.......	20	60	325
60.......	35	85	230
90.......	60	120	170
120.......	80	160	120
150.......	100	200	100
180.......	120	240	80
250.......	150	350	60
400.......	250	550	40

[1]Grades 1, 6 and 8 are narrow-range grades for exacting work in cutting and polishing fine diamond dies, sapphire bearings, etc. Grades 3X and 8X are wide-range grades desired for some purposes.

[2]United States Standard Sieve series. Sieve numbers are included for reference only. It does not necessarily follow that powders passing the sieve indicated for a grade will meet the grain size requirements of that grade, nor that powders retained on the sieve necessarily fail to meet the grain-size requirements.

DIE—Device for cutting or forming material in a press or by hand with the aid of mechanical devices. Term also applies to separate pieces of such a device. A die, or dies, may consist of a male section (punch) and female section (matrix). A thread-cutting die may be of one piece or of several pieces.

(The term is used rather indiscriminately singular or plural.)

DIE (SETS)—The assembly, consisting of the punch and die with guide posts. Formerly called a sub-press die. Standardized names for the various parts are: *Punch Holder*—The upper member of the set; *Die Holder*—The lower member of the set; *Guide Posts*—The members which keep the punch and die in alinement; *Guide Bushings*—The bushings in the punch plate; *Guide Holes*—The openings in either punch or die for the guide posts or die for the guide posts or bushings; *Shank*—The projecting portion of the upper member which enters the ram of the press; and *Flange*—The portion of either the die holder or punch holder by which they are bolted or clamped to the press. The term is sometimes used to designate thread cutting dies for different diameters. See *Punch and Die Sets.*

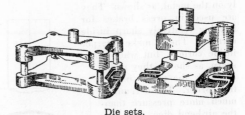

Die sets.

DIE(S), ACORN—A form of threading die for use in screw machines. The cutting portion resembles an acorn. Its shape, the holder and the adjusting cap are shown.

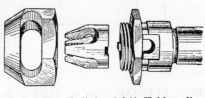

Acorn die: (Left to right) Holder, die, adjusting cap.

DIE(S), AIR-BEND—Dies which do not strike solidly on the metal being bent or formed, as shown. Here the metal is formed by contact only at the point of the upper die and the two edges of the lower die. These are used in press brakes for the heavier gages of metal.

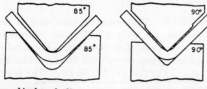

Air-bend dies.   Bottoming dies.

DIE(S), BLANKING—Dies which cut a piece from sheet stock to form a blank for further operations. Sometimes combined with punches and called multiple blanking dies, or tools.

DIE(S), BLASTED—Forming dies in which the surfaces have been sand blasted to impart a matte finish on the work.

DIE(S), BOLT—Threading dies for cutting screw threads on bolts. They are of many types.

DIE(S), BOTTOMING—Dies that strike solidly on the metal, as shown. They are used in press brakes for forming relatively sharp inside corners. These make sharper inside corners, but when made sharp, as shown, they nick, or mark the metal inside the corner. These require much more pressure than the air-bend dies.

as shown. In some special cases oil pressure inside the work is used to expand the shell to the desired shape.

DIE(S), BURNISHING—Burnishing or polishing dies producing a smooth and polished surface by friction between the work and the die. For a tube, the die is a trifle smaller at the bottom than at the top and the tube is polished as it is forced through the die.

Button dies.

DIE(S), BUTTON—Small adjustable dies for screw machines and similar work, supported in a ring holder. A cone pointed adjusting screw enters the slot, while another set screw on the side closes the die in contact with the adjusting screw.

DIE-CASTING—See page 76.

DIE CHASER—See page 77.

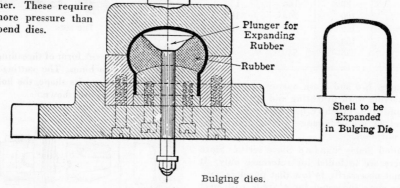

Plunger for Expanding Rubber

Rubber

Shell to be Expanded in Bulging Die

Bulging dies.

DIE(S), BULGING—Dies in which a sheet metal cup or tube is enlarged at some point of its diameter, or "bulged" by exerting pressure at the right place. A common example is the tops of many salt cellars and shakers. In the die shown, the rubber disk goes up inside the shell and as the punch descends the rubber is forced outward, enlarging or bulging the work

DIE(S), COINING—These are really embossing dies in which the metal blank is forced up into depressions in the face of the die by heavy pressure on the surrounding metal. They are used in making coins, medals and similar pieces. The term is sometimes applied to the notching of the edges of coins, although this is usually called "milling."

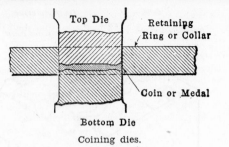

Coining dies.

DIE(S), COMBINATION—Dies for use in a single acting press in which the piece is blanked out and formed at the same stroke of

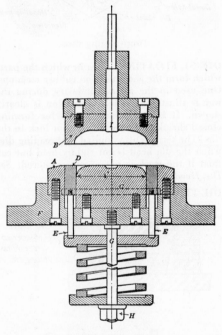

Combination dies.

the press. A spring forces the piece out of the die after it is formed. The punch B cuts the blank to shape on the edge of the die A. The ring D is then forced down as the punch descends and forms the blank over the draw post, or form, C. The pressure pin E acts against the heavy spring by means of the plate surrounding the post G. The pressure can be regulated by the nut H. The ring D which returns to its normal position on the up-stroke of the press, forces the work out of the die.

DIE(S), COMPOUND—These dies have both die and punch in the upper part and a punch in the lower part. The blanking and outer drawing is shown at A, while a central die B receives the lower punch C. This cuts out the center of the blank so that the metal can be drawn down on both inside and outside of D. When the work is forced down, the ring E compresses the rubber cushion beneath, which acts as a spring to eject the piece on the return stroke.

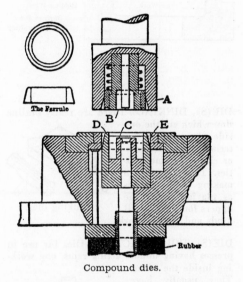

Compound dies.

DIE(S), CONTINENTAL—Punches and dies for short run, or temporary use, made from flat cold rolled steel plates, usually from $\frac{1}{8}$ to $\frac{1}{4}$ inch thick. The punch is usually fastened to a guide plate so as to match the opening in the die. In some cases they are merely laid on the sheet to be cut, in proper position over the die. When case-hardened, such punches and dies have cut from 100 to 150 pieces of sheet aluminum such as is used in airplane construction. Used with magnetized upper and lower die plates, they require no other fastening.

DIE(S), CUPPING—These are drawing dies used to form a cup shaped piece from a flat blank.

DIE(S), CURLING—Dies which curl the edges of drawn metal pails or cans, which stiffens the edge and also removes the sharp edge. The illustration shows the curling of a shell. When a wire is rolled inside the curled edge the tool is called a wiring die.

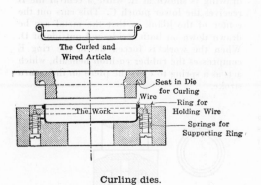

Curling dies.

DIE(S), DINKING—These are really outline dies which cut the outside edges of such materials as paper, leather cloth or some plastics. They are used in making such articles as playing cards, the uppers for shoes of all kinds and similar work

Dinking dies.

DIE(S), DOUBLE-ACTING—Dies for use in presses having double acting rams, one working inside the other. They usually have different lengths of strokes. As shown, the part A operates in advance of B and holds the sheet while it is formed by B. This holds the sheet while the blank is being drawn and prevents wrinkling of the metal. A holds the work against the recess C.

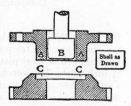

Double-acting dies.

DIE(S), DROP FORGING—Dies for use in a drop forging hammer. A typical die is shown with the various parts named. The first blow is struck in the bender, at the right, which shapes it so that the edge, from which it goes to the blocking impression, from here to finishing die at the right in which the flash, or surplus metal, flows into the gutter. The flash is then trimmed in another die.

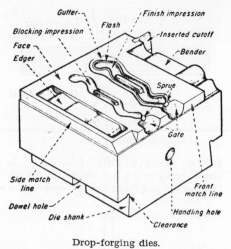

Drop-forging dies.

DIE(S), FLOATING—Dies in which the parts which form the sheet float on rubber cushions. One used in the aircraft industry during the war is illustrated. The construction is clearly shown. It is particularly useful for forming closed shrink flanges which do not lock in the die. The term is also applied to threading dies when the die head is not rigidly held but can float if the work is not exactly centered. See *Die Heads.*

DIE FENCES—See page 77.

Floating Dies.

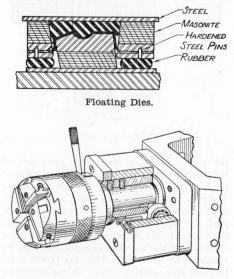

Floating die holder for rigid type die heads.

70

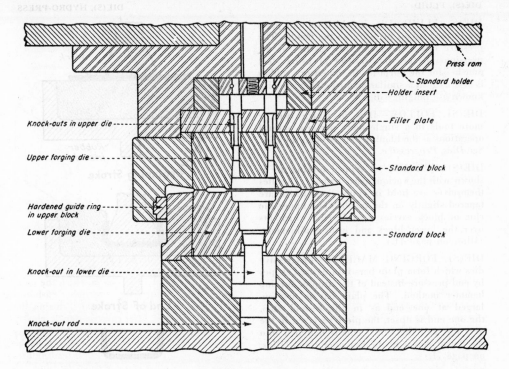

Press ram

Standard holder

Holder insert

Knock-outs in upper die

Filler plate

Upper forging die

Standard block

Hardened guide ring
in upper block

Lower forging die

Standard block

Knock-out in lower die

Knock-out rod

FORGING DIES.

Typical press die in which impressions are sunk in round inserts supported in
in standard blocks. Hardened guide ring slips over lower dies to match dies.

(Definition on page 72.)

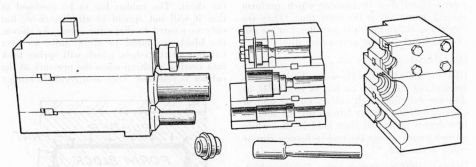

FORGING MACHINE DIES.

Set of dies and punches for producing a gear blank in the forging machine.
Stock is gathered in the bottom groove, upset to final dimensions in the center
and punched from the bar at the top. The material punched from the work
remains on the bar and is used in forming the next piece.

(Definition on page 72.)

DIE(S), FLUID—Dies in which tubular parts are formed by oil pressure on the inside. The pressure forces the metal into cavities or depressions in the dies instead of using steel punches for the purpose. In some work rubber is also used in a similar manner. They are also known as "bulging" dies.

DIE(S), FOLLOW—Dies in which two or more tools in a single body perform several operations as the blank is fed through the dies. See *Dies, Progressive.*

DIE(S), FORGING—A typical forging die is shown with the various parts named. The dies themselves are held in guide rings which are tapered slightly on the inside. The upper die ring or block carries a guide ring which fits over the lower block and insures alinement. (Illus. on page 71.)

DIE(S), FORGING MACHINE—Progressive dies which form plain bars into desired shapes by end pressure instead of the drop or forging hammer method. The plain bar is first enlarged at one end as in the second step, the one end is upset, the piece reversed in the next die, and the coned end is flattened into the flange shown in the last operation. (Illus. on page 71.)

DIE(S), FORMING, RUBBER—Dies in which rubber is used to form sheet metal around a punch, as shown. The sides of the punch have a taper that will allow the metal to be bent beyond the vertical so as to spring back to the desired straight sides.

DIE(S), GANG—These have two or more punches and dies in tandem which perform several operations at the same time. They are sometimes called multiple punches, but are not the same as follow or progressive dies.

DIE HEAD—See page 78.

DIE(S), HEADING—These may be either dies for making bolt heads on hot or cold rods, or dies for forming small collars on the end of cartridge shells. In the latter case, the shell is first drawn plain and then held in dies while an end punch upsets the end to form a rim or collar at the end.

DIE(S), HORN—Punch press dies in which the work is supported by a projection, or horn, while being punched or formed. The illustration shows an operation where the hole punched at the first stroke of the press is used to index the work so as to locate the second hole in its proper position.   (Illus. on page 73.)

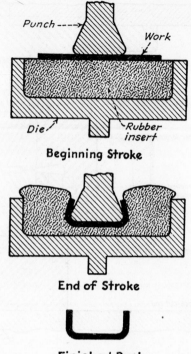

Beginning Stroke

End of Stroke

Finished Part

Rubber forming dies. Tapered punch and rubber pad compensate for spring-back.

DIE(S), HYDRO-PRESS—Dies used in a hydro-press having a heavy rubber cushion to form the metal around the form block under the sheet. The rubber has to be confined so that it will not spread in all directions, but only as wanted to shape the sheet. As shown, the block is shaped to allow quite an over bending of the edges, which will spring back into vertical position when the pressure of the rubber is released. (See also *Hydroforming.*)

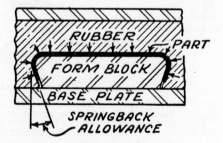

Hydro-press dies.

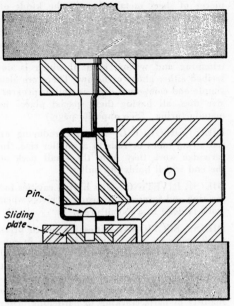

Horn dies.

DIE(S), INDEX—Dies for cutting notches or punching holes at specified intervals, usually in a round blank, such as disks used in building up an armature for a motor or generator. These dies feed the blank step by step past the punches.

DIE(S), MAGNETIC—Both the punch and the die are held in position by magnets in both the ram and the bed of the press. The punches and dies can be of case hardened material, as in continental dies, or they can be made of regular die steels. The use of magnets makes the usual methods of fastening both punch and die unnecessary.

DIE(S), NOTCHING—Literally dies which cut notches. Usually applied to an indexing die which feeds the work so as to cut successive notches. A well known notching die punches the notches in the laminations of an armature to receive the coils of wire, or windings. The round blank is rotated one space at a time and the notches punched. Where production warrants, special dies are made to punch all the notches at once.

DIE(S), PERFORATING—Multiple punches and dies for perforating a number of holes at the same time. The work is held against the face of the die by a pressure pad while the

punches are forced through the blank. As shown, the small punches are easily replaced, when broken or dulled.

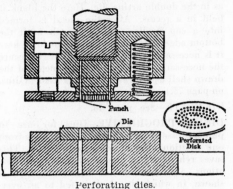

Perforating dies.

DIE(S), PIPE—See *Pipe Dies.*

DIE(S), PIERCING—Practically the same as perforating dies. These are sometimes made with two or more sets of punches, not always in the same plane, so that holes can be punched in two or more sides of a piece at the same time. These side punches are usually actuated by wedges in the same way as in compound bending dies. They are then known as compound piercing dies.

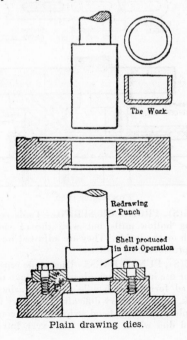

Plain drawing dies.

73

DIE(S), PLAIN DRAWING—These can only be used for drawing shallow cups, as the metal will wrinkle unless there is a pressure plate as in the double acting die. Here the blank is held in a recess. After the metal is formed into a cup it clings to the punch until the bottom edge strips it from the punch. Where it is necessary to use two operations to secure the necessary reduction in the diameter of the drawn shell a "re-drawing" die is used. (Illus. on page 73.)

DIE-PLATE—See page 78.

DIE(S), PROGRESSIVE—Dies for use in punch presses where the stock *progresses* from one position of operation, to the next. This saves rehandling of the work between operations. A simple two-station progressive die is shown, in which the stock is fed to an overhanging stop at the left. The first station pierces the slot. The strip is then fed to the left where the end is rounded. The next movement brings the rounded end against the stop and the slot is pierced at station 1 while station 2 cuts the ends of the second piece square and also rounds the end of the second piece.

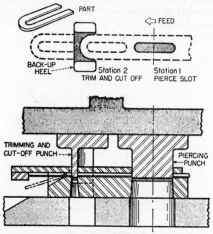

Progressive dies.

DIE(S), PRONG OR SPRING—Tools resembling hollow mills but with thread cutting teeth on the inside. They are adjusted for size by pressure from collars.

DIE(S), PUNCH PRESS—Dies made especially for use in the punch press. These take many varied forms and handle a great variety of work, some of it very difficult. They vary from simple dies which bend strip stock to complicated dies which cut and form very intricate

pieces of sheet metal. Among the kinds of punch press dies are those for bending, blanking, bulging, burnishing, coining, curling, cupping, drawing, heading, indexing, perforating, piercing, reducing, riveting, shearing, swaging, trimming and wiring, each of which is described either above or below. There are also simple and compound dies, as well as progressive dies, all having their special places in manufacturing. (See opposite page.)

DIE(S), REDUCING—Dies for reducing or redrawing tubes or rods to a smaller size. In cartridge work they form the small neck at the end which holds the bullet.

DIE(S), RIVETING—Dies having cavities for locating and forming the heads on rivets when work is done in a punch press.

DIE(S), SECTIONAL—Dies for punch press work made in sections both for ease in construction and to enable parts to be renewed without remaking the whole die. Care must be exercised in locating the points of separation, both for ease in making and to reduce liability of parts cracking in hardening. Dies should not usually be split through corner arcs or tangents to a circle. Illustration indicates both methods.

DIE(S), SHAVING—Dies for final finishing of parts which must be very accurate as to size, such as gears for fine clocks. In some cases, two shaving operations are used. The first may remove 0.003 inch and the final operation only half this amount. This requires accurate positioning of the blank.

DIE(S), SHEARING—Dies used in shearing operations of various kinds. The die shown simply cuts off pieces of the required length. The shearing blade has angular cutting edges which start the cut at the outside instead of requiring maximum power for each cut.

DIE(S), SPLIT—Sectional dies, usually made in two parts.

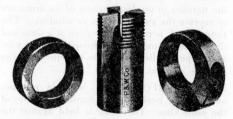

Prong dies (or spring threading dies).

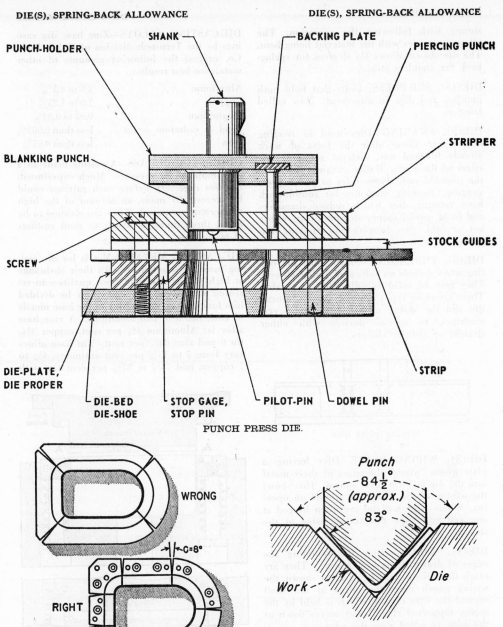

PUNCH PRESS DIE.

Labels: SHANK, BACKING PLATE, PIERCING PUNCH, PUNCH-HOLDER, STRIPPER, BLANKING PUNCH, STOCK GUIDES, SCREW, STOP GAGE, STOP PIN, PILOT-PIN, DOWEL PIN, STRIP, DIE-PLATE, DIE PROPER, DIE-BED, DIE-SHOE

Sectional dies. A large section die should not be split through the corner arcs, as above. Use break lines as shown to reduce machining problems.

C=8°

WRONG

RIGHT

Punch
84½°
(approx.)
83°

Work

Die

Spring-back allowance for dies. Added spring-back allowance must be made for stainless steel.

DIE(S), SPRING-BACK ALLOWANCE FOR
—The amount allowed for over-bending so as to have the piece at a right angle after it has

sprung back following the operation. The allowance varies with the material being bent. The die shown allows 1½ degrees for spring-back for stainless steel.

DIES(S), SUB-PRESS—Units that hold both punches and dies in alinement. Now called Die-Sets.

DIE(S), SWAGING—Dies used in swaging operations. These alter the form of work already blanked out, such as rounding the edges of flat parts. Bullet swaging dies form the rounded end. These refer to punch press swaging. Swaging machines for round work have rotating dies which reduce diameters and form special shapes on round bars, either hot or cold. See *Swaging* and *Swaging Machines.*

DIE(S), THREADING—Small tools for cutting screw threads on bolts and similar objects. They may be solid or adjustable as to size. There are many types in use, from the "acorn" die and the spring or prong die for screw machines, to special devices with either straight or circular chasers.

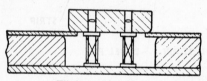

Wiping plate dies.

DIE(S), WIPING PLATE—Dies having a plate which "wipes" the edges of sheet metal into the die to form it, as shown. This shows the wiping of the flange all around an opening. Single wiping plates are often hinged at one end and wipe the outside edge of the sheet.

DIE(S), WIRING—Dies for rounding the edges of drawn shells over a wire. They are much the same as curling dies. As shown, the wiring punch curls the edges of the shell around the wire ring A, which is held by the spring supported ring B and moves down as the edge is rolled over the wire.

DIE CASTING—The forming of parts by forcing molten metal into metal molds. Alloys of zinc or aluminum are commonly used. Brass has also been cast successfully by this method. Similar to the molding of plastic material.

DIE-CASTING ALLOYS—Zinc base die castings by the Ternstedt division of Fisher Body Co. suggest the following amounts of other metals for best results:

Aluminum .... 3.9 to 4.3%
Copper .... 1.0 to 1.25%
Magnesium .... ˙ .... 0.03 to 0.04%
Lead + cadmium + tin ..... less than 0.003%
Iron .... less than 0.05%

DIE-CASTING, BRASS—A casting made in a steel mold under pressure. Much experimenting was necessary before such castings could be successfully made, on account of the high temperature required. They are claimed to be about three times as strong as sand castings of 60-40 brass.

DIE-CASTING METALS—Metals for die casting must be selected on both their shrinkage at high temperature and their qualities in resisting such shrinkage. They may be divided into four classes, depending on the base metals of zinc, tin, lead and aluminum. A zinc base alloy is: Aluminum 1¼ per cent, copper 3½, tin 6 and zinc 89¼ per cent. Tin base alloys vary from 7 to 13¾ per cent antimony, 4¼ to 7 copper, and 78½ to 87½ per cent tin, with

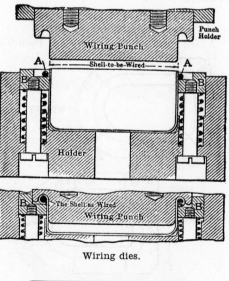

Wiring dies.

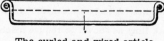

The curled and wired article.

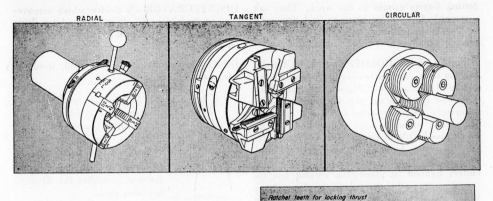

RADIAL   TANGENT   CIRCULAR

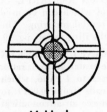

Hobbed   **Inserted**

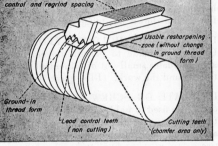

Ratchet teeth for locking thrust control and regrind spacing

Usable resharpening zone (without change in ground thread form)

Ground-in thread form

Lead control teeth (non cutting)

Cutting teeth (chamfer area only)

Tangential die chaser.

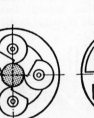

Circular   **Tangent**

Die heads or holders.

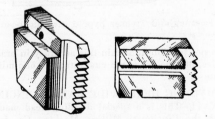

Die chasers.

low tin alloy having 4 per cent of lead. Lead base alloys run from 8½ per cent antimony, 0 to 3 copper, 25 to 84½ lead and 5 to 61½ per cent tin. Aluminum base alloys are grouped into aluminum-copper; aluminum-copper-silicon, and aluminum-silicon. Magnesia, manganese and nickel are sometimes added to give colors, toughness or wearing qualities. One authority limits the advisable weight of castings from these alloys to 3 pounds for aluminum base; 10 pounds for lead; 8 pounds for tin, and 6 pounds for zinc. Improved practice will probably increase these limits.

DIE CHASERS—The separate cutting tools used in die heads, which actually cut the screw threads. They are of three general types: Radial, with the cutting edges on the ends of the chasers; tangential, with the cutting edges along the length of the chaser, and circular, in which the chaser is round with a section cut away to give a cutting edge.

DIE FENCES—Safety guards, usually made of expanded sheet metal, which surround a punch press or other die, and prevent operators from getting fingers caught in the work. They are removable for putting work in and removing it. This is sometimes done automatically while the press is idle.

DIE HEADS OR HOLDERS—Holders for the chasing tools used in cutting screw threads on bolts and similar work. These permit the chasers to be removed for grinding and replaced accurately. Some types of die heads open automatically when the work is threaded and can be removed without reversing the work of the die. These are known as automatic die heads. Four die heads are shown. The first has fixed cutters hobbed in place—the second has inserted cutters—the third has circular cutters which are turned when sharpened. All three have the cuttters radial to the work. The fourth one shown has tangential cutters.

DIE HEADS OR HOLDERS, FLOATING— Die holders made to permit movement that accommodates small out of alinement between the die and the work. (Illus. page 70.)

DIE-PLATE OR SCREW STOCK—A frame or handle used to hold standard threading dies for hand use. In some cases the die and stock are in one piece, but this is not common practice.

DIEING MACHINE—A trade name for an automatic punch press made especially for manufacturing small sheet metal parts at a rapid rate.

DIELECTRIC STRENGTH—The point at which insulation breaks down under electric pressure. It is measured by dividing the thickness of the insulating materials in *mils* (thousandths of an inch) by the voltage necessary to break down the insulation, with standard alternating current at sixty cycles.

DIFFERENTIAL GEARING—See *Gearing, Differential.*

DIMENSIONING—The method of showing sizes of different parts of any mechanism on the drawings from which it is to be made. These may show not only the overall sizes but also the relation of different parts to each other. See *Drawing.*

DIP BRAZING—While much brazing is done in a fire or with a torch, there are times when it is better to dip the parts to be brazed into a molten bath of the brazing metal, heated to its proper temperature. This is known as dip brazing. See *Brazing, Dip.*

DISINTEGRATOR—A device which removes broken studs, taps or other objects by melting or disintegrating the broken part with an electric arc.

DISKS—Flat plates, usually round, used for various purposes.

DIVIDER—A mechanic's or draftsman's tool for measuring and locating spaces or desired distances. In the spring divider shown, the spring tends to force the points apart while the nut regulates the distance between them.

Divider.

DIVIDING HEAD, BROWN & SHARPE—A well known dividing head which can be used for either direct or differential indexing. The main parts are named in the illustration, pg. 79.

DIVIDING HEAD, KEARNEY & TRECKER HYPOID—Instead of the usual 40 to 1 ratio, this dividing head has a 5 to 1 ratio, which gives 40,000 different leads from 0.0219 to 2.918 inches. They also make an astronomical attachment by which the circle can be divided into 1,296,000 parts, which gives seconds of arc, one second equalling 0.000024 inch on the periphery of a circle 10 inches in diameter. It

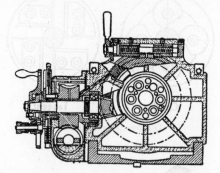

Kearney and Trecker hypoid dividing head.

is not possible to obtain this accuracy in practice, but the heads are guaranteed to one minute of arc.

DIVIDING HEAD, WIDE RANGE, CINCINNATI—This is a special dividing head made by the Cincinnati Milling Machine Co. for rapidly selecting divisions between 2 and 400,000 and any angle in degrees, minutes and seconds. The main crank operate 40 to 1 and the small crank 100 to 1. Details are available from the maker.

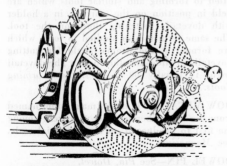

Cincinnati wide-range dividing head.

DOCTOR—A local term for a piece which acts as a separator between different parts. It may be a bushing between a shaft and an oversize hole. Also may mean a piece used to patch up a poor piece of work. Some use the term "dutchman" in the same manner.

DODECAGON—A figure having 12 equal sides. See *Polygon*.

DOG—This has a variety of meanings. In lathe work it is a carrier which drives work between centers. In planer and shaper work it is a movable piece which contacts a mechanism that reverses the travel of the planer table or shaper ram. Sometimes applied to a pawl in a ratchet mechanism of any kind. See *Pawl*. Several lathe dogs are shown on page 80.

DOG POINT SCREWS—See *Screws, Dog Point*, page 361.

DOLLY BAR—A term used in some localities for the "hold on" or part which backs up the blows of the riveting hammer in riveting boilers and other structures. It acts as an anvil to hold the rivet in place as it is being headed over.

DOLOMITE—A type of limestone used as a flux in melting iron. Also used for lining basic steel furnaces and in the production of magnesium.

DOUBLE END BOLT—See *Bolt, Double End*.

DOUZIEME—A watchmaker's measurement which is 0.0074 inch. See *Watchmaker's Measurements*.

DOVETAILS—Angular sided slots or recesses to guide or to locate parts of any mechanism. The angle prevents the inner or male member from being lifted out of the recess. Wear and

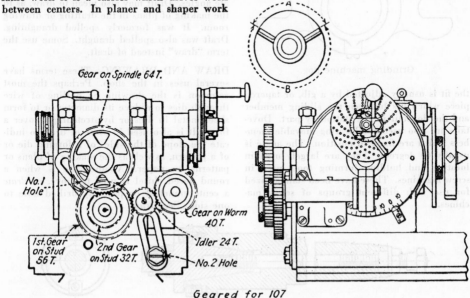

Gear on Spindle 64 T.

No. 1 Hole

1st. Gear on Stud 56 T.

2nd Gear on Stud 32 T.

Gear on Worm 40 T.

Idler 24 T.

No. 2 Hole

Geared for 107

Dividing head, Brown and Sharpe.

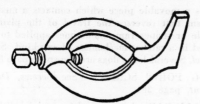

Bent tail dog.

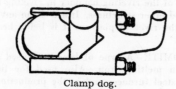

Clamp dog.

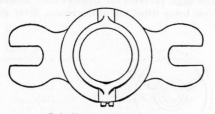

Straight tail dog.

Grinding machine dog.

the fit is usually adjusted by a gib, or tapered piece which fits between the sliding member and the dovetail in the stationary part. Dovetails are also used for locating movable members which are fixed in position. The angle is usually 60 degrees. They are largely used in locating and holding forming tools used in screw machines. These have been standardized for use with different groups of screw machines.

DOVETAILS, DIMENSIONING — See *Drawings, Dimensioning, Dovetails.*

DOVETAIL TOOLS—The term is usually applied to forming and similar tools which are held in position on the machine in a holder with dovetails matching those on the tool. The same term is also applied to tools which are formed at the proper angle for cutting dovetails in slides or other parts. The dovetail angle is usually 60 degrees. See *Forming Tools.*

DOW METAL—A brand of magnesium named from the Dow Chemical Co. who were among the first to produce it on a commercial scale. See *Magnesium.*

DOWEL PIN—See *Pin, Dowel.*

DOWN TIME—The time a machine or other equipment is out of use because of need of repairs or adjustment. Some apply it to the time needed to prepare, or set the machine up for a new job, but this is usually known as "setting up time."

DRAFT—The angle or slope in forging dies or in patterns and core boxes for castings, to enable the work to be removed easily. In forging dies the draft angle varies from 5 to 12 degrees with 7 and 9 degrees as the intermediate angles. Draft may also mean to draw, as in the making of plans in the drafting or drawing room. It was formerly spelled draughting. Draft was also spelled draught. Some use the term "draw" instead of draft.

DRAW AND DRAWING—These terms have several uses in the shop. Perhaps the most common is the drawing or pulling of wire through dies to reduce its diameter or to form sheet metal in dies or by stretching it over a form. It is also used in place of draft to indicate the slope of the sides of a forging die or of a pattern, as well as the making of plans or patterns on paper. Another use is when a round nosed chisel is used to move, or *draw* a center-punched or partially drilled hole to one side. See *Draft.*

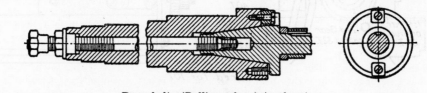

Draw bolt. (Pulling arbor into place.)

DRAW BOLT—A bolt used in milling machines and other machine tools to hold cutter arbors firmly in place in the spindle. While they were sometimes used with the older "self-holding" tapers they are necessary with the new 3½-inch tapers now standard in milling and some other machines.

DRAW-CUT—In machine tools, a cutting action which draws the tool toward the base of the machine. A draw-cut shaper cuts toward the column of the machine instead of away from it.

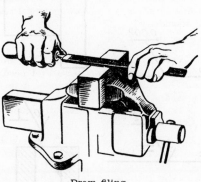

Draw filing.

DRAW-FILING—Filing by moving the file in the long direction of the work instead of across it. The file is moved sideways instead of from point to heel. It was formerly used to give a fine finish to shaft bearings and in other places where a pleasing finish was desired. This has largely been replaced by grinding.

DRAW KEY—See *Key, Draw.*

DRAW REDUCTION RATIO FOR ROUND SHELLS—There is a definite ratio between the diameter and the height, or depth, to which metal can be drawn or cupped, in one operation. These depend on (1) ratio of height to diameter; (2) ductility of material, and (3) corner radius. The corner radius should be four times the shell thickness.

DRAWINGS, ANGLE OF PROJECTION—The approved method of showing more than one view of any mechanism is indicated here, using a punch and die. This is known as "third-angle-projection." The view from the right hand side goes at the right of the front view, as shown. This method has now been adopted by British engineers, who formerly

put the view of the right side at the left side of the front view. This is called "first-angle-projection."

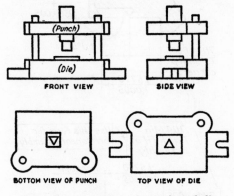

Normal arrangement of punch-and-die drawings.

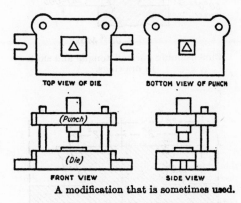

A modification of punch-and-die drawings that is sometimes used.

DRAWING BATHS—See *Heat Treatment, Drawing Baths.*

DRAWING COMPOUND—Any lubricant used on sheet metal to make it slide over the surface of dies and punches in deep drawing.

DRAWINGS, DIMENSIONING DOVETAILS—The standardized method of showing the dimensions of dovetails is indicated. This includes dimensions and tolerances permitted on plain surfaces and on the angles. (See illustration, page 82.)

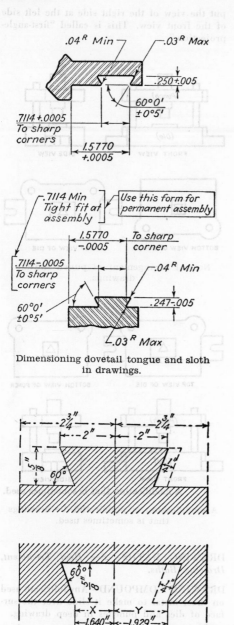

Dimensioning dovetail tongue and sloth in drawings.

Dimensioning sides and gibs in drawings.

DRAWINGS, INDICATING SURFACE QUALITY — Standard symbols for surface quality have been adopted, as shown.

SYMBOLS FOR SURFACE QUALITY

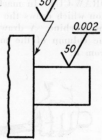

a

b

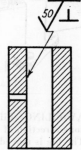

c

d

e   **SYMBOLS FOR LAY**

PARALLEL   PERPENDICULAR   ANGULAR

MULTI-DIRECTIONAL   CIRCULAR   RADIAL

Indicating surface quality in drawings.

DRAWINGS, INDICATING TWO POSITIONS—

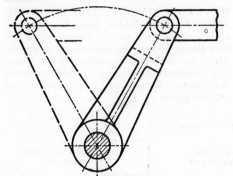

Drawings—indication of alternate positions.

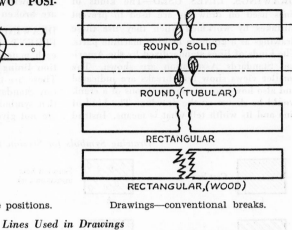

ROUND, SOLID

ROUND, (TUBULAR)

RECTANGULAR

RECTANGULAR, (WOOD)

Drawings—conventional breaks.

Lines Used in Drawings

Outline of Parts	1	THICK	The outline should be the outstanding feature and the thickness may vary to suit size of drawing.
Section lines	2	THIN	Spaced evenly to make a shaded effect.
Hidden lines	3	MEDIUM	Short dashes, closely and evenly spaced.
Center lines	4		Alternate long and short dashes, closely and evenly spaced.
Dimension and Extension lines	5	$3\frac{1}{2}$	Lines unbroken, except at dimensions.
	6	$2'-3\frac{1}{2}$	Lines unbroken, dimensions above line for civil eng. and struct. practice only.
Cutting Plane line	7		Long and two short dashes alternately and evenly spaced.
Break lines	8		Free hand line for short breaks.
	9		Ruled line and free hand zig-zag for long breaks.
Adjacent Parts and Alternate Positions	10		Broken line made up of long dashes.
Ditto line	11		Indication of repeated detail. Short double dashes evenly spaced.

Lines used in drawings (American Standard). Character of lines.

DRAWINGS, LINES USED—The kinds of lines used on drawings are used to prevent mistakes by workmen when they use these drawings as a guide in making machine parts. The kinds of lines standardized by the American Standards Association are shown. The smaller views show how breaks are indicated and also how two extreme positions of a crank would be shown on the drawing. The kind of line and its width tell what is means. Instead of showing long bars in their full length they are broken as shown. (Illus. p. 83.)

DRAWINGS, LINES, SECTIONS, FOR DIFFERENT MATERIALS—Instead of calling each material by name, distinctive cross section lining is used in most cases, as shown. These are the recommendations of the American Standards Association. It will be noted that symbols for cast steel and malleable iron are not given.

Drawing Symbols for Section Lines

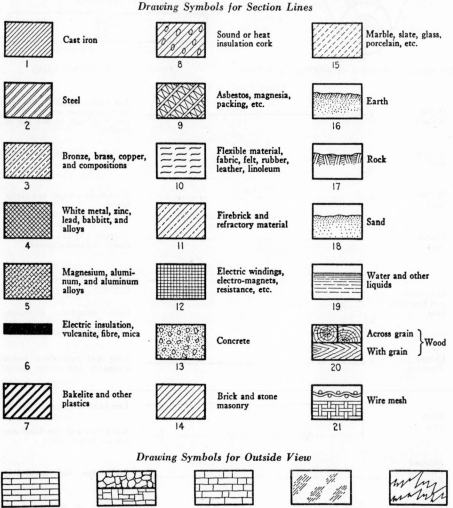

1 Cast iron
2 Steel
3 Bronze, brass, copper, and compositions
4 White metal, zinc, lead, babbitt, and alloys
5 Magnesium, aluminum, and aluminum alloys
6 Electric insulation, vulcanite, fibre, mica
7 Bakelite and other plastics
8 Sound or heat insulation cork
9 Asbestos, magnesia, packing, etc.
10 Flexible material, fabric, felt, rubber, leather, linoleum
11 Firebrick and refractory material
12 Electric windings, electro-magnets, resistance, etc.
13 Concrete
14 Brick and stone masonry
15 Marble, slate, glass, porcelain, etc.
16 Earth
17 Rock
18 Sand
19 Water and other liquids
20 Across grain / With grain } Wood
21 Wire mesh

Drawing Symbols for Outside View

Brick   Uncoursed and   Ashlar   Transparent   Marble
                     coursed rubble   materials,
                                                                 glass, etc.

DRAWINGS, MECHANICAL — Drawings

which show the construction and sizes of complete machines or of parts. They are made to scale, which varies with the size of the finished machine. Parts for very small mechanisms are frequently drawn several times as large as the part itself, while parts and assemblies of large machines are drawn to a very small scale, such as ⅛ of an inch on the drawing to 12 inches on the finished machines. This is called "⅛ inch to the foot." Drawings should not be measured to secure sizes. These should be plainly marked in figures in their proper places. Even if drawings could be accurately measured, the changes in the paper due to atmospheric conditions would prevent accurate results.

DRAWINGS, SCREW THREAD—Instead of

making complete and artistic drawings of screw threads, as was done 50 or more years ago, we now indicate them by standard symbols as shown in either the *regular* or the *simplified* symbols. Similar methods are used for pipe threads. Square thread and Acme thread drawings are shown. These save many hours of time. (See also *Screw Thread Drawings*, page 86.)

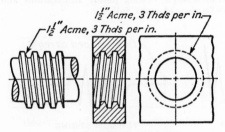

Drawing—Modified square thread.

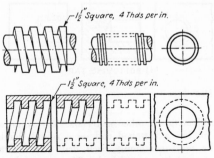

Drawing—Acme thread.

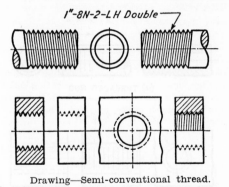

Drawing—Semi-conventional thread.

DRAWINGS, SPRING — Simplified symbols

for compression, torsion and tension springs are standardized, as shown.

DRAWINGS, STANDARD SIZES OF—The

American Standards Association has adopted five standard sizes for mechanical drawings, as follows: A—8½ x 11 inches; B—11 x 17 inches; C—17 x 22 inches; D—22 x 34 inches; and E—34 x 44 inches.

Sizes A and B are usually filed flat, but the larger sizes may be folded as shown. When necessary, fold the 11 x 17 inch drawing in the center, making it 8½ x 11 inches. Position of drawing number and title is indicated.

DRAWN WORK — The term is usually ap-

plied to sheet metal work in which a sheet which was originally flat is formed into shapes which require stretching the metal in places to force it to assume the desired shape. Common examples are tinware dishes used in every kitchen, automobile fenders and bodies, cartridges and similar work.

DRIFT—A common name for a flat piece of

steel used to remove taper shank drills and other tools from their holder. Sometimes called a key center. The term *drift* is also used for a tapered tool used to force mismated holes in line for riveting or bolting. Older mechanics used it for a short broach which was driven through mismated holes for the same purpose.

DRIFT HOLE—A hole or slot in a drill socket

or other tool holding part, to admit a drift or drive key, for forcing the tool out of the socket.

DRIFT KEY—See *Key, Drift*.

DRIFT PIN—A round, tapered steel pin used

to bring plates which are to be riveted into

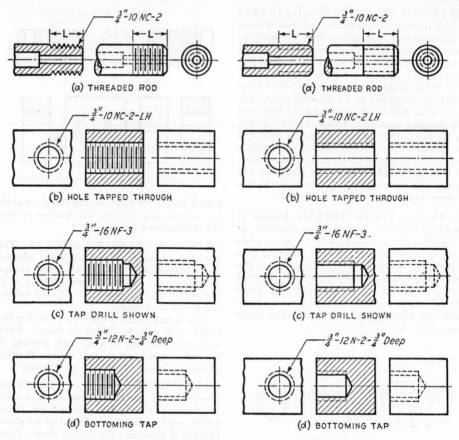

Screw Thread Drawings

alinement to permit putting rivets in place easily. Used largely in making boilers and tanks and also in structural work.

DRIFT SLOT—Another name for a drift hole.

DRILL—(See also *Drilling Machines.*) Primarily a rotating tool for cutting holes in solid metal or other materials. The simplest form has a flattened end on a round shank. The most commonly used drill has helical flutes cut in a round body. They are made in many sizes but usually have a 118-degree included angle cutting point. Illustrations and definition of parts follow.

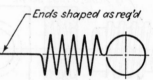

COMPRESSION SPRING

TORSION SPRING

TENSION SPRING

Ends shaped as req'd

SPRING DRAWINGS.

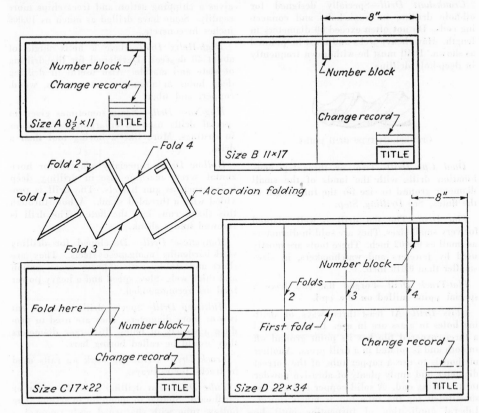

TITLE BLOCK, CHANGE RECORD, AND FOLDING

STANDARD SIZES FOR DRAWINGS.

Types of Drills

Bakelite Drill — Have a wide, polished flute adapted for use in bakelite, fiber, and hard rubber. Generally made of high-speed steel to resist abrasion.

Blacksmith's Drill — A short, stocky drill with a straight shank, flattened on one side for holding with a set screw.

Bobbin Bit Drill — Developed for drilling deep holes in wood. Its chip cleaning ability makes it useful in drilling celluloid.

Bonding Drill — Designed and tempered for drilling holes for bonding wires in track-circuit signal work. Shorter and heavier than regular drills.

Brass Drill — Usually carbon steel with special shape. Superior to regular drills for

brass work. Also satisfactory for magnesium alloys.

Center Drill — A short drill for preparing the ends of turned work to receive the lathe centers on which the work turns. These combine a small drill point with a reamer that cuts a 60 degree angle behind the small drill point to fit the angle of the lathe center.

Combination Drill — Rotary cutting tools for special work, such as combined drill and countersink.

Core Drill — A hollow tool made with cutting edges on the end of a tube. Instead of removing all the metal it leaves a center core which can be tested and analyzed to test the kind of material in the piece being drilled. The same type of drill is also used in securing samples of rock for various purposes.

87

Crankshaft Drill—Specially designed for oil-hole drilling in crankshafts and connecting rods. Do not often exceed 60 diameters in length. Have heavy webs and must be pointed as shown. Drill must be withdrawn frequently in deep-hole drilling.

Crankshaft type drill point.

Dual Cut Drill—Two- or three-step combination drills with the lands of the small diameter ground to size for the full length of the flutes. See *Drilling, Step.*

Flat Drill—The flat drill is well adapted for very small sizes. They are sold in diameters as small as 0.0002 inch. These tools are mostly used by jewelers and watchmakers, in sizes smaller than 0.010 inch.

Flat-Track Drill—Forged flat and have a special point milled on the end.

Glass Drill—At least three ways of drilling holes in glass are in use. In one method a three-cornered file has its point ground off smooth and is rotated in a drill press. Another method is to use a copper tube of the correct diameter and apply plenty of abrasive powder to its cutting end. A solid copper rod may be substituted for the tube but is much slower. Liberal application of turpentine must be made in all cases.

Grobet Drill—A flat drill, made in diameters of 0.002 to 0.080 inch. The smaller sizes vary by half-thousandths of an inch. The drill blade is five times its diameter. They are high speed steel drills, and are used for precision drilling.

Gun-Barrel Drill—A drill for drilling gun barrels. They are usually short drills brazed or welded to steel tubes through which oil is pumped at high pressure to remove the chips. They frequently have but one cutting edge and are run at high speed.

Hammer Drill—A drill to be used in percussion tools, such as the air hammer, for drilling holes in stones, concrete or other material too hard and too abrasive for a rotating drill. In steel drills, the point is usually in the shape of a cross, but the newer carbide drills are triangular in shape, the carbide tip being brazed to the steel shank. This shape gives a chipping action and frees chips more readily. Some have drilled as much as 10,000 inches in concrete.

High-Helix Drill—Have a helix angle of about 40 degrees. Developed for the drilling of slate and marble. Also useful in drilling deep holes in aluminum, magnesium, wood, copper, and fiber.

Hog-Nose Drill—Name sometimes given to special drills used in enlarging cored holes in castings. More like a boring tool than a drill.

Hollow Drill—Especially adapted for horizontal screw machine use in drilling deep holes, such as gun barrels. The drill is provided with a threaded shank. A hole through this shank runs into the flutes. The drill is screwed into a shank.

Manganese Drill—Developed for drilling work-hardening manganese steels. They are short and stubby with a heavy cross section and thick web. Slow speed and a heavy power feed are recommended.

Multistep Drill—Special drills made to cut two or more diameters. They are used to produce a variety of holes. In larger diameters they would be called boring bars.

Track Drill—Drills for work on rails used in tracks for railways.

Tube Drill—For drilling holes in paper or cardboard. Similar to spoon bit in action. The hollow tube with sharpened ends removes a solid core.

Spoon Bit Drill—For drilling stacked layers of paper, cardboard, or thin wood. Has a crescent-moon section with sharp edges. They remove a central core of the material.

Oil Hole Drill—A drill with a hole through which oil or other lubricants can be forced to the cutting edges of the drill. The drill is made with straight flutes and the oil hole drilled through the solid portion or land. The drill is then heated and twisted to the desired helix.

Oil Tube Drill—A drill with an oil tube for carrying oil, under pressure, to the cutting edges. A slot is milled in the land of the drill body and a small tube soldered or otherwise fastened in this groove, so as to avoid contact with the hole being drilled.

Percussion Drill—A drill for use in brick or masonry work, which forces its way by a series of blows which break away the particles of masonry. It is really more of a chisel than a drill, as it seldom rotates, but is sometimes turned back and forth by the operator. See *Hammer Drill*.

Ratchet Drill—A hand-operated drill, for use where it is not possible or convenient to use a continuous movement. The use of a ratchet on the spindle of the drill permits the use of a small portion of a turn in which the pawl of the ratchet engages the spindle and then releases it while the handle is moved back for the next stroke. They are frequently made reversible so that the drill spindle can be moved in either direction. This is particularly useful when used to drive a tap into a drilled hole, and then to remove it.

Roll-Forged Drill—A drill with flutes forged between rollers instead of being milled from a solid bar.

Sheffield Drills—A special drill made by the Sheffield Twist Drill & Steel Co., England, for drilling holes for taper pins. It has a taper of ¼ inch per foot and also has serrated cutting lips. It really combines a drill and reamer. In this country we step-drill the holes, using drills of different sizes before reaming to the correct taper.

Shell Drill—Similar to reamers; used in enlarging holes. They are fitted to a shank, usually tapered. They may have either straight or helical flutes.

Skin or Body Drill—A drill having a very short length of flutes for drilling through sheet metal, such as used in automobile bodies.

Star Drill—A drill for rock or brickwork, having a point shaped like a four-pointed star. See *Hammer Drill*.

Stack Drill—A drill with flutes at a steeper angle with the center axis, for use in drilling stacks of tin plates.

Stove Burner Drill—A drill designed for drilling burner castings of gas stoves. Has a short flute. A strong drill.

Straight-Flute Drill—Originally known as the Farmer drill after its inventor. The flutes are straight instead of helical and do not clear themselves of chips as readily as the twist drill. They are preferred, however, when drilling holes that intersect other holes, as the drill is stiffer and has less tendency to "run" or be diverted from its true path.

Tapping Drill—Drills used for holes that are to be tapped must allow for sufficient depth of thread to hold the screw or bolt without danger of stripping the thread. A tapped hole ¾ of the thread depth is sufficient in all regular work. The following rule by H. W. Bearce, formerly with the Bureau of Standards, is very convenient. "Deduct the pitch of the thread, in threads per inch, from the outside diameter of the tap. For a 1-inch, 8-pitch tap, deduct ⅛ inch and get ⅞ as the tap drill. For ¼-inch, 20-thread tap deduct 1/20 inch, or 0.05 inch, giving a drill 0.20 inch in diameter.

Tell-Tale Drill—A drill used for drilling holes in the ends of staybolts used in boilers to show when a bolt breaks inside the boiler sheet.

Three- and Four-Groove Drill(s)—These are made for second operations, following holes made by the usual two-lipped drill. They enlarge holes already made in the same way as reamers.

Wood Drill—Drills for boring holes in wood; usually called "bits." There are three general types of wood drills for use where the regular twist drill is not satisfactory. The pod drill has a single flute and is really half a cylinder. The bit point has a spur, the same as wood augers, while the single flute drill has special uses. This is usually made of smaller diameter after a short straight length of full size. This reduces friction as the drill gets deeper into the hole.

Drills—Classification, Based on Number of Flutes

Two Flute Drills—These are the conventional drills used for originating holes.

Single Flute Drills—Drills used principally for drilling wood and other soft substances.

Three Flute Drills (Core Drills)—These drills are used for enlarging and finishing holes. They will not originate holes because they do not have any cutting edges at the center.

Four Flute Drills—These drills are used interchangeably with three flute drills. They are of the same construction except for the number of flutes.

Twist Drill Nomenclature

Axis—The axis is the longitudinal center line through the drill.

Back Taper (Longitudinal Relief)—Drills are usually made slightly smaller in diameter at the shank end than at the point. This is known as back taper. It is about 0.0005 inch per inch of length.

Body—The body is the portion of the drill extending from the shank or neck to the outer corners of the cutting lips.

Body Diameter Clearance—That portion of the land that has been cut away so it will not rub against the walls of the hole is designated as body diameter clearance. It is sometimes called land clearance. Its purpose is to reduce friction.

Chisel Edge—The edge at the end of the web that connects the cutting edges is designated as the chisel edge.

Chisel Edge Angle (Center Angle)—The angle included between the chisel edge and the cutting edge as seen from the end of the drill is called the chisel edge angle.

Clearance Diameter—The clearance diameter is the diameter of the relieved portion of the drill body.

Flutes—The helical grooves cut or formed in the body of the drill to provide cutting edges, to permit removal of chips, and to allow cutting fluid to reach the cutting edges are called flutes. (Straight fluted drills may be obtained.)

Flute Length—The flute length is the length from the outer corners of the cutting lips to the extreme back end of the flutes. This is often referred to as the length of waist.

Helix Angle—The helix angle is the angle of the leading edge of the land with the axis of the drill. The helix angle is identical with the rake angle of the cutting edges at the periphery of the drill. A straight flute drill would have zero-degree helix angle.

Land—The land is the periphery of that portion of the drill body not cut away by the flutes.

Lips—The cutting edges of the drill extending from the chisel edge to the periphery are called the lips.

Lip Relief Angle—This is the angle measured between a tangent on the surface back of the cutting edge at the periphery, and a line at right angles to the axis of the drill.

Margin—The margin is that portion of the land which is not cut away to provide clearance. The margin forms the full diameter of the drill.

Neck—The neck is the diametrically relieved portion between the body and the shank of the drill.

Overall Length—The length from the shank end to the outer corners of the cutting lips is called the overall length. It does not include the conical cutting point.

Point—The cutting end of a drill, made up of the ends of the lands and the web forming the lips. It is usually roughly conical in form.

Point Angle—The angle included between the lips is known as the point angle.

Rake Angle (In Relation to Work)—The rake angle is the angle between the leading edge of the land and the axis at the drill point.

Shank—The shank is that part of the drill by which it is held and driven.

Tang—The tang is the flattened end of the shank, intended to fit into a driving slot in the

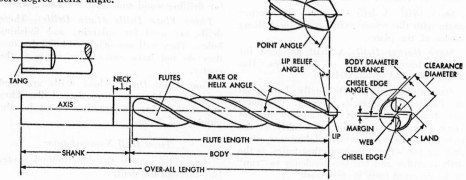

Names of parts of twist drills.

drill holder or socket. Tangs are most common on taper shanks.

Web—The central portion of the body that joins the lands is called the web. The extreme end of the web forms the chisel edge.

Web Thickness—The minimum thickness of the web at the point, unless another specific location is indicated, is the web thickness.

Web Thinning—The operation of reducing the web thickness at the point to reduce drilling thrust, is called web thinning.

Drills—Classification, Based on Kind of Shank

Straight Shank Drills—Drills having cylindrical shanks. The shank may be of the same or of a different diameter from that of the body of the drill. It may be made with or without driving flats, tang, or grooves.

Taper Shank Drills—Drills having conical shanks suitable for direct fitting into tapered holes in drilling machine spindles or driving sockets. The tapered shanks generally have a driving tang.

Taper Square Shank Drills—Drills having tapered shanks with four flat sides for fitting ratchets and braces.

Drills—Classification, Based on Hand of Rotation

Right-Hand Drills—The great majority of drills are made "right hand;" that is, when looking toward the point of these drills with the shank extending away, they must be rotated in a counterclockwise direction in order to cut.

Left-Hand Drills—These drills are made to cut when rotated in a clockwise direction. They are not used except where close center distances between drills in multiple drilling heads make it necessary to use gears that reverse the direction of alternate drills.

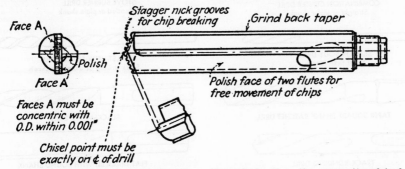

A two-lip gun drill gives production three times faster than the conventional tool when drilling forged barrels.

TWO-STEP TAPER SHANK DRILL

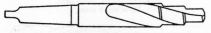

THREE-STEP CORE DRILL

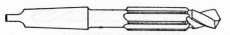

COMBINATION DRILL AND REAMER

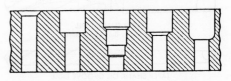

MULTI-LAND DRILL AND REAMER

TWO DIAMETER MULTI-LAND DRILL

HOLES PRODUCED WITH MULTI-LAND DRILLS

TYPES OF DRILLS.
(Continued on page 92)

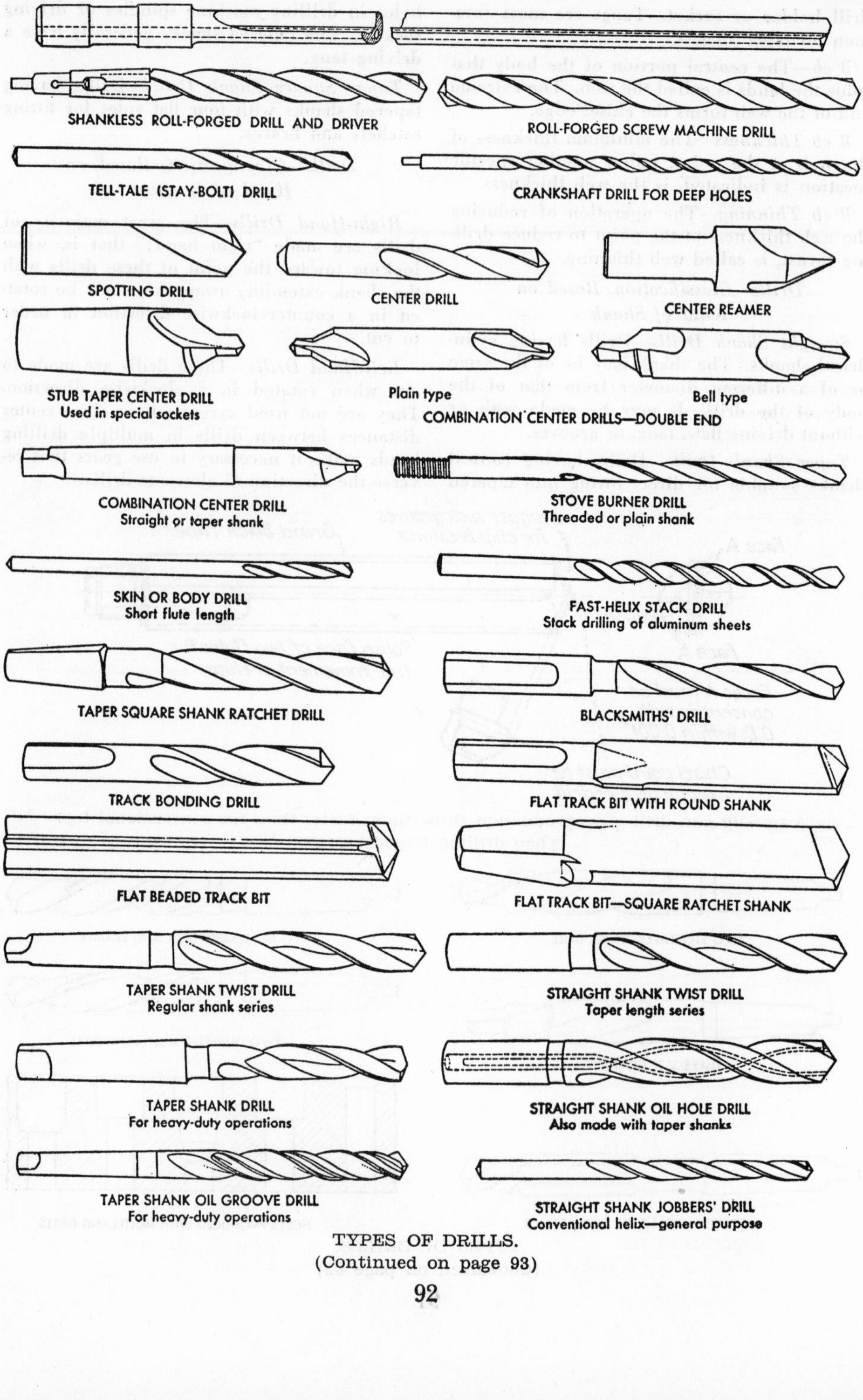

SHANKLESS ROLL-FORGED DRILL AND DRIVER

ROLL-FORGED SCREW MACHINE DRILL

TELL-TALE (STAY-BOLT) DRILL

CRANKSHAFT DRILL FOR DEEP HOLES

SPOTTING DRILL

CENTER DRILL

CENTER REAMER

STUB TAPER CENTER DRILL
Used in special sockets

Plain type

COMBINATION CENTER DRILLS—DOUBLE END

Bell type

COMBINATION CENTER DRILL
Straight or taper shank

STOVE BURNER DRILL
Threaded or plain shank

SKIN OR BODY DRILL
Short flute length

FAST-HELIX STACK DRILL
Stack drilling of aluminum sheets

TAPER SQUARE SHANK RATCHET DRILL

BLACKSMITHS' DRILL

TRACK BONDING DRILL

FLAT TRACK BIT WITH ROUND SHANK

FLAT BEADED TRACK BIT

FLAT TRACK BIT—SQUARE RATCHET SHANK

TAPER SHANK TWIST DRILL
Regular shank series

STRAIGHT SHANK TWIST DRILL
Taper length series

TAPER SHANK DRILL
For heavy-duty operations

STRAIGHT SHANK OIL HOLE DRILL
Also made with taper shanks

TAPER SHANK OIL GROOVE DRILL
For heavy-duty operations

STRAIGHT SHANK JOBBERS' DRILL
Conventional helix—general purpose

TYPES OF DRILLS.
(Continued on page 93)

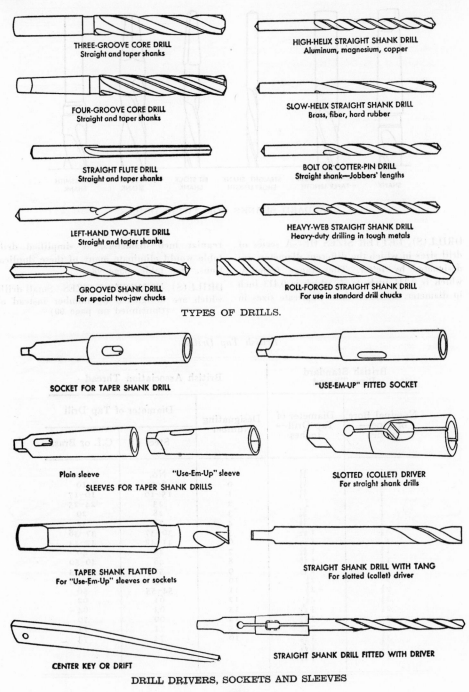

THREE-GROOVE CORE DRILL
Straight and taper shanks

HIGH-HELIX STRAIGHT SHANK DRILL
Aluminum, magnesium, copper

FOUR-GROOVE CORE DRILL
Straight and taper shanks

SLOW-HELIX STRAIGHT SHANK DRILL
Brass, fiber, hard rubber

STRAIGHT FLUTE DRILL
Straight and taper shanks

BOLT OR COTTER-PIN DRILL
Straight shank—Jobbers' lengths

LEFT-HAND TWO-FLUTE DRILL
Straight and taper shanks

HEAVY-WEB STRAIGHT SHANK DRILL
Heavy-duty drilling in tough metals

GROOVED SHANK DRILL
For special two-jaw chucks

ROLL-FORGED STRAIGHT SHANK DRILL
For use in standard drill chucks

TYPES OF DRILLS.

SOCKET FOR TAPER SHANK DRILL

"USE-EM-UP" FITTED SOCKET

Plain sleeve   "Use-Em-Up" sleeve
SLEEVES FOR TAPER SHANK DRILLS

SLOTTED (COLLET) DRIVER
For straight shank drills

TAPER SHANK FLATTED
For "Use-Em-Up" sleeves or sockets

STRAIGHT SHANK DRILL WITH TANG
For slotted (collet) driver

CENTER KEY OR DRIFT

STRAIGHT SHANK DRILL FITTED WITH DRIVER

DRILL DRIVERS, SOCKETS AND SLEEVES

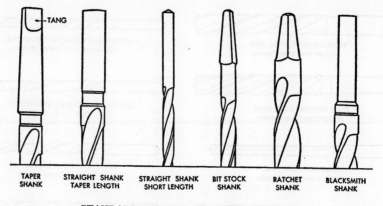

| TAPER SHANK | STRAIGHT SHANK TAPER LENGTH | STRAIGHT SHANK SHORT LENGTH | BIT STOCK SHANK | RATCHET SHANK | BLACKSMITH SHANK |

STANDARD SHANKS FOR TWIST DRILLS.

DRILL(S), LETTER SIZES OF—A series of drill sizes in which the different diameters are designated by letter. They range from A, which is 0.234 inch, to Z, which is 0.413 inch in diameter. Some of these duplicate sizes in regular inch diameters. A simplified drill table would eliminate many of these duplications. See table, page 98.

DRILL(S), NUMBER OF SIZES—Small drills which are designated by number instead of (Continued on page 99)

British Tap Drills

British Standard Pipe Thread		British Association Thread		
Nominal Bore of Pipe— Inches	Diameter of Tap Drill— Inches	Designating Number	Diameter of Tap Drill	
			Steel	C.I. or Brass
			No.	No.
$\frac{1}{8}$	$1\frac{1}{32}$	0	8–9	10
$\frac{1}{4}$	$1\frac{5}{32}$	1	15–16	16–17
$\frac{3}{8}$	$1\frac{1}{2}$	2	23	24–25
$\frac{1}{2}$	$\frac{3}{4}$	3	28	29
$\frac{5}{8}$	$\frac{25}{64}$	4	31	32
$\frac{3}{4}$	$3\frac{1}{2}$	5	36–37	37–38
$\frac{7}{8}$	$1\frac{7}{64}$	6	41–42	42–43
1	$1\frac{3}{32}$	7	45	46
$1\frac{1}{4}$	$1\frac{35}{64}$	8	48	49–50
$1\frac{1}{2}$	$1\frac{3}{32}$	9	51	52–53
$1\frac{3}{4}$	$2\frac{3}{32}$	10	53	54–55
2	$2\frac{1}{2}$	11	54–55	56
$2\frac{1}{4}$	$2\frac{7}{8}$	12	61	62
$2\frac{1}{2}$	$2\frac{7}{8}$	13	63	64
$2\frac{3}{4}$	$3\frac{9}{64}$	14	69	70
3	$3\frac{25}{64}$	15	71	71
$3\frac{1}{4}$	$3\frac{19}{32}$	16	74	74
$3\frac{1}{2}$	$3\frac{27}{32}$			
$3\frac{3}{4}$	$4\frac{11}{32}$			
4	$4\frac{11}{32}$			

Tap Drills for Small Sizes of American National Fine Thread—Class 3 Fit*

Size of Screw and Threads	Dia. Body or Major Diameter Screw	Basic Pitch Dia.	LIMITS Tapped Hole	LIMITS Screw	Internal Thread Minor Diameter	TAP DRILL SIZES Full Thr'd 75% to 80% (Wrought Brass, Nickel, Babbitt, Wr. Alum. Alloy, Fiber, White Metal, Hd. Rubber)	Full Thr'd 70% to 75% (Mild Steel, Cast Alum., Cast Iron, Cast Brass)	Full Thr'd 65% to 75% (Bronze, Tool Steel, Drop Forgings, Stainless Steel, Cast Steel, Nickel Copper)	Clearance Drill
00-96	0.047 +0.0000 −0.0032	0.0402	+0.0010 −0.0000	+0.0000 −0.0010	0.0357 +0.0024 −0.0000	64 (0.036)	63 (0.037)	63 (0.037)	55 (0.052)
0-80	0.060 +0.0000 −0.0034	0.0519	+0.0013 −0.0000	+0.0000 −0.0013	0.0465 +0.0027 −0.0000	55 (1.052) 56 (0.0465)	55 (0.052)	55 (0.052)	51 (0.067)
1-72	0.073 +0.0000 −0.0036	0.0640	+0.0013 −0.0000	+0.0000 −0.0013	0.058 +0.0030 −0.0000	53 (0.0595)	53 (0.0595)	52 (0.0635)	47 (0.0785)
2-64	0.086 +0.0000 −0.0038	0.0759	+0.0014 −0.0000	+0.0000 −0.0014	0.0691 +0.0033 −0.0000	50 (0.070)	49 (0.073)	48 (0.076)	42 (0.0935)
3-56	0.099 +0.0000 −0.0040	0.0874	+0.0015 −0.0000	+0.0000 −0.0015	0.0797 +0.0037 −0.0000	46 (0.081)	45 (0.082)	44 (0.086)	36 (0.065)
4-48	0.112 +0.0000 −0.0044	0.0985	+0.0016 −0.0000	+0.0000 −0.0016	0.0894 +0.0043 −0.0000	43 (0.089)	42 (0.0935)	41 (0.096)	31 (0.120)
5-44	0.125 +0.0000 −0.0046	0.1102	+0.0016 −0.0000	+0.0000 −0.0016	0.1004 +0.0045 −0.0000	38 (0.1015)	37 (0.104)	35 (0.110)	29 (0.136)
6-40	0.138 +0.0000 −0.0048	0.1218	+0.0017 −0.0000	+0.0000 −0.0017	0.1109 +0.0049 −0.0000	33 (0:113)	32 (0.116)	31 (0.120)	26 (0.147)
8-36	0.164 +0.0000 −0.0050	0.1460	+0.0018 −0.0000	+0.0000 −0.0018	0.1339 +0.0052 −0.0000	29 (0.136)	29 (0.136)	28 (0.1405)	17 (0.173)
10-32	0.190 +0.0000 −0.0054	0.1697	+0.0019 −0.0000	+0.0000 −0.0019	0.1562 +0.0056 −0.0000	21 (0.159)	20 (0.161)	19 (0.166)	7 (0.201)

*These tap drill sizes for different materials have been adopted by Kollsman Instrument Division, Square D Co., to provide the accuracy required in aviation instruments. The tolerances on pitch diameter apply only to Class 3 fit and up to ½ in. length of thread engagement.

Basic Thread Dimensions and Tap Drill Sizes

American Thread

Nominal Size	Outside Diameter in Inches	Pitch Diameter in Inches	Root Diameter in Inches	Commercial Tap Drill to Produce Approx. 75% Full Thread	Decimal Equivalent of Tap Drill
1/16–64	0.0625	0.0524	0.0422	3/64	0.0469
72	0.0625	0.0535	0.0445	3/64	0.0469
5/64–60	0.0781	0.0673	0.0563	1/16	0.0625
72	0.0781	0.0691	0.0601	52	0.0635
3/32–48	0.0938	0.0803	0.0667	49	0.0730
50	0.0938	0.0808	0.0678	49	0.0730
7/64–48	0.1094	0.0959	0.0823	43	0.0890
1/8–32	0.1250	0.1047	0.0844	3/32	0.0937
40	0.1250	0.1088	0.0925	38	0.1015
9/64–40	0.1406	0.1244	0.1081	32	0.1160
5/32–32	0.1563	0.1360	0.1157	1/8	0.1250
36	0.1563	0.1382	0.1202	30	0.1285
11/64–32	0.1719	0.1505	0.1313	9/64	0.1406
3/16–24	0.1875	0.1604	0.1334	26	0.1470
32	0.1875	0.1672	0.1469	22	0.1570
13/64–24	0.2031	0.1760	0.1490	20	0.1610
7/32–24	0.2188	0.1919	0.1646	16	0.1770
32	0.2188	0.1985	0.1782	12	0.1890
15/64–24	0.2344	0.2073	0.1806	10	0.1935
1/4–20	0.2500	0.2175	0.1850	7	0.2010
24	0.2500	0.2229	0.1959	4	0.2090
27	0.2500	0.2260	0.2019	3	0.2130
28	0.2500	0.2268	0.2036	3	0.2130
32	0.2500	0.2297	0.2094	7/32	0.2187
5/16–18	0.3125	0.2764	0.2403	F	0.2570
20	0.3125	0.2800	0.2476	17/64	0.2656
24	0.3125	0.2854	0.2584	I	0.2720
27	0.3125	0.2884	0.2644	J	0.2770
32	0.3125	0.2922	0.2719	9/32	0.2812
3/8–16	0.3750	0.3344	0.2938	5/16	0.3125
20	0.3750	0.3425	0.3100	21/64	0.3281
24	0.3750	0.3479	0.3209	Q	0.3320
27	0.3750	0.3509	0.3269	R	0.3390
7/16–14	0.4375	0.3911	0.3447	U	0.3680
20	0.4375	0.4050	0.3726	25/64	0.3906
24	0.4375	0.4104	0.3834	X	0.3970
27	0.4375	0.4134	0.3894	Y	0.4040
1/2–12	0.5000	0.4459	0.3918	27/64	0.4219
13	0.5000	0.4501	0.4001	27/64	0.4219
20	0.5000	0.4675	0.4351	29/64	0.4531
24	0.5000	0.4729	0.4459	29/64	0.4531
27	0.5000	0.4759	0.4519	15/32	0.4687
9/16–12	0.5625	0.5084	0.4542	31/64	0.4844
18	0.5625	0.5264	0.4903	33/64	0.5156
27	0.5625	0.5384	0.5144	17/32	0.5312

(Continued on next page.)

Basic Thread Dimensions and Tap Drill Sizes—Continued

American Thread

Nominal Size	Outside Diameter in Inches	Pitch Diameter in Inches	Root Diameter in Inches	Commercial Tap Drill to Produce Approx. 75% Full Thread	Decimal Equiva-lent of Tap Drill
5/8–11	0.6250	0.5660	0.5069	17/32	0.5312
12	0.6250	0.5709	0.5168	35/64	0.5469
18	0.6250	0.5889	0.5528	37/64	0.5781
27	0.6250	0.6009	0.5769	19/32	0.5937
11/16–11	0.6875	0.6285	0.5694	19/32	0.5937
16	0.6875	0.6469	0.6063	5/8	0.6250
3/4–10	0.7500	0.6850	0.6201	21/32	0.6562
12	0.7500	0.6959	0.6418	43/64	0.6719
16	0.7500	0.7094	0.6688	11/16	0.6875
27	0.7500	0.7259	0.7019	23/32	0.7187
13/16–10	0.8125	0.7476	0.6826	23/32	0.7187
7/8– 9	0.8750	0.8029	0.7307	49/64	0.7656
12	0.8750	0.8209	0.7668	51/64	0.7969
14	0.8750	0.8286	0.7822	13/16	0.8125
18	0.8750	0.8389	0.8028	53/64	0.8281
27	0.8750	0.8509	0.8269	27/32	0.8437
15/16– 9	0.9375	0.8654	0.7932	53/64	0.8281
1 – 8	1.0000	0.9188	0.8376	7/8	0.8750
12	1.0000	0.9459	0 8918	59/64	0.9219
14	1.0000	0.9536	0.9072	15/16	0.9375
27	1.0000	0.9759	0.9519	31/32	0.9687
1 1/8 – 7	1.1250	1.0322	0.9394	63/64	0.9844
12	1.1250	1.0709	1.0168	1 3/64	1.0469
1 1/4 – 7	1.2500	1.1572	1.0644	1 7/64	1.1094
12	1.2500	1.1959	1.1418	1 11/64	1.1719
1 3/8 – 6	1.3750	1.2668	1.1585	1 7/32	1.2187
12	1.3750	1.3209	1.2668	1 19/64	1.2969
1 1/2 – 6	1.5000	1.3917	1.2835	1 11/32	1.3437
12	1.5000	1.4459	1.3918	1 27/64	1.4219
1 5/8 –5 1/2	1.6250	1.5070	1.3888	1 29/64	1.4531
1 3/4 – 5	1.7500	1.6201	1.4902	1 9/16	1.5625
1 7/8 – 5	1.8750	1.7451	1.6152	1 11/16	1.6875
2 – 4 1/2	2.0000	1.8557	1.7113	1 25/32	1.7812
2 1/8 – 4 1/2	2.1250	1.9807	1.8363	1 29/32	1.9062
2 1/4 – 4 1/2	2.2500	2.1057	1.9613	2 1/32	2.0312
2 3/8 – 4	2.3750	2.2126	2.0502	2 1/8	2.1250
2 1/2 – 4	2.5000	2.3376	2.1752	2 1/4	2.2500
2 3/4 – 4	2.7500	2.5876	2.4252	2 1/2	2.5000
3 – 3 1/2	3.0000	2.8145	2.6288	2 23/32	2.7187
3 1/4 – 3 1/2	3.2500	3.0645	2.8788	2 31/32	2.9687
3 1/2 – 3 1/4	3.5000	3.3002	3.1003	3 3/16	3.1875
3 3/4 –3	3.7500	3.5335	3.3170	3 7/16	3.4375
4 3	4.0000	3.7835	3.5670	3 11/16	3.6875

Basic Thread Dimensions and Tap Drill Sizes
American Machine Screw

Nominal Size	Outside Diameter in Inches	Pitch Diameter in Inches	Root Diameter in Inches	Commercial Tap Drill to Produce Approx. 75% Full Thread	Decimal Equivalent of Tap Drill
0–80–F	0.0600	0.0519	0.0438	³⁄₄	0.0469
1–56	0.0730	0.0614	0.0498	54	0.0550
64–C	0.0730	0.0629	0.0527	53	0.0595
72–F	0.0730	0.0640	0.0550	53	0.0595
2–56–C	0.0860	0.0744	0.0628	50	0.0700
64–F	0.0860	0.0759	0.0657	50	0.0700
3–48–C	0.0990	0.0855	0.0719	47	0.0785
56–F	0.0990	0.0874	0.0758	45	0.0820
4–32	0.1120	0.0917	0.0714	45	0.0820
36	0.1120	0.0940	0.0759	44	0.0860
40–C	0.1120	0.0958	0.0795	43	0.0890
48–F	0.1120	0.0985	0.0849	42	0.0935
5–36	0.1250	0.1078	0.0889	40	0.0980
40–C	0.1250	0.1088	0.0925	38	0.1015
44–F	0.1250	0.1102	0.0955	37	0.1040
6–32–C	0.1380	0.1177	0.0974	36	0.1065
36	0.1380	0.1200	0.1019	34	0.1110
40–F	0.1380	0.1218	0.1055	33	0.1130
7–30	0.1510	0.1294	0.1077	31	0.1200
32	0.1510	0.1307	0.1104	31	0.1200
36	0.1510	0.1330	0.1149	⅛	0.1250
8–30	0.1640	0.1423	0.1207	30	0.1285
32–C	0.1640	0.1437	0.1234	29	0.1360
36–F	0.1640	0.1460	0.1279	29	0.1360
40	0.1640	0.1478	0.1315	28	0.1405
9–24	0.1770	0.1499	0.1229	29	0.1360
30	0.1770	0.1553	0.1337	27	0.1440
32	0.1770	0.1567	0.1364	26	0.1470
10–24–C	0.1900	0.1629	0.1359	25	0.1495
28	0.1900	0.1668	0.1436	23	0.1540
30	0.1900	0.1684	0.1467	22	0.1570
32–F	0.1900	0.1697	0.1494	21	0.1590
12–24–C	0.2160	0.1889	0.1619	16	0.1770
28–F	0.2160	0.1928	0.1696	14	0.1820
32	0.2160	0.1957	0.1754	13	0.1850

C = coarse-thread standard.   F = fine-thread standard.

Letter Sizes of Drills

Diameter, Inches	Decimal Equivalent	Diameter, Inches	Decimal Equivalent	Diameter, Inches	Decimal Equivalent
A ¹⁵⁄₆₄	.234	J	.277	S	.348
B	.238	K ⁹⁄₃₂	.281	T ²³⁄₆₄	.358
C	.242	L	.290	U	.368
D	.246	M ¹⁹⁄₆₄	.295	V ³⁄₈	.377
E ¼	.250	N	.302	W ²⁵⁄₆₄	.386
F	.257	O ⁵⁄₁₆	.316	X	.397
G	.261	P ²¹⁄₆₄	.323	Y ¹³⁄₃₂	.404
H ¹⁷⁄₆₄	.266	Q	.332	Z	.413
I	.272	R ¹¹⁄₃₂	.339		

Tap Drills for Uniform Pitch Thread Series*

8 Pitch = 0.1250 inch		12 Pitch = 0.0833 inch				16 Pitch = 0.0625 inch	
Nominal Size Inches	Drill Size Inches	Nominal Size Inches	Drill Size Inches	Nominal Size Inches	Drill Size Inches	Nominal Size Inches	Drill Size Inches
1	7/8	1/2	0.417	3 1/4	3.167	3/4	11/16
1 1/8	1	9/16	0.479	3 1/2	3.417	7/8	13/16
1 1/4	1 1/8	5/8	0.542	3 3/4	3.667	1	15/16
1 3/8	1 1/4	11/16	0.604	4	3.917	1 1/8	1 1/16
1 1/2	1 3/8	3/4	0.667	4 1/4	4.167	1 1/4	1 3/16
1 5/8	1 1/2	13/16	0.729	4 1/2	4.417	1 3/8	1 5/16
1 3/4	1 5/8	7/8	0.792	4 3/4	4.667	1 1/2	1 7/16
1 7/8	1 3/4	15/16	0.854	5	4.917	1 5/8	1 9/16
2	1 7/8	1	0.917	5 1/4	5.167	1 3/4	1 11/16
2 1/8	2	1 1/16	0.979	5 1/2	5.417	1 7/8	1 13/16
2 1/4	2 1/8	1 1/8	1.042	5 3/4	5.667	2	1 15/16
2 3/8	2 1/4	1 3/16	1.104	6	5.917	2 1/8	2 1/16
2 5/8	2 1/2	1 1/4	1.167			2 1/4	2 3/16
3	2 7/8	1 5/16	1.229			2 1/2	2 7/16
3 1/4	3 1/8	1 3/8	1.292			2 3/4	2 11/16
3 1/2	3 3/8	1 7/16	1.354			3	2 15/16
3 3/4	3 5/8	1 1/2	1.417			3 1/4	3 3/16
4	3 7/8	1 9/16	1.542			3 1/2	3 7/16
4 1/4	4 1/8	1 11/16	1.667			3 3/4	3 11/16
4 1/2	4 3/8	1 3/4	1.792			4	3 15/16
4 3/4	4 5/8	2	1.917				
5	4 7/8	2 1/4	2.167				
5 1/4	5 1/8	2 1/2	2.417				
5 1/2	5 3/8	2 3/4	2.667				
5 3/4	5 5/8	3	2.917				
6	5 7/8						

*H. W. Bearce, Bureau of Standards.

by diameter measurements. They run from No. 80 to No. 1, or from 0.0135 inch to 0.228 inch in diameter. No. 80 is the smallest. See table p. 100.

DRILL(S), PREFERRED SIZES OF—A series of drill sizes which have been selected to cover practically all needs between 0.0156 and 0.500 inch and which omits many sizes which appeared in old drill lists. Many of those omitted overlapped sizes in fractional, letter, wire gage and metric lists. The preferred list lessened the number of drill sizes to be carried in stock and was recommended by the American Standards Association. The list is intended to cover all necessary sizes for the great majority of work. It has not been generally adopted, and may be discarded.

DRILL(S), TAP—Drills for holes that are to be tapped. It is common to allow metal for these threads about ¾ of full depth.

DRILL(S), TWIST, STANDARD SHANKS— Twist drill shanks are made in six forms: taper shank; straight shank, taper length; straight shank, short length; bit stock (square and tapered); ratchet shank (also square but a shorter taper); and the shank for blacksmiths' drills.

DRILL DIAMETERS—Drills are designated by number, by letter and by fractions, in English measurements, and in metric measurements. See table under Drills, Letter Sizes of.

Number Sizes of Drills

Number by Gauge	Equivalent Decimal	Number by Gauge	Equivalent Decimal
1	.2280	41	.0960
2	.2210	42	.0935
3	.2130	43	.0890
4	.2090	44	.0860
5	.2055	45	.0820
6	.2040	46	.0810
7	.2010	47	.0875
8	.1990	48	.0760
9	.1960	49	.0730
10	.1935	50	.0700
11	.1910	51	.0670
12	.1890	52	.0635
13	.1850	53	.0595
14	.1820	54	.0550
15	.1800	55	.0520
16	.1770	56	.0465
17	.1695	57	.0430
18	.1730	58	.0420
19	.1660	59	.0410
20	.1610	60	.0400
21	.1590	61	.0390
22	.1570	62	.0380
23	.1540	63	.0370
24	.1520	64	.0360
25	.1495	65	.0350
26	.1470	66	.0330
27	.1440	67	.0320
28	.1405	68	.0310
29	.1360	69	.0292
30	.1285	70	.0280
31	.1200	71	.0260
32	.1160	72	.0250
33	.1130	73	.0240
34	.1110	74	.0225
35	.1100	75	.0210
36	.1065	76	.0200
37	.1040	77	.0180
38	.1015	78	.0160
39	.0995	79	.0145
40	.0980	80	.0135

DRILL DRIFT—A tapered flat piece of steel used to force taper shank drills out of drilling machine spindles or out of sockets. Frequently called "keys."

DRILL DRIVER—Generally applies to any device for driving drills. It is, however, specifically applied to a split tapered shank with a straight hole which receives and holds the shank of a twist drill. These have been standardized by the A. S. A. for drills from 0.0390 to 0.6875 inches in diameter. They are of heat treated chrome-nickel steel and held to close tolerances. They include tapers from number 0 to 4, as shown on page 101.

DRILL END LENGTH—The distance from the outer cutting edge of a drill to the point, measured along the axis. The depth of the conical hole between the full diameter of the drill and the point. With the standard 118-degree included angle, it is 0.3 times the drill diameter. It is more with a sharper angle and less with one more obtuse, or blunt.

DRILL FITTINGS—Couplings for connecting lengths of pipe used in deep hole drilling in oil fields and similar places. The fittings are standardized so as to be interchangeable in different fields. They are largely used in "core" drilling, as well as in straight drill work. The term "reaming shell" is now used in place of "swell coupling" in this connection.

DRILL FITTINGS, DIAMOND CORE—Used in oil fields and for other prospecting. They vary from 1¹³⁄₁₆ to 3½ inches in outside diameter and from 1½ to 3 inches in inside diameter. They have modified square threads with 5-degree side angles.

DRILL HEAD, MULTIPLE—A mechanism carrying a number of drill spindles for drilling a number of holes at once. These are usually separate mechanisms for use on standard single spindle drilling machines, all the spindles being driven from the main spindle of the drilling machine. The spindles may be in fixed positions in the head or may be adjustable as to center distances.

DRILL PIPES—Pipe made for use in drilling oil and other wells. Standard sizes are from 2⅞ to 6⅝ inches outside diameter, with specials 2⅜, 7⅜ and 8⅜ inches. Lengths of from 20 to 30 feet are available. These have been standardized by the A. P. I., the American Petroleum Institute. These are also used for well casings.

DRILL POINTS, SPECIAL — Drill point angles which differ from the standard 118-degree included angle are suggested for special uses by the Chicago-Latrobe Twist Drill

A.S.A. STANDARD ON DRILL DRIVERS

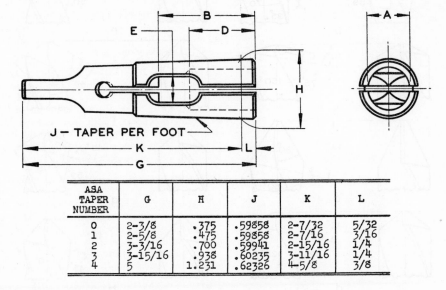

ASA TAPER NUMBER	G	H	J	K	L
0	2-3/8	.375	.59858	2-7/32	5/32
1	2-5/8	.475	.59858	2-7/16	3/16
2	3-3/16	.700	.59941	2-15/16	1/4
3	3-15/16	.938	.60235	3-11/16	1/4
4	5	1.231	.62326	4-5/8	3/8

Works, and shown on the next page. They are recommended as follows:

a—crankshaft and deep hole drilling;
b—manganese rails and hard materials;
c—wood, rubber, fiber and aluminum;
d—heat treated steel and drop forgings; alloys;
e—copper and similar metals with copper;
f—bakelite, plastics and molded materials;
g—brass and soft bronze; and
h—cast iron and die castings and as an alternate for c.

DRILL POINT THINNING—The drill point, which is the distance between the flutes at the

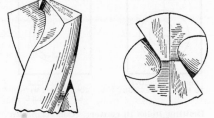

Thinning the point on drills.

end of the drill, has very little cutting action. This is frequently "thinned" by grinding away some of the metal in the flutes, as shown. This reduces the amount of dead space and makes a drill cut better.

DRILL PRESS—The name formerly given to vertical drilling machines. See *Drilling Machines, Vertical.*

DRILL ROD—A high carbon steel rod originally made for making drills. Now used for a variety of purposes. Drill rods are drawn very true to size, and frequently ground to a tolerance or plus or minus 0.0005 inch. On cold drawn rods the usual tolerance is plus or minus 0.001 inch. The rods are made in sizes from No. 80, or 0.0135 inch, to about 1½ inches, with a nominal tolerance of 0.005 inch, plus or minus.

DRILL ROUTER BITS—Made in an endless variety of styles and shapes. Widely used in woodcarving and engraving machines.

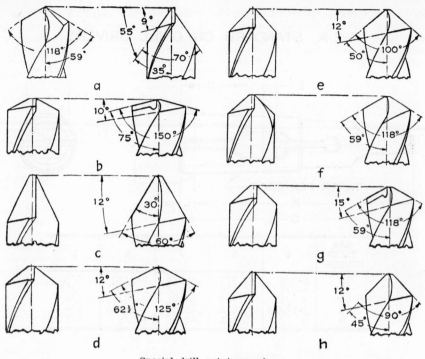

Special drill points—angles.

DRILL, SHELL—Used for the same purpose as three-or four-fluted drills. Made with tapered hole and fit on an arbor. One size of arbor will hold a large range of shell drills.

DRILL SOCKET—A device for holding drill shanks while they are being used. They are usually tapered on the outside to fit a tapered hole to receive the shank of drills smaller than the hole in the spindle.

DRILL SOCKETS, "USE-EM-UP"—A well known patented device for driving taper shank drills where the tang has been twisted off the end. The tapered shank is flattened to fit the socket or collet and is driven by the flattened portion of the shank.

DRILL SPEEDER—A device which goes in the spindle of a large drilling machine or a boring machine to increase the speed of small drills far beyond the speed of the main spindle of the machine.

DRILLING HOLES IN CENTER—Drills frequently "run" away from the desired center and must be brought back into position. The illustrations show how this is done with a "draw chisel" by cutting a grove in the right position so as to "draw" the drill point back into the center. See also *Chisel, Draw*.

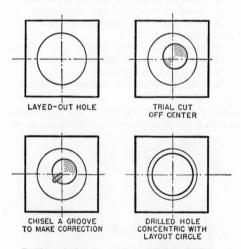

Drilling holes in center. (Correcting an off-center drilled hole.

DRILLING MACHINE, BENCH — A small vertical spindle drilling machine mounted on a bench instead of with a base of its own. Usually made in small sizes. Generally used for precision work. See *Drilling Machine, Precision.*

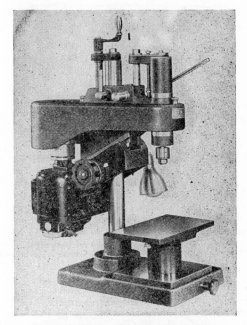

Hamilton-Muhlmatt precision drilling machine.

DRILLING MACHINE, GANG—A drilling machine with several separately driven spindles in a row so that work is moved from one to the other. They are really a collection of several single spindle machines usually on a single base. Not a multiple drill.

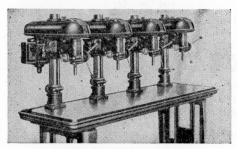

Gang drilling machine.

DRILLING MACHINE, MULTIPLE SPINDLE—Drilling machine with head carrying almost any number of spindles which are driven from one central source. In many cases these spindles can be adjusted for spacing holes as desired, but for mass manufacturing the spindles are fixed for each particular job. Should not be confused with "gang" drilling machines.

DRILLING MACHINE, PRECISION — A bench type machine in which care is taken to insure accuracy in all the bearings and in the alinement of the spindle and table. Used largely in watch and fine instrument work. See *Drilling Machine, Bench.*

DRILLING MACHINE, PORTABLE—A small unit containing a motor for driving a single drill spindle, usually for drills under 3/8 inch in diameter. They are usually driven by an electric motor, but some are driven by an air motor instead. They are carried to the work and largely used in erection work of various kinds.

DRILLING MACHINE, RADIAL—A machine tool in which the drilling head is mounted on an arm which swings around a vertical column. The drilling head can be moved to any desired point on the arm to drill holes at any radius from the column, which gives it its

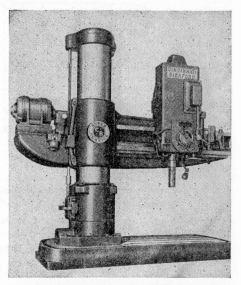

Cincinnati-Bickford radial drilling machine.

name. Formerly driven by belting over the arm that drove the drill no matter what is position on the arm, modern machines have an electric motor mounted on the drilling head, or on the column, power being transmited to the drilling spindle by gearing and shafting. Usually called Radial Drill.

DRILLING MACHINE, VERTICAL—A machine tool with a vertical drilling spindle mounted in a fixed frame and having a work table which can be adjusted under the spindle to give different distances between table and drill. They are made with power feed and to be fed by hand. The latter are called "sensitive drills" because the hand of the operator is sensitive to the resistance encountered by the drill. These were formerly known as "drill presses."

DRILLING MACHINE, WAY—A drilling machine having several drilling heads located so as to drill several different faces of the work at the same time. They are built up from drilling head units located to suit the special work to be done. While they have a multitude of spindles, they should not be confused with multiple spindle drilling machines.

DRILLING, OFF-CENTER — Using a drill with the lips of uneven length. This will drill larger than the diameter of the drill, as shown. The lips should be of the same length and the same angle.

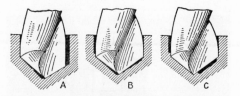

Off-center drilling. How badly ground drills cut. A, B, and C show action due to different errors in grinding the point.

DRILLING, STEP—Using drills of different diameters to produce the desired hole. The large hole is first drilled as deep as needed, the other drills following to the proper depth for each. This is common practice in drilling holes which are to be reamed by a taper reamer, as it leaves little metal to be removed by the reamer itself. This is shown herewith.

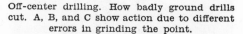

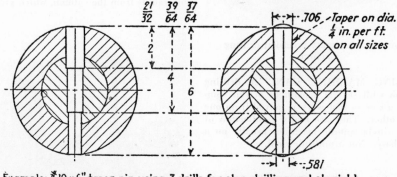

Example: #10 x 6" taper pin using 3 drills for step drilling and straight fluted reamers

If helical fluted taper reamers, as shown above, are used instead of step drilling and straight fluted reamers. The diameter at the small end of the pin is the size for the through drill

Step drilling for taper-pin reamers.

DRILLING, THRUST LOADS ON DRILLS—The thrust load, or pressure required to feed the drill into the work, depends on the rate of feed per revolution and the material being drilled, as well as the condition of the cutting edges of the drill itself. The table gives the the pressures shown in the table for drilling cast iron, machine steel, cast steel and carbon steel with feeds varying from 0.001 to 0.020 inch per revolution. These assume drills to be in good cutting condition.

Thrust Load on Drills (or Feeding Pressure)

Drill Diam.	Feed per Revolution	In Steel Pounds	In Cast Iron Pounds
½ inch	0.010	750	200
⅝	0.011	1000	275
¾	0.012	1275	325
⅞	0.013	1590	400
1	0.014	1910	500
1⅛	0.015	2275	600
1¼	0.016	2650	700
1⅜	0.016	2925	775
1½	0.016	3200	850

Data by Carl G. Oxford—National Twist Drill Co.

DRILLING, UPSIDE-DOWN—Drilling work where the drill feeds into the bottom of the work instead of the top as usual. Used occasionally when it seems best to have the chips fall out of the hole instead of being fed up by the helical flutes or washed out by lubricant.

DRIVE FIT—See *Fits, Force.*

DRIVING FIT—See *Fits, Force.*

DROP HAMMER—See *Hammer, Power.*

DROP HANGER—See *Hanger, Shafting.*

DROP TEST FOR RAILWAY AXLES—The axle is placed on supports 3 feet apart and the tup, or weight, 2,240 pounds, must strike it midway between the supports. The axle must be rotated between 40 and 120 deg. F. when tested. The axles are rotated 180 degrees between first and third blows. Maximum set permissble is shown in the last column of the table.

DROSS—Oxidized refuse which forms on the surface of melted metal and which is usually skimmed off. Sometimes allowed to remain as a retainer of heat while the metal is poured off from under the scum.

DRUM TYPE MILLING MACHINE—See *Milling Machine, Drum.*

DRY CYANIDING—See *Cyaniding, Dry.*

Standard Drop Test for Railway Axles

A.A.R. Class	Size of Journal, In.	Diameter of Axle at Center, In.	Length of Axle, In.	Height of Drop, Ft.	Number of Blows	Maximum Permanent Set, In.
		4¼		18		8¾
A	3¾ by 7	4⅜	83¼	19	5	8⅜
		4½		20		8
		4¾		22½		7½
B	4¼ by 8	4⅞	84¼	23½	5	7¼
		5		25		7
		5⅜		29		6¼
C	5 by 9	5½	86½	30	5	6
		5⅝		31½		5¾
		5⅞		34½		5½
D	5½ by 10	6	88½	36	5	5¼
		6⅛		37½		5
		6 7/16		41½		4¾
E	6 by 11	6 9/16	90¾	43	5	4½
		6 11/16		44½		4¼

DRY-ICE FITS—Another name for expansion fits, in which male parts are frozen by dry ice to reduce their diameter for insertion into holes that will be a tight fit when the part reaches room temperature. Used largely in fitting valve seats in cylinder blocks of automobile engines. It is necessary to know the coefficient of expansion of the metals to know what allowance to make for the drop in temperature that can be obtained. See *Expansion Fit* and *Coefficients of Expansion*.

DRY SAND MOLDS—Molds which have been baked in ovens before the metal is poured into them.

DUAL CONTROL—Any method whereby operation of a machine can be controlled from two points, or where it requires both hands to safeguard the operator of such a machine as a punch press.

DUCTILE—Capable of being easily worked, like the metals from which wire is made, or the sheets used in forming automobile fenders and other intricate shapes.

DUPLEX MACHINES—Machines having two heads in operation at once.

DUPLEX METAL—Sheet or plate made of two different metals, rolled together. Long used in jewelry, newer in other industries.

DUPLICATING MACHINE—A type of milling machine, also known as a "profiler," used in reproducing desired shapes or recesses in a work piece. The movement of the milling spindle is controlled by a "follower" which directs it from the surfaces of a master form. A small machine of this kind is shown, in which the movements are mechanically controlled, as in the regular profiler. Machines are now built in which the controls are by electrical contact and largely automatic. Such a machine is the Hydro-Tel, built by the Cincinnati Milling Machine Company; also the Gorton Machine shown here.

DURALUMIN—An alloy which probably originated in Germany, with about 94 per cent aluminum, 4 per cent copper, 1 per cent manganese and 1 per cent magnesium. It is much stronger than pure aluminum and is widely used in many industries.

DURONZE—A high silicon bronze alloy of

the Bridgeport Brass Co. It is made in several grades for various purposes. It melts at a lower point than copper and is somewhat stronger.

DUST EXHAUST — Provision for removing dust which comes from grinding wheels or other operations. See *Exhaust Systems*.

DUTCHMAN—A local shop term for a wedge or liner used to make a poor job usable. Also used to designate a patch to cover a defect and a round key holding a bored hub on a shaft. Seldom used at present.

Gorton duplicating machine.

DYNAMIC BALANCE — See *Balance, Dynamic*.

DYNAMO—A machine which produces electric current by revolving wires in a magnetic field. These are now called generators in nearly all cases.

DYNAMOMETER—A machine for measuring the amount of power being developed by a prime mover of any kind. Friction devices, controlled by springs or weights and mechanisms for recording the power being absorbed, make up the apparatus.

EAR—A lobe or projection, usually made for the attachment or connection of some other part.

EATONITE—An alloy developed by the Eaton Company for valve seats.

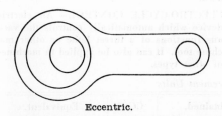

Eccentric.

ECCENTRIC—The opposite of concentric, where the centers of two diameters are not at the same point. In machine work a disk mounted on a shaft which is not in the center. A cam which produces a uniform movement. Eccentrics are largely used in steam engine and similar work for moving valves admitting steam to the cylinder. They convert rotary motion into longitudinal motion the same as a crank. Used to some extent in sewing machines and other mechanisms. The throw, or movement secured by an eccentric, is twice the distance between the *center* of the *shaft* and the *center* of the *eccentric*.

ECCENTRIC BLADE — See *Eccentric Strap* and *Eccentric Rod*.

ECCENTRIC MOTIONS — Mechanisms for converting rotary into lateral or reciprocating motion. They consist of an eccentric disk surrounded by a band or "strap" attached to a rod, arm or "blade" which connects with any sliding or rocking mechanism. They may act solely as a crank in operating piston pumps, or to control the opening and closing of parts to admit steam or air to an engine cylinder. They are widely used in steam locomotives and stationary engines. When so used the eccentrics are set with definite relations to the crank pins so as to admit and exhaust steam at the proper time. They are also used in many small mechanisms, such as sewing machines, to secure small, non-rotary movements. See illustrations of eccentric and rod.

ECCENTRIC ROD—The rod or blade through which the eccentric transmits motion to the moving part.

ECCENTRIC STRAP OR BAND—The band or part surrounding the eccentric disk through which the motion is transmitted to the part to be moved laterally. See *Eccentric Motions*.

ECCENTRIC, THROW OF—This refers to the total motion secured by one revolution of the eccentric. It is twice the distance between the center of the shaft and the center of the eccentric disk. It is the same as a crank of the same length as this center distance. *Crank throw*, however, is the distance between the center of the shaft and the center of the crank pin. The two terms should not be confused.

ECHOLS THREADED TAPS — See *Tap, Echols*.

ECHOLS TAP—See *Screw Machine Tools*.

EDGE HOLE SAWS—See *Saw, Edge Hole*.

EDGE JOINT—See *Welding, Types of Joints*.

EJECTOR—Any device for removing unwanted material. In punch press work it may be a ring, collar or disk used to remove blanks from a die. The disk or ring may be a spring or a piece of rubber.
Other ejectors utilize a jet of water or steam to create a vacuum and move water or other liquid from one place to another.

ELASTOMERS—See *Rubber, Synthetic*.

ELECTRALIGN—Trade name of a Brown & Sharpe device for aligning the swiveling table on plain and universal grinding machines.

ELECTRIC ARC—See *Arc, Electric*.

ELECTRIC STEEL FURNACE—See *Furnace, Electric, Steel*.

ELECTRIC WELDING CURRENT—The polarity of welding current is either "straight" or "reversed." In *straight* current the electrode is negative and the work positive. In *reverse* current the electrode is positive and the work negative. With bare or slightly covered electrodes straight polarity is generally used.

ELECTRICAL STANDARDS FOR MACHINE TOOLS—Standards for electrical equipment of machine tools have been adopted by the National Machine Tool Builders Association. They include diagrams to be supplied with the motors, switches, protection against overload, control enclosures, mountings, wiring, horsepower ratings, wiring, identification of wiring, conduits, grounding and electrical accessories and other devices. These can be obtained from the N. M. T. B. A., Cleveland, Ohio.

ELECTRICAL STEEL—See *Steel, Electrical.*

ELECTRICAL MEASUREMENT UNITS—See table.

ELECTRICHEK GAGES — See *Gages, Electricheck.*

ELECTRO-ARCING PROCESS—A method of cutting by making the work the anode and maintaining an arc between the work and the cathode. A pulsating d. c. current is used with an electrolyte which is a moderate conductor as water glass solutions. Especially suitable for rapidly cutting off hard materials and carbides. The finish may be somewhat rough but it is fast. Voltages of less than 25 are generally used.

ELECTRO-CYCLE CONTROL — An electric device which automatically controls the various functions of a turret lathe or other machine tool. It can also be applied to machines of other types.

Electrical Measurement Units

Name	Symbol	Unit of	How Obtained.	CGS*	Equivalent.
Ohm	R	Resistance	The electrical resistance of a column of mercury 106 centimeters long and 1 square millimeter section.	10^9	1 true ohm = 1,0112 British Association ohm.
Ampere	C	Current	Is that current of electricity that decomposes .00009324 gram of water per second.	10^1	Deposits 1.118 milligrams of silver per second.
Volt	E	Electromotive force	One ampere of current passing through a substance having 1 ohm of resistance = 1 volt.	10^8	.926 of a standard Daniel cell.
Coulomb	Q	Quantity	A current of 1 ampere during 1 second of time.	10^1	Deposits 1.118 milligrams of silver.
Farad	K	Capacity	The capacity that a current of 1 ampere for 1 second (= 1 coulomb) charges it to potential of 1 volt.	10^9	2.5 knots of D. U. S. cable.
Microfarad	K	....	1-millionth of farad.	10^{15}	
Watt	Pw.	Power	Power of 1 ampere current passing through resistance of 1 ohm.	10^7	.0013405 $\left(\text{or} \ \dfrac{1}{746} \right)$
Joule	W.j.	Work	Is the work done by 1 watt of electrical power in 1 second.	10^7	of a horsepower. .238 unit of heat (Therm).

*C. G. S. = Electro-magnetic units. Consult technical works in electricity.

Electricity

Volts × ampers = watts.
1000 watts = 1 kw.
746 watts = 1 hp.

1.34 hp. = 1 kw.
1 kw. = 44,257 ft. lb. per minute.
1 hp. = 33,000 ft. lb. per minute.
1 hp. = 42.41 B. T. U. per minute.
1 B. T. U. = 778 ft. lb.
1 B. T. U. = .2930 watt-hours.

ELECTRO-EROSION—A term used in Great Britain for machining by the use of the electric arc. In this country we have called it Electrical Discharge Machining. It is a new process and is still largely experimental.

ELECTRO-FORMING—The forming of metal by electroplating over a form or matrix. The form may be of almost any substance but must have a coating of some conductor, such as graphite. In some cases wax is used and then melted out of the finished part. The metal can be deposited to any desired thickness, which can be readily controlled.

ELECTRO-SPARKING METHOD OF RE-MOVING STOCK—Stock is removed by making the work one of the electrodes in a properly designed circuit. A rapidly pulsed current, usually ocillatory, is used, a discharged spark being passed between the work and the other electrode in a dielectric fluid. It is especially suited for small diameter deep holes of any shape. Voltage ranges from 40 to 300. It is an electro-mechanical process, not electro-chemical as in the electrolytic process.

ELECTRODES—In machine shop work, the rods which are used in electric cutting or welding. An arc is drawn between the electrode and the part to be cut or welded. In either case it is simply applying heat at the desired point. The usual method, according to C. H. Jennings, research engineer for Westinghouse, is to use direct current with a carbon negative electrode, but alternating current can be used. The cuts are not as smooth as with a gas torch but the cost is less.

ELECTROLIMIT GAGE—See Gage, Electrolimit.

ELECTROLYSIS—The eating away of metal substances by action of an electric current. This is noticeable in underground pipes in some localities.

ELECTROLYTIC GRINDING—See Grinding, Electrolytic.

ELECTROLYTIC TOOL SHARPENING—A method of sharpening tools in which the tool and the grinding wheel are connected in a direct current circuit, with the tool forming the anode and the wheel the cathode. The action of the direct current in the electrolyte continuously removes metal from the surface of the tool. It is said that a softer wheel can be used than in regular tool grinding.

ELECTROLYZING—An electrolytic process which binds chromium to any part of a tool so that some degree of fusing or impregnation actually exists. It is said to be much harder than regular chrome plating or flash-chrome plating. The bonded skin is over 80 Rockwell-C in hardness, and porosity is less than with regular plating. The process is said to involve a combination of electrolytic and heat treatment. It does not affect the surface finish and the co-efficient of friction between tool and work is said to be about $\frac{1}{6}$ that of untreated, hardened and ground steel. The base metal is only heated to about 350° F. The thickness is from 0.00002 to 0.00005 inch. The base should be hardened.

ELECTRON—The most elementary charge of negative electricity. The opposite of proton.

ELECTRONICS—A general term which includes the use of radio type tubes of various kinds for controlling the flow of electric current to motors and to other apparatus.

ELECTRONIC HEATING—A method in which electronic impulses are passed through the substance to be heated, so as, by effect on the molecules of the material, to produce heat enough to fuse the joints of plastic and other materials. The contacts, or electrodes, do not become heated, all the effect being confined to the material between them. In some cases it is even necessary to warm the contacts to prevent their cooling the material between them. See Induction Heating.

ELECTRONIC INDICATOR—A device in which a high frequency alternating current and electronic tube convert a minute mechanical movement into an electrical charge which magnifies the movement many times. A typical indicator has a power unit which contains an oscillator, amplifier, rectifier and an on-off switch with indicating light. It enables much finer measurements to be taken than with any mechanical device. The indicator is a micro-ammeter calibrated in very small fractions of an inch.

ELECTROPLATE—Metal deposited on other metals or on any conducting surface. Leather and other materials can be electroplated if coated with graphite, which is a conductor of electric current. Both the material to be plated and the metal from which the plating comes are immersed in a bath which will assist in the passage of the plating material from one to the other.

EMERY—An impure variety of corundum usually mixed with magnesite. Used in grinding before the production of artificial abrasives.

EMPIRICAL—This refers to any rule or practice which is based on custom or experience rather than on mathematical or physical considerations.

EMULSIFICATIONS—In shop usage, the suspension of oily substances in water. Used in coolants to secure the lubricating effects of oil and the cooling properties of water, when metal is being cut.

EMULSIFIERS—Any materials that aid in mixing liquids that are not soluble in each other.

EMULSION—The suspension of liquids in other liquids in which they are not soluble. Oil and water used as a cutting lubricant or coolant is made into an emulsion with soap as the emulsifier.

In machine terms any liquid coolant in which minute particles of an oily substance remain in suspension in water in the same way that globules of fat are suspended in milk. These emulsions usually have a milky appearance.

ENAMEL—A painted, sprayed or baked coating which hardens into a hard, glossy surface.

END MEASURING ROD—A rod made to precise measurements from one end to the other. The diameter is not particularly important. Generally used on jig boring and grinding machines in setting the work table.

END MILLING CUTTER—See *Milling Cutters, Miscellaneous.*

ENDLESS BELT—See *Belt, Endless.*

ENDLESS SCREW—See *Screw, Endless.*

ENERGIZER — Any device which provides energy. Usually applied to an electric coil, as in a magnetic chuck, which energizes the chuck for holding work.

ENGINE—Generally a mechanism which produces or supplies power, but the term is used in several ways. The engine lathe is a power lathe, but so are most other lathes and it does not supply power. Engine turning is a term which applied to the engraving of circular designs on watch cases and similar work, but this is seldom heard now. In many fields the term engine has given way to "motor," as

with electric motors and largely with internal combustion power producers.

ENGINE LATHE—A turning lathe with means for cutting or chasing screw threads.

ENGINE TURNING—An old designation for a geometrical engraving formerly used on watch cases and similar jewelry. The lines are arcs formed by a tool set off-center from the work itself. Similar markings are found in surface grinding with a cup wheel.

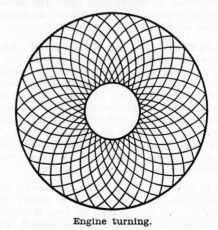

Engine turning.

ENGRAIL—Largely a term used by engravers for the irregular edges on coins or other border designs.

ENGRAVE—To make designs of any kind by cutting with a tool, as in making medals and coins. This may be done either by hand or by machine. It is sometimes applied to designs made by acids, which is really an etching process.

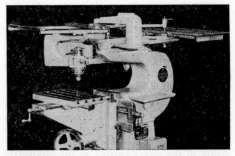

Gorton engraving machine.

ENGRAVING MACHINE—A machine for engraving name plates or designs of any kind.

They have pantagraph motions by which the engraving cutter is guided by a master design made in a much larger scale. In this way all imperfections are greatly reduced in the finished work. The engraving tool is a small end milling cutter of the desired shape.

ENLARGED PINIONS AND REDUCED GEARS—See *Gears, Pinions, Enlarged.*

ERICHSEN VALUES—One of the methods of indicating the properties of sheet steel for deep drawing work. It uses a round ended conical punch on a test sheet held by a blank holder, forcing the punch into the piece until it fractures. The depth of the cup, in millimeters, is the Erichsen value.

ESCUTCHEON—A plate of shield generally used to cover, or protect, softer or more delicate materials or actions.

ETCHING—The marking of steel or other materials by eating away portions of the surface with acid or with an electric arc. With acid, the surface is protected with wax or other material which resists the acid, often called a "resist." The desired design, scratched through the wax, allows the acid to work on the steel. A common etching acid is nitric acid 75 parts, nitrate of silver 2 parts, water 23 parts. In shop use the nitrate of silver is often omitted. This attacks the exposed parts of the steel and etches the desired letters or design. This has given way to the use of a small electric arc in many cases. Although not exactly etching in the old sense, is usually known by that name.

EUTECTOID STEEL — Carbon steels with complete pearlitic structure. This is the structure developed under normal hot working conditions and cooling with about 0.8 per cent carbon. *Hyper*-eutectoid steel has more carbon and *hypo*-eutectoid steel has less carbon. Note the difference in the prefixes "hyper" and "hypo."

EVANS VARIABLE SPEED DRIVE — See *Cone Drive Countershaft.*

EVENER — Any bar or connection which equalizes the pressures or power exerted on any part of machinery.

EVEN-GEARED LATHE—A lathe is said to be "geared even" when gears having the same number of teeth are placed on both the stud and the lead screw. The lathe will then cut a thread of the same pitch as the lead screw.

EXCAVATOR—In machine work, a tool used in digging metal out of dies.

EXHAUST SYSTEMS FOR GRINDING ROOMS—These remove dust and small particles of metal and grinding wheels by suction or exhaust fans which draw the dust from the hoods which enclose the wheels, as shown. This greatly improves working conditions and is obligatory in most sections. See diagram on following page.

EXPANDED METAL—Sheets of metal which are slit in alternating places so they can be expanded by pulling, to form a mesh.

EXPANDING METALS—This usually refers to metals which expand in cooling instead of shrinking as most metals do. Type metal is perhaps the best known. One mixture is lead 9 parts, antimony 2 parts, bismuth 1 part. Other expanding metals are in the "Cerro" family. See *Cerro Matrix* under *Cerro Metals.*

EXPANSION FIT—The reverse of a shrink fit, which expands the outer member by heat. In this case the inner member is contracted by extreme cold with dry ice or similar freezing methods. See *Shrink Fit.*

EXPANSION OF METALS—Nearly all metals expand when heated. The table shows the expansion per linear inch for each degree of temperature, Fahrenheit. Special alloys such as type metal expand in cooling. See table on following page.

EXPENDABLE TOOLS—Tools which wear out and must be replaced at frequent intervals, such as drills, taps, reamers and cutting tools of all kinds. These have been generally called "perishable" tools, but the name has been subject to considerable misinterpretation.

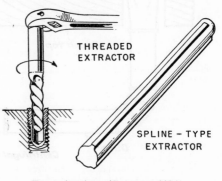

THREADED EXTRACTOR

SPLINE – TYPE EXTRACTOR

Tap extractor. (See page 113.)

Material	Inches	Micro-Inches	Material	Inches	Micro-Inches
Aluminum	0.00001234	12.3	Lead	0.00001571	15.7
Alcad	0.00001220	12.2	Solder, plumber's	0.00001388	13.9
Aluminum alloy 3S	0.00001280	12.8	Magnesium	0.00001430	14.3
Aluminum-silicon 43	0.00001220	12.2	Manganese	0.00001280	12.8
Antimony	0.00000627	6.3	Mercury	0.00001000	10.0
Bismuth	0.00000975	9.8	Molybdenum	0.00000695	6.9
Copper	0.00000887	8.9	Monel metal	0.00000777	7.8
Aluminum bronze	0.00000916	9.2	Nickel	0.00000305	3.0
Brass	0.00000957	9.6	"No solvit" (Boro-		
Bronze	0.00000986	9.8	silicate Glass)	0.00000470	4.7
Bronze, gun metal	0.00001000	10.0	Platinum	0.00000479	4.8
Nickel silver	0.00001020	10.2	Platinum-Iridium	0.00000488	4.9
Diamond	0.00000065	0.6	Quartz	0.00000030	0.3
"DoALL" Gages	0.00000640	6.4	Silver	0.00001079	10.8
Gold	0.00000786	7.8	Steel	0.00000636	6.3
Granite	0.00000460	4.6	Stellite	0.00000856	8.5
Indium	0.00001833	18.3	Tin	0.00001163	11.6
Iridium	0.00000356	3.5	Titanium	0.00000396	3.9
Iron, cast	0.00000556	5.5	Tungsten	0.00000220	2.2
Iron, wrought	0.00000648	6.5	Tungsten carbide	0.00000330	3.3
Allegheny metal	0.00000961	9.6	Zinc	0.00001407	14.0
Invar	0.00000044	0.4			
Stainless steel	0.00000611	6.1			

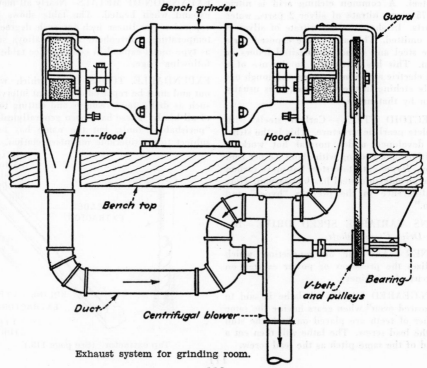

Exhaust system for grinding room.

EXPLOSIVE RIVET—See *Rivet, Explosive.*

EXTRACTOR, OIL—A machine for extracting oil from metal chips. The chips are placed in a container which is perforated on the outside and whirled rapidly. The oil is forced out by centrifugal action.

EXTRACTOR, TAP—A tool for removing broken taps. It has prongs which go down into the flutes of the broken tap and turn the tap out of the hole. Another method is to disintegrate the broken part of the tap with an electric arc. This is known by different trade names.

EXTRUSION—The forcing of material through dies which give it the desired cross section. Macaroni is made by extrusion, the dough being naturally plastic. In the case of metals they must be capable of flowing through the dies with sufficient pressure behind them. It is the opposite of wire drawing, which is pulling cold metal through dies. Extrusion produces sections which would be difficult to machine and saves much time in many forms of construction.

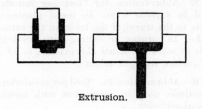

Extrusion.

F

F P M—Abbreviation for "feet per minute." Used in various ways. In metal planing it refers to the travel of the table on the cutting stroke. In turning or cutting with revolving tools or work the usual abbreviation is S F M or "surface feet per minute."

F P R—Abbreviation for "feed per revolution." Sometimes used in connection with turning operations.

F P T—Abbreviation for "feed per tooth." Sometimes used in connection with milling or other machining where several cutting teeth or edges are involved.

FACE ANGLE OF GEARS—See *Gears, Bevel.*

FACE PLATE—A term applied to several parts of machines. Engine lathes have face plates screwed or otherwise fastened to the end of the spindle. Boring mill tables are sometimes called face tables. The back plate of a lathe chuck is also called a face plate.

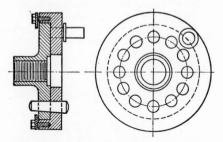

Indexing faceplate for multiple threads.

FACE PLATE, INDEXING—A face plate, for a lathe or other machine, which can be used to secure accurate spacing in cutting multiple threads or for other purposes. In the plate shown there are twelve holes in the outer plate and one in the inner, or main plate. The two plates are located by the taper pin shown. This permits threads with 1, 2, 3, 4, 6 or 12 starts to be cut by moving the index plate while the work is positively driven by the stud shown.

FACE-PLATE WORK—In lathe or vertical boring mill work, the locating and driving of work on the face-plate of the machine.

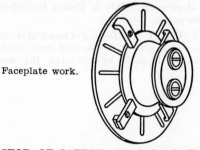

Faceplate work.

FACTOR OF SAFETY—A calculated allowance below the estimated breaking point of any material, at which it should be safe. If a steel rod of 1 square inch section, from stock which shows a breaking point of 50,000 pounds, is only loaded to 10,000 pounds per square inch, the factor of safety is 5, as the load is 1/5 the pressure breaking point of the steel. It is usually better to calculate from the point at which the steel begins to stretch or "yield," rather than from the breaking point. This is called the "yield point."

FAGGOT—An old term used by workers in wrought iron to describe a bundle of rods or pieces to be worked over into desired shapes by hammering or rolling.

FAHRENHEIT—Thermometer scale used in this and some other countries, in which the freezing point is 32 and the boiling point 212. To convert to Centigrade, subtract 32, divide the remainder by 9, and multiply by 5.

FALSE JAWS—Jaws attached to the permanent jaws of a chuck for holding special work.

FANGS—Name sometimes applied to the ends of metal belt fasteners, which go into the belt.

FAST HELIX—See *Helix, Fast.*

FAST TAPER—See *Taper, Fast.*

FAYING SURFACE—The mating or contact surfaces where two or more pieces are riveted together.

FEATHER KEY—A parallel key fastened in either the shaft or in the hub of a member sliding on it. When fastened in the shaft it must be long enough to hold or drive the sliding member in any of its positions on the shaft. When in the sliding member the key need only be as long as the hub.

FEED—This usually refers to the advance of a tool at each revolution of the tool or of the work. In the case of milling cutters, it usually means the chip thickness per tooth. Feed is also given in inches per minute. It should not be confused with the depth of cut. One large maker of boring machines refers to the feed as "lead or pitch," comparing it with the advance of a single-point thread tool or a tap or die. This is, however, not the usual understanding of the term.

FEED BOX—The box or case containing the feeding mechanism on any machine. The term refers to the whole feeding mechanism.

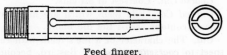

Feed finger.

FEED FINGER—A device for feeding stock into a machine. In an automatic screw machine, it is a sleeve or tube slotted to allow squeezing of the fingers on the bar stock which goes through it. At the proper time the fingers close on the bar and move forward to move stock into position for machining the next piece.

FEED OF MILLING CUTTERS—See *Milling, Direction of Feed.*

FEED, RADIAL—Where the tool is fed radially, or from the center of a revolving piece of work.

FEED, TANGENTIAL—A method of feeding, such as in hobbing gears or worms, where the hob is fed tangentially with reference to the work. The hob for this method is made with the end teeth tapering. See *Hobbing.*

FEEL—In shop terms this may be called "sensitivity of touch," or ability to know when a caliper or a micrometer goes over a shaft or gage, or into a hole, with the same resistance every time. Some good mechanics hold the caliper should go over the piece by its own weight, while other shops consider that a small amount of force should be used. The difference may amount to several ten-thousandths of an inch, or more. The same is true in using feeler gages between two surfaces, as spark plug points. Most accurate measurements eliminate the human touch entirely. In measuring screw threads with wires, Van Keuren suggests a pressure of 14 to 16 ounces for threads finer than 20 per inch and $2\frac{1}{4}$ to $2\frac{1}{2}$ pounds for coarser threads.

FELDSPAR—A group name for minerals used in making pottery and glass. They are also used as fluxes in melting metals.

FEMALE—This always refers to the receiving portion of any mechanism or element, and is almost universal in shop language. It is the ring gage which measures the work placed inside it. It refers to threaded parts as well as to plain parts of any shape.

FERRO-ALLOYS—Combinations (alloys) of different metals, having iron as a base, mixed (alloyed) with chromium, manganese, etc.

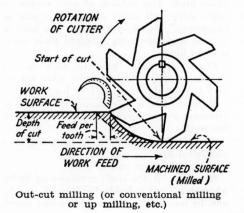

Out-cut milling (or conventional milling or up milling, etc.)

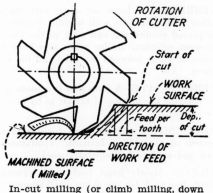

In-cut milling (or climb milling, down milling, etc.)

FERRO-CHROMIUM—A master alloy, high in chromium, which is used to add chromium to iron and steel.

FERROGRAPH—A device for the hand sorting of ferrous parts. It uses a low frequency of 26 cycles, based on the fact that an appreciable effect is obtained from "remanent" magnetism (the opposite of permanent magnetism). The operation is based on the harmonic analysis of the induced voltage in the secondary of the test transformer in which the sample becomes the core. The indications may be related to the analysis of the material or to its hardness. It is practically an instrument to aid in sorting materials which have become mixed. Steels have been sorted with differences of only 15 points, or 15 per cent.

FERRO-MANGANESE—A master alloy of iron and manganese used to deoxidize steel and to add manganese to iron, steel or bronze.

FERRO-PHOSPHOROUS—Iron with a high content of phosphorous, to be used in steel making.

FERRO-SILICON—A master alloy of iron and silicon for making silicon steels.

FERRO-TITANIUM—A combination of titanium and iron to be used as a purifying agent in iron and steel.

FERROUS—A basic name for iron or its products, such as the various kinds of steel.

FERROUS METALS—All metals in the iron and steel family, including cast, forged and rolled parts.

FERROUS SULPHATE—A mixture of iron and sulphur, sometimes known as iron sulphate or green vitriol.

FERRULE—A band or ring surrounding other parts. In tools with wooden handles, it is placed around the end next to the tool to prevent splitting. Boiler tubes also have ferrules at times, between the tube and the tube sheet.

FERRUMINATE—A term that is seldom used to describe the uniting of metals as by brazing or soldering.

FETTLING—A mixture used for lining the hearth of a puddling furnace. A mixture of ore and cinders is frequently used.

FILE(S)—Mostly hand tools with comparatively fine teeth for removing small amounts of material. They are made in a great variety of shapes and sizes, some of which are described on following pages. Many files are adapted for special kinds of work. Some are also made for use in filing machines.

Files are designated by the way in which the teeth are cut and the cross-section of the file body, and also by the purpose for which they used.

File Terms

Back. The convex side of Half Round, Cabinet, Pitsaw and other files of similar cross-section.

Bastard Cut. File coarseness between "Coarse" and "Second Cut."

Bellied. Used to describe a file having a fullness in the middle.

Blank. A file in any process of manufacture before being cut.

Blunt. Used to describe a file with parallel edges and sides; *i.e.,* which preserves its sectional size throughout from point to tang.

Coarse Cut. Coarsest of all cuts.

Curved Cut. File teeth which are made in curved contour across the file blank.

Cut. The character of a file's teeth with respect to *coarseness* (Coarse, Bastard, Second Cut, Smooth, Dead Smooth) or their *type* (single, double, rasp, curved, special).

Dead Smooth Cut. The finest of the standard cuts of regular files.

Double Cut. A file tooth arrangement formed by two series of cuts—the overcut, followed, at an angle, by the upcut.

Filing Block. A piece of hard, close-grained wood having grooves of varying sizes upon one or more of its sides. Used for holding small rods, pins, etc., in the jaws of the vise while being filed. Also a block of zinc, copper or other fairly soft metal as one of a pair of "protectors" placed between the vise jaws to prevent work becoming damaged while being held for filing.

Float. Sometimes used to refer to the coarser grades of single-cut files when cut for very soft metals (like lead) or for wood.

Hopped. A term used among file makers to represent a very wide skip or spacing between file teeth.

Overcut. The first series of teeth put on a double-cut file.

Point. The front end of a file.

Rasp Cut. A file tooth arrangement under which teeth are individually formed, one by one, by means of a narrow, punch-like chisel.

116

Re-cut. A worn-out file which has been re-cut and re-sharpened after annealing ("softening") and grinding off the old teeth. (Similar to "regrooving" as applied to automobile tires.) Dull files are sometimes sharpened by sandblasting.

Safe Edge (or *Side*). Used to denote that a file has one or more of its edges or sides smooth or uncut, so that it may be presented to the work without injury to that portion or surface which does not require filing.

Scraping. As applied to machine shops, the process of removing an exceedingly small portion of the wearing surfaces of machinery by means of scrapers, in order to bring such surfaces to a precision fit or finish not attainable by ordinary filing means.

Second Cut. File coarseness between "Bastard" and "Smooth."

Section (or *Cross-section*). The end view of a file if cut off squarely at the greatest width and thickness from its tang.

Set. To blunt the sharp edges or corners of file blanks before and after the overcut is made, in order to prevent weakness and breakage of the teeth along such edges or corners when file is put to use.

Single Cut. A file tooth arrangement formed by a single series of cuts.

Smooth Cut. File coarseness between "Second Cut" and "Dead Smooth."

Superfine (or *Super*) *Cut.* The British equivalent of the file cut which American file manufacturers term "Dead Smooth."

Tang. The narrowed portion of a file which engages the handle.

Taper. Used to denote the shape of a file, as distinguished from the Blunt. Custom has also established it as a short name for the Triangular Handsaw File. Graded variations are Slim Taper, Extra Slim Taper and Double Extra Slim Taper.

Upcut. The series of teeth superimposed on the overcut, and at an angle to it, on a double-cut file.

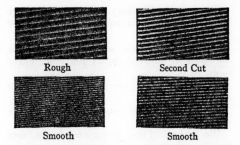

Rough   Second Cut

Smooth   Smooth

Actual tooth spacing of single-cut flat files.

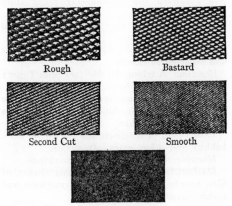

Rough   Bastard

Second Cut   Smooth

Dead Smooth

Actual tooth spacing of double-cut flat files.

Types of Files

Aluminum "A." A special-cut file for work on aluminum stock or castings.

Auger Bit. A file with double ends (each with different cut) for sharpening auger bits.

Brass. A file for use on brass and similar soft metals.

Broach. Jewelers' steel-wire files of many gauges.

Cabinet (File or Rasp). Used by cabinetmakers and woodworkers.

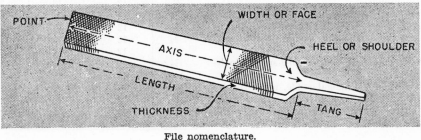

File nomenclature.

Contact. A file for dressing "make-and-break" points of electrical circuits (also called Tungsten).

Corrugating. A file made for corrugating the edges of barbers' shears and other edged tools.

Crosscut. A file for sharpening cross-cut saws.

Die Cast. A file for use on aluminum or zinc castings.

Die Sinkers. Files, of various shapes, used by die makers.

Double Ender. A saw file cut from the points toward the middle—for filing from either end.

Foundry. A file used on castings formed from foundry molds.

Hand. A double-cut file with parallel edges and tapering thickness.

Handsaw. A triangular file (see Slim Taper) for sharpening handsaws.

Knife. A file whose cross-section resembles the blade of a knife—thick at one edge, thin or sharp at the other.

Lead Float. A single-cut file for use on lead, babbitt and other extra-soft metals.

Machine. Files used in filing machines.

Machinists'. Applied to various shapes of files, mostly double-cut, used in machine and repair shops.

Mill. A single-cut (tapered or blunt) file which acquired its name from its early use in filing mill or circular saws.

Needle. Special small files for tool makers. Clock and watchmakers also have special sizes and shapes.

Pillar. A parallel-edge file with rectangular cross-section of narrow width and extra thickness.

Pippin. A file with a cross-section resembling a pippin (apple) seed.

Pitsaw. A file used for sharpening pit or frame saws.

Plastic. Files, of various types, used in flash removal and other finishing work on molded plastic products.

Rifflers. Fine-point and vari-shaped files used by die sinkers and silversmiths.

Screw Head. A file for clearing out the slots in the heads of screws.

Shear Tooth. A coarse, long-angle, single-cut file.

Slim Taper. Triangular file, more slender than the regular Taper, used mainly for handsaw sharpening. Also Extra Slim Taper and Double Extra Slim Taper.

Stainless Steel. A special-cut file for use on stainless and other extra-tough steels.

Swiss Pattern. Small files from Swiss designs used for various kinds of small work.

Taper. Used to denote the shape of a file as distinct from Blunt. Custom has also established it as a short name for the triangular Handsaw File.

Three Square. A file whose cross-section is triangular. Usually applied when such file is double-cut.

Warding. A file named after its original or most common use—filing ward notches on keys and locks.

FILE(S), CARBIDE—Special files made with carbide inserts, which are replaceable. The serrations have a 30 degree angle and the rake is negative at 15 degrees, with 20 and 30 teeth per inch. They are used for removing burs from steel, brass or other metals and have a very long life.

FILE(S), CROSSING—Files having two convex surfaces, but with different radii for each.

FILE(S), NEEDLE—Small files, of the Swiss pattern, used in finishing punch and die work. The teeth are cut in grades from No. 00 to No. 6, the latter being the finest. Handles are either round or rectangular in shape.

FILE(S), ROTARY—Hand cut milling cutters with teeth similar to a well cut hand file. They work well on cast iron and similar metals. They resemble "burs" and the term is sometimes used interchangeably. See *Bur*; see illustration on following page.

Rotary Files—Teeth Per Inch

	Rough cut	Standard cut	Fine cut
⅛	14	20	30
3/16	14	20	30
¼	14	20	30
5/16	12	18	27
⅜	12	18	27
7/16	12	18	27
½	12	18	27
9/16	12	18	27
⅝	12	18	27
¾	12	18	27
⅞	12	18	27
1	10	15	24
1⅛	10	15	24
1¼	10	15	24
1½	10	15	24

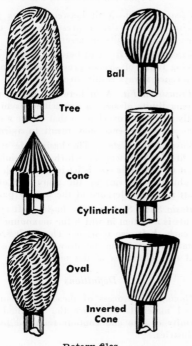

Rotary files.

FILE(S), SLOT—Narrow files with smooth, parallel sides. Also called pillar files.

FILE(S), SWISS PATTERN—A group of small files made in a variety of shapes and cuts of teeth, some of the shapes having a very small point. They are used in fine tool making and die-sinking and in jewelry work. They vary from 3 to 10 inches in length and from No. 00 to No. 6, this being the finest.

FILE(S), VIXEN—Flat files in which the teeth are milled in an arc across the face of the file. They are very useful in working on soft metals. Vixen files are also known by other names.

FILING, DRAW—See *Draw-Filing.*

FILING MACHINE—Any machine in which the file is operated by power. The first machine moved the file vertically through a hole in the table and the work was held against it. Later machines attach short files to a steel band which runs over large pulleys, as with a band saw. They are much faster, as they cut continuously.

FILLET—A concave corner which is rounded to avoid a sharp angle. In metal work, it lessens the likelihood of failure through cracking. This is the reason for the adoption of the rounded bottom on screw threads. In pattern work, the fillet is usually made with leather or wax after the pattern is made.

FILM-THICKNESS GAGES—Gages for measuring the thickness of various coatings from one side. See *Magne-Gage* and *Filameter.*

FILAMETER—An instrument for measuring the thickness of non-conducting coatings on non-magnetic metals. It measures the thickness of paint, varnish, shellac, enamel, plastics and ceramics from zero to 0.005 inch very accurately. Its action is based on the inductance effect that the coated base metal has on the coil of an inductor or searching coil, when applied to the coating. Current flowing in this coil induces eddy currents in the base metal, the intensity of these currents varying with the thickness of the coating. The General Electric Co. also makes a gage for similar use, known as a "thickness gage."

FIN—The thin edge or projection left by the parting of a mold or die, in castings or forgings. In forgings it may be called a "flash." Also, a rough edge raised by grinding or cutting action.

FINS AND RAGS—A defect in forgings. See *Forging Defects.*

FINE THREADS—Screw threads of finer pitch than the standard or coarse pitch threads. There is also an "extra fine" series of pitches, as well as instrument threads, which are of very fine pitch. See *Screw Threads.*

FINES—A term used in connection with diamond powder for grinding and lapping, to designate particles below the desired size. They should not be over 10 per cent in grade 40 and coarser and not over 50 per cent in grade 25 and smaller, nor constitute over 3 per cent of the total weight.

FINGER—Any small projection used for locating or for moving or guiding other parts.

FINING—Sometimes used to describe the finishing operation in buffing or polishing. Also, the converting of pig iron into wrought iron in a charcoal furnace.

FIRE CLAY—A clay that stands very high heat without cracking. Used in lining furnaces.

FIRE HOSE COUPLING—See *Screw Threads, Hose Coupling*, for standards which have been adopted to make it possible to use hose from one city in any other city.

FISH JOINT—A joint made with fish plates. See *Fish Plate.*

FISH PLATE—In railroad practice, the plate used on each side of a rail joint, with track bolts through them and the rails, to make a rigid joint.

FISH TAIL—A term applied to milling or similar cutters having two points, or cutting edges, shaped like the tail of a fish. Sometimes called fly-cutters, although, correctly speaking, a fly-cutter has but one point. Some also use the term in connection with the gage used in setting thread cutting tools.

FITS (OF METAL PARTS)—All measurements for accurate fitting are based on a room temperature of 68 deg. F., or 20 deg. C. In interchangeable manufacure, parts are supposed to go together without fitting and to function satisfactorily.

1. The standard or basic size, as physically represented by a correct standard master gage, represents the line at which this interference begins between mating parts.

2. It is the minimum size of the external members of all mating parts of standardized practice, regardless of the kind of fit.

3. It is the maximum size of internal members of all mating parts where interference begins or that fit metal to metal.[1]

4. The limits of the component as physically represented by the limit master gages shall not be exceeded as a result of either tolerance or wear of the gages.

5. "Go" gages, or the equivalent verification of all the factors involved in the fit, are necessary to prevent interference of mating parts.

In the case of force fits, "go" gages are necessary to determine the maximum amount of interference between mating parts.

6. "Not go" gages, or the equivalent verification of the determining factor, are necessary to prevent the maximum looseness of mating parts exceeding the limits specified.

In the case of force fits, "not go" gages are necessary to determine the minimum amount of interference between mating parts.

Types and Systems of Fits

Clearance Fit—A fit between mating parts having limits of size so prescribed that clearance always results in assembly.

Interference Fit—A fit between mating parts having limits of size so prescribed that an interference always results in assembly.

Transition Fit—A fit between mating parts having limits of size so prescribed as to partially or wholly overlap, so that either a clearance or interference may result in assembly.

Basic Hole System—The basic hole system of fits is a system in which the minimum limit of each hole size is basic. The fit desired is obtained by varying the allowance of the shaft and the tolerance of the mating parts.

Basic Shaft System—The basic shaft system of fits is a system in which the maximum limit of each shaft size is basic. The fit desired is obtained by varying the allowance of the hole and the tolerances of the mating parts.

Definitions

Gaging—A process of measuring manufactured materials to assure the specified uniformity of size and contour required by the industries.

Gage—A device for determining whether or not one or more of the dimensions of a manufactured part are within specified limits.

1. *Ring Gage*—One whose inside measuring surfaces are circular in form. The measuring surfaces may be cylindrical or conical.

2. *Plug Gage*—One whose outside measuring surfaces are arranged to verify the specified uniformity of holes. A plug gage may be straight or tapered and of any cross-sectional shape.

3. *Receiving Gage*—One whose inside measuring surfaces are arranged to verify the specified uniformity of size and contour of manufactured material.

4. *Indicating Gage*—One that exhibits visually the variation in the uniformity of dimensions or contour, the amount of the variation being indicated by lever on graduated scale, dial, flush pin, plunger gages, etc.

5. *Snap Gage*—A fixed gage arranged with inside measuring surfaces for calipering diameters, lengths, thicknesses, etc.

6. *Caliper Gage*—One which, for internal members, is similar to a snap gage, and for external members, is similar to a plug gage.

Standard—A physical representation of a form, dimension or size established by law or by general usage and consent.

Standard Sizes—A series of recognized or accepted sizes corresponding to various subdivisions of a recognized unit of length, such as the yard or the meter. These are usually expressed in inches or in millimeters, sometimes by arbitrary numbers or letters.

Note: The industries, by common consent, have chosen several different series important for interchangeable manufacture. For instance, the common fractions of an inch are commonly called standard sizes, such as $\frac{1}{8}$, $\frac{3}{16}$, $\frac{1}{4}$, $\frac{5}{16}$ inch, etc.

Nominal Size—A designation given to the subdivision of the unit of length having no specified limits of accuracy, but indicating a close approximation to a standard size.

Basic Size—The exact theoretical size from which all limiting variations are made.

Allowance (Neutral Zone)—An intentional difference in the dimensions of mating parts; or the minimum clearance space which is intended between mating parts. It represents the condition of the tightest permissible fit, or the largest internal member mated with the smallest external member. It is to provide for different classes of fit.

Example: A shaft dimensioned 0.874 inch and a hole dimensioned 0.875 inch represents an allowance of 0.001 inch. The same hole with a shaft dimensioned 0.876 inch represents an allowance of 0.001 inch also; but, as the shaft is larger than the hole, this allowance becomes a negative quantity.

Tolerance—The amount of variation permitted in the size of a part.

Note: In the example under Allowance, the ideal condition and the tightest fit permissible have been given; but in manufacturing large numbers of pieces, these sizes could not be produced exactly, so variations must be made that will not prevent their proper functioning but will enable them to be produced. These variations must therefore tend toward greater looseness. Then, if a manufacturing tolerance of 0.001 inch is required on each member, they would be dimensioned as follows:

Shaft	0.874 inch + 0.000 inch
	− 0.001 inch
Hole	0.0875 inch + 0.001 inch
	− 0.000 inch

This defines a condition in which the greatest looseness is 0.003 inch, and the greatest tightness gives a clearance of 0.001 inch.

Neutral Zone—See Allowance.

Limits — The extreme permissible dimensions of a part.

Master Gage—A gage whose gaging dimensions represent as exactly as possible the physical dimensions of the component. It is the gage with which all other gages and all dimensions of manufactured material are finally checked or compared, either by direct check or by comparison.

Inspection Gages—Gages for the use of the manufacturer or purchasers in accepting the product. These gages must not accept any product which the master gages will reject.

Working Gages—Gages used by the manufacturer to check the work as it is produced. These gages should not accept any product which the inspection gages will reject.

Classification of Fits

Standard fits for mating parts have been classified in accord with the way in which they are to be used. Eight classes have been recommended by the Standardization Committee, as follows:

Loose Fit (Class 1) — Large Allowance — This fit provides for considerable freedom and embraces certain fits where accuracy is not essential.

Examples: Machined fits of agricultural and mining machinery; controlling apparatus for marine work; textile, rubber, candy, and bread machinery; general machinery of a similar grade; some ordnance material.

Free Fit (Class 2) — Liberal Allowance — For running fits with speeds of 600 revolutions per minute, or over, and journal pressures of 600 pounds per square inch, or over.

Examples — Dynamos; engines; many machine-tool parts; and some automotive parts.

Medium Fit (Class 3)—Medium Allowance —For running fits under 600 revolutions per minute and with journal pressures of less than 600 pounds per square inch; also for sliding fits; and the more accurate machine-tool and automotive parts.

Snug Fit (Class 4)—Zero Allowance—This is the closest fit which can be assembled by hand and necessitates work of considerable precision. It should be used where no perceptible shake is permissible and where moving parts are not intended to move freely under a load.

Wringing Fit (Class 5)—Zero to Negative Allowance—This is also known as a "tunking fit," and it is practically metal-to-metal. Assembly is usually selective and not interchangeable.

Tight Fit (Class 6)—Slight Negative Allowance—Light pressure is required to assemble these fits and the parts are more or less permanently assembled, such as the fixed ends of studs for gears, pulley, rocker arms, etc. These fits are used to drive fits in thin sections or extremely long fits in other sections and also for shrink fits on very light sections. Used in automotive, ordnance, and general machine manufacturing.

Medium Force Fit (Class 7)—Negative Allowance. Considerable pressure is required to assemble these fits, and the parts are considered permanently assembled. These fits are used in fastening locomotives, wheels, car wheels, armatures of dynamos, and motors and crank discs to their axles or shafts. They are also used for shrink fit on medium sections or long fits. These fits are the tightest which are recommended for cast-iron holes or external members, as they stress cast iron to its elastic limit.

Heavy Force and Shrink Fit (Class 8)—Considerable Negative Allowance. These fits are used for steel holes where the metal can be highly stressed without exceeding its elastic limit. These fits cause excessive stress for cast-iron holes. Shrink fits are used where heavy force fits are impractical, as on locomotive wheel tires, heavy crank discs of large engines, etc.

FITS, COMPOUND—Shrink fits in which the outer member is expanded by heat and the inner member shrunk by extreme low temperature. The use of both methods is not often considered necessary. The term might also be applied to fits on more than one diameter, but this is not usual practice.

FITS, FORCE—The forcing of parts together where the male piece is somewhat larger than the hole into which it is forced. Most of the distortion takes place in the hole, as the shaft can compress very little. If the difference in

diameter is too great, the piece with the hole may be stressed beyond its elastic limit and result in a loose fit. Car axles and wheels are probably the best and most common examples of force fits. Driving wheels of steam locomotives have keys in addition to the force fits on account of the stresses imposed in turning the wheels. This is frequently called "press fit," on account of the presses used in forcing the axles into the wheels. The amount of variation in diameter varies somewhat with the length of the fit. The pressure required can be varied considerably by the kind of lubricant used.

FITS, LIMITS, STANDARD—Cylindrical fits have been discussed for years. The American Standards Association suggests the following preferred basic sizes and the tolerances to be used with them.

Table 1—Preferred Basic Sizes

	0.0100	⁵⁄₁₆ 0.3125	1⅞ 1.8750	
	0.0125	⅜ 0.3750	2 2.0000	
¹⁄₆₄	0.01562	⁷⁄₁₆ 0.4375	2⅛ 2.1250	
	0.0200	½ 0.5000	2¼ 2.2500	
	0.0250	⁹⁄₁₆ 0.5625	2⅜ 2.3750	
¹⁄₃₂	0.03125	⅝ 0.6250	2½ 2.5000	
	0.0400	¹¹⁄₁₆ 0.6875	2⅝ 2.6250	
	0.0500	¾ 0.7500	2¾ 2.7500	
¹⁄₁₆	0.0625	⅞ 0.8750	2⅞ 2.8750	
	0.0800	1 1.0000	3 3.0000	
³⁄₃₂	0.09375	1⅛ 1.1250	3¼ 3.2500	
	0.1000	1¼ 1.2500	3½ 3.5000	
⅛	0.1250	1⅜ 1.3750	3¾ 3.7500	
⁵⁄₃₂	0.15625	1½ 1.5000	4 4.0000	
³⁄₁₆	0.1875	1⅝ 1.6250		
¼	0.2500	1¾ 1.7500		

All dimensions are given in inches.

Table 2—Tolerances and Allowances

0.0001	0.0006	0.0025	0.0100*
0.00015	0.0008	0.0030	0.0120
0.0002*	0.0010*	0.0040	0.0150
0.00025	0.0012	0.0050*	0.0200*
0.0003	0.0015	0.0060	0.0250
0.0004	0.0020*	0.0080	0.0300*
0.0005*			

All dimensions are given in inches.

*Preferred values.

FITS, PRESS, LOCOMOTIVE—See pages 123 and 124.

Press Fits of Locomotive Driving Axles—Mounting Pressures in Tons

Diameter Wheel Fit, in Inches	Wheel Centers			
	Cast Iron	Variation	Steel	Variation
4½	40 to 49	9	64 to 79	15
5	45 to 55	10	72 to 88	16
5½	49 to 60	11	79 to 96	17
6	54 to 66	12	86 to 105	19
6½	58 to 71	13	93 to 114	21
7	63 to 77	14	104 to 133	29
7½	67 to 82	15	112 to 143	31
8	72 to 88	16	119 to 153	34
9	76 to 93	17	127 to 162	35
9½	81 to 99	18	135 to 172	37
10	85 to 104	19	142 to 181	39
10½	90 to 110	20	150 to 191	41
11	94 to 115	21	157 to 200	43
11½	99 to 121	22	165 to 210	45
12	103 to 126	23	173 to 220	47
12½	108 to 133	25	180 to 229	49
12½	112 to 138	26	188 to 239	51
13	116 to 143	27	195 to 248	53
13½	121 to 150	29	203 to 258	55
14	125 to 155	30	210 to 267	57

Press Fits of Locomotive Crankpins—Mounting Pressures in Tons

Diameter Wheel Fit, in Inches	Wheel Centers			
	Cast Iron	Variation	Steel	Variation
3	13 to 16	3	21 to 26	5
3½	18 to 22	4	28 to 35	7
4	22 to 27	5	36 to 44	8
4½	27 to 33	6	43 to 52	9
5	31 to 38	7	50 to 61	11
5½	36 to 44	8	57 to 70	13
6	40 to 49	9	64 to 79	15
6½	45 to 55	10	72 to 88	16
7	49 to 60	11	79 to 96	17
7½	54 to 66	12	86 to 105	19
8	58 to 71	13	93 to 114	21
8½	63 to 77	14	100 to 123	23
9	67 to 82	15	108 to 132	24
9½	71 to 88	17	115 to 141	26
10	76 to 94	18	122 to 150	28
10½	81 to 100	19	129 to 159	30
11	85 to 105	20	136 to 168	32

Press Fits of Locomotive Truck Axles—Mounting Pressures in Tons

Diameter Wheel Fit, in Inches	Wheel Centers			
	Cast Iron	Variation	Steel	Variation
3½	18 to 22	4	27 to 33	6
4	22 to 27	5	33 to 40	7
4½	27 to 33	6	40 to 49	9
5	31 to 38	7	46 to 57	11
5½	36 to 44	8	54 to 66	12
6	40 to 49	9	60 to 73	13
6½	45 to 55	10	67 to 82	15
7	49 to 60	11	73 to 90	17
7½	54 to 66	12	81 to 99	18
8	58 to 71	13	88 to 107	19
8½	63 to 77	14	95 to 116	21
9	67 to 82	15	101 to 124	23
9½	72 to 88	16	108 to 132	24
10	76 to 93	17	115 to 141	26
10½	81 to 100	19	122 to 150	28

Press Fits of Car or Locomotive Tender Axles—Mounting Pressures in Tons

Size of Journal	Diameter Wheel Fit, in Inches	Wheel Centers			
		Cast Iron	Variation	Steel	Variation
4 × 8	5¾	35 to 60	25	55 to 80	25
4¼ × 8	5¾	35 to 60	25	55 to 80	25
5 × 9	6½	40 to 65	25	70 to 100	30
5¼ × 9	6½	40 to 65	25	70 to 100	30
5½ × 10	7	45 to 70	25	75 to 110	35
6 × 10	7⅝	50 to 75	25	80 to 120	40
6 × 11	7⅝	50 to 75	25	80 to 120	40
6½ × 11	7¹³⁄₁₆	52 to 77	25	80 to 120	40
6½ × 12	8⅛	54 to 79	25	85 to 130	45

FITTING-UP BOLTS—See *Bolt, Fitting-Up.*

FIXTURE—A loosely used term describing devices for holding work of various kinds to be machined. It is frequently used interchangeably with "jig." Many consider that a fixture is fastened to the table of the machine, while a jig may be located by hand and moved at will. See *Jigs.*

FLAMATIC HARDENING — See *Hardening, Flamatic.*

FLAME ANNEALING—Annealing by direct heat from a flame to remove surface tension or stresses. It is largely used to relieve welded structures of the stresses imposed by the local heating of the welding torch.

FLAME CUTTING—The cutting or disintegration of ferrous metals with an oxy-acetylene torch. After the cut is started by the use of both gases the acetylene supply is shut off and only oxygen fed to the cut. With the heat of the metal, this practically makes the metal burn itself away, or disintegrate. Cuts of 12 or more inches deep are made with comparatively little loss of metal, as the kerf, or width of cut, need not exceed ⁷⁄₃₂ inch on a cut of 6 inches deep. The cutting torch is sometimes called a "lance."

FLAME HARDENING—A method of local hardening by heating with an oxy-acetylene torch, or torches, and quenching in a cooling medium. It is not a new method, but methods and mechanisms have been greatly improved so that it is now a commercial process.

FLANGE MOUNTED MOTORS — Electric motors which require no base, but are mounted and supported by a flange at the end. These were designed especially for use on machine tools, as they can form a part of the machine itself in most cases.

FLANK — The side of a piece, as the side or contacting surface of a gear tooth.

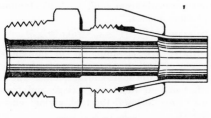

Flared tube fitting.

FLARED TUBE FITTING — A device for holding thin tubing securely without threading or soldering. One such device is shown.

FLASH — Excess metal forced out between the dies of a forging operation, or in die castings.

FLASH AND FIRE POINTS OF OILS — The temperatures at which the oil flashes or catches fire. These points have no bearing on the lubricating quality of the oils, only on their safety when stored in warm places.

FLASH WELDING — See *Welding, Flash.*

FLASK — A frame for holding the sand in which patterns are molded before casting can be poured. They may be of wood or metal. They are made in two or more parts, depending on the pattern. The top part is the "cope," the bottom is the "drag," and any intermediate parts are known as "cheeks."

FLASK, SNAP — A molding flask for foundry work with the sides held in place by latches of some sort. These are usually of small size.

FLAT CAM — See *Cam, Flat.*

FLAT FORGINGS — Forgings made with flat dies instead of with dies having depressions for producing more or less intricate shapes.

FLATTER — A blacksmith's tool having a rather broad flat face which is laid on the work and struck with a sledge, to smooth out the surface of a forging.

FLEXIBLE SHAFT — Usually a closely coiled spring or chain used to transmit small amounts of power to parts not in line with the motor. It runs inside a flexible tube which permits it to be curved at reasonably sharp angles. Flexible shafts are also sometimes made of a series of small parts with some sort of universal joint between them to permit curving while driving the adjoining member. They are contained in a flexible tube the same as the coiled spring.

FLINT — A very hard stone which gives sparks when struck with steel. Formerly used to ignite powder in firearms. Now used in pottery work as an abrasive.

FLOATING DIE — See *Dies, Floating.*

FLOGGING CHISEL — See *Chisel, Flogging.*

FLOGGING HAMMER — See *Hammer, Flogging.*

FLOOR FASTENINGS — Methods of securing and leveling machines in shops of various kinds. The Westinghouse standard method is shown and provides for anchor bolts in concrete foundations where necessary.

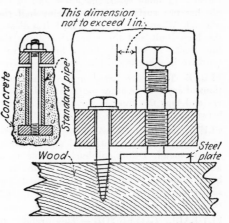

Floor fastenings for machine tools.

FLOOR STANDS — See *Stands, Floor.*

FLOSS — A sort of fluid glass which forms in puddling furnaces from the fusion of slag and other impurities. Really another name for slag.

FLUID CLUTCH — See *Clutch, Fluid.*

FLUID DIES — See *Dies, Fluid.*

FLUID FRICTION — See *Laminar Oil Flow.*

FLUOROSCOPIC INSPECTION—The use of a fluorescent screen instead of photographic film, with X-ray inspection. This enables the operator to see what would be recorded on a film and saves time when a permanent record is not necessary. As the eye is not as sensitive as the film, it is not quite as accurate as an X-ray photograph.

FLUORSPAR—A mineral used as a flux in steel making. Sometimes called fluorite.

FLUSH—In shop terms, when two surfaces are even with each other they are said to be flush. The term is also used to describe the washing or cleaning out of chips and dirt by forcing oil or water through all inside passages of any device.

FLUSH MEASURING WIRES — See *Screw Thread Measurements, Flush Wires.*

FLUSH PIN GAGE—A type of gage in which the measuring is done by a pin which slides in the gage body and indicates the size by the position of the outer end with relation to the surface of the gage body. When the pin is flush or even with the surface, the work is correct. In some cases, the outer end of the pin has two surfaces, each covering half the pin end. When one surface is flush it indicates the high limit and the other end shows the low limit. A worker's finger becomes very sensitive in detecting slight variations in size.

FLUTE—The space between two raised portions of any tool or other part. In drills, reamers and taps the flute is the portion cut out between the lands. See *Drill*, page 90.

FLUX—Any substance which will aid the flow of solder (or similar materials) and its adherence to metal. Dilute sulphuric acid or muriatic acid, in which small particles of zinc have been dissolved, were once widely used, but soldering pastes of various kinds have largely replaced the use of liquids.

FLY-BALL GOVERNOR — This refers to any device for governing the speed of engines, or other mechanisms by use of fan blades or weighted balls. With fan blades, an increase in speed adds to the resistance and slows the mechanism. With revolving balls, as on a stationary steam engine, increase in speed forces the balls to travel in a larger diameter and reduces the supply of steam to the cylinder.

FLY-CUTTER—Strictly speaking, this is a single point cutter used for milling or boring.

The term is also used for cutters with two or even four teeth or points, to distinguish them from the usual multi-tooth cutter.

FLYWHEEL—A heavy wheel or pulley for steadying the rotation of a shaft or spindle. On a reciprocating engine, it carries the crankpin past the center and helps give a uniform motion. Now largely used on milling machine spindles to prevent slowing of cutter as its teeth contact the work.

FOIL—Very thin sheets of metal, usually pure. They are made from gold, tin, lead, aluminum and other metals.

FOLLOW BOARD—See *Mold Board.*

FOLLOW RESTS—Supports to prevent deflection of work from pressure of a tool, usually single point tools and in a lathe. The rest is fastened to the tool carriage and travels with it, or "follows" the tool, giving constant support.

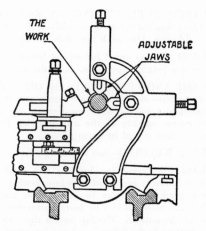

Follower rest mounted on lathe saddle.

FOOT PRESS—See *Press, Foot.*

FOOTSTOCK—The part of any machine tool which carries the dead center and which does not apply power to the work. Some special machines have power applied at both ends of the work, and so have no foot stock. In some cases, as with car axle lathes, there are two foot stocks, the power being applied in the center of the axle.

FORCE FIT—See *Fits, Force.*

FORELOCK BOLT—See *Bolt, Forelock.*

126

FORCE—A master punch used in a powerful press to form an impression in a die. Forces are used in making coining and other embossing dies, as well as in silverware and in making dies for plastic molding. In some trades they are called "hubs" and also "hobs." The latter term should only be used in connection with gear cutting.

FORGE—An open fireplace in which metals are heated for forging. A forced draft, by blower or bellows, makes a hot flame. The name is applied to the shaping of hot metals by hammering or by pressure. In some cases an entire forging plant is called a "forge."

FORGINGS—Parts formed by hammering or forcing metal to assume desired shapes. In most cases the metal is heated to a high temperature so as to flow into the desired shapes before it cools. Originally made by hand hammers or sledges, using hand-held formers to secure desired shapes. Then came drop hammers, steam hammers and forging presses. These give greater accuracy of form and uniformity of grain structure. Most small and medium sized forgings are now formed in dies.

FORGING ALLOYS, NON-FERROUS—Forging alloys and their properties for different uses, as suggested by the Copper and Brass Research Associates, are shown herewith. These forging brasses include: Copper; plain; non-leaded brasses; leaded brasses; tin brasses; and silicon bronzes.

FORGING, BRASS—The forming of parts in brass which has been heated, by forcing it between dies, as in steel forgings by machine methods rather than with the hammer.

FORGING DEFECTS—Forgings may have numerous defects, each having its own name, which follow:

Burnt and Overheated Metal — Usually caused by soaking the stock too long in the fire.

Cold Shuts—Short cracks, usually at corners and at right angles to the surface, caused by metal forming against itself during forging. They may be caused by incorrect placing of stock in dies. If they occur too frequently, they may be due to poor forging design or improper dies.

Fins and Rags—Small pieces of loose metal

Non-Ferrous Forging Alloys

Metals %	Forging Ratio	Hot Working	Cold Working	Soft Soldering	Brazing	Welding		Machine-ability %
						Gas	Arc	
Copper 99.9	65	Excel.	Excel.	Excel.	Good	Poor	Fair	20
Copper 91 Alum. 7 Tin 2	75	Fair	Poor	Fair	Fair	Fair	Fair	55
Copper 44-46 Nickel 9-11 Rest Zinc	85	Excel.	Poor	Excel.	Good	Good	Good	40
Copper 59-62 Tin 0.5-1.0 Rest Zinc	90	Excel.	Fair	Excel.	Good	Fair	Poor	30
Copper 59-63 Rest Zinc	90	Excel.	Fair	Excel.	Good	Fair	Poor	70
Copper 58.5-62 Lead 1.5-2.5 Rest Zinc	100	Excel.	Poor	Excel.	Good	Fair	Poor	80

127

forced into the forging, which produce small nicks and unfilled sections.

Mismatched Parts—Forgings in which the dies are not properly matched. The die may shift through bad mountings or from lack of alinement in the machine. Dies with offset parting lines sometimes cause the dies to shift position.

Mistrimmed Forgings—Surplus metal, not properly removed in trimming. May be caused by improper placing of forging in the trimming dies, or if the trim dies are not properly designed.

Out of Tolerance—Where long, irregular sections have uneven shrinkage so that centers are not within specified tolerance, even though general dimensions may be correct.

Ruptured Fiber—The structure of the metal fiber to detect broken grain flow lines can be shown only by etching. This defect is usually caused by a too rapid flow of metal. See *Forgings, Grain Flow.*

Scale Pits—Shallow depressions caused by scale being forced into the surface of the metal. Its removal leaves pits in the surface.

Unfilled Sections—Lack of metal in parts of the forging. May be caused by wrong size of stock, by poor forging design, or by improper dies. Sometimes due to underheated stock or stock misplaced in dies.

FORGINGS, GRAIN FLOW—Grain flow is the way in which the fibers of metal arrange themselves when they are forced into desired shapes by forging, especially in forging dies. The illustration shows the flow as obtained by cutting a forging in half and etching the surface. It will be noted that the cast metal has no fiber but is granular. Forgings produced in hammers, forging machines and presses each show the characteristic grain flow.

FORGING HEAT—The temperature to which metals to be forged should be heated. This varies with the metal. For low-carbon steel one large automobile plant prefers 2,250 deg. F. to 2,400 deg. F. as a maximum, for the center of the metal. Some consider 3 minutes per inch of diameter or thickness as minimum time, others prefer a slower rate. Pre-heating is suggested for steels with over 1 per cent carbon, soaking up to 1,300 or 1,400 deg. F., and then rapid heating to forging temperature. Tables are given for different metals on following pages.

Magnesium Alloys—Maximum Forging Temperatures

Alloy	Blocking °F.	Finishing °F.
AT35	820	800
AZ61X	720	700
AZ80X	720	650

FORGING MACHINE—Any machine which forms hot metal by pressure instead of by hammering. Forging machine or upsetter also employs a type of closed impression die in which the hot plastic metal is forged by the squeeze pressure exerted by punches carried in the header ram. Forging suitable for production by this method range in weight from less than a pound to about 500 pounds. See also *Forging Press.*

FORGING MACHINE DIES—See *Dies, Forging Machine.*

FORGING PRESS—A machine for forging metal into dies to secure the desired shape. Also known as a forging machine. They use

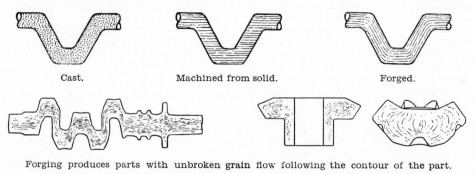

Cast.   Machined from solid.   Forged.

Forging produces parts with unbroken grain flow following the contour of the part.

FORGING GRAIN FLOWS.

Small National forging machine.

Large forging machine.

is in almost its finished state. At G the flash has been trimmed from the outside and the thin web of metal in the bearing hole has been punched out. The rod is now ready for machining. See following pages.

Bar stock is heated on one end for upsetting in the forging machine. In most cases the stock is handled by hand as it is shifted from one die cavity to the next. Frequently the completed work is sheared or punched from the bar in the final pass of the header slide. This is a 2-in. machine.

a steady pressure instead of hammer blows to shape the metal. Similar in some ways to a bulldozer except that the latter usually bend bars into shape instead of forging them.

FORGING, ROLL—Instead of hammer blows, roll forging shapes the metal by steady pressure applied by rolls. One type of roll forging is shown where a car wheel is being formed by the pressure of two dies as they revolve. In some cases one die may be stationary. Another type of forging roll is used to forge such parts as gun barrels, as shown.

FORGING, STEPS IN—The seven steps in forging a connecting rod show three preliminary steps before the rod begins to assume the finished outline, as at D. At A it has been struck by the first die, or the first time in that die. The surplus metal is being forced out as flash. This is more evident in F, where the rod

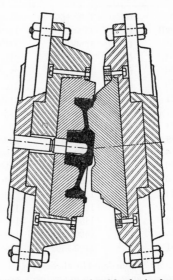

Roll forging from circular blanks is done between revolving dies. Angle die is fixed and vertical die moves on the end of hydraulic ram.

Carbon Steel—Forging and Heat-Treating Typical Temperatures

SAE No.	Forge* °F.	Normalize °F.	Process Anneal °F.	Full Anneal °F.	Quench °F.	Die-Life Ratio	Relative Machin-ability
1010	2400	1650-1800	1000-1350	1600-1700	1650-1700	105	84
1020	2350	1600-1750	1000-1350	1600-1700	1575-1675	100	100
1030	2320	1600-1675	1250-1400	1575-1650	1550-1625	98	104
1035	2320	1575-1650	1250-1400	1575-1625	1525-1600		93
1040	2280	1575-1650		1550-1600	1500-1575	95	85
1045	2280	1550-1650		1550-1600	1475-1550		78
1050	2220	1550-1625		1550-1600	1450-1525	90	76
1060	2160	1525-1600		1500-1575	1425-1550	85	
1070	2100	1500-1575		1475-1550	1455-1550		
1080	2050	1500-1575	1250-1400	1475-1550	1400-1525		
1095	2020	1500-1575	1250-1400	1475-1550	1400-1525		69

*Mamimum temperature for reducing atmospheres.

Stainless Steel—Forging, and Heat-Treating Typical Temperatures

Type	Group[a]	Preheating, °F	Begin Forging °F	Finish Forging °F	Annealing Temp. °F.	Stress Relieve
302	C	1500-1600	2100-2200	Above 1700	1850-2050	400-750
302B	C	1500-1600	2100-2150	Above 1700	1850-2050	400-750
303	C	1500-1600	2100-2200	Above 1700	1850-2050	400-750
304	C	1500-1600	2100-2200	Above 1700	1850-2050	400-750
309	C	1500-1600	2200-2300	Above 1800	1850-2050	400-750
310	C	1500-1600	2100-2200	Above 1800	1900-1950	400-750
321	C	1500-1600	2150-2200	Above 1700	1700-1950	450-750
347	C	1500-1600	2150-2200	Above 1800	1700-2000	400-750
403	A	1400-1500	2000-2100	1450-1500	1550-1650[b]	450-700
410	A	1400-1500	2000-2100	1600-1700	1550-1650[b]	450-700
416	A	1400-1500	2100-2200	1500-1600	1550-1650[b]	450-700
420	A	1400-1500	1950-2050	1650-1700	1550-1650[b]	450-700
430	B	1400-1500	1900-2000	1350-1400	1450-1550	
430F	B	1400-1500	2000-2100	1350-1400	1250-1450	
440	A	1400-1500	1850-2000	1700-1750	1625-1675[b]	300-700
442	B	1400-1500	1900-2000	1300-1400	1450-155	
446	B	1400-1500	1900-2000	1300-1400	1450-155	
501	A	1400-1500	1950-2000	1650-1700	1550-1575	

a Group: A hardenable chromium, B non-hardenable chromium, C austenitic chrome-nickel.
b Process annealing temperatures are about 200 deg. F. lower.

Copper Alloys—Forging and Heat-Treating Typical Temperatures

Alloy	Forging Range °F.	Annealing °F.	Die-Life Ratio	Machinability SAE 0120-=100	Free-cutting Brass = 100
Copper	1400-1600	490-500 up	110	125	20
Forging brass	1250-1550	800-1100	115	200	20
Naval Brass	1200-1300	800-1100	110	160	30
Leaded naval brass	1200-1350	800-1100			70
Manganese brass	1200-1300	800-1100	85	80	
600 Bearing metal	1250-1350				
Muntz metal	1150-1300	800-1100		75	40
Silicon bronze (Type A)	1200-1500	900-1300	83	75	30
Silicon bronze (Type B)	1200-1500	900-1250	83	75	30
Aluminum bronze......	1450-1700	950-1500		110	20
Nickel silver	1300-1500				80

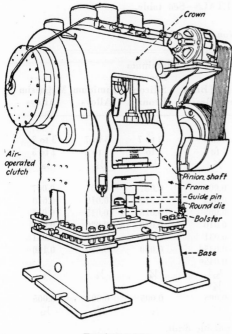

Forging press.

FORGINGS—Pieces of metal formed by pressure or hammering to secure desired shapes and to improve the quality of the metal. There is a variety of methods, which include upset-ting, rolling and working by various types of machines.

FORGINGS, TERMS USED — *Extrusion* — Forcing the metal through a die. *Ironing*—Producing smooth surfaces. *Finishing*—Bringing the piece to final size. *Re-Striking*—Second operation with a die to secure better surfaces or sizes. *Shearing*—Cutting off surplus or cutting metal needed from a bar. *Sizing*—Also called coining. Similar to re-striking except it is usually done cold. *Trimming*—Shearing the flash or excess metal from the forging. *Weldless Rings*—Made by slitting a piece of flat or bar stock, opening the slit and forming the piece into a ring of solid metal.

Magnesium Forgings—Minimum Dimensions and Tolerances

	Hammer	Press
Sectional thickness, in. ..	$\frac{1}{8}$ to $\frac{3}{16}$	$\frac{1}{8}$ to $\frac{3}{16}$
Machining allowance, in..	$\frac{1}{16}$ to $\frac{1}{8}$	$\frac{1}{16}$ to $\frac{1}{8}$
Size tolerance, in.	$\pm\frac{1}{32}$	$\pm\frac{1}{64}$ to $\frac{1}{32}$
Flatness tolerance, in. ...	$\frac{1}{32}$	$\frac{1}{32}$
Trimming tolerance, in...	$\frac{1}{16}$	$\frac{1}{16}$
Draft, deg.	7	1 to 3

FORGINGS, UPSET—Forgings made by enlarging the ends of bars by pressure, in much the same way as a rivet head is formed by spreading the end to a larger diameter than the body of the rivet. See *Upset Forgings*.

131

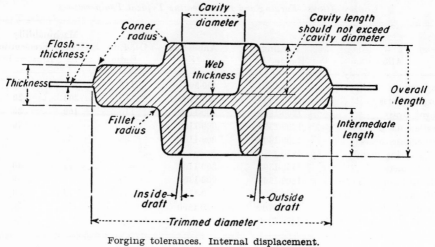

Forging tolerances. Internal displacement.

FORGING TOLERANCES (NON-FERROUS METALS—See table.

Forging Tolerances (Non-ferrous Metals)

	Copper	Forging Brass Naval Brass	Aluminum Bronze Silicon Bronze	Aluminum Alloys	Magnesim Alloys
Outside draft[a], deg.					
hammer	3 to 7	3 to 7	3 to 7	3 to 7	3 to 7
press	1 to 5	1 to 5	1 to 5	1 to 5	1 to 5
Fillet and corner radii, in.[b]	⅛	⅛	⅛	⅛	⅛
Dimensions, in. [c]					
up to 1 in.	0.007	0.005	0.007	0.007	0.007
2 in.	0.010	0.008	0.010	0.010	0.010
4 in.	0.007	0.005	0.015	0.015	0.015
6 in.	0.015	0.010	0.020	0.020	0.020
over 6 in.	0.031	0.031	0.031	0.031	0.031
Web thickness, in.	0.080	0.035[d] 0.045[e]	0.080	0.080	0.100
Flash thickness, in.	¼	³⁄₃₂[d] ⅛[e]	¼	¼	⅜
Flatness per inch	0.005	0.005	0.005	0.005	0.005
Machining allowance, in.	¹⁄₃₂	¹⁄₃₂	¹⁄₃₂	¹⁄₃₂	¹⁄₃₂

a Inside draft will be somewhat greater than outside draft.

b These radii are minimum desirable for maximum die life, fillets with much smaller radii can sometimes be made.

c Minimum of ± 0.007 should be allowed for all dimensions crossing the parting line.

d Forging brass.

e Naval brass.

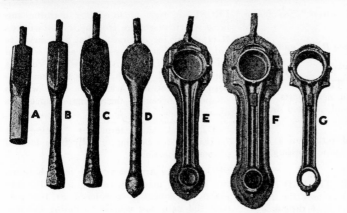

A, B, C, D and E cover all of the operations performed in the pre-forming and blocking impressions while F and G show the result of subsequent operations in the finishing dies. Although the forging operations are unquestionably the most important, failure to obtain good punch fits and proper relief angles might easily ruin the forging in trimming.

Steps in forging connecting rods.

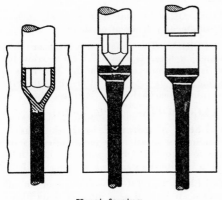

Upset forging.

FORK TRUCKS — Power driven trucks or tractors which carry pallets or platforms on forks ahead of the machine. Also called scooters, jitneys, chisels, hoists and lifts.

FORM GRINDING—Grinding with an abrasive wheel that has its face formed or shaped to the contour desired on the work. While this is usually a finishing operation, many contours are now ground from the rough without previous machining. Thread grinding is now done from the solid, using wheels which are formed by crushing to shape. See *Crushed Wheel Grinding*.

FORM RELIEVED—A method of grinding milling cutters. See *Milling Cutters, Form Relieved*.

FORM TURNING—Turning special shapes with tools formed to the desired outline. The tools are either flat or round, with a section cut away to provide a cutting edge. The form tools may be used on one or on both sides of the work, being fed toward the center. This refers to tools which cut radially. Forming is also done with tools which cut tangentially and pass under or over the work. This is know as "skiving." See *Skiving*. Both flat and circular tools are shown.

FORMED GEAR TOOTH CUTTERS — See *Milling Cutters*.

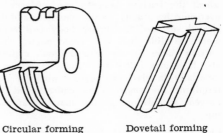

Circular forming tool.   Dovetail forming tool.

FORMING TOOLS—Tools with their cutting edges shaped to some particular form which is to be reproduced in the work. The term usually refers to tools for lathe work of some kind. The usual form is either round or flat as shown. When ground on the face they maintain the form until used up. Some cut the work tangentially instead of radially. Formed tools for milling machine work are called "formed cutters." See *Screw Machine Tools.*

FOUNDATION BOLT—See *Bolt, Foundation.*

FOX BOLT—See *Bolt, Fox.*

FRACTIONAL PITCH THREADS — Screw threads which are not in even parts of an inch. An 11½-pitch thread is used in one pipe size.

FRAISE—A seldom used term for a small milling cutter and for a stone working tool, resembling a reamer.

FRANKLIN INSTITUTE THREAD—Name formerly applied to what is now the American National Standard form of thread.

FREE MACHINING — A shop term for metals which can be turned or otherwise machined at relatively high speeds without developing too much heat, and which can be cut so as to leave a relatively smooth surface. With modern carbide tools the speeds which can be called high seem fantastic as compared with a few years ago. Some shops are buying both metals and machine tools on the basis of specified cutting speeds.

FRENCH CURVE—A draftsman's device contaig a number of curved surfaces, of different radii. Used in blending curved lines in some classes of mechanical drawing.

FRICTION, ANGLE OF — The angle at which the friction between two surfaces is overcome by gravity. With smooth, well-lubricated surfaces, the upper body will commence to slide at a very slight angle. The friction varies greatly with different materials. It is also called the "angle of repose," especially in civil engineering work in determining the angle of an embankment to prevent the sliding of the material at the top.

FRICTION CLUTCH—See *Clutch, Friction.*

FRICTION GEARING—See *Gear, Friction.*

FRIT — An imperfectly vitrified material used as a binder or binding agent in making grinding wheels and other similar products.

FROG—In railroad work, the casting or other parts which connect rail ends at points where tracks diverge in any way. They are used in connection with switches to guide trains from one track to another.

FROST—A type of finish for machine surfaces which resembles frosting, or snowflakes. It is mostly for decoration, but also serves to hold oil on flat surfaces, such as the ways of a lathe. It is frequently done with a rotating abrasive wheel or cloth. Serves the same purpose as "spotting," which is done with a scraper, to break up the flat appearance of a plane surface.

FROZEN—A shop term for "seizing" or "sticking" of a bearing, usually from lack of proper lubrication.

FRUSTRUM—Any part of a solid between two surfaces made by cutting the solid into pieces. Frequently considered as the part near the base, not usually including the top, should that be cut off. The part of a cone below a line where the top is cut off. Rarely used in the shop, being mostly a geometric term.

FUEL OIL—Any oil used as fuel, such as distillate of petroleum or shale.

FULCRUM—The point on which, or about which, a lever is moved. With a crow bar, it is the point on which the bar rests in being used as a pry. In pliers, it is the rivet or pin which holds the jaws together.

FULCRUM PIN—See *Pin, Collar.*

FULLER—A tool used by blacksmiths for shaping hot metal. The anvil fuller fits into a hole in the anvil face, while the hand fuller has a handle the same as a hammer or sledge.

FULLERS EARTH—A soft clay of an oily nature. It is used as a filter in some bleaching processes.

FULMINATE — Various materials used in percussion and detonating devices.

FURBISH—To burnish or scour to a bright surface. To polish. Not often used in the shop.

FURNACE—Any device for heating metals for forging or hardening. There are many types devised for special kinds of work.

FURNACE, AIR—A furnace in which a natural draft moves the heat of combustion through the furnace and over the work being heated.

FURNACE ATMOSPHERE—Three types of furnace atmosphere are recognized by those who heat-treat metals: oxidizing, neutral and reducing. The *oxidizing* atmosphere has less air than required for combustion and affects the surface of the work. The *reducing* atmosphere has too little air and an excess of gas or whatever fuel is used. A truly *neutral* atmosphere is almost impossible to obtain.

FURNACE, BLAST—A furnace in which a forced draft, or blast, carries the heat to and over the work. In the Bessemer process it carries the blast of air through the material being melted.

FURNACE, ELECTRIC, STEEL—A furnace having large carbon electrodes projecting through the roof of a brick lining. The steel is melted by arcs drawn between the electrodes and the metal. These furnaces are mounted on trunions and tilt for pouring. Electrodes wear rapidly and are automatically adjusted for proper position. These furnaces hold up to 85 tons of steel and take from 4 to 6 hours per charge.

FURNACE, GAS FIRED—A furnace in which the heat is produced by burning gas. There are many kinds designed to meet different requirements in heat treating metals and other materials.

FURNACE HEATING—The heating of metals in some sort of furnace. In most cases it is considered better to prevent the flame from coming in direct contact with the metal, by using baffles which divert the flame away from the metal being heated. Fire brick is frequently used for these baffles and is frequently called a "muffled" furnace.

FURNACE, HYDROGEN—A furnace in which the heating chamber is kept in an atmosphere of hydrogen. This excludes the air and prevents oxidization. It is very successful in many kinds of soldering and brazing work.

FURNACE, INDUCTION—An electrically heated surface in which the heating coils surround the heating chamber, or the work itself, but are not in contact with it.

FURNACE, MUFFLE—A furnace so designed that direct flames do not contact the material being heated. The material is protected by baffles or partitions which divert the flow of the flame.

FURNACE, OIL FIRED—A furnace in which the heat comes from burning oil. It

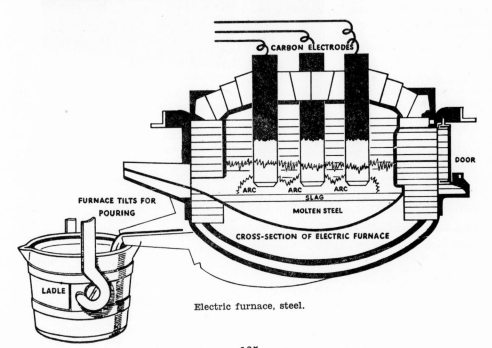

Electric furnace, steel.

is sprayed into the furnace and gives very similar results to gas in many cases.

FURNACE, REVERBERATORY — In this type of furnace a low arched roof throws the heated air down on the material being melted.

FURNITURE—In machine shops this applies to tool racks, lathe pans, tote boxes, angles, blocking clamps, bolts and similar small parts.

FUSED QUARTZ—See *Quartz, Fused.*

FUSIBLE ALLOYS — Low melting alloys that usually melt below 121 deg. F. Used in automatic sprinkler heads for fire protection.

FUSIBLE METAL — An alloy of metals which will melt at a low heat. Used in automatic sprinkler heads to allow water to flow when a room gets to a dangerous temperature. An alloy of 2 parts tin, 3 parts lead and 5 parts bismuth will melt below the boiling point of water.

FUSIBLE PLUG—A plug, usually brass, having a center of fusible metal that will melt at a temperature that will prevent explosion or damage. Generally used on steam boilers to relieve pressure when the water level becomes too low.

FUSION—The joining of two metals by heat, or the act of melting metals of any kind.

FUSION WELDING—See *Welding, Fusion.*

G

GAGE—Instruments or tools used in checking sizes or dimensions of work. Some of the most common types are shown, including plug and ring gages, receiving gages, indicating gages, snap and caliper gages. The last two are very similar, one type combining both inside and outside gages in one piece. Many other types are described under various headings, all under gages. The term is usually applied to non-adjustable devices such as plug and ring gages, gage blocks and the like. See also *Gaging.*

GAGE, BORING BAR CUTTER—A gage for setting cutters in boring bars to bore the correct diameter desired. Three methods are shown.

GAGE, CENTER—A sheet steel gage with three 60-degree angles. Used for checking the angle of lathe and other centers and for setting thread tools when chasing screw threads. Should not be confused with a "center square." See *Center Square.*

GAGE, DEPTH—A tool for measuring the depth of a hole or recess. In the type shown the body is placed across the hole and the blade pushed down into contact with the desired surface.

Depth gage.

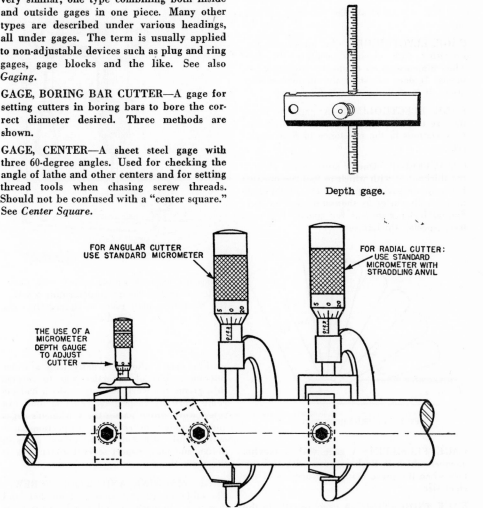

Boring bar cutter gage. The use of standard micrometer instruments to adjust the center.

137

GAGE, DRILL—Usually a flat piece of steel with holes made by drills of different sizes. In some cases it has a narrow V-shaped opening with the sizes marked at points where drills of different sizes fit the slot.

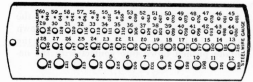

Drill gage.

GAGE, ELECTRICHEK—An inspection gage operating with electrical contacts to show when dimensions do or do not meet requirements. It does not show the amount of variation. It is made by the Sheffield Corp.

GAGE, ELECTROLIMIT—A gage in which the size of pieces being measured is indicated by variations in the resistance to flow of current.

GAGE, FEELER—One or more blades of varying thicknesses with which to feel the opening between two parts or points. The blade thickness usually varies by thousandths of an inch. Special feeler gages, as for spark plug gaps, have special thicknesses.

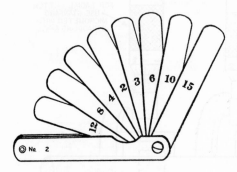

Feeler or thickness gage.

GAGE, FLUSH-PIN—A gage with a moving member which is flush or even with the surface when the piece being measured is of the right size.

GAGE, INDICATING—A gage, usually in the form of a watch or clock, with a hand which

indicates the size of the work being measured. It does not actually measure the work as does a plug or ring gage, but indicates the approximate size of the piece within very close limits. In some cases there are no measured graduations, merely marks which indicate that if the pointer stays between them the piece being checked is within specified limits.

GAGE, INSPECTION—Gage used by inspectors to check accuracy of work after it has been machined. May be a duplicate of the

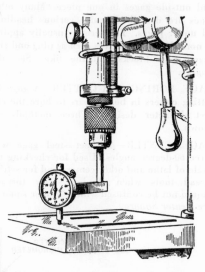

Indicating gage. A simple set-up with a dial indicator makes it easy to determine whether the table of a drill press is square with the spindle.

working gages, though usually with a wider tolerance. The old practice was to reverse this, giving the workmen gages which had become worn by inspectors. This method can reject work which passes the workmen's gages and has now been reversed. Inspection gages may be quite different from workers' gages in design and may inspect several dimensions at the same time.

GAGE, MACHINE AND WOOD SCREW—The table on page 140 shows the numbers and daimteers of machine and wood screws from No. 000 to No. 50, in decimals of an inch.

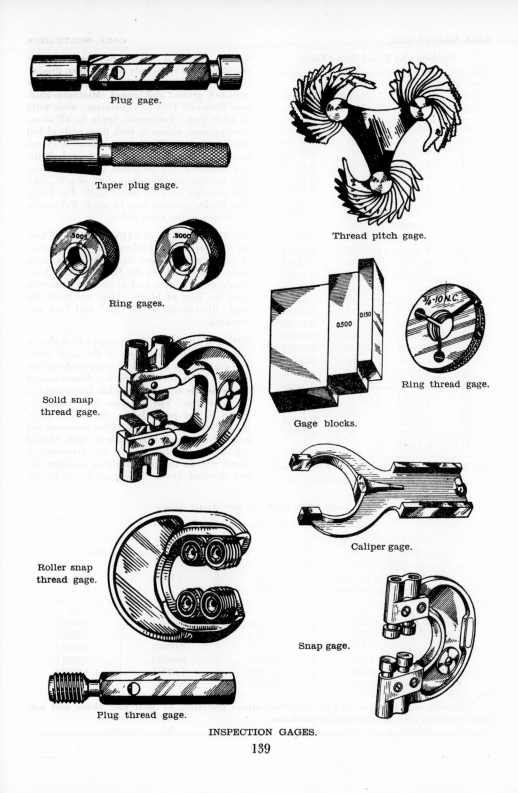

Plug gage.

Taper plug gage.

Ring gages.

Thread pitch gage.

Solid snap
thread gage.

Gage blocks.

Ring thread gage.

Caliper gage.

Roller snap
thread gage.

Snap gage.

Plug thread gage.

INSPECTION GAGES.

Machine and Wood Screw Gage

No. of Screw Gage	Size in Decimals	No. of Screw Gage	Size in Decimals
000	0.03152	25	0.38684
00	0.04468	26	0.40000
0	0.05784	27	0.41316
1	0.07100	28	0.42632
2	0.08416	29	0.43948
3	0.09732	30	0.45264
4	0.11048	31	0.46580
5	0.12364	32	0.47896
6	0.13680	33	0.49212
7	0.14996	34	0.50528
8	0.16312	35	0.51844
9	0.17628	36	0.53160
10	0.18944	37	0.54476
11	0.20260	38	0.55792
12	0.21576	39	0.57108
13	0.22892	40	0.58424
14	0.24208	41	0.59740
15	0.25524	42	0.61056
16	0.26840	43	0.62372
17	0.28156	44	0.63688
18	0.29472	45	0.65004
19	0.30788	46	0.66320
20	0.32104	47	0.67636
21	0.33420	48	0.68952
22	0.34736	49	0.70268
23	0.36052	50	0.71584
24	0.37368		

The increment between sizes is 0.01316 inch.

GAGE, MASTER DISK—Standards set by the Bureau of Standards for the War Production Board, Sept. 15, 1945. Disks are to be seasoned, ground and lapped. Minimum hardness Rockwell C-63 or equivalent. Sizes 0.015 to 8.010 inch. Tolerances apply to all diameters between points $\frac{1}{16}$ inch from ends of full working surface. Total variations from roundness and for taper not to exceed one-half the size tolerance. To be tested with comparator with suitable amplification at 68 deg. F., with 1-lb. pressure for sizes under 4.510. For larger sizes $2\frac{1}{2}$-lb. pressure may be used. Tolerances are shown in the table below.

GAGE, MASTER SETTING DISK—These are disks or short cylinders used for setting or checking micrometers and other measuring tools. Those made by the Sheffield Corp. have plastic grips at each end to prevent distortion from the heat of hands. They are made for single dimensions or for "go" and "not go" checking.

GAGE, MULTICHECK—A gage which checks more than one dimension at the same time. The gage shown is an Electrigage made by the Sheffield Corp. for checking five dimensions of the projectile shown in the left foreground at the same time. The five gage head lights are shown in the panel below the master light. If all the dimensions are within tolerance the master light shows everything is right. Should any dimension be outside the tolerance it shows red on the proper panel location, the rest showing green. The gage is set by the

Tolerance on Diameter for Master Disks

(Classes XX, X, Y, gage makers' tolerances)

Size		Total Tolerance[1] on Nominal Size		
Above	Up to and including	Class XX	Class X	Class Y
in.	in.	in.	in.	in.
0.105	0.825	0.00002	0.00004	0.00007
0.825	1.510	0.00003	0.00006	0.00009
1.510	2.510	0.00004	0.00008	0.00012
2.510	4.510	0.00005	0.00010	0.00015
4.510	6.510	0.000065	0.00013	0.00019
6.510	8.010	0.00008	0.00016	0.00024

[1]Tolerance may be taken in plus direction, minus direction, or split half above and half below nominal size, as specified by purchaser.

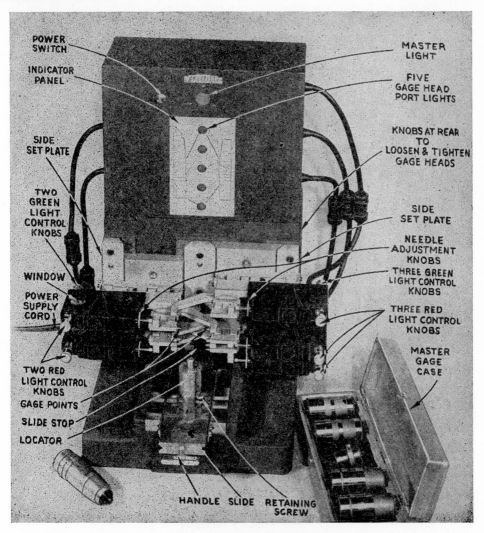

POWER
SWITCH

INDICATOR
PANEL

MASTER
LIGHT

FIVE
GAGE HEAD
PORT LIGHTS

SIDE
SET PLATE

KNOBS AT REAR
TO
LOOSEN & TIGHTEN
GAGE HEADS

TWO
GREEN
LIGHT
CONTROL
KNOBS

SIDE
SET PLATE

NEEDLE
ADJUSTMENT
KNOBS

WINDOW

THREE GREEN
LIGHT CONTROL
KNOBS

POWER
SUPPLY
CORD

THREE RED
LIGHT CONTROL
KNOBS

MASTER
GAGE
CASE

TWO RED
LIGHT CONTROL
KNOBS

GAGE POINTS

SLIDE STOP

LOCATOR

HANDLE   SLIDE   RETAINING
SCREW

Sheffield Multicheck Electrigage.

master plugs shown in the box at the lower right. The various elements are indicated by arrows.

GAGE, PIPE THREAD — The illustrations on page 142 show gages used for American national pipe threads. Notations show how the gages are used.

GAGE, RECEIVING—Any gage into which the work to be gaged is placed. A gage which "receives" the part to be measured. A ring gage *receives* the work it is to check.

GAGE, ROCK PIN—A pin with rounded ends used in checking diameter of a bore. The pin is shorter than the diameter of the bore and the amount the free end can be *rocked* gives diameter in addition to the length of the pin. This practice is seldom used at present, as most shops have inside micrometers for such work.

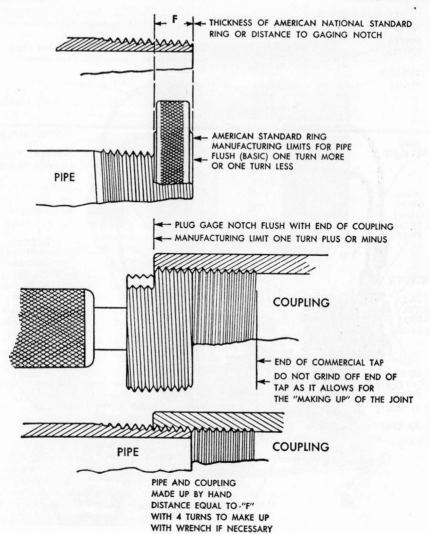

F — THICKNESS OF AMERICAN NATIONAL STANDARD RING OR DISTANCE TO GAGING NOTCH

AMERICAN STANDARD RING MANUFACTURING LIMITS FOR PIPE FLUSH (BASIC) ONE TURN MORE OR ONE TURN LESS

PIPE

PLUG GAGE NOTCH FLUSH WITH END OF COUPLING
MANUFACTURING LIMIT ONE TURN PLUS OR MINUS

COUPLING

END OF COMMERCIAL TAP
DO NOT GRIND OFF END OF TAP AS IT ALLOWS FOR THE "MAKING UP" OF THE JOINT

PIPE   COUPLING

PIPE AND COUPLING MADE UP BY HAND DISTANCE EQUAL TO "F" WITH 4 TURNS TO MAKE UP WITH WRENCH IF NECESSARY

Pipe thread gage. Gages and their relation to taper pipe threads. The gages indicated here are American National Standard Plug and Ring Nitrigages. The work being gaged is a correctly threaded pipe and fittings.

GAGE, SCRATCH—A tool for marking or scratching a line at a given distance from one side of a piece. The movable bar carrying the scratching element is frequently graduated.

GAGE, SCREW THREAD PITCH—Thin sheet steel with V notches showing the number of threads per inch. Made in different forms with blades of various shapes or with the notches on the edge of a disk. The type of blade shown on page 143 permits the gage to be used in small diameter holes.

GAGE, SHEET ZINC — The thickness and weight of sheet zinc made by the Illinois Zinc Company are shown herewith.

Illinois Zinc Company's Zinc Gage

No.	Lbs. per Square Foot	Thickness in Inches
3	0.22	0.006
4	0.30	0.008
5	0.37	0.010$\frac{1}{100}$
6	0.45	0.012
7	0.52	0.014
8	0.60	0.016
10	0.75	0.020$\frac{1}{50}$
11	0.90	0.024
12	1.05	0.028
13	1.20	0.032
14	1.35	0.036
15	1.50	0.040$\frac{1}{25}$
16	1.68	0.045
17	1.87	0.050
18	2.06	0.055
19	2.25	0.060$\frac{1}{17}$
20	2.62	0.070
21	3.00	0.080
22	3.37	0.090
23	3.75	0.100$\frac{1}{10}$
24	4.70	0.125$\frac{1}{8}$
25	9.40	0.250$\frac{1}{4}$
26	14.00	0.375$\frac{3}{8}$
27	18.75	0.500
28	37.50	1.000

GAGE, SNAP—A solid caliper which measures diameters or lengths between its points, which are fixed. See illustrations of *Gages.*

GAGE, STAR—A gage having three or more radial points for checking the bore of long holes such as cannon. They are usually adjustable from the end of the supporting rod.

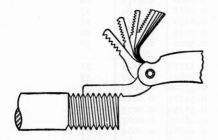

Screw thread pitch gage.

GAGE, SURFACE—A tool for measuring or gaging the height between flat surfaces, such as a planer bed, or from a surface plate. Some have a micrometer adjustment on the needle for fine work. Some also have magnetic bases so as to stick on any iron or steel surface, whether horizontal or vertical.

GAGE, TAPER—Gages for measuring either internal or external tapered parts. Gages for internal tapered holes may be either solid tapered plugs or flat tapered plates. Internal tapers can also be measured by indicating mechanisms which show both correctness or taper and irregularities. Either plug or plates are usually *blued* before inserting to note if the bearing is uniform the whole length. Measuring external tapers can be readily done in a device as shown, where two straight blades are fastened at the desired taper so that light will show whether there is a full bearing or not.

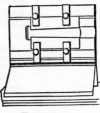

Taper gage.

GAGE, THREAD—See *Gage, Screw Thread Pitch.*

GAGE(S) USED FOR DIFFERENT MATERIALS—American or Brown & Sharpe gages are used for sheet brass, copper and nickel silver sheets and for wire of the same materials. Birmingham and Stubs iron wire gages are used for soft iron wire rods, but not for steel drill rods. American Steel & Wire (or Washburn & Moen's) gages are used for iron or copper telegraph and telephone wire, but not for wire used in electrical instruments. These wires are measured in thousandths of an inch or "mils." Stubs steel wire gages are used for drill rods (should not be confused with Stubs iron wire gage). United States standard gages are used for iron and steel sheets only. See *Tables.*

GAGE, V—A gage which has a V opening into which the part to be gaged is placed. Its position in the V indicates its size. Some wire and drill gages are made in this way.

GAGE, WIRE—A tool for measuring diameter of wires. Made both as shown for drill gages and in circular form. It is also made with a narrow V-slot having wire sizes marked along the side of the slot, but this is not as satisfactory as the type shown under *Gage, Drill.*

Adoption of the method used by the electrical industry, with wires measured by "mils," or thousandths of an inch, would eliminate all gages except micrometers and save much time and confusion.

GAGE(S), WIRE AND SHEET—Many different wire gages have been used in the United States over the years. The American or Brown & Sharpe, Birmingham, Stubs and Music Wire gages are probably the most used at present. They should not be confused. The practice of the electrical industry in designating wire by "mils," or thousandths of an inch, instead of by numbers, has much to commend it. Eleven gages are given for reference. They should

MANUFACTURERS' STANDARD GAGE FOR SHEET STEEL

Gage-thickness equivalents are based on 0.0014945 inch per ounce per square foot; 0.023912 inch per pound per square foot (reciprocal of 41.82 lb. per square foot per inch thick); 3.443329 inches per pound per square inch.

Manufacturers' Standard Gage No.	Ounces per Square Foot	Pounds per Square Inch	Pounds per Square Foot	Inch Equivalent for Steel Sheet Thickness	Manufacturers' Standard Gage No.
3	160	0.069444	10.0000	0.2391	3
4	150	0.065104	9.3750	0.2242	4
5	140	0.060764	8.7500	0.2092	5
6	130	0.056424	8.1250	0.1943	6
7	120	0.052083	7.5000	0.1793	7
8	110	0.047743	6.8750	0.1644	8
9	100	0.043403	6.2500	0.1495	9
10	90	0.039062	5.6250	0.1345	10
11	80	0.034722	5.0000	0.1196	11
12	70	0.030382	4.3750	0.1046	12
13	60	0.026042	3.7500	0.0897	13
14	50	0.021701	3.1250	0.0747	14
15	45	0.019531	2.8125	0.0673	15
16	40	0.017361	2.5000	0.0598	16
17	36	0.015625	2.2500	0.0538	17
18	32	0.013889	2.0000	0.0478	18
19	28	0.012153	1.7500	0.0418	19
20	24	0.010417	1.5000	0.0359	20
21	22	0.0095486	1.3750	0.0329	21
22	20	0.0086806	1.2500	0.0299	22
23	18	0.0078125	1.1250	0.0269	23
24	16	0.0069444	1.0000	0.0239	24
25	14	0.0060764	0.8750	0.0209	25
26	12	0.0052083	0.7500	0.0179	26
27	11	0.0047743	0.6875	0.0164	27
28	10	0.0043403	0.6250	0.0149	28
29	9	0.0039062	0.5625	0.0135	29
30	8	0.0034722	0.5000	0.0120	30
31	7	0.0030382	0.43750	0.0105	31
32	6.5	0.0028212	0.40625	0.0097	32
33	6	0.0026042	0.37500	0.0090	33
34	5.5	0.0023872	0.34375	0.0082	34
35	5	0.0021701	0.31250	0.0075	35
36	4.5	0.0019531	0.28125	0.0067	36
37	4.25	0.0018446	0.26562	0.0064	37
38	4	0.0017361	0.25000	0.0060	38

not be confused. See above. See also suggestions of *Wire and Sheet Metal Gages.*

Wire and Sheet Metal Gages

Wire and sheet metal gages were originally evolved by individual manufacturers in order that certain sizes could be reproduced upon customer demand. Their unconformity was an advantage, for it bound the user to his original source of supply. There are now at least 30 systems, with about 1,225 sizes, in active use in the United States.

Even though some systems are almost obsolete, it is impossible to be familiar with all phases of their application, particularly because of the inconsistencies and duplications in use. Until final standardization, confusion and mistakes may be held to a minimum by observing these rules:

1. Always give name of the gage in addition to the number on drawings, specifications and orders.

2. Be sure that the correct gage system is used for the material in question.

3. Use decimal equivalents, preferably in conjunction with the gage name and number.

As an aid to carrying out these rules, the accompanying tabulation is given.

STUBS' STEEL WIRE SIZES, AND WEIGHT IN POUNDS PER LINEAR FOOT

Letter and No. of Gage	Dia. in Inches	Weight per Foot	No. of Wire Gage	Dia. in Inches	Weight per Foot	No. of Wire Gage	Dia. in Inches	Weight per Foot
Z	.413	.456	10	.191	.098	46	.079	.017
Y	.404	.437	11	.188	.095	47	.077	.016
X	.397	.422	12	.185	.092	48	.075	.015
W	.386	.399	13	.182	.089	49	.072	.014
V	.377	.380	14	.180	.087	50	.069	.013
U	.368	.362	15	.178	.085	51	.066	.012
T	.358	.335	16	.175	.082	52	.063	.011
S	.348	.324	17	.172	.079	53	.058	.009
R	.339	.307	18	.168	.075	54	.055	.008
Q	.332	.295	19	.164	.072	55	.050	.007
P	.323	.280	20	.161	.069	56	.045	.006
O	.316	.267	21	.157	.066	57	.042	.0047
N	.302	.244	22	.155	.064	58	.041	.0045
M	.295	233	23	.153	.063	59	.040	.0042
L	.290	.225	24	.151	.061	60	.039	.0040
K	.281	.211	25	.148	.059	61	.038	.0039
J	.277	.205	26	.146	.057	62	.037	.0037
I	.272	.192	27	.143	.055	63	.036	.0035
H	.266	.189	28	.139	.052	64	.035	.0033
G	.261	.182	29	.134	.048	65	.033	.0029
F	.257	.177	30	.127	.043	66	.032	.0027
E	.250	.167	31	.120	.039	67	.031	.0026
D	.246	.162	32	.115	.035	68	.030	.0024
C	.242	.159	33	.112	.034	69	.029	.0022
B	.238	.152	34	.110	.032	70	.027	.0020
A	.234	.146	35	.108	.031	71	.026	.0018
1	.227	.138	36	.106	.030	72	.024	.0015
2	.219	.128	37	.103	.028	73	.023	.0014
3	.212	.120	38	.101	.027	74	.022	.0013
4	.207	.115	39	.099	.026	75	.020	.0011
5	.204	.111	40	.097	.025	76	.018	.0009
6	.201	.108	41	.095	.024	77	.016	.0007
7	.199	.106	42	.092	.023	78	.015	.0006
8	.197	.104	43	.088	.020	79	.014	.0005
9	.194	.101	44	.085	.019	80	.013	.0004
			45	.081	.018			

United States Standard Gage (U.S.S.G.)

Use: Uncoated steel sheets and plates; also long terne plates and light tin plates (occasional).

Range: 7/0 to 38. Extended by custom to 44. Heaviest commercial size is 3.

General: Established by the United States Government and based on the weight per square foot with the equivalent thickness calculated on the basis of 0.2833 lb. per cu. in.

Galvanized Sheet Gage (G.S.G.)

Use: Galvanized Sheet Steel

Range: 8 to 34.

General: Identical with U.S.S.G. except for addition of 2½ oz. per sq. ft. to cover weight of galvanizing.

Tin Plate Gage (T.P.G.)

Use: Tin plate and small terne plate.

Range: 55 to 435 lb.

General: Differs from ordinary gages as the thickness is not measured by gage number but by the weight of a "base box." This consists of 112—14 x 20-in. sheets or any other combination having the same area of 31,360 sq. in. The weight of the box varies with the thickness of the sheets from 55 lb. for sheets with a thickness of No. 38 U.S.S.G. to 435 lb for sheets of approximately No. 18 U.S.S.G. Symbols such as IC, IX, DX, etc., have been adopted by the trade for certain widely used weights.

Sheet Zinc Gage

Use: Zinc Sheets.

Range: 1 to 28.

General: The gage numbers increase with greater thickness of the sheets.

Steel Wire Gage (Stl. W. G.)

Use: Steel wire, except steel telephone and telegraph wire, music wire and tool steel wire. Also frequently used for non-ferrous wire for weaving into cloth.

Range: 7/10 to 50.

General: Practically identical with American Steel & Wire Co., Roebling and Washburn and Moen Wire Gages and supersedes them.

Music Wire Gage (M.W.G.)

Use: Music or piano wire.

Range: 6/10 to 45.

General: The gage numbers increase with the size of the wire. There are several different music wire gages in general use, two of which are the American Steel & Wire Co. and the American Screw & Wire Gage Co. gages.

Brown & Sharpe Gage (B. & S.G.), American Wire Gage (A.W.G.)

Use: Non-ferrous wire, brazed non-ferrous tubing and all non-ferrous sheets except soft and hard copper sheets; ribbon and clock spring steel.

Range: 6/50.

General: Each size is approximately 89% of the next larger.

Music Wire Sizes

No. of Gage	Diameter	No. of Gage	Diameter	No. of Gage	Diameter	No. of Gage	Diameter
6—0	0.004	8	0.020	21	0.047	34	0.100
5—0	0.005	9	0.022	22	0.049	35	0.106
4—0	0.006	10	0.024	23	0.051	36	0.112
3—0	0.007	11	0.026	24	0.055	37	0.118
2—0	0.008	12	0.029	25	0.059	38	0.124
0	0.009	13	0.031	26	0.063	39	0.130
1	0.010	14	0.033	27	0.067	40	0.138
2	0.011	15	0.035	28	0.071	41	0.146
3	0.012	16	0.037	29	0.075	42	0.154
4	0.013	17	0.039	30	0.080	43	0.162
5	0.014	18	0.041	31	0.085	44	0.170
6	0.016	19	0.043	32	0.090	45	0.180
7	0.018	20	0.045	33	0.095		

Due to the fact that the wire gage of the American Steel Wire Company was most extensively used this gage has been recommended by the Bureau of Standards. On this account it has seemed best to publish only these sizes, as given above.

STUBS IRON WIRE GAGE, WARRINGTON WIRE GAGE (W.W.G.), BIRMINGHAM WIRE GAGE (B.W.G)

Use: All steel tubing and seamless non-ferrous tubing, steel plates, bands, hoops, sheet spring steel, cold rolled steel strips, steel or iron telephone and telegraph wire, soft and hard copper sheets

Range: 5/0 to 36.

General: In ordering soft or hard copper sheets, use the name "Stubs" in preference to B.W.G. or W.W.G.

STUBS STEEL WIRE GAGE

Use: Drill rod and tool steel wire.

Range: 1 to 80.

TWIST DRILL GAGE (T.D.G.)

Use: Small sizes of twist drills.

Range: 1 to 80.

General: Slightly larger than same numbers of Stubs Steel Wire Gage. It is also known as "Manufacturers' Standard."

OLD ENGLISH OR LONDON GAGE

Use: Non-ferrous wire for weaving into cloth (occasional).

Range: 4/0 to 40.

AMERICAN SCREW GAGE

Use: Wood and machine screws.

Range: 3/0 to 50.

BRITISH IMPERIAL STANDARD WIRE GAGE

Abbreviations: Great Britain, W. G., B.W.G. United States, I.S.W.G.

Use: All wire in Great Britain. Occasionally in U. S. for copper telephone wire.

Range: 7/0 to 50.

BRITISH STANDARD GAGE FOR IRON AND STEEL SHEETS AND HOOPS (B.G.)

Use: Iron and steel sheets and hoops in Great Britain.

Range: 7/0 to 50.

General: Also know as New Birmingham Gage.

GAGE, WIRE TYPE PLUG—A type of plug gage credited to Van Keuren. It has an aluminum handle with measuring plugs of tool steel, high speed steel, chrome plated steel or carbide material. It is light to handle, the wear life depending on the material in the measuring plugs.

GAGE(S), WORKING—Gages used in production of machine parts. When these have less

tolerance than inspection gage, any parts they pass will be accepted by inspection gages.

GAGE BLOCKS—See *Blocks, Measuring.*

GAGGER—A piece of iron sunk in a sand mold to strengthen and hold it in place when the pattern has been withdrawn.

GAGING—

Gaging is the process of measuring manufactured materials to assure the specified uniformity of size and contour required by the industries.

Standard—The standard for gaging is a physical representation of a form, dimension, or size established by law or by general usage and consent.

Standard Sizes are recognized or accepted sizes corresponding to various sub-divisions of a recognized unit of length. These are usually expressed in inches or in millimeters, but sometimes by arbitrary numbers or letters.

Basic Size is the exact theoretical size from which all limiting variations are made.

Nominal Size is a designation given to the sub-division of the unit of length having no specified limits of accuracy, but indicating a close approximation to a standard size.

Gages are devices for determining whether or not one or more of the dimensions of a manufactured part are within specified limits. The type of common manufacturing gages employed for measuring the accuracy, or variation from standard, of a manufactured article are: Ring, plug, receiving, snap, caliper, indicating, and fixture.

Ring Gage—One whose inside measuring surfaces are circular in form.

Plug Gage—One whose outside measuring surfaces are arranged to verify the specified uniformity of holes. A plug gage may be straight or tapered, and of any cross-sectional shape.

Receiving Gage—One whose inside measuring surfaces are arranged to verify the specified uniformity of size and contour of material.

Snap Gage—A fixed gage arranged with inside measuring surfaces for calipering.

Caliper Gage—One which, for external use, is similar to a snap gage, and for internal use, is similar to a plug gage.

Indicating Gage—One that exhibits visually the variations in the uniformity of dimensions or contour, the amount of the variations being usually indicated by lever on a graduated scale or dial.

Fixture Gage—The name given to a combination of any or all of the above types, and is employed for the purpose of measuring more than one point on an irregular piece at one setting, or for determining the accuracy of one point in relation to another.

Master Check—One whose gaging dimensions represent as exactly as possible the physical dimensions of the component. It is the gage to which all other gages, and all dimensions are checked.

Working Gage—One used by the workman to check the work as it is produced. The working gage should not accept any product that the inspection gage will reject.

Inspection Gage—A gage used by the manufacturer or purchaser in accepting the finished product. These gages are checked against the master gage or against the drawing of the part.

GAGING, AIR—Air gaging is really measuring the pressure of air which escapes between the surfaces being measured and the gaging surface. The diagram shows a Sheffield gage

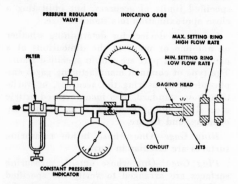

Air gaging. Principle of mechanized back-pressure air gage. Back pressure is controlled by ratio of orifice to air escaping when the gaging head contacts maximum or minimum part.

for checking the bore of rings. Air at constant pressure comes through the filter, pressure regulator and restricting orifice to the gaging head. Two setting rings, of maximum and minimum diameter, are put over the gaging head and the pressure on the indicating gage is noted, for both rings. If the indicating gage hand moves between the two central marks on the gage, they represent the limits which are

permissible. Rings to be measured are put over the gaging head and the position of the gage hand noted. The back pressure caused by the escaping air between the gaging head and the work shows on the gage. As the width of the rings being measured affects the back pressure, the rings used for setting the gage must be of the same width as the work to be measured.

GAGING, CONVERSION OF INTERFERENCE BANDS TO MICRO-INCHES—With a monochromatic light having interference bands of 11.6 millionths of an inch, the values in micro-inches are given in the table. See *Light Wave Bands*.

GAGING SCREW THREADS—Screw threads are gaged or measured in two ways—by screwing them into a gage and noting the fit, or by measuring the pitch diameter with standard steel wires, this being the more accurate. Three wires are generally used, although some use but two. The wires are held in the angle of the thread and the distance between the outside wires on each side is carefully measured with a micrometer or similar device. See *Screw Threads, Measuring*.

GALLIUM—Melts at about 86° F. or when held in the hand. Boils at about 3750 ° F. Found in some zinc ores, mainly in Germany and South Africa. Chemical behavior resembles aluminum. Few practical uses as yet. Has replaced mercury in very high temperature thermometers.

GALLOWS FRAME—The frame of any piece of machinery which supports bearings at the top, as with vertical steam engines with the crankshaft over the cylinders, and sometimes a walking beam to transmit power from the cylinder to the engine shaft. This was used in both stationary and marine engines.

GALVANIZED IRON — Iron sheets coated with zinc by dipping them into the molten zinc.

GAMMA-RAY INSPECTION—Using radium salts which emit gamma rays. These are similar to X-rays but their shorter wave length gives them greater penetrating power. Capsules containing up to 500 milligrams of radium salts are used in making radiographs of large castings. Placed inside a large hollow casting, as a turbine casting, film can be placed at as many points on the outside as desired and the various portions X-rayed at the same time.

GANG DRILL—See *Drilling Machine, Gang.*

GANG TOOL—Any combination of a number of cutting tools in a single tool holder. They usually divide the depth of the cut into several stages. The term also applies to tools used for turning different diameters or for locating shoulders. In planer work, gang tools are used for a variety of purposes and have as many as 20 or more tools.

GANGUE—Non-metallic impurities in steel.

GAS-CYLINDER THREADS—See *Screw Threads, Gas Cylinder.*

GASH—Usually a roughing cut in the making of gear teeth. This was common in the making of gears with single cutters. It was common to "gash" or rough cut the teeth with a gang of two or three cutters, and then finish with a single cutter.

GASHING—Taking a roughing cut to be followed by a finishing cut. The term is mostly used in gear cutting by the older method of using single or double formed cutters.

GASKET—A packing between two parts where it is necessary to have a tight joint. Gaskets may be round, to go between pipe flanges, or of special shapes as those used on automobile cylinder heads or crankcases. They are usually made of some resilient material, such as cork, or of a softer metal such as copper, and corrugated continuously around the opening.

GATE VALVE—See *Valve, Gate.*

GEAR(S) (The term is used rather indiscriminately singular or plural.) Usually a disk having teeth cut around its periphery. Generally round in shape but occasionally made elliptical or of other form to impact varying velocities to the shaft on which it is mounted, or to a mating gear. Larger gears may be spoked wheels or otherwise made to secure lightness. The many types of gears are described and illustrated. When the mating gear is of smaller diameter it is called a "pinion."

Gearing embraces all kinds of toothed wheels for securing positive motion between revolving parts in all kinds of machinery, from watches to rolling mills and steam turbines.

Alphabetically in the following pages are *GEAR(S)* plural, *GEAR* singular, *GEAR* adjectivally, and *GEAR(ING)*.

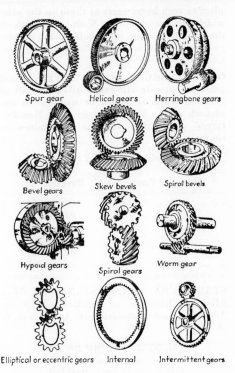

Common types of gears.

GEAR(S), ADDENDUM OF, LONG AND SHORT—In some gear applications, designers put the pitch line of the pinion nearer the outside diameter, which gives the tooth a short addendum (or distance from pitch line to outside diameter) and a long dedendum. This requires a long addendum and a short dedendum on the teeth of the mating gear. This makes a stronger pinion. Some gears are made with pitch line nearer the top of the tooth, giving a short addendum. In others the pitch line is nearer the base of the tooth, making a long addendum. The tooth curve or profile is then modified to give the desired bearing between the mating surfaces.

GEAR(S), ANGULAR—Name sometimes given to bevel gears and to those having angular or helical teeth, such as skew gears.

GEAR(S), ANNULAR—Toothed rings, such as are used in some universal chucks, with teeth on any one or more of the four faces. When the teeth are on the inside surface they are known as internal gears. The term is also applied to such bevel gears as those on the axles which drive automobiles. With spiral teeth on the side, as in some universal chucks, annular gears are sometimes called "scrolls." See also *Cutters for Bevel Gears.*

GEAR(S), BACKLASH OF BEVEL— Bevel gears are usually allowed a given amount of backlash which is etched or stamped on one or both gears. The American Gear Manufacturers' Association suggests the values as shown.

Backlash of Bevel Gears

Diametral Pitch	Backlash, In.
2	0.012-0.016
3	0.008-0.010
4- 5	0.006-0.008
6- 9	0.004-0.006
10-19	0.002-0.004
20-up	0.000-0.002

GEAR(S), BACKLASH, STANDARD OF— Allowable backlash, as standardized by the American Gear Manufacturers' Association, is as follows:

A. G. M. A. Standard Backlash

C.P.	Backlash
4	0.032-0.050
2	0.017-0.025
1	0.009-0.014
½	0.005-0.007
¼	0.003-0.005
⅛	0.002-0.004

GEAR(S), BASE CIRCLE OF—To find the base circle for spur gears, multiply the pitch diameter by the cosine of the pressure angle. The cosine of commonly used pressure angles are given.

Cosines of Common Pressure Angles

Degrees	
10	= 0.98481
14½	= 0.96815
17½	= 0.95372
20	= 0.93969
22½	= 0.92388
25	= 0.90631
27½	= 0.88701
30	= 0.86603

GEAR(S), BEVEL—Gears with teeth cut on angular surfaces so as to transmit power with the shafts at an angle. When the shafts are at right angles, and the gears are of the same size, they are sometimes called miter gears. There are several types of bevel gears. Plain bevels have teeth that are radial from the center. Skew bevel gears have teeth at an angle not parallel with axis; spiral bevel gears have taken their place. Spiral bevel gears have angular curved teeth. Zerol bevel gears have curved teeth but without an angle. See *Gears, Spiral; Gears, Zerol Bevel.* See also *Gears, Backlash of Bevel.*

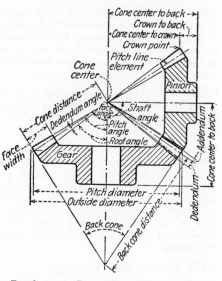

Bevel gears. Conventional bevel gear nomenclature.

GEAR BLANK—The disk on which gear teeth are cut, usually on the periphery.

GEAR(S), BLOCK GAGING OF—A method of checking the accuracy of gear tooth spacing

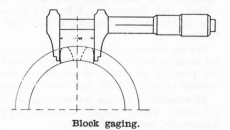

Block gaging.

by measuring across several teeth. Special tables are prepared for use where this system of measurement is used. It involves measurement across the profiles of the teeth as well as the pressure angle, number of teeth in the block measured and total number of teeth in the gear. Beam vernier calipers or micrometers with special jaws are used in making the measurements.

GEAR BURNISHING MACHINE—A machine for running soft or "green" gears with hardened master gears to burnish, and so work harden, the green gears. It may also make slight corrections in the tooth form.

GEAR(ING) CHAIN—See *Chain, Gearing.*

GEAR(S), CHANGE—Gears used to vary the relation between the driving mechanism and the part which it actuates. An engine lathe has a set of change gears which can be used to vary the ratio of movement between the work and the lathe carriage, carrying the tools for cutting screw threads. Change gears are also provided for varying the rate of feed on milling machines and to secure the proper divisions with a dividing head.

GEAR(S), CONTROL—This is similar to a sample gear, except that the number of teeth may be different. It is used for control, or reference purposes. These are not used in worm or bevel gearing.

GEAR(S), CROWN—A gear with the teeth on the end or side of its cylindrical surface. The driving pinion is at a right angle so that it does the work of a bevel gear. Seldom used except for very light powers.

GEAR CUTTER—This may mean either the machine on which gears are cut or the cutter used in forming the teeth. It is best to designate which is meant, as rotary gear cutter, hobbing machine, gear planer or gear shaper, when the machine is meant. The cutting tools should be named according to the particular work they are to do.

GEAR CUTTERS, FORMED—Milling cutters shaped to produce the desired form of gear

Brown & Sharpe Involute Gear-Tooth Cutters

	Will Cut Wheels from
No. 1	135 teeth to a rack
No. 1½	80 to 134 teeth
No. 2	55 to 134 teeth
No. 2½	42 to 54 teeth
No. 3	35 to 54 teeth
No. 3½	30 to 34 teeth
No. 4	26 to 34 teeth
No. 4½	23 to 25 teeth
No. 5	21 to 25 teeth
No. 5½	19 to 20 teeth
No. 6	17 to 20 teeth
No. 6½	15 to 16 teeth
No. 7	14 to 16 teeth
No. 7½	13 to 14 teeth
No. 8	12 to 13 teeth

Tooth Proportions for 1 Diametral Pitch

(Axes at 90 deg.)

$$\text{Ratio} = \frac{\text{number of gear teeth}}{\text{number of pinion teeth}}$$

Ratio	Pinion addendum	Gear addendum	Pinion circular thickness	Gear circular thickness
1.00	1.000	1.100	1.5708	1.5708
1.01 to 1.14	1.100	0.900	1.6436	1.4980
1.15 to 1.33	1.200	0.800	1.7164	1.4252
1.34 to 1.70	1.300	0.700	1.7892	1.3524
1.71 to 2.78	1.400	0.600	1.8620	1.2796
2.79 and higher	1.450	0.550	1.8984	1.2432

Dimension are in inches.
Where pinions and gears are to be hardened, consideration of top lands may require modification of addendum proportions.

tooth as they pass across the face of the gear blank. The forms are practical compromises with ideal shapes and produce satisfactory gears for many uses. There are 15 cutters in a full set, although many use only the cutters bearing whole numbers. These are now used mostly in jobbing and repair shops, as the great majority of gears are either made with a gear shaper or hobbed. The standard formed cutters are shown and also the work they do.

To measure a gear cutter use the distance

Depth of Space and Thickness of Tooth in Spur Wheels When Cut with These Cutters

Pitch of cutter	Depth to be cut in gear, in.	Thickness of tooth at pitch, line, in.
1¼	1.726	1.257
1½	1.438	1.047
1¾	1.233	0.898
2	1.078	0.785
2¼	0.958	0.697
2½	0.863	0.628
2¾	0.784	0.570
3	0.719	0.523
3½	0.616	0.448
4	0.539	0.393
5	0.431	0.314
6	0.359	0.262
7	0.308	0.224
8	0.270	0.196
9	0.240	0.175
10	0.216	0.157
11	0.196	0.143
12	0.180	0.131
14	0.154	0.112
16	0.135	0.098
18	0.120	0.087
20	0.108	0.079
22	0.098	0.071
24	0.090	0.065
26	0.083	0.060
28	0.077	0.056
30	0.072	0.052
32	0.067	0.049
36	0.060	0.044
40	0.054	0.039
48	0.045	0.033

from the pitch line to the bottom of the space. Cutters for bevel gears are made approximately to the width of the space at the small end of the teeth where the face is one-third the apex.

GEAR CUTTERS FOR BEVEL GEARS—Standard cutters for spur gears are used for cutting bevel gears in milling machines. As bevel gear teeth are tapered, a cutter is selected for the narrow space at the inner end of the teeth. After making one cut the blank is shifted enough off-center to give the right width of space at the outer end. The amount of set-over depends on the ratio of the apex distance, or center of the cone of which the gear is a part, to the width of the gear face. The table shows the amount of "set-over" for different ratios. If the apex cone is 4 inches and the gear face 1 inch, the set-over distance is given in the column with the 4 over the 1.

Table moved in this direction for this cut

Cutter for bevel gears. Setting work off-center to widen tooth space at outer end.

GEAR CUTTERS FOR GEAR SHAPERS—The cutters are practically hardened gears with cutting edges on one side, as shown. They are sharpened by grinding on the cutting face. As both cutter and gear blank revolve in unison, they generate teeth of the desired form.

Cutters for Use in Cutting Bevel Gears

-	12	13	14	15	16	17	18	19	20	21	22	23	24	25	26	27	28	29	30
12	7-7																		
13	6-7	6-6																	
14	5-7	6-6	6-6																
15	5-7	5-6	5-6	5-5															
16	4-7	5-7	5-6	5-6	5-5														
17	4-7	4-7	4-6	5-6	5-5	5-5													
18	4-7	4-7	4-6	4-6	4-5	4-5	5-5												
19	3-7	4-7	4-6	4-6	4-6	4-5	4-5	4-4											
20	3-7	3-7	4-6	4-6	4-6	4-5	4-5	4-4	4-4										
21	3-8	3-7	3-7	3-6	4-6	4-5	4-5	4-5	4-4	4-4									
22	3-8	3-7	3-7	3-6	3-6	3-5	4-5	4-5	4-4	4-4	4-4								
23	3-8	3-7	3-7	3-6	3-6	3-5	3-5	3-5	3-4	4-4	4-4	4-4							
24	3-8	3-7	3-7	3-6	3-6	3-6	3-5	3-5	3-4	3-4	3-4	4-4	4-4						
25	2-8	2-7	3-7	3-6	3-6	3-6	3-5	3-5	3-5	3-4	3-4	3-4	3-4	3-3					
26	2-8	2-7	3-7	3-6	3-6	3-6	3-5	3-5	3-5	3-4	3-4	3-4	3-4	3-3	3-3				
27	2-8	2-7	2-7	2-6	3-6	3-6	3-5	3-5	3-5	3-4	3-4	3-4	3-4	3-4	3-3	3-3			
28	2-8	2-7	2-7	2-6	2-6	3-6	3-5	3-5	3-5	3-4	3-4	3-4	3-4	3-4	3-3	3-3	3-3		
29	2-8	2-7	2-7	2-7	2-6	2-6	3-5	3-5	3-5	3-4	3-4	3-4	3-4	3-4	3-3	3-3	3-3	3-3	
30	2-8	2-7	2-7	2-7	2-6	2-6	2-5	2-5	3-5	3-5	3-4	3-4	3-4	3-4	3-4	3-3	3-3	3-3	3-3
31	2-8	2-7	2-7	2-7	2-6	2-6	2-6	2-5	2-5	2-5	3-4	3-4	3-4	3-4	3-4	3-3	3-3	3-3	3-3
32	2-8	2-7	2-7	2-7	2-6	2-6	2-6	2-5	2-5	2-5	2-4	2-4	3-4	3-4	3-4	3-3	3-3	3-3	3-3
33	2-8	2-8	2-7	2-7	2-6	2-6	2-6	2-5	2-5	2-5	2-4	2-4	2-4	3-4	3-4	3-4	3-3	3-3	3-3
34	2-8	2-8	2-7	2-7	2-6	2-6	2-6	2-5	2-5	2-5	2-4	2-4	2-4	2-4	2-4	3-4	3-3	3-3	3-3
35	2-8	2-8	2-7	2-7	2-6	2-6	2-6	2-5	2-5	2-5	2-4	2-4	2-4	2-4	2-4	2-4	2-3	3-3	3-3
36	2-8	2-8	2-7	2-7	2-6	2-6	2-6	2-5	2-5	2-5	2-5	2-4	2-4	2-4	2-4	2-4	2-3	2-3	2-3
37	2-8	2-8	2-7	2-7	2-6	2-6	2-6	2-5	2-5	2-5	2-5	2-4	2-4	2-4	2-4	2-4	2-3	2-3	2-3
38	2-8	2-8	2-7	2-7	2-6	2-6	2-6	2-5	2-5	2-5	2-5	2-4	2-4	2-4	2-4	2-4	2-4	2-3	2-3
39	2-8	2-8	2-7	2-7	2-6	2-6	2-6	2-5	2-5	2-5	2-5	2-4	2-4	2-4	2-4	2-4	2-4	2-3	2-3
40	1-8	2-8	2-7	2-7	2-6	2-6	2-6	2-5	2-5	2-5	2-5	2-4	2-4	2-4	2-4	2-4	2-4	2-3	2-3
41	1-8	1-8	2-7	2-7	2-6	2-6	2-6	2-6	2-5	2-5	2-5	2-5	2-4	2-4	2-4	2-4	2-4	2-3	2-3
42	1-8	1-8	2-7	2-7	2-6	2-6	2-6	2-6	2-5	2-5	2-5	2-5	2-4	2-4	2-4	2-4	2-4	2-4	2-3
43	1-8	1-8	1-7	2-7	2-6	2-6	2-6	2-6	2-5	2-5	2-5	2-5	2-4	2-4	2-4	2-4	2-4	2-4	2-3
44	1-8	1-8	1-7	1-7	2-6	2-6	2-6	2-6	2-5	2-5	2-5	2-5	2-4	2-4	2-4	2-4	2-4	2-4	2-3
45	1-8	1-8	1-7	1-7	1-7	2-6	2-6	2-6	2-5	2-5	2-5	2-5	2-4	2-4	2-4	2-4	2-4	2-4	2-3
46	1-8	1-8	1-7	1-7	1-7	2-6	2-6	2-6	2-5	2-5	2-5	2-5	2-4	2-4	2-4	2-4	2-4	2-4	2-3
47	1-8	1-8	1-7	1-7	1-7	1-6	2-6	2-6	2-5	2-5	2-5	2-5	2-4	2-4	2-4	2-4	2-4	2-4	2-3
48	1-8	1-8	1-7	1-7	1-7	1-6	1-6	2-6	2-5	2-5	2-5	2-5	2-4	2-4	2-4	2-4	2-4	2-4	2-3
49	1-8	1-8	1-7	1-7	1-7	1-6	1-6	1-6	2-5	2-5	2-5	2-5	2-4	2-4	2-4	2-4	2-4	2-4	2-3
50	1-8	1-8	1-7	1-7	1-7	1-6	1-6	1-6	2-5	2-5	2-5	2-5	2-4	2-4	2-4	2-4	2-4	2-4	2-4
51	1-8	1-8	1-7	1-7	1-7	1-6	1-6	1-6	1-5	2-5	2-5	2-5	2-4	2-4	2-4	2-4	2-4	2-4	2-4
52	1-8	1-8	1-7	1-7	1-7	1-6	1-6	1-6	1-5	1-5	2-5	2-5	2-4	2-4	2-4	2-4	2-4	2-4	2-4
53	1-8	1-8	1-7	1-7	1-7	1-6	1-6	1-6	1-5	1-5	1-5	2-5	2-4	2-4	2-4	2-4	2-4	2-4	2-4
54	1-8	1-8	1-7	1-7	1-7	1-6	1-6	1-6	1-5	1-5	1-5	1-5	2-4	2-4	2-4	2-4	2-4	2-4	2-4
55	1-8	1-8	1-7	1-7	1-7	1-6	1-6	1-6	1-5	1-5	1-5	1-5	1-4	2-4	2-4	2-4	2-4	2-4	2-4

Gear (row axis label)

These tables apply only to bevel gears with axis at right angles.   Pinions at top.

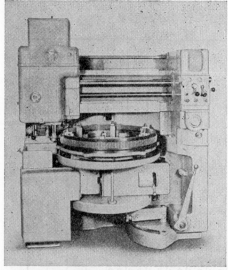

Fellows standard gear shaper.

Fellows 10-spindle gear shaper.

GEAR CUTTER, WORM, SNAIL-BACK—
A fly tool for cutting worm wheels where the cost of a hob is not warranted. The carbide tip is supported by a substantial body of steel with proper relief on all sides. For a single thread worm the tool support can be three-quarters of a complete turn, less for multiple

thread worms. These tools have also been made with a second straight blade opposite the first. They were designed by the Gould & Eberhardt Co. See also *Gear* (pages previous); *Gears* (pages following).

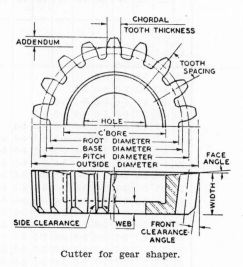

Cutter for gear shaper.

GEAR CUTTING MACHINES — Machines which cut gears with rotary cutters are of the milling machine type. This includes hobbing machines in which the work and cutter revolve continuously and require no indexing. Machines with reciprocating tools, as the Fellows or Gleason, are called gear shapers or gear planers. They are all gear cutters.

GEAR CUTTING ON MILLING MACHINES
—See *Milling Machine, Gear Cutting.*

GEAR CUTTING, SYKES METHOD— A shaping process of cutting gears, similar in many ways to the Fellows method, which preceded it. The Sykes machine used cutters on a horizontal spindle instead of a vertical. In cutting herringbone gears, he used two cutters, one coming in from each side of the gear. By proper timing of each spindle, it was possible to make herringbone gears with no groove, or clearance space in the center. See *Gear Shaping Machine; Gear Grinder.*

GEAR(ING), DIFFERENTIAL— The most common differential gearing is in the rear axles of automobiles. Here combinations of gears permit the engine to drive each rear wheel at a different rate going around curves and at the same rate in straight driving. With one

154

wheel jacked up or on ice, that wheel turns at twice the normal rate while the other does not turn at all. These differential gears may be either spur or bevel type, but are now made bevel in most cases.

Another type of differential gear is where a worm gear is made in two parts, one having 100 teeth and the other 99 teeth. The worm will drive both halves but the 99-tooth gear will gain one tooth at each revolution of the gear. With graduations on the 99 tooth gear,

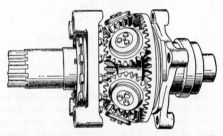

Differential gearing. In this case the idler gears are laid at an angle to shaft. Speed reduction depends on number of teeth in pinion and stationary gear.

a pointer will indicate 1 when the large gear has made one revolution, or for each 100 revolutions of the work. This method has been largely used on revolution counters for shafting.

GEAR(S), ECCENTRIC—Round gears which have the shaft off-center. As with elliptical gears, they give a varying rate of revolution to the driven wheel or shaft.

GEAR(S), ELLIPTICAL—Gears in the shape of an ellipse, with the shafts so located that they will run together and give a varying motion to the driven shafts. See *Gearing*.

GEAR(S), FRICTION—Any device for transmitting motion by surface friction rather than by gear teeth or other positive mechanical means, usually at varying speeds. All locomotives drive by friction of the driving wheels on the rails, and there have been many devices for securing variable speeds by friction wheels or disks of various kinds. See *Variable Speed Drives*.

GEAR(S), FINE TOOTH—Fine tooth gear tables by the Fellows Gear Shaper Co. show teeth from 30 to 200 diametral pitch. The table includes teeth with a circular pitch from

0.0524 to 0.0079 inch and depths of from 0.0729 to 0.013 inch.

GEAR GRINDER—Grinder for finishing gear teeth after hardening.

Gear tooth grinder.

GEAR(S), HELICAL—Gears having teeth cut at an angle across their face to give a more constant pull. This also gives a side or end thrust to the gear shaft. They are sometimes called "skew" and "spiral" gears. See *Gears, Herringbone*.

GEAR(S), HELICAL, ANGLES OF—Meshing helical gears on parallel shafts must have the same helix angle at the pitch circle, but of opposite hands. The angle between the helix and the axis is the lead angle, the same as in a screw thread. The helix angle is the difference between the lead angle and 90 degrees. As both mating gears must have the same helix angle, the lead angle varies in proportion to the difference in the pitch diameters. The illustration shows how this works on 3 and 6 inch diameter gears.

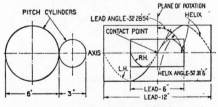

Helical gear angles. Pitch cylinder and helix angles.

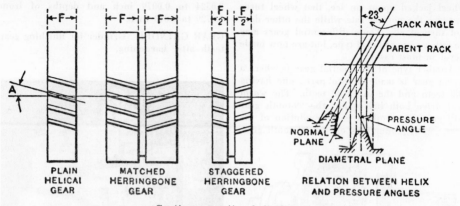

PLAIN HELICAL GEAR   MATCHED HERRINGBONE GEAR   STAGGERED HERRINGBONE GEAR   RELATION BETWEEN HELIX AND PRESSURE ANGLES

Continuous action helical gear.

GEAR(S), HELICAL, CONTINUOUS ACTION—To provide continuous action with helical gear teeth it is necessary to have the face wide enough to insure constant tooth contact. Much depends on the angle of the helix used. The illustration shows the necessary face width for Fellows stub-tooth gears for various pitches and helix angles.

GEAR(S), HELICAL, THREE PITCHES—Helical gears have two normal pitches. The normal pitch of the involute curve lies in the rotational plane of the gear, commonly called the transverse plane. This is commonly known as the *base* pitch. The normal circular pitch lies in a plane at right angles to the helix angle of the area. This normal circular pitch is one used in reference to helical gears, worms, etc. These two pitches should not be confused. The third is the circular pitch shown at the ends of the teeth.

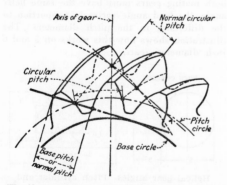

The three pitches common to helical gears.

GEAR(S), HERRINGBONE—These might be called double helical gears, because they have teeth running at opposite angles from the center of the gear face. When cut with rotary cutters it is necessary to leave a space in the center for cutter clearance. With the shaping process, some machines do not require this clearance and give continuous teeth. Herringbone gears are sometimes made by using two gears with teeth at opposite angles, with their sides in contact.

GEAR HOB—A continuous gear cutting tool. The teeth resemble a screw thread with gashes at right angles to the helix of the thread. The sides of the teeth are straight, but the movement of the hob as the work rotates generates gear teeth of the proper form. The tooth form of the hob is the same as the basic rack. The illustration names the various parts of the hob. See illus. following page.

GEAR HOBBING—Hobbing is a continuous method of cutting gear teeth, using a cutter called a "hob," which resembles a worm, with flutes cut across the threads, usually at a right angle to the thread. A hob and the worm gear which drives the gear blank are shown. The blank is geared to turn at a speed that will make a straight tooth in a spur, and at a different rate when a gear with helical teeth is required. The turning of the gear blank during the cutting makes it possible to use a hob with practically straight sided teeth when an involute gear tooth is desired. In addition to the gear blank being turned as it is cut, it is also fed under the hob, so that either a straight spur tooth or a helical tooth is cut across the

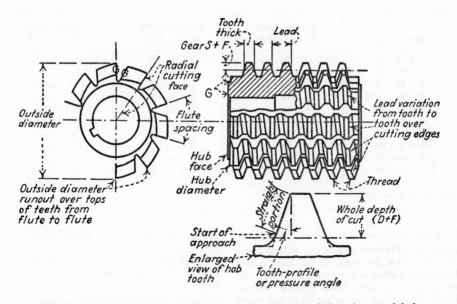

Gear hob. Terms used for parts of single, right-hand-thread ground hob.

face. Other forms of gear teeth can be cut by the hobbing process, but the hob teeth must be properly designed to give the form desired. An involute gear tooth will mesh with a straight sided rack tooth.

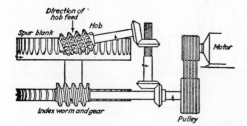

Gear hobbing. Gears in hobbing machine.

GEAR HOBBING, DIFFERENTIAL AND NON-DIFFERENTIAL METHODS — Two

types of gear hobbing machines are used, differential and non-differential. With the differential method, a second cut can be taken merely by disconnecting the feed and moving the cutter slide to its original position. When the feed is disconnected, with the non-differ-

ential method, the relation of the lead between the hob and the blank is changed, and it is necessary to reset both the cutter and the blank very carefully to have the hob act uniformly on both sides of the teeth already cut. The differential machine is somewhat more complicated and costs more, but has advantages in many cases. There are, however, many places where the non-differential method is perfectly satisfactory.

GEAR(S), HORSEPOWER OF—The American Gear Manufacturers' Association suggests that gears and pinion pitches should bear a reasonable relation to the power they are to transmit. For steel gears they suggest the following table, where P.L.V. means "pitch line velocity." Thus for 10 horsepower at 1,000 feet pitch line velocity a gear with 4 diametral pitch should be used. This means 4 teeth per inch of diameter at the pitch line of the gear.

GEAR(S), HOUR-GLASS WORM—A worm gear in which the worm is curved to fit the contour of the worm wheel, and resembles an hour glass. The object is to give greater contact between the worm and the worm wheel. It is known as the Hindley worm and also as

157

Horsepower Rating of Gears

Hp rating	Up to 1,000 P.L.V.* D.P.	1,000 to 2,000 P.L.V. D.P.	Over 2,000 P.L.V. D.P.
¼ to 1	8 to 10	10 to 12	12 to 16
1 to 2	7 to 8	8 to 10	10 to 12
2 to 3	6 to 7	7 to 8	8 to 10
3 to 7½	5 to 6	6 to 7	7 to 8
7½ to 10	4 to 5	5 to 6	6 to 7
10 to 15	3 to 4	4 to 5	5 to 6
15 to 25	2½ to 3	3 to 4	4 to 5
25 to 60	2 to 2½	2½ to 3	3 to 4
60 to 100	1¾ to 2	2 to 2½	2½ to 3
100 to 150	1½ to 1¾	1¾ to 2	2 to 2½

*Pitch-line velocity.

the Cone worm, and dates back many years.

GEAR(S), HYPOID—These are helical bevel gears in which the teeth are so formed that the driving pinion is not in a center line with the gear, as in plain bevel gearing. It was designed to give a similar action to the worm gear and also to permit the driving shaft to be above or below the center of the gear. These bevel gears are known as "spiral bevels," even though the term is not entirely correct. They were devised by the Gleason Works. See *Gearing.*

GEAR, IDLER—A gear which simply transmits motion, but has no effect on the rate of speed of the driven gear. A single idler gear reverses the direction of motion of the driven gear.

GEAR(S), INTERMITTENT—Gears in which the teeth are not continuous around their periphery, but have plain surfaces between the teeth. The driven gear has a plain, concave surface which fits the plain surface of the driver. When the geared section contacts the driven gear it is turned through a portion

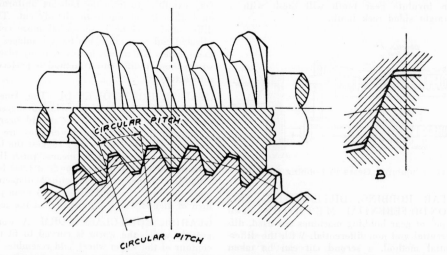

Hourglass worm. In addition to the line contact along the gear tooth, cone drive gearing also provides full depth contact, resulting in larger area contact plus more teeth in contact.

158

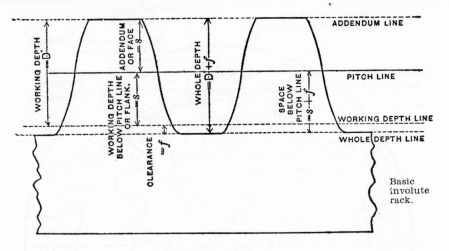

Basic involute rack.

of a revolution. The number of teeth must be alike in both driver and driven gears, or the gear be a multiple of the teeth in the pinion. Subtract twice the addendum from the pitch standard internal diameter.

GEAR(S), INTERNAL—Gears with teeth inside a ring or recessed part. Sometimes called ring gears, although this term is usually reserved for external gears which shrink, or otherwise fasten on a plain pulley surface. The illustration on page 160 shows the action and the names of the parts. They involve problems of tooth form to prevent interference as can be seen, which are helped by using stub teeth.

GEAR, LANTERN—Gear build up by bars or rods between two flanges or disks, the bars acting as gear teeth. Used in mill work when gearing was made of wood. Sometimes found in old clock mechanisms, of brass disks and steel pins.

GEAR(ING), LEWIS GEAR TOOTH FORMULA—A formula developed by Wilford Lewis, a well-known engineer. The Lewis formula, used for the determination of the size of gear teeth, has often been rearranged for the purpose of facilitating its use in practical work. The following arrangement of the Lewis form-

Rules and Formulas for Finding Elements of Internal Spur Gears

Dimension Wanted	Rule	Formula
Pitch diameter	Divide number of teeth by diametral pitch.	$PD = \dfrac{N}{DP}$
Center distance	Divide difference between number of teeth in gear and pinion by twice diametral pitch.	$CD = \dfrac{NG - NP}{2 \times DP}$
Internal diameter	Substract twice the addendum from the pitch diameter.	$1\,D = PD - (Z \times A)$
Root diameter	Add twice the whole depth of tooth to the standard interial diameter.	$RD = 2 \times WD + 1\,D$
Base circle diameter	Multiply pitch diameter by the cosine of the pressure angle.	$BCD = PD \times Cos.\ PA$

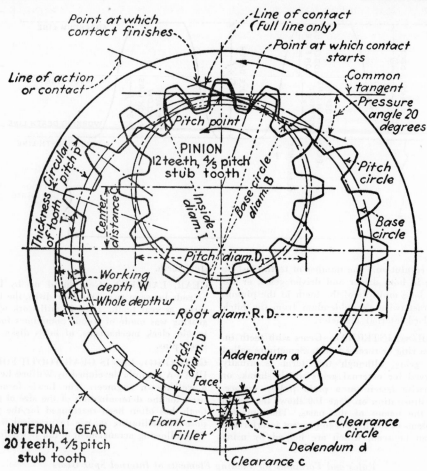

Internal gears. The various elements of internal gear and pinion.

ula has been found advantageous for quick, accurate solution. It minimizes the amount of figuring to be done, therefore reduces the labor of providing the permanent record. The horsepower transmitted by a pair of gears in operation is,

$$hp. = \frac{\text{Tooth pressure } (W) \times \text{Pitch-line velocity } (V) \text{ in ft. per min.}}{33,000}$$

GEAR, MASTER—The American Gear Manufacturers Association defines a master gear as one of known accuracy in every respect. It is usually hardened and ground and proved to be highly accurate by measurements with re-

spect to runout, pitch error, accumulated error, and lead or helix angle. Master gears are used primarily on fixtures which roll gears to determine the cumulative effect of errors in individual elements and show whether these errors compensate for each other or build up in excess of specifications. Backlash may or may not be included in the master gear. If it is, it is usually sized for the average backlash required.

Green (soft) master gears are used to check green gears. They may be made off-standard to match off-standard production gears to allow for changes in hardening. They are sometimes made with teeth enough thinner than standard to allow for grinding in the hardened gear.

GEAR(S), MASTER FOR HELICAL, ZEROL BEVEL AND HYPOID

Master straight tooth bevel gears are not hardened and ground. Master spiral and zerol bevel, as well as master hypoid gears, are frequently hardened and ground. Green master gears, thin tooth master gears and sample gears are commonly used for bevel gearing. Tolerances for these gears are 75 per cent of the most accurate classes listed. Backlash is stipulated in each case.

GEAR(S), MASTER, STANDARD FOR

The American Gear Manufacturers' Association has issued tentative Standard 235.01 entitled "Gear Inspection and Tolerances, Section 5—Master Gears." This standard applies to gears of the following types:

Spur and helical gears, up to 12-in. diameter and 2-in. face, 3 to 16 diametral pitch.

Worms and worm gears.

Straight, spiral and zerol bevel gears.

Hypoid gears.

Definitions—A master gear is one of known accuracy in every respect. It is usually hardened and ground, and by measurement proved to be highly accurate with respect to runout, pitch error, accumulated error, profile error, and lead or spiral-angle error.

Master gears are used primarily on gear-rolling fixtures for a running check of gears to determine the cumulative effect of errors in individual elements, and provide the means of determining whether these errors compensate for each other or build up in excess of specification. They determine backlash, runout, and smoothness of operation.

Backlash may or may not be provided in a master gear. When it is, a master is usually sized for the average backlash desired.

A green master gear is one that is used to check green gears. It may purposely be made off standard with respect to pitch, profile, lead or spiral angle, or tooth thickness, to match production gears made off-standard to allow for changes during heat treatment. Such gears are hardened and ground.

Thin-tooth master gears are a type of green master gear commonly utilized in the production of hardened and ground spiral and zerol bevel, and hypoid gears. The teeth, being thinner by the amount of grinding stock allowed in the mating production gears, permit meshing with the green production gear on a testing machine.

GEAR(S), MEASURING, CONJU-GAGE METHOD

See *Conju-Gage Gear Measurement*.

GEAR(ING)—MEASURING INTERNAL DIMENSIONS

with wires. Spring-steel clamps holds wires in position for measuring with micrometer. See illustration.

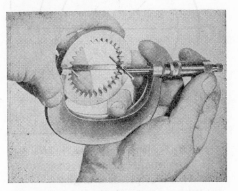

Measuring internal dimensions of gearing with wires.

GEAR(S), MEASURING WITH V-BLOCKS

V-blocks of special size and shape are also used in measuring gear diameters on the pitch line, instead of wires. For gears with even numbers of teeth, two single blocks are used, while for odd-tooth gears, a single and a double V-block are used. Both are shown with formulas for their use.

GEAR(S), MEASURING WITH WIRES

Pitch diameters of gears are measured with wires in the same way that screw threads are now measured. For spur gears the measurement is taken over two wires as shown. Three sizes of wires are used, a wire diameter of 1.728 divided by the diametral pitch of the gear being preferred. For internal gears similar wires are held in place by a spring and measured as in-

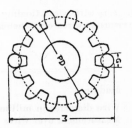

Wire measurement of gears.

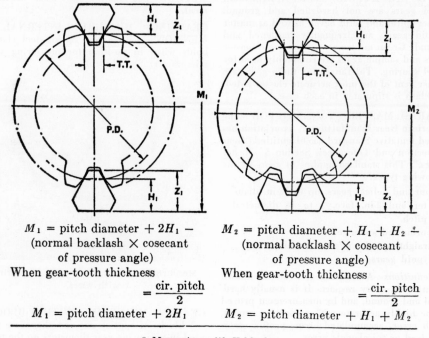

Even Number of Teeth	Odd Number of Teeth

M_1 = pitch diameter $+ 2H_1 -$
(normal backlash $\times$ cosecant
of pressure angle)
When gear-tooth thickness
$$= \frac{\text{cir. pitch}}{2}$$
M_1 = pitch diameter $+ 2H_1$

M_2 = pitch diameter $+ H_1 + H_2 \div$
(normal backlash $\times$ cosecant
of pressure angle)
When gear-tooth thickness
$$= \frac{\text{cir. pitch}}{2}$$
M_2 = pitch diameter $+ H_1 + M_2$

Measuring with V-blocks.

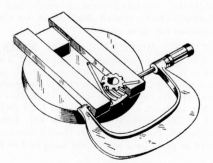

Measuring gears with wires. Holding and aligning measuring wires on a helical gear.

dicated. Different tables are needed for internal parts The standard measuring pressure
is 1 pound. Tables are obtainable for different
pressure angles and for odd and even numbers
of teeth Small helical gears are measured as
shown, with wires held by accurate gage strips
and measured over these strips, their thickness
being deducted from the measurement.

GEAR(S), MODULE OR METRIC — The
French system of designating gears. The module is the pitch diameter in millimeters divided by the number of teeth in the gear.

GEAR(S), MODULE, WIRE DIAMETERS
FOR MEASURING—See table, bottom of
page.

Module Gears

Module	$= \dfrac{\text{pitch diameter in millimeters}}{\text{number of teeth}}$
Wire diameter in millimeters	$= 1.728 \times$ module
Measurement over wires in millimeters	$=$ table value $\times$ module

162

GEAR(ING) NOMENCLATURE:

Active Face—The width of gear tooth face which actually comes in contact with a mating gear. On herringbone gears it includes both surfaces of the angular teeth, minus groove between them, if any.

Addendum — Radial or perpendicular distance between the pitch circle and the top of the tooth. This applies to all types of gearing.

Addendum Angle—The angle between elements of the pitch cone and the face cones in a plane containing the axis of the gear, as applied to bevel gearing.

Angle, Axis Pressure — The angle in an axial plane between the side of the tooth or thread and a line perpendicular to the axis. This applies to both helical and worm gearing.

Angle, Back—In a bevel gear, the angle between an element of the back cone and a plane of rotation. It is usually equal to the pitch angle. The angle between the plane of the pitch circle and a plane tangent to the large end of the tooth.

Angle, Base Helix—Helix angle on the base cylinder involute. (Helical and worm gearing.)

Angle, Dedendum—The angle between elements of the pitch and root cones in a plane containing the axis of the gear. (Bevel gearing only.)

Angle, Face—The angle between an element of the face cone and its axis. (Bevel gearing only.)

Angle, Helix—The angle between a tangent to a helix and an element of the cylinder. Unless otherwise specified, the pitch helix is referred to. Base and pitch helix angles are also included. (Helical and worm gearing.)

Angle, Front—The angle between the plane of the pitch circle and a plane tangent to the small end of the tooth. (Bevel gearing only.)

Angle, Lead—The angle between any helix and a plane of rotation. It is the complement of the helix angle and is used for convenience in worms and hobs. Unless otherwise specified it is taken at the pitch diameter. In screw thread practice the term *lead angle* has largely replaced helix angle.

Angle, Normal Pressure—The pressure angle in a plane normal to the pitch line elements of a helical or spiral bevel gear. In spiral bevel gears it is the normal pressure angle at the mean cone distance.

Angle of Recession—The arc of the pitch circle through which a tooth travels from the time it is in contact with a mating tooth at the pitch point until contact stops. It applies to all types of gearing.

Angle, Outside Helix—The helix angle on the outside of the cylinder. It is sometimes used for trial settings. (Helical and worm gearing.)

Angle, Pitch — In bevel gears, the angle between an element of a pitch cone and its axis. In external and internal bevel gears the pitch angles are respectively less than and greater than, 90 degrees.

Angle, Pressure—The angle between a tooth profile and the radial line at its pitch point. In involute teeth, it is also described as the angle between the line of action and the line tangent to the pitch circle. *Standard pressure angles* are established in connection with standard gear tooth proportions. A given pair of involute profiles will transmit smooth motion at the same velocity ratio even when the center distance is changed. Changes in center distance, however, in gear design and manufacture are accompanied by changes in pitch diameter, pitch, and pressure angles. Different values of pitch diameter and pressure angle may occur in the same gear under different conditions.

Angle Root—The angle between the element of the root and its axis. (Bevel gearing.)

Angle, Shaft—The included angle between the shafts upon which a pair of mating gears are to operate. (Helical, bevel and worm gearing.) Of the four angles at which the two axes of bevel gears cross, the shaft angle is the one containing the teeth in engagement. In crossed helical gears and in worm gears the shaft angle is the sum of the two helix angles. In external bevel gears the shaft angle is the sum of the two pitch angles. In internal bevel gears the shaft angle is the sum of the two pitch angles. In internal bevel gears it is the difference between the pitch angles.

Angle, Spiral—In a spiral bevel gear the angle between the tooth spiral and an element of the pitch cone. It corresponds to the helix angle in helical teeth. Unless otherwise specified it is understood to be at the mean cone distance.

Arc of Action—The arc of the pitch circle through which a tooth travels from the time it first makes contact with a mating tooth until this contact stops. It applies to all types of bevel gearing. The virtual pitch circles are used.

Arc of Approach—The arc of the pitch circle through which a tooth travels from the time it first makes contact with a mating tooth until it is in contact at the pitch point. It applies to all types of gearing.

Axial Contact Ratio—The ratio of face width to the axial pitch, in helical teeth.

Axial Base Pitch—The base pitch of helical involute tooth surfaces in an axial plane.

Axial Pitch—The circular pitch in the axial plane and in the pitch surface between corresponding sides of adjacent teeth, in helical and worm gears. The term "axial pitch" is preferred to the term "linear pitch."

Axial Thickness—In helical and worm gears the tooth thickness in the axial cross section at the pitch line.

Backing—The distance parallel to the axis from the pitch circle to a hub or shoulder extension. (Bevel gearing.)

Backlash—The amount by which the width of a tooth space exceeds the thickness of the engaging tooth at the pitch circle. The clearance between the mating teeth.

Base Diameter—The diameter of a circle from which the involute curve is generated. Applies to all involute gearing.

Base Pitch—In an involute gear the pitch on the base circle or along the line of action. Corresponding sides of involute gear teeth are parallel curves and the base pitch is the constant distance between them in a plane of rotation.

Base Tooth Thickness—The distance on the base circle between the involutes of the same tooth. Applies to all forms of involute gearing.

Bias Bearing—A tooth bearing which is at an angle to the pitch line. Applies particularly to bevel gearing.

Bore Diameter—Diameter of the hole in any gear.

Bottom Land—Surface of the gear at the bottom of the teeth.

Center Distance—The shortest distance between the axes of gears on parallel shafts, or the crossed axes of crossed helical gears and of worm gears.

Central Plane—In a worm gear a plane perpendicular to the gear axis and containing the common perpendicular of the gear and

worm axes. With the axes at right angles, as usual, it contains the worm axis.

Chordal Addendum—Radial distance from the circular thickness chord to the top of the tooth. Applies to all gears.

Chordal Thickness—The thickness of a gear tooth measured on the chord of the circular thickness arc.

Circular Pitch—Distance on the circumference of the pitch circle between corresponding points on adjacent teeth.

Circular Thickness—The thickness of a gear tooth on the pitch circle. In helical gears Normal Circular Thickness is an arc of the normal helix.

Clearance—The space between the top of a tooth and the bottom of the space between the mating teeth.

Cone Center—The apex or meeting point of lines drawn from the pitch lines of mating bevel gears.

Cone Distance — Distance from the cone center to a point on the pitch circle of bevel gears. The Inner Cone Distance is measured to the inner ends of the teeth. The Mean Cone Distance is measured to the center of the face width.

Contact Ratio—Ratio of arc of contact to circular pitch in all gearing. See *Number of Teeth in Contact*.

Contact Ratio, Face—Ratio of face advance to circular pitch. (Helical and spiral-bevel gearing.)

Contact Ratio, Total—The ratio of the sum of the arc of action and the face advance to the circular pitch. (Helical and spiral-bevel gearing.)

Crown Backing—The distance parallel to the axis from the crown to a shoulder or hub, in bevel gearing.

Crown Circle—The circle formed by the intersection of face cone and back cone in bevel gearing.

Dedendum — The radial or perpendicular distance between the pitch circle and the bottom of the tooth space, in all gearing.

Diametral Pitch — Ratio of number of teeth to number of inches in pitch diameter. It is the number of teeth per inch of gear diameter of any gear.

Edge Round—A radius on the outer edge of gear teeth of all kinds.

Equivalent Pitch Radius—The radius of the pitch circle in a cross section of gear teeth in any plane except the plane of rotation. The radius of curvature of the pitch surface in a given cross section.

Face Advance—The distance on the pitch circle that a gear tooth travels from the time pitch point contact is made at one end of the tooth until similar contact is made at the other end of the tooth. (Helical and spiral-bevel gearing.)

Face Width—The width of the pitch surface. For herringbone gears this includes both angular surfaces, plus the center groove, if any.

Gear Ratio—The ratio of the number of teeth in mating gears.

Groove Depth—Depth of clearance groove in herringbone gears where teeth are not continuous.

Groove Width—Width of center groove in herringbone gears, if any.

Heel—The large end of a bevel gear tooth.

Hub Diameter—The diameter of the hub of a gear which extends beyond the body, spokes or web.

Hub Extension—The distance a hub extends beyond the face of the gear body.

Interference—Contact between mating teeth at the point not along the line of normal action.

Internal Diameter—The diameter of the circle touching the tops of the teeth of an internal gear.

Large End of Tooth—The outer end of a bevel gear tooth.

Lead—The axial advance of the helix of helical or worm gearing, in one complete revolution.

Length of Worm—The length of the fully threaded portion of a worm.

Line of Action—The portion of the common tangent to the base circles where contact occurs between mating involute surfaces.

Line of Centers—A line connecting the centers of the pitch circles of two meshing gears. Also the common perpendicular of the axes in crossed helical gears and worm gears. When one gear is a rack the line of centers is perpendicular to the pitch line.

Linear Pitch—The distance, parallel to the axis, of corresponding sides of adjacent teeth on a worm. The same as axial pitch.

Module—In metric gearing, the ratio of pitch in millimeters to the number of teeth. Some use the same term for the ratio of the pitch diameter in inches to the number of teeth. Its use is however generally confined to metric gears.

Mounting Distance—The distance parallel to the axis from the cone center to the shoulder or hub against which the bevel gear is mounted.

Normal Chordal Thickness—The chordal thickness in the plane normal to the pitch helix, or the tooth curve at the center of the tooth.

Normal Circular Pitch—The shortest distance on the pitch surface between corresponding pitch line elements of adjacent teeth. The length of the arc along the normal helix between helical teeth or threads in helical and spiral-bevel gears.

Normal Diametral Pitch—The diametral pitch corresponding to the normal circular pitch in helical and spiral-bevel gearing.

Normal Tooth Profile—The outline formed by the intersection of a tooth surface and a plane perpendicular to its pitch line element. (Helical and spiral-bevel gearing.)

Outside Diameter—The diameter at the tops of the teeth.

Pitch—The distance between similar, equally spaced tooth surfaces, in a given direction and along a given line or curve. The single word "pitch" should not be used in specifying whether *axial, circular* or *diametral* pitch is meant.

Pitch Circle—The circle through the pitch point of contact, in all except bevel gearing. In bevel gearing, it is the circle formed by the intersection of the pitch cone and a plane perpendicular to the axis of the gear.

Pitch Cylinder—The cylinder corresponding to the pitch circle.

Pitch Diameter—The diameter of the pitch circle.

Pitch Helix—The helix formed by the intersection of the surface of a helical tooth or thread with the pitch cylinder.

Pitch Line Element—A straight or curved line formed by the intersection of pitch surface and tooth surface, in all gears.

Pitch Plane—The plane which is tangent to both the pitch cylinder of the worm and the pitch cylinder of the gear, in worm gearing.

Pitch Point—The intersection between the axes of the line of centers and the common tangent to the base circles, in all types of involute gearing.

Pitch Surface—The surface of the pitch cylinder or the pitch cone, which rolls with the surface of the mating member.

Root Circle—The circle indicating the root or bottom of gear teeth.

Root Cone—The right circular cone which contains the bottom lands of a bevel gear.

Root Diameter—The diameter of the root circle in all gears.

Small End of Tooth—The end of a bevel gear tooth nearest the center of the mating gear. At the small diameter.

Space Bottom—A line joining the two fillets at the bottom of gear teeth.

Teeth in Contact, Number of—The number of profile contacts in a pair of mating gears. For average number of teeth in contact see *Contact Ratio*.

Teeth, Left-Hand—Teeth which twist to the left or counter-clockwise, when viewed from the end in helical and spiral-bevel gearing.

Teeth, Long and Short Addendum—Teeth having longer addendum on the teeth of one member of mating gears.

Teeth, Matched—Herringbone gears in which the teeth join or intersect if there is no groove between them.

Teeth, Right Hand—Teeth of helical and spiral-bevel gears which twist to the right or clockwise as viewed from the end.

Teeth, Staggered—Herringbone gears in which the teeth would not join if there is no center groove. Narrow faced spur gears are also sometimes mounted so that the teeth do not form a continuous line across the face. This gives a more continuous action, similar to that of helical gears.

Throat Diameter—The outside diameter of a worm gear in its central plane.

Throat Increment—The amount added to the throat diameter of a worm gear to give the maximum diameter of the worm wheel blank.

Toe—The small end of a bevel gear tooth.

Tooth Bearing—The portion of a gear tooth surface which actually contacts its mate.

Tooth Chamfer—The bevel at the end of a tooth to break the sharp edge or corner.

Tooth Fillet—Curved line joining the tooth flank and bottom of tooth space.

Tooth Flank—Surface between pitch line and bottom land, including fillet.

Tooth Surface—Total area of tooth face and flank, in all gearing.

Tooth Top—The outer end of any gear tooth.

Top Land—Surface on top of any gear tooth.

Undercut—The portion of a tooth surface which is inside a radial line passing through an imaginary intersection of the involute curve and the base circle, in any gear. It is done to avoid interference with mating teeth.

Whole Depth—The radial distance between the outside circle and the root circle of any gear.

Working Depth—The greatest depth to which a tooth of one gear extends into the tooth space of the mating gear.

GEAR(S), NOTATION FOR—The notation adopted by the A.G.M.A. in March, 1944, is recommended. This designates the diametral pitch by a capital P and pitch diameter by a capital D. Whenever possible capital letters are used for the gear and small letters for the pinions. See *Gearing Nomenclature*.

GEAR(S), PHENOLIC—Gears made of phenolic laminated materials such as cotton fabric, impregnated with plastics of various kinds. They are somewhat elastic and run with less noise than metallic gears.

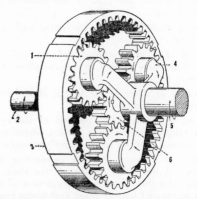

Planetary gears. Driving sun pinion engages three idler (planetary) gears. These three gears are mounted on a spider connected to take-off shaft. Idlers roll on outer gear ring. (1) Idler gear. (2) Drive shaft. (3) Stationary ring gear. (4) Spider. (5) Take-off shaft. (6) Drive pinion.

GEAR, PICK-OFF—A gear that is "picked off" and replaced by another to change the range of feeds or speeds. Many users of high-speed production machines which are kept on one operation for a long run find this much more economical than to have to change gear boxes built into the machine. By changing one gear they secure another range, or series, of feeds or speeds suitable for a new operation. Sometimes referred to as a "slip-gear."

GEAR, PIN—A gear in which the teeth are formed by pins instead of being cut from the solid. The old lantern gear was a good example. The term also applies to gears with short projecting pins in place of regular teeth, as used in some feeding devices.

GEAR(S), PINIONS, ENLARGED, FOR—Pinions are sometimes enlarged to reduce the undercutting of the flanks of the teeth. An oversize blank is selected and teeth are cut to standard depth. This makes the teeth thicker at the pitch diameter than the space between them. To maintain standard center distances the outside of the mating gear must be reduced.

GEAR(ING), PITCH CONE ANGLE—The angle between a line through the axis of a bevel gear and a line through the pitch line of the gear teeth. See *Gears, Bevel.*

GEAR PLANERS—Machines which cut gear teeth with tools having reciprocating action, as in a planer. The term is usually confined to

Types of Bevel Gearing

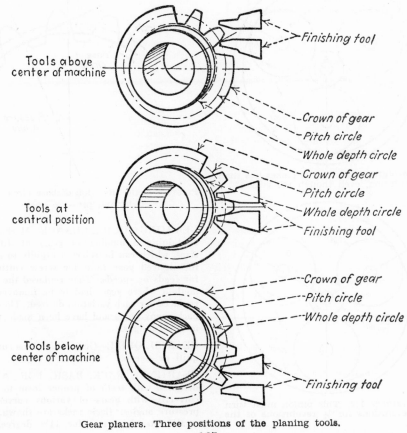

Gear planers. Three positions of the planing tools.

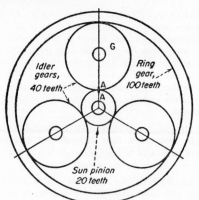

Here's what it looks like at rest. When sun pinion is turned one...

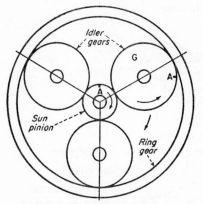

... revolution, the idler G makes less than ½ revolution, even though the gear . . .

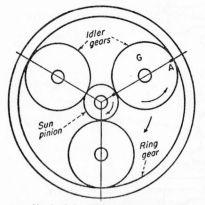

... ratio is 1:2. This pinion must turn 1.2 revolutions for ½ revolutions of the idler.

machines for making bevel gears, as the Bilgram or Gleason. Both generate the tooth form, using a type of planer tool on each side of the tooth being cut, as shown.

GEAR(S), PLANETARY—A combination of gears in which some of them run around a central gear which may be either internal or external. There have been many forms of planetary gearing, the best known being in early automobile transmissions, including the Model T Ford. The stationary gear is known as the "sun" gear. The drawings at left show the action of these gears.

GEAR(S), PRESSURE ANGLE OF—The angle at which teeth of gears in contact press against each other. The diagram shows the relation between the base circle, the pitch circle and the pressure angle.

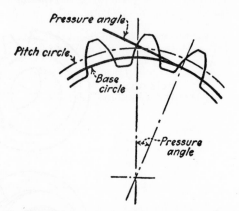

Pressure angle. Relation of base circle, pitch circle, and pressure angle.

GEAR(ING), QUICK CHANGE—Mechanisms containing a number of gears of different sizes, which can be selected rapidly to secure the desired gear ratio for screw cutting or for feeds or speeds. They replaced the older method where gears had to be removed and replaced for each variation desired. They date back many years and have been made in numerous designs.

GEAR(S), QUILL—Gears or pinions cut on a quill or sleeve.

GEAR(ING), RACK, BASIC FOR—A rack designed with teeth of proper form to mesh correctly with gears of various curves and pressure angles. Basic racks are shown. The small cuts show two for 14½ degree, full depth teeth—the other for both 14½ and 20 degree teeth for stub and full depth.

GEAR(S), RAWHIDE—Gears made of layers of rawhide pressed together and usually held by metal flanges. They were made to reduce the noise of metallic gearing. The rawhide was generally used for the smaller gear, or pinion. It was affected by dampness and was not altogether satisfactory, as it swelled to some extent. It also gathered particles of dirt from the air and acted as a lap, wearing the cast iron gears with which it ran. It has largely been replaced by plastics, or cloth impregnated with plastics and known under various trade names.

GEAR(S), ROLLED—Several attempts have been made to make gears by rolling the teeth by having master gears work on hot gear blanks. Probably the most successful attempt was by Anderson of Cleveland, about 1920. Starting with gear blanks of the pitch diameter of the gear, the teeth were formed much as in thread rolling. The flow of the metal made a strong tooth, as with thread rolling. Anderson

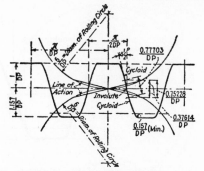

Basic rack for 14½-deg. composite system (full-depth tooth.)

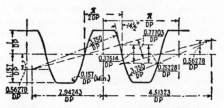

Approximation to basic rack for 14½-deg. composite system (full-depth tooth).

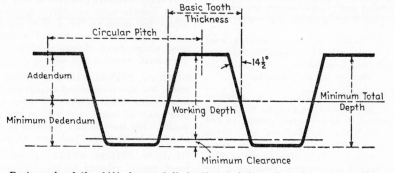

Basic rack of the 14½-degree full depth involute system for spur-gearing.

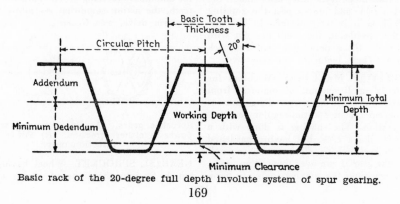

Basic rack of the 20-degree full depth involute system of spur gearing.

169

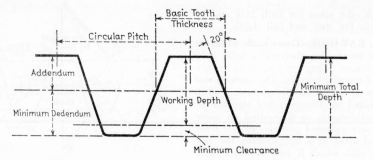

Basic rack of the 20-degree stub involute system for spur gearing.

even rolled herringbone bevel gears. It is probable that the total cost, including the machinery necessary, the dies and their upkeep and other expense, made it unprofitable. A new process has been developed by the Ben Grob Corp., Grayton, Wis., for producing external gears by rolling them in cold steel blanks.

GEAR, SAMPLE—A gear identical with production gears, but which is kept for reference. It is hardened and ground only if the production gears are finished in the same way.

GEAR, SEGMENT—A gear extending over part of a circle only. It is used to secure a limited rotation, being driven by a pinion, or driving a pinion, as the case may be.

GEAR-SHAPING MACHINE — A machine which cuts gear teeth by a planing or shaping motion instead of with a rotary cutter. In two of these machines, the Fellows and Sykes machines, the cutter is practically a hardened gear which reciprocates past the gear blank as they both revolve, generating the tooth form. Sometimes the cutter takes the form of a rack and moves past the rotating gear blank as it is reciprocated. In one machine, the Speed-Cut, the teeth are cut with formed tools, there being one tool for each tool space. These teeth are not generated.

GEAR-SHAVING MACHINES—Machines for removing a small amount of material from teeth after they have been cut. This removes slight inaccuracies left in the regular gear cutting operation. The shaving is done with a tool made like a rack, but having hardened teeth with small cutting edges that shave small chips as the gear is run over them at an angle. In some machines the shaving tools are hard-

ened gears with the same kind of teeth as in the rack just mentioned.

GEAR, SHROUDED—A gear with flanges or raised sides, to prevent end motion by the mating gear or pinion. Sometimes used with rawhide or plastic gears, but not common practice in most industries.

GEAR, SLIP—A gear provided for use in feeding mechanisms to change the rate of feed. It is really a change gear, but is only provided when definite rates of change are desired to adjust the machine for a different class of work. Slip gears are changed by hand and used where quick change mechanism is not warranted. Same as pick-off gear.

GEAR(S), SPIRAL—These are really helical gears, but the term spiral is still used in too many cases. Some confine the term to 45 degree gears of equal size, with shafts at right angles. The term is also retained in the case of spiral bevel gears. See *Gear, Hypoid.*

GEAR(S), SPIRAL BEVEL—A curved tooth bevel gear developed by the Gleason Works for automobile driving gears. With the curved teeth, the action somewhat resembles that of a worm drive. See *Gearing.*

Sprocket gears. (A) Sprocket can transmit power in either direction. (B) Power in one direction only.

GEAR(S), SPROCKET—Wheel having teeth which fit into the links of chains used in transmitting motion and power. Most sprocket gears are made to drive in either direction. Some are made for one direction only. *Silent chain gears* have teeth of special shape to fit the projections on the chains.

GEAR(S), SPUR—Spur gears are primarily those with teeth cut across the outer surface of a disk or gear blank. Since the introduction of gears with helical teeth the term "spur" means a gear with teeth straight across the face. This has also led to use of the term "spur" in connection with internal gears to indicate that the teeth are straight across the face instead of at an angle.

GEAR(S), SPUR, RULE FOR CALCULATING—To find the base circles for spur gears multiply the pitch diameter by the cosine of the pressure angle. The cosines of the pressure angles of 14½ and 20 degrees, in common use are—0.96815 and 0.93969. Example: A 10 pitch gear with 30 teeth and a 14½ degree pressure angle. Dividing 30 by 10 gives 3 in. as pitch diameter. 3×0.96815 gives 2.9044 in. as base circle. See *Gear, Pressure Angle.*

Spur and Helical Ground Master Gear Tolerances

All dimensions in inches

	All Classes		
Hole size within		+0.0002	
(Preferred hole size ¾, 1¼, 1¾)		—0.0000	
Face runout of locating surfaces with respect to hole,			
total indicator reading per in. of diam., not to exceed		0.0001	
Outside diameter size within		±0.0010	
Runout of outside diameter, with respect to hole		0.0010	
	Class		
	1	2	3
Runout (as measured by pin, cone, or ball)			
4 diameter and smaller	0.0005	0.0004	0.0003
4 + to 8 diameter	0.0009	0.0007	0.0005
8 + to 12 diameter	0.0013	0.0010	0.0007
	All Classes		
Gear-tooth measurement over pins		+0.020	
(See footnote 1)		—0.000	
Pitch error (tooth-to-tooth variation, not over pins)			
4 diameter and smaller		0.0002	
4 + to 8 diameter		0.0003	
3 + to 12 diameter		0.0004	
	Spur	Helical	
Profile error (total variation, not plus and minus)			
4 diameter and smaller	0.0002	0.0003	
4 + to 8 diameter	0.00025	0.00035	
8 + to 12 diameter	0.0003	0.0004	
	All Classes		
Circumferential lead error per in. of face			
(or parallelism of spur teeth with axis)		0.0002	

1. Circular tooth thickness at standard pitch diameter to be marked on each master gear.

2. Tolerances of root diameter are purposely omitted because they affect only the clearance at the root of the teeth, and therefore are considered unessential.

3. Material recommended is high-speed steel hardened to a minimum of Rockwell C63.

4. The tolerances suggested in this table are to be considered binding on a manufacturer or seller only when specifically agreed to in writing.

GEAR(ING), STAGGERED TEETH—Teeth which do not form a continuous line across the face of a gear. They are usually made by assembling several thin gears on the same shaft with the teeth offset from each other. The action is more like a helical gear. One helical gear is made by this method, using thin plates for each gear and riveting them into a solid gear. Since the helical gear became common, there are few staggered gears in use. In herringbone gears with a groove in the center, the teeth on one side are sometimes staggered from those on the other.

GEAR STANDARD, SPUR AND HELICAL—This standard is based on use of master gears in variable center distance devices. Fixed center distance fixtures are not recommended, owing to the expense of making the necessary master gears to the extreme accuracy required, both as to runout and size over pins in the teeth. Tolerances for spur and helical ground master gears are shown in the accompanying table.

GEAR(S), STUB TOOTH—Gear teeth shorter than normal. Stub teeth usually have a greater pressure angle than full length teeth. See *Gear Teeth, Fellows;* and *Gear Teeth, Stub.*

GEAR TEETH, BEAM STRENGTH OF—The strength of a gear tooth considered as a beam fixed at the end where it joins the body of the gear.

GEAR TEETH BEARING, SPIRAL BEVEL—The bearing surfaces between gear teeth depend on both the shape of the teeth and the way in which the shafts supporting them are mounted as with all gearing. Both tooth form and method of mounting are important.

GEAR TEETH, BEVEL, PROPORTIONS FOR—For gears at right angles (90 degrees) and of 1 diametral pitch, tooth proportions are shown in the table.

GEAR TEETH, CHORDAL THICKNESS—The thickness of either the gear cutter or the gear tooth at the pitch line, measured *across* the tooth or tooth space in a straight line, instead of on the arc or curve of the circular pitch line. Tables are available for both standard and stub teeth.

GEAR TEETH CUTTERS—Cutters for involute gear teeth have been standardized by the Brown & Sharpe Co. to cut teeth from a rack to a gear with 135 teeth. See *Gear Cutters, Formed.*

GEAR TEETH, CYCLOIDAL CURVE—The Fellows Gear Shaper Co. shows how the cycloidal curve for rack teeth and gear teeth is laid out. Taking a disk with a hole near the edge and holding it against a ruler, the cycloidal curve for a rack is drawn by rolling the disk along the ruler as shown. Drawing the teeth for gears requires two disks of the pitch diameter of the gears that are to run together. The hole should be just at the edge

Bevel Gear Tooth Proportions

Diametral Pitch	Normal Pitch	Helix Angles "A"	Lead of Helix in Inches	Minimum Width of Face "F" in Inches
5/7	5.184	15°-20′	41.270	2¹⁹⁄₆₄
5/7	5.456	23°-35′	25.904	1⅞₆
6/8	6.209	14°-55′	41.270	1³¹⁄₃₂
6/8	6.518	23°	25.904	1¹⁵⁄₆₄
7/9	7.254	15°-12′	41.270	1²¹⁄₃₂
7/9	7.629	23°-25′	25.904	1³⁄₆₄
8/10	8.279	14°-55′	41.270	1³¹⁄₆₄
8/10	8.691	23°	25.904	¹⁵⁄₁₆
9/11	9.324	15°- 9′	41.270	1¹⁹⁄₆₄
9/11	9.801	23°-20′	25.904	¹³⁄₁₆
10/12	10.349	14°-55′	41.270	1³⁄₁₆
10/12	10.863	23°	25.904	¾
12/14	12.418	14°-55′	41.270	⁶³⁄₆₄
12/14	13.036	23°	25.904	⅝

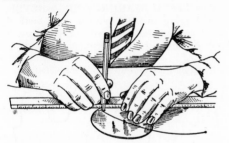

Drawing a cycloidal curve for a rack tooth.

Drawing a cycloidal curve gear tooth.

of the disks. Rolling one disk around the other draws the curve for teeth for gears of the sizes of the disks. It is a curved line generated by a point on a circle rolling away from the gear or rack with which it meshes.

GEAR TEETH DEPTH GAGE—For measuring the depth of gear teeth. It requires a different gage for each pitch of gear tooth.

GEAR TEETH, ELLIPTOID—A gear tooth slightly thicker in the center to prevent bearing at the ends. Devised by the National Broach & Tool Co. Similar to the coniflex tooth in form.

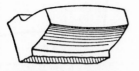

Elliptoid gear tooth form.

GEAR TEETH, FELLOWS STUB TEETH—The Fellows system of stub gear teeth uses a 20 degree pressure angle and a fraction to show how the tooth depth compares with standard gear teeth. The numerator of the fraction shows the number of teeth per inch of diameter, commonly known as the pitch of the gear,

while the denominator shows standard gear having the same tooth depth. A 7/9 Fellows gear has 7 teeth per inch of diameter but the tooth depth is the same as a 9 pitch gear of standard tooth length. The lesser tooth depth, or length, gives a stronger tooth and is very largely used.

GEAR TEETH, FORMATE—A development of the hypoid, where the relative rolling action of both work and cutter generates the correct

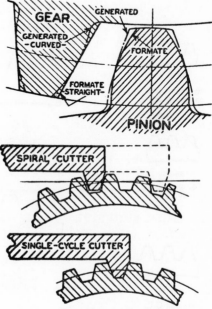

Formate gear teeth.

tooth form. With the formate tooth, however, the work does not roll and only the cutter is in motion.

GEAR TEETH, GENERATED—Generated gear teeth are cut by tools which represent mating gears, in machines which move both the gear blank and the cutter in the same way

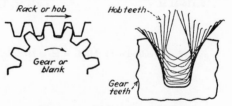

How gear teeth are generated.

Actual Gear-Teeth Sizes

20 P.

0.1571 C.P.
1.270 M.M.

10 P.

0.3142 C.P.
2.540 M.M.

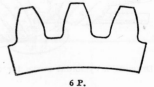

6 P.

0.5236 C.P.
4.233 M.M.

18 P.

0.1745 C.P.
1.411 M.M.

9 P.

0.3491 C.P.
2.822 M.M.

16 P.

0.1963 C.P.
1.587 M.M.

5 P.

0.6283 C.P.
5.080 M.M.

14 P.

0.2244 C.P.
1.814 M.M.

8 P.

0.3927 C.P.
3.175 M.M.

12 P.

0.2618 C.P.
2.116 M.M.

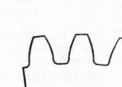

7 P.

0.4488 C.P.
3.628 M.M.

4 P.

0.7854 C.P.
6.350 M.M.

C.P. = Circular Pitch.   M.M. = m/m Module.

Gear-Teeth Parts

20° Stub Pitches and Modules   Fellows Gear Shaper Company Standards

20° Stub Tooth English (DP)	20° Stub Tooth Module (M)	Circular Thickness (C Th)	Addendum (A)	Dedendum (D)	Whole Depth of Tooth (WD)	Double Depth of Tooth (DD)
3/4		.5236	.2500	.3125	.5625	1.1250
	8/6	.4947	.2362	.2952	.5314	1.0628
	7½/5¾	.4638	.2264	.2830	.5094	1.0188
	7¼/5¾	.4484	.2264	.2830	.5094	1.0188
	7/5¼	.4329	.2067	.2584	.4651	.9302
	6¾/5¼	.4174	.2067	.2584	.4651	.9302
	6½/5	.4019	.1969	.2461	.4430	.8860
4/5		.3927	.2000	.2500	.4500	.9000
	6¼/4¾	.3865	.1870	.2338	.4208	.8416
	6/4½	.3710	.1772	.2215	.3987	.7974
	5¾/4½	.3556	.1772	.2215	.3987	.7974
	5½/4	.3401	.1575	.1969	.3544	.7088
	5¼/4	.3247	.1575	.1969	.3544	.7088
5/7		.3142	.1429	.1786	.3215	.6430
	5/3¾	.3092	.1476	.1845	.3321	.6642
	4¾/3½	.2938	.1378	.1722	.3100	.6200
	4½/3¼	.2783	.1279	.1599	.2878	.5756
	4¼/3¼	.2628	.1279	.1599	.2878	.5756
6/8		.2618	.1250	.1563	.2813	.5626
	4/3	.2473	.1181	.1476	.2657	.5314
	3¾/2¾	.2319	.1082	.1352	.2434	.4868
7/9		.2244	.1111	.1389	.2500	.5000
	3½/2½	.2164	.0984	.1230	.2214	.4428
	3¼/2½	.2010	.0984	.1230	.2214	.4428
8/10		.1964	.1000	.1250	.2250	.4500
	3/2¼	.1855	.0885	.1106	.1991	.3982
9/11		.1745	.0909	.1137	.2046	.4092
	2¾/2	.1700	.0787	.0984	.1771	.3542
10/12		.1571	.0833	.1042	.1875	.3750
	2½/2	.1546	.0787	.0984	.1771	.3542
11/14		.1428	.0714	.0893	.1607	.3214
	2¼/1¾	.1391	.0689	.0861	.1550	.3100
12/14		.1309	.0714	.0893	.1607	.3214
	2/1¾	.1236	.0689	.0861	.1550	.3100
13/16		.1208	.0625	.0781	.1406	.2812
14/18		.1122	.0556	.0694	.1250	.2500
	1¾/1½	.1082	.0591	.0738	.1329	.2658
16/21		.0982	.0476	.0591	.1068	.2136
	1½/1¼	.0927	.0492	.0611	.1103	.2206
18/24		.0873	.0417	.0520	.0937	.1874
20/26		.0785	.0385	.0482	.0866	.1737
	1¼/1	.0773	.0394	.0492	.0886	.1772
22/29		.0714	.0345	.0434	.0779	.1558
24/32		.0655	.0313	.0395	.0708	.1416
	1/¾	.0618	.0295	.0374	.0670	.1340
26/35		.0604	.0286	.0363	.0649	.1298
28/37		.0561	.0270	.0344	.0615	.1230
30/40		.0524	.0250	.0320	.0570	.1140
32/42		.0491	.0238	.0306	.0544	.1088
	¾/½	.0464	.0197	.0256	.0453	.0906
34/45		.0462	.0222	.0287	.0509	.1018
36/48		.0436	.0208	.0270	.0478	.0956
38/50		.0413	.0200	.0260	.0460	.0920
40/54		.0393	.0185	.0242	.0427	.0854

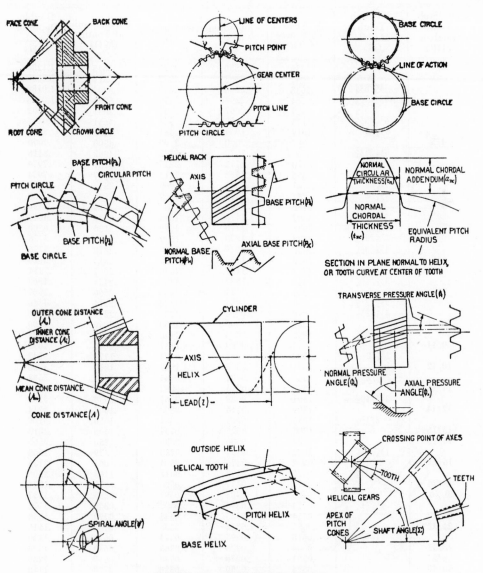

NAMES OF GEAR TEETH PARTS.

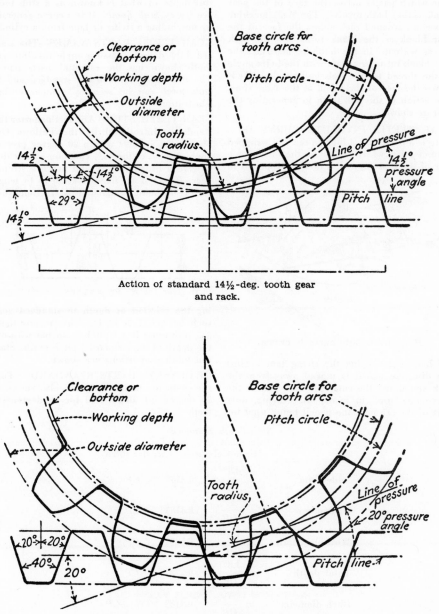

Action of standard 14½-deg. tooth gear
and rack.

Action of 20-deg. stub-tooth gear and rack.

as mating gears. In the Fellows and Sykes machines the cutter represents a hardened gear which passes across the face of the gear blank as they both revolve. The Maag machine moves a hardened rack across the face of the gear blank as the blank turns and the rack moves with it. In the hobbing machine, the gear blank turns in unison with the helix angle of the thread on the hob and the hob feeds across the face of the blank at the same time. The action of the hob teeth in generating the gear is shown.

GEAR TEETH, INVOLUTE CURVE OF—Here is a cord with a loop in the end wrapped around a disk which should be the pitch diameter of the gear wanted. Placing the pencil in

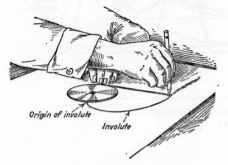

Origin of involute

Involute

How an involute curve is drawn.

the loop and keeping the string taut against the disk, the pencil is moved away from the disk and draws the curve shown. This is the curve now used in nearly all gearing, only part of the arc near the pencil being used for the gear tooth. The amount of this curve used depends on whether the gear tooth is to be full depth or what is known as a stub tooth. See *Gears, Stub Tooth*. It is a curve generated by unwinding a string or tape from a cylinder.

GEAR TEETH, PARTS NAMES—The standard 14½ degree pressure angle involute gear tooth shown has the essential parts named. The difference between the standard and the stub tooth can be seen by comparing both illustrations.

GEAR TEETH, STUB—Any teeth shorter than standard. Introduced by the Fellows Gear Shaper Co. in 1899 with a 20 degree pressure angle instead of the 14½ common at that time, to give a broader flank and make a stronger gear. There is no fixed relation as to length, stub teeth being designated by fractions show-

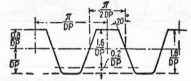

Stub gear teeth. Proportions for stub gears.

ing the relation of depth to standard gears, such as 4/5, 7/9, 12/14. This means that a 4/5 stub tooth is a 4 pitch tooth but with only the depth of the standard 5 pitch tooth. Standard tooth proportions are shown.

GEAR TEETH PARTS, STANDARDS—Tooth shown in the table. They are also shown for 20 degree full depth and for 20 degree stub teeth.

Stub-Tooth Standards

	Diametral Pitch	Circular Pitch
Addendum	$= \dfrac{0.8''}{DP}$	$0.2546'' \times CP$
Dedendum	$= \dfrac{1''}{DP}$	$0.3183'' \times CP$
Working depth	$= \dfrac{1.6''}{DP}$	$0.5092'' \times CP$
Total depth	$= \dfrac{1.8''}{DP}$	$0.5729'' \times CP$
Pitch diameter	$= \dfrac{N}{DP}$	$0.3183 \times N \times CP$
Outside diameter	$= \dfrac{N + 1.6''}{DP}$	$PD + (2 \times \text{addenda})$

Gear-Teeth Parts*

14½-deg. and 20-deg. Involute Full-length Tooth Form

Diametral pitch	Dimensions, in.				
	Circular thickness	Addendum	Dedendum plus clearance	Whole depth of tooth	Double depth of tooth
6	0.2618	0.1667	0.2083	0.3750	0.7500
7	0.2244	0.1429	0.1786	0.3215	0.6430
8	0.1964	0.1250	0.1563	0.2813	0.5626
9	0.1745	0.1111	0.1389	0.2500	0.5000
10	0.1571	0.1000	0.1250	0.2250	0.4500
11	0.1428	0.0909	0.1136	0.2045	0.4090
12	0.1309	0.0833	0.1042	0.1875	0.3750
14	0.1122	0.0714	0.0893	0.1607	0.3214
16	0.0982	0.0625	0.0781	0.1406	0.2812
18	0.0873	0.0556	0.0705	0.1261	0.2522
20	0.0785	0.0500	0.0650	0.1150	0.2300
22	0.0714	0.0455	0.0604	0.1059	0.2118
24	0.0654	0.0417	0.0566	0.0983	0.1966
26	0.0604	0.0386	0.0533	0.0919	0.1838
28	0.0561	0.0357	0.0507	0.0864	0.1728
30	0.0524	0.0333	0.0483	0.0816	0.1632
32	0.0491	0.0313	0.0462	0.0775	0.1550
34	0.0462	0.0294	0.0394	0.0688	0.1376
36	0.0436	0.0278	0.0377	0.0655	0.1310
38	0.0413	0.0263	0.0363	0.0626	0.1252
40	0.0393	0.0250	0.0350	0.0600	0.1200

Fellows Gear Shaper Company Standard.

*Note that this tables gives circular tooth thickness instead of circular pitch.

GEAR TEETH PARTS, STUB TOOTH— Fellows stub-tooth standards are shown in the table, page 180.

GEAR TEETH SPUR, PROPORTIONS—See next page.

GEAR TEETH WEAR—The American Gear Manufacturers Association Standard 111.01, dated March, 1944, designates gear tooth wear as follows:

Abrasion—A general wearing away of the tooth surface at a rapid rate. It usually results from the presence of foreign matter such as dirt, grit, or metallic particles.

Burning—Discoloration of the tooth surface caused by high temperatures. May be caused by overspeed, overload, or poor lubrication.

Chipping—The breaking off of small particles from the tooth edge or face. Usually indicates excessive hardness. Sometimes called "spalling."

Cracking or checking—Occurrence of single or scattered cracks in the tooth surface, which may not result in failure. When numerous small cracks occur it is called "checking." May be caused by excessive hardness.

Fatigue and breakage—This is tooth breakage resulting from repeated overloading. It usually begins with the formation of cracks at highly stressed points.

179

Gear-Tooth Parts*

20-deg. Pressure Angle, Stub-tooth Form

Diametral pitch	Dimensions, in.				
	Circular thickness	Addendum	Dedendum plus clearance	Whole depth of tooth	Double depth of tooth
6/8	0.2618	0.1250	0.1563	0.2813	0.5626
7/9	0.2244	0.1111	0.1389	0.2500	0.5000
8/10	0.1964	0.1000	0.1250	0.2250	0.4500
9/11	0.1745	0.0909	0.1136	0.2045	0.4090
10/12	0.1571	0.0833	0.1042	0.1875	0.3750
11/14	0.1428	0.0714	0.0893	0.1607	0.3214
12/14	0.1309	0.0714	0.0893	0.1607	0.3214
14/18	0.1122	0.0556	0.0705	0.1261	0.2522
16/21	0.0982	0.0476	0.0626	0.1102	0.2204
18/24	0.0873	0.0417	0.0566	0.0983	0.1966
20/26	0.0785	0.0386	0.0533	0.0919	0.1838
22/29	0.0714	0.0345	0.0494	0.0839	0.1678
24/32	0.0654	0.0313	0.0462	0.0775	0.1550
26/35	0.0604	0.0286	0.0435	0.0671	0.1342
28/37	0.0561	0.0270	0.0420	0.0641	0.1282
30/40	0.0524	0.0250	0.0350	0.0600	0.1200
32/42	0.0491	0.0238	0.0338	0.0576	0.1152
34/45	0.0462	0.0222	0.0322	0.0544	0.1088
36/48	0.0436	0.0208	0.0309	0.0517	0.1034
38/50	0.0413	0.0200	0.0300	0.0500	0.1000
40/54	0.0393	0.0185	0.0285	0.0470	0.0940

Fellows Gear Shaper Company Standard.

*Note that this table gives circular tooth thickness instead of circular pitch.

Designation of diametral pitch on stub teeth shows the relation of pitch to depth as compared with standard length teeth. A 6/8 pitch, for example, indicates 6 diametral pitch but that the tooth only has the depth of an 8-pitch tooth of standard length.

Galling—An aggravated condition of scoring. May be caused by small particles of metal being torn from the teeth. It is sometimes referred to as "seizing" or "welding."

Gouging—Occurs in soft or unhardened gears when there is interference between the flank of the driving pinion and the tip of the driven gear.

Initial pitting—The formation of small *pits* in the tooth surface, usually starting at the pitch line and occurring during the initial period of operation. If they occur gradually and do not increase rapidly they may disappear with normal wear.

Normal wear—A gradual smoothing and polishing of the working surfaces from the sliding and rolling action of the teeth.

Overloading and breakage—Although similar to fatigue and breakage it is usually caused by a sudden shock from an overload. This may be caused by the jamming of some parts of the machine on which the gear is mounted.

Progressive pitting—When the pits continue

Full Depth Tooth Proportions for Spur Gears

	Diametral Pitch[1] In Terms of (Inches)	In Terms of Circular Pitch[1] (Inches)
1. Addendum	$= \dfrac{1}{DP}$	$0.3183 \times CP$
2. Minimum Dedendum[2]	$= \dfrac{1.157}{DP}$	$0.3683 \times CP$
3. Working Depth	$= \dfrac{2}{DP}$	$0.6366 \times CP$
4. Minimum Total Depth[2]	$= \dfrac{2.157}{DP}$	$0.6866 \times CP$
5. Pitch Diameter	$= \dfrac{N}{DP}$	$0.3183 \times N \times CP$
6. Outside Diameter	$= \dfrac{N+2}{DP}$	$0.3183 \times (N+2) \times CP$
7. Basic Tooth Thickness on Pitch Line	$= \dfrac{1.5708}{DP}$	$0.5 \times CP$
8. Minimum Clearance[2,3]	$= \dfrac{0.157}{DP}$	$0.05 \times CP$
9. Radius of Fillet	$= 1\frac{1}{2} \times$ Clearance	

N = Number of Teeth.   DP = Diametral Pitch.   CP = Circular Pitch.

[1] NOTE: The term Diametral Pitch is used up to 1 DP inclusive and the term Circular Pitch is used for 3 inches CP and over.

[2] NOTE: A suitable working tolerance should be considered in connection with all minimum recommendations.

[3] NOTE: Minimum clearance refers to the clearance between the top of the gear tooth and the bottom of the mating gear space, and is specified as "minimum" so as to allow for necessary cutter clearance for all methods of producing gears. At the present time this value cannot be standardized.

Stub Tooth Proportions for Spur Gears[4]

		In Terms of Diametral Pitch[1] (Inches)	In Terms of Circular Pitch[1] (Inches)
1.	Addendum	$= \dfrac{0.8}{DP}$	$0.2546 \times CP$
2.	Minimum Dedendum[2]	$= \dfrac{1}{DP}$	$0.3183 \times CP$
3.	Working Depth	$= \dfrac{1.6}{DP}$	$0.5092 \times CP$
4.	Minimum Total Depth[4]	$= \dfrac{1.8}{DP}$	$0.5729 \times CP$
5.	Pitch Diameter	$= \dfrac{N}{DP}$	$0.3183 \times N \times CP$
6.	Outside Diameter	$= \dfrac{N + 1.6}{DP}$	$PD + (2 \text{ Addendums})$
7.	Basic Tooth Thickness on Pitch Line	$= \dfrac{1.5708}{DP}$	$0.5 \times CP$
8.	Minimum Clearance [2,3]	$= \dfrac{0.2}{DP}$	$0.0637 \times CP$

N = Number of Teeth.   DP = Diametral Pitch.   PD = Pitch Diameter.   CP = Circular Pitch.

[1] NOTE: The term Diametral Pitch is used up to 1 DP inclusive and the term Circular Pitch is used for 3 inches CP and over.

[2] NOTE: A suitable working tolerance should be considered in connection with all minimum recommendations.

[3] NOTE: A minimum root clearance of 0.2 inch/Diametral Pitch is recommended for new cutters and gears. There is correct tooth action, however, between gears cut to this standard system and those cut to the Nuttall system, the only dimension affected being the clearance. Where the proposed gear tooth meshes with a Nuttall gear space there is a clearance of 0.1425 inch/Diametral Pitch, and where the Nuttall tooth runs with the proposed gear space there is a clearance of 0.2146 inch/Diametral Pitch.

[4] NOTE: These proportions are identical with those of the A. G. M. A. recommended practice for Herringbone Gears.

---

to increase both in number and in size so that the unpitted areas cannot carry the load.

Rolling or peening—This refers to a plastic flow of the tooth surface to form fins at the tooth ends. Metal is probably too soft for the load it is to carry.

Scoring—This usually results from excessive loading or poor lubrication, or both.

Scratching—Similar to abrasion except that the marks are deeper and more widely separated. It is caused by coarse particles being carried between the teeth.

GEAR TRAIN—Two or more gears operating together to transfer motion from one shaft to another constitute a gear train. The speeds of the different shafts depend on the number of teeth in each gear.

GEAR(S), TUMBLER—Gears held on a "tumbler plate" so that either gear can engage a main gear and so reverse the motion of the driven gear at will. These were formerly common on engine lathes, but are now replaced with the quick change gearing of modern engine lathes.

Gear-Wire Sizes

P	Wire diameter for enlarged pinions, in. $G = \dfrac{1.92 \text{ in.}}{P}$	Wire diameter for external gears, in. $G = \dfrac{1.728 \text{ in.}}{P}$	Wire diameter for internal gears, in. $G = \dfrac{1.44 \text{ in.}}{P}$	Alternate series, in. $G = \dfrac{168 \text{ in.}}{P}$
2	0.960	0.864	0.720	0.840
2½	0.768	0.6912	0.576	0.672
3	0.640	0.576	0.480	0.560
4	0.480	0.432	0.360	0.420
5	0.384	0.3456	0.288	0.336
6	0.320	0.288	0.240	0.280
7	0.27428	0.24686	0.20571	0.240
8	0.240	0.216	0.180	0.210
9	0.21333	0.192	0.160	0.18666
10	0.192	0.1728	0.144	0.168
11	0.17454	0.15709	0.13091	0.15273
12	0.160	0.144	0.120	0.140
14	0.13714	0.12343	0.10286	0.120
16	0.120	0.108	0.090	0.105
18	0.10667	0.096	0.080	0.09333
20	0.096	0.0864	0.072	0.084
22	0.08727	0.07855	0.06545	0.07636
24	0.080	0.072	0.060	0.070
28	0.06857	0.06171	0.05143	0.060
32	0.060	0.054	0.045	0.0525
36	0.05333	0.048	0.040	0.04667
40	0.048	0.0432	0.036	0.042
48	0.040	0.036	0.030	0.035
64	0.030	0.027	0.0225	0.02625
72	0.02667	0.024	0.020	0.02333
80	0.024	0.0216	0.018	0.021
100	0.0192	0.01728	0.0144	0.0168
120	0.0160	0.0144	0.012	0.014
128	0.0150	0.0135	0.01125	0.01312
200	0.0096	0.00864	0.0072	0.0084

NOTE: The Fellows stub tooth is expressed as a fractional P, such as 7/9. The numerator (7) represents the P which is used for figuring the circular pitch and the pitch diameter and the denominator (9) the P that is used to figure the addendum and the dedendum. A 7 P gear wire should therefore be used for a 7/9 P Fellows gear.

Van Keuren gear-measuring wires are 1⅛ in. long and are held within 25 millionths of an inch for roundness and exact size.

They are standardized at 1 lb. pressure between flat measuring contacts.

GEAR WIRE SIZES—Wires to be used in measuring pitch diameters of gears.

GEAR(S), WORM—Worm gears or wheels can be cut with either a single cutter or a hob, the latter being the better. Frequently a single cutter is used to rough out, or *gash* the teeth, which are then finished by a hob. In some cases the hob is tapered on the end and fed tangentially, beginning with the tapered end, until it is at full depth. In other cases the hob is straight and is fed radially into the wheel until it reaches the proper depth.

GEAR(S), WORM AND WORM GEAR STANDARDS — Master *worms* are usually

Gear Wire Systems

From the wide acceptance and use of the Van Keuren 1.728″/P gear wire system, other **systems** for special requirements have come into use. These system are as follows:

	System	Relation	Use
(1)	$\dfrac{1.92''}{P}$		(a) Enlarged pinions. Wires project above outside diameter. (b) Specified for ASA-B5.5—1946—30° external splines. Wires require no flats. (c) Specified in a new SAE standard for 45° involute external and internal serrations.
(2)	$\dfrac{1.728''}{P}$	$\dfrac{(1.92'' - 10\%)}{P}$	(a) External spur and helical gears. Wires project well above outside diameter. Adopted by AGMA for fine pitch gears. (b) Alternate size for ASA-B5.15 — 1946 — 30° internal splines above 18 teeth. Wires require no flats.
(3)	$\dfrac{1.68''}{P}$	$\dfrac{(1.92'' - 12\frac{1}{2}\%)}{P}$	(a) Suitable for 20° internal gears above 20 teeth and 30° internal gears above 8 teeth. Wires project below inside diameter. (b) Alternate size for ASA-B5.15—1946—30° involute internal splines from 8 to 18 teeth. Wires require no flats.
(4)	$\dfrac{1.44''}{P}$	$\dfrac{(1.92'' - 25\%)}{P}$	(a) Recommended for the most accurate measurement of $14\frac{1}{2}°-17\frac{1}{2}°-20°-25°$ and 30° internal gears. Wires make the best contact on the internal involute gear tooth but do not project below the inside diameter. (b) Wires flatted to .8 x dia. are specified for measuring ASA-B5.15—1946—30° involute internal splines from 6 teeth up.

hardened and ground. Tooth thickness is easily controlled. Sample worms are made to match gears produced by particular hobs with respect to tooth profile and lead. Master *worm gears* are not hardened and ground.

Often the first worm and gear set from a lot is properly matched and retained as a sample set.

GEAR(S), WORM, DIMENSION OF—Dimensions of a worm wheel depend on various ele-

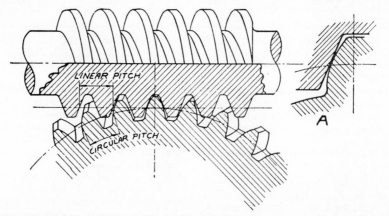

Conventional worm gear of the single enveloping type. Provides theoretical line contact, with point contact in section. Actually, under load there is of course some area contact.

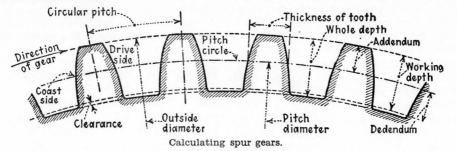

Calculating spur gears.

ments indicated herewith. Rules for making calculations follow. Terms used are shown in the illustration.

P = circular pitch of wheel and linear pitch of worm.
l = lead of worm.
n = number of threads in worm.
S = addendum.
d = pitch diameter of worm.
D = pitch diameter of worm wheel.
o = outside diameter of worm.
O = throat diameter of worm wheel.
O' = diameter of worm wheel over sharp corners.
b = bottom diameter of worm.
N = number of teeth in worm wheel.
W = whole depth of worm tooth.
T = width of thread tool at end.
B = helix of thread tooth at end.
$-B$ = helix angle of worm.
U = radius of curvature of worm-wheel throat.
C = center distance.

Zerol bevel gear.

Dimensions of worm gear. C = center distance between gear and worm. D = outside diameter of gear. A = outside angle of worm gear teeth. b = bottom diameter of worm thread. d = pitch diameter of worm. O = outside diameter of worm.

GEAR(S), ZEROL BEVEL—Gears with curved teeth but with zero-degree curve. They make a more continuous drive than bevel gears with straight teeth and in some ways resemble spiral bevel gears.

GEAR(ING)—Gearing embraces all kinds of toothed wheels for securing positive motion between revolving parts in all kinds of machinery, from watches to rolling mills and steamship turbines.

Twelve types are shown, on page 149.

GENERATORS—Machines which produce electric current by revolving wires in a magnetic field. They are divided into two classes, direct and alternating current generators. In the first, impulses caused by passing both the north and south poles are separated, or

"commuted," by a commutator and give what is called direct current. In alternating generators, current is taken off by collector rings and reverses its direction, usually 60 times per second in this country. Direct current generators were formerly called dynamos.

GENEVA MOTION—A device largely used in watches and in some other cases, to give a positive, but intermittent, motion to the driven wheel, at the same time preventing movement

Geneva motion.

of the driven wheel without the driver. As shown, the driver has but one tooth, which is usual, but it could have more if the operation required it.

GERMAN SILVER—A white alloy of copper, nickel and zinc. The term is now prohibited in marketable products, as the alloy contains no silver.

GERMANIUM—A by-product of cadmium-zinc recovery. Has a non-metallic crystal structure similar to the diamond, but resembles a metal. A semi-conductor useful in electronic fields. Alloyed with gold or silver it gives a very fine grained structure suggesting use in jewelry or dentistry.

GIB—A comparatively thin strip of metal which forms one mating surface between two parts of any mechanism. The inner side of the gib and of the part it contacts are tapered slightly, so that moving the gib affects the fit between the pieces in contact. Gibs are generally used to control the fit between a sliding and a stationary part of a machine. Adjustment is made by moving the gib endwise, on the tapered surface.

GIBBET—The arm of a crane or derrick which supports the load, aided, of course, by the brace which runs from this to the base of the upright. In some localities it may be used in the same way as "shears," or the supporting legs of builders and similar hoisting apparatus.

GIMBAL—A device, which probably originated in seafaring circles, by which an object, as a lamp, can remain vertical regardless of the rolling or pitching of a vessel. The lamp is supported in a ring from two opposite points, this ring being supported in turn at two other points, at right angles to the first supports. It is sometimes called a gimbal joint.

GIN—A local name for a windlass type of mechanism used for moving heavy weights. The best known gin is for removing seeds from cotton bolls.

GLAND—A bushing or sleeve which surrounds a stem or shaft, as with a globe or gate valve. It fits into a stuffing box, holding the valve stem packing in place, usually by means of a nut.

GLASS—A transparent substance made by fusing silica with a basic oxide, such as soda ash.

GLAZE—In shop language, a surface in which the pores of the metal have been filled or otherwise closed. A glazed bearing runs with little friction as long as the surfaces are separated by a lubricant. Should the surfaces run dry, they may become abraded, or "galled," and severely damaged.

GLOBE VALVE—See *Valve, Globe.*

GLORY HOLE—A hole in the door wall of a furnace through which the furnace man can inspect the contents.

GOLD LEAF—Very thin sheets of gold used in gilding picture frames and even such large surfaces as the domes of some churches. Gold, being a very malleable metal, can be beaten into sheets only a few thousandths of an inch in thickness. Thin gold sheets are placed between leaves of what is called "gold beaters' skin"—a sort of parchment, and beaten by hand until the sheets become unbelievably thin.

GOOSENECK — Anything shaped or arched like the neck of a goose or swan. The term is used in connection with pipe bends, and also tools for lathes, planers, or shapers. As a tool, its object is to permit the cutting point of the tool to spring back if it meets a hard spot in the metal. Its use is comparatively limited under present shop conditions, with the greatly increased power of machines and the use of carbide tools.

GOOSENECK TOOL—A tool with the cutting edge at the end of a curved neck to allow a slight spring. Sometimes used to bring the

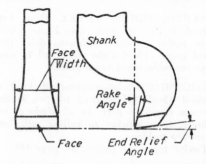

A gooseneck end-cut finishing tool of tool steel, for planing cast iron.

cutting edge in line with, or below, the bottom of the tool shank. Also called a "spring tool" in some localities.

GOVERNOR — Any device for regulating speed or other important functions of a machine.

GRAB HOOK — A hook for grabbing or clutching pieces to be raised or moved by cranes or other power handling devices. See *Sling*.

GRAIN FLOW — See *Forgings, Grain Flow*.

GRAIN STRUCTURE — The tough, fibrous grain structure found in metals which is formed by forging or compressing the metal in the forging process.

GRANULATED BONE — Bone that has been crushed to sizes used in carbonizing or case-hardening. Rogers & Hubbard make several sizes from $\frac{1}{4}$ inch to $\frac{1}{2}$ inch in diameter. The smaller the work to be carbonized the finer the bone used. When packed around parts of low carbon steel and heated sufficiently, carbon from the bone enters the steel and makes it possible to harden the outer surface.

GRAPHIC CHARTS — Charts or diagrams which give information without use of tables. The chart shown is by Kearney & Trecker for machine performance. Select the desired cutting speed and find the number nearest to it in the diagonal column. Suppose 50 feet is desired and 47 is the number nearest to it. If

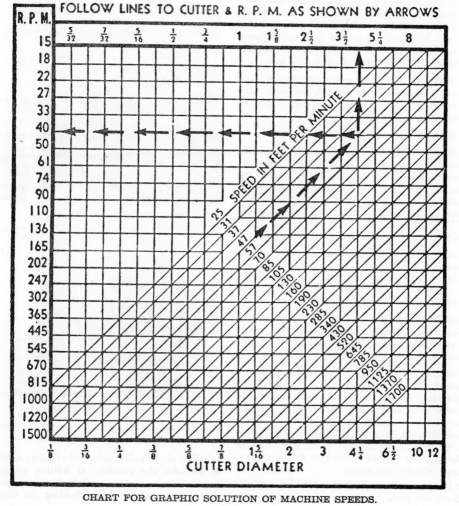

CHART FOR GRAPHIC SOLUTION OF MACHINE SPEEDS.

187

GRINDING MACHINES.

Bryant internal grinder.

the cutter diameter is 4½ inches, follow diagonal line to this number (shown both top and bottom of the chart); then look to the left, to the column showing R.P.M.'s for a cutter of this size to give 47 feet per minute cutting speed. For smaller cutters, follow the diagonal lines down to the left. For a ⅞ in cutter, for example, the spindle speed should be 202 R.P.M.

GRAPHITE—A natural variety of carbon. Also called plumbago and black lead.

GRAPHITE METALS—Bearing metals, such as babbitt or bronze, in which graphite has been incorporated to assist in lubrication.

GRASSHOPPER—The use of beams and other mechanims to transmit power, such as the old type steam engines with walking or working beams by which the pistons transmitted power from the cylinders to the crank. Many old steamboat engines were built in this way.

GRAZING IRON—In making lead pipe joints it is good practice to smooth the joint. The tool used is called a grazing iron, which resembles a soldering iron.

GREASE GUN—See *Gun, Grease.*

GREEN SAND—Any fine sand used in making molds for metals. Its color is not particularly important. If the mold is baked before the metal is poured into it, it is called a dry sand mold.

GRIDIRON VALVE—See *Valve, Gridiron.*

GRINDER—See also *Grinding Wheels.*

GRINDER, CENTERLESS—A grinding machine in which round work is supported from the outside instead of on centers. First used on outside of cylindrical work, the Heald machine handles internal work.

GRINDER, DISK—A grinding machine having a steel disk covered with abrasive cloth. Some disks have spiral grooves to act as cushions under the abrasive cloth.

GRINDER, SWING—A grinding machine in which the wheel is mounted in a frame which permits it to swing both horizontally and vertically. This permits it to follow either straight or irregular outlines under guidance of the operator. It is used for rough grinding or dry snagging in foundry work and on large forgings. It may be either belt driven or powered with its own motor.

GRINDER, TOOL AND CUTTER — While there are plain bench grinding machines for

Heald centerless internal grinder.

Cincinnati centerless grinder.

grinding single point tools, tool grinding usually includes the grinding of milling cutters, reamers and other general tools. These machines have provisions for holding the work

Cincinnati heavy duty roll grinder.

to be ground so as to secure the desired angles, the helix on helical cutters, and other useful features. There are also special tool grinders for taps, drills, hobs and other tools.

GRINDING—A method of removing metal or other material by abrasion, either by abrasive disks or belts. The type of grinding machines are: belt, centerless, cylindrical, disk, internal, form, surface, swing, and tool. While all grinding is really surface work, the term refers to flat surfaces. See *each type for details.*

Grinding Terms

Abrasive—A substance used for abrading—grinding, polishing, lapping—such as the natural materials, corundum, emery, diamond, etc., and the manufactured or artificial materials, aluminum oxide (Al_2O_3), silicon carbide (SiC) and boron carbide (B_4C).

Alumina—Unfused aluminum oxide.

Aluminum Oxide—An abrasive made by fusing the mineral bauxite (Al^2O^3).

Alundum — Norton Co.'s registered trademark for fused alumina, an abrasive made by melting the mineral bauxite in an electric furnace.

Arbor—The spindle of the grinding machine on which the wheel is mounted.

Arbor Hole—The hole in a grinding wheel sized to fit the machine arbor.

Area of Contact—The total area of the circumference of a grinding wheel touching the work being ground.

Arc of Contact — The total arc of the grinding surface of a grinding wheel in contact with the work being ground.

Arkansas Oilstones—A natural stone quarried in the Ozark Mountains and a producer of the finest cutting edges.

Artificial Abrasive—One that is manufactured; not a natural mineral.

Balance (dynamic)—A piece in static balance is in dynamic balance, if, upon rotating, there is no vibration nor "whip" action due to unequal distribution of its weight throughout its length.

Balance (static)—A grinding wheel is in static balance when, centered on a frictionless horizontal arbor, it remains at rest in any position.

Balancing—Testing for balance, adding or subtracting weight to put a piece into either static or dynamic balance.

Bauxite—A mineral ore high in aluminum oxide content, from which Alundum abrasive is manufactured.

Bearing—Point of support. The part of a machine in which the spindle revolves.

Bench Stand—An off-hand grinding machine, mounting either one or two wheels mounted on a horizontal spindle, attached to a bench.

Blotter—A disc of compressible material usually of blotting paper stock, used between a wheel and flanges when mounting.

Bond—The material in a grinding wheel which holds the abrasive grain together.

Boron Carbide (B_4C)—The Norton Co. registered trade-mark Norbide. See *Norbide.*

Brick—A block of bonded abrasive used for such purpose as rubbing down castings, scouring castings, general foundry and machine shop use, scouring chilled iron rolls, polishing marble, and work of like nature.

Burning (the work)—A change in the work being ground caused by the heat of grinding, usually accompanied by a surface discoloration.

Burr—A turned over edge of metal resulting from punching a sheet and sometimes from grinding or cutting off operations.

Burring—Act of removing burrs from metal.

Bushing—The material, usually lead or babbitt, which sometimes serves as a lining for the hole in a grinding wheel.

Center Hole Lapping—The cleaning or lapping of center holes with a bonded abrasive wheel cemented onto a steel spindle.

Centerless Grinding—Grinding the outside or inside diameter of a round piece not mounted on centers.

Centers—Conical steel pins of a grinding machine upon which the work is centered and rotated during grinding.

Ceramics—Science and art of clay working and various related industries. The use of vitrified bonds brings abrasive wheel manufacture under this classification.

Chatter Marks—Surface imperfections on the work being ground, usually caused by vibrations between the wheel and the work.

Chuck—A device for holding grinding wheels of special shape or the work piece being ground.

Coated Abrasives—Paper or cloth having abrasive grains bonded into the surface.

Collets—See *Flanges.*

Cone Wheel—A small wheel shaped like a bullet nose which is used for portable grinding.

Controlled Structure—A process of manufacturing grinding wheels whereby the relationship between the abrasive and bond is definitely controlled.

Coolant—The liquid or solution used to cool the work and to prevent it from rusting.

Coping—Sawing stone with a grinding wheel.

Corner Wear—The tendency of a grinding wheel to wear on a corner so that it does not grind sharp corners without fillets.

Corundum—A natural abrasive of the aluminum oxide type, of higher purity than emery.

Crank Wheel—An expression used to designate wheels for grinding crankshafts.

Critical Speed—Every spindle with a wheel or point mounted on it has a certain critical speed at which vibration due to deflection or whip tends to become excessive.

Crush Dressing—The process of using steel rolls to form or dress grinding wheels to a wide variety of shapes.

Crystal—A solid symmetrical particle, bounded by plane surface.

Crystalline—Made up of crystals.

Crystallize—To convert into crystals.

Crystolon—A silicon carbide abrasive made by the Norton Co.

Cup Wheel—A grinding wheel shaped like a cup or bowl.

Cutters—The part of a grinding wheel dresser that comes in contact with the wheel and does the cutting.

Cutting-Off Wheel—A thin wheel, usually made with an organic bond, for cutting off.

Cutting Rate—The amount of material removed by a grinding wheel per unit of time.

Cutting Surface—The surface or face of the wheel against which the material is ground.

Cylinder Wheel—A grinding wheel of similar characteristics to a straight wheel but with large hole size in proportion to its diameter and usually of several inches height.

Cylindrical Grinding—Grinding the outside surface of a cylindrical part mounted on centers.

Diamond Tool—A diamond dresser.

Diamond Wheel—A grinding wheel in which the abrasive is natural bort diamond.

Disk Grinder—A machine on which abrasive disks are used for grinding.

Disk Wheel—A grinding wheel shaped similar to a straight wheel, but usually mounted on a plate and using the side of the wheel for grinding.

Discoloration—See *Burning* (the work).

Dish Wheel—A wheel shaped like a dish.

Dog—A device attached to the work piece by means of which the work is revolved.

Dressers—Tools used for dressing a grinding wheel.

Dressing—A grinding wheel is dressed to improve or alter its cutting action.

Ductile—Capable of being readily pressed or drawn or otherwise formed into various shapes.

Emery—A natural abrasive of the aluminum oxide type.

External Grinding—Grinding on the outside surface of an object as distinguished from internal grinding.

Face—That part of a straight wheel on which cylindrical and surface grinding is usually done.

Feed, Cross—Surface grinding. The distance of horizontal feed of the wheel across the table.

Feed, Down—Surface grinding. The rate at which the abrasive wheel is fed into the work.

Feed, Index—Cylindrical grinding. Measurement indicated by the index of the machine. On most machines this measurement refers to the diameter of the work; on a few to the radius.

Feed Lines—A pattern on the work produced by grinding. The finer the finish the finer and more evident are these lines. Some types of feed lines indicate incorrect grinding condition.

Feed, Plunge — Surface grinding where wheel is fed radially—or "plunged" into the work.

Fin—A thin projection on a casting or forging.

Finish—The surface quality or appearance, such as that produced by grinding or other machining operation.

Finishing—The final cuts taken with a grinding wheel to obtain accuracy and the surface desired.

Flanges—The circular metal plates on a grinding machine used to drive the grinding wheel.

Flaring Cup—A cup wheel with the rim extending from the back at an angle so that the diameter at the outer edge is greater than at the back.

Floor Stand Grinder—An off-hand grinder, mounting either one or two wheels running on a horizontal spindle fixed to a metal base attached to the floor.

Fluting—Grinding the grooves of a twist drill, tap or reamer.

Freehand Grinding—Grinding by holding the work against the wheel by hand, usually called offhand grinding.

Gate—The part of a casting formed by the opening in the mold through which the metal is poured.

Generated Heat—Heat resulting from the removal of metal by a grinding wheel.

Glazing—The dulling of the cutting particles of a grinding wheel resulting in a decreased rate of cutting.

Grade—The strength of bonding of a grinding wheel, frequently referred to as its hardness.

Grain — Abrasive classified into predetermined sizes for use in polishing, in grinding wheels and in coated abrasive.

Grain Size—The size of the cutting particles of a grinding wheel or polishing abrasive.

Grain Spacing—The relative position of the cutting particles in a grinding wheel.

Grinding—Removing material with a grinding wheel.

Grinding Action — Refers to the cutting ability of, and the finish produced by, a grinding wheel.

Grinding Machine—Any machine on which a grinding wheel is operated.

Grinding Wheel—A cutting tool of circular shape made of abrasive grains bonded together.

Grindstone—A flat, circular grinding wheel cut from natural sandstone, sometimes used for sharpening tools.

Hand Grinding—See *Offhand Grinding*.

Hemming Machines—Machines used for grinding flat surfaces such as cutlery blades and skates—named after the inventor, C. H. Hemming.

Honing — An abrasive operation typically performed on internal cylindrical surfaces and employing bonded abrasive sticks in a special holder to remove stock and obtain surface accuracy.

Hoods—Metal guards used for protection against wheel breakage.

Huntington Dresser — A tool using star shaped cutters for truing and dressing grinding wheels, invented by a man named Huntington.

India—Registered trade-mark of Norton Co. for oilstones for producing keen cutting edges. Made from alundum abrasive and oil-impregnated.

Inserted Nut—Disk, segment or cylinder wheels having nuts embedded in the back surface for mounting on the machine.

Internal Grinding—Grinding the inside surface of the hole in a piece of work.

Lapping—A finishing process typically employing loose abrasive grain, but now often including similar types of operation with bonded abrasive wheels or coated abrasives.

Loading—Filling of the pores of the grinding wheel surface with the material being ground, usually resulting in a decrease in production and poor finish.

Lubricant—The liquid or solution used to lubricate the wheel and promote a more efficient cutting action.

Mounted Points and Wheels—Small bonded abrasive shapes and wheels that are mounted on steel spindles.

Mounting—Putting a grinding wheel on the arbor or spindle of the machine.

Natural Abrasive—A hard mineral found in nature. See *Abrasive*.

Norbide—A Norton boron carbide, the hardest material ever made commercially.

Off-Grade—Bonded abrasive materials which are not of exact grade.

Offhand Grinding—Where the work is held in the operator's hand, otherwise known as freehand grinding.

Oilstone—A natural or manufactured abrasive stone impregnated with oil and used for sharpening keen edged tools.

Operating Speed—The speed of revolution of a grinding wheel expressed in either revolutions per minute or surface feet per minute.

Organic Bond—A bond made of organic materials such as the synthetic resins, rubber or shellac.

Peripheral Speed—The speed at which any point or particle on the face of the wheel is traveling when the wheel is revolved, expressed in surface feet per minute (s.f.p.m.). Multiply the circumference in feet by the wheel revolutions per minute.

Periphery—The line bounding a rounded surface—the circumference of a wheel.

Planer Type—A type of surface grinding machine built similar to an open side planer.

Plate Mounted—Disk, segment or cylinder wheels cemented to a steel back plate having projecting studs or other means for mounting on the machine.

Polishing—Act of smoothing off the roughness or putting a high finish on metal by applying to a polishing wheel or belt.

Polishing Wheel—A wheel which can be made of several different kinds of materials, which has been coated with abrasive grain and glue.

Portable Grinder—One that is used manually and can be easily transported.

Pouncing Paper—An abrasive paper used in the felt industry.

Precision Work—Work which is required to be exact in measurements, finish, etc. Work that must be ground with great care.

Production—The quantity of product turned out or the amount of work done in a given time or during the life of a grinding wheel.

Profilometer—An instrument for measuring the degree of surface roughness in micro-inches.

Protection Flanges—See *Safety Flanges*.

Protection Hoods—See *Hoods*.

Puddled Wheel—Wheel made by a process wherein the mixture is of such a consistency that it can be poured into molds.

Recessed Wheels—Grinding wheels made with a depression in one side or both sides to fit special types of flanges or sleeves provided with certain grinding machines.

Resinoid Bond—A bonding material described commercially as synthetic resin.

Rest—That part of a grinding wheel stand which is used to support the work, dresser or truing tool when applied to the grinding wheel.

Roll Grinding Machine—A machine for grinding cylindrical rolls used for rolling metal, paper, or rubber.

Rough Grinding—The first grinding operation for reducing stock rapidly without regard to the finish the wheel leaves.

R. P. M.—Revolutions per minute.

Rubber Bond—A bonding material, the principal constituent of which is natural rubber or synthetic rubber

Rubber Wheels—Wheels made with rubber bond.

Safety Devices—Devices for the protection of operators and machines in case of accident.

Safety Flanges—Special types of flanges designed to hold together the broken parts of a wheel in case of breakage, thus protecting workmen.

Saucer Wheel—A shallow, saucer-like wheel.

Saw Gummer—A grinding wheel used for gumming saws.

Saw Gumming—Saw sharpening and sharpening with a grinding wheel.

Scale—A black, scaly coating on the surface of heated steel and upon other metals—as in forging and rolling.

Scleroscope—An instrument for determining the relative hardness of materials by a drop and rebound method.

Scratches—Marks left on a ground surface caused by a dirty coolant or a grinding wheel unsuited for the operation.

Scythe Stone—A long, narrow stone for sharpening or whetting scythes by hand.

Segments—Bonded abrasive section of various shapes to be assembled to form a continuous or intermittent grinding shape.

S.F.P.M.—Surface feet per minute. See *Peripheral Speed*. Multiply the circumference in feet by the wheel revolutions per minute.

Sharpening Stone—A natural or manufactured abrasive stone usually of oblong shape, used for sharpening or whetting tools.

Shellac Bond—A bonding material, the principal constituent of which is shellac.

Silica—Silicon oxide (SiO_2).

Silicate Bond—Type of bond matured by baking, in which silicate of soda is an important bonding constituent.

Silicon Carbide—An abrasive made from coke and silica sand—(SiC).

Snagging—Grinding the gates, fins and sprues from castings or forgings.

Spindle—See *Arbor*.

Stand—See *Bench Stand* and *Floor Stand Grinder*.

Steadyrest—A support for pieces being ground on a cylindrical grinding machine.

Straight Wheel—A grinding wheel of any dimension which has straight sides, a straight face, and a straight or tapered arbor hole, and is not recessed, grooved, dovetailed, beveled or otherwise changed from a plain straight wheel.

Structure—A general term referring to the proportion and arrangement of abrasive and bond in an abrasive product.

Structure Number—A Norton term designating the relative grain spacing in an abrasive product. Dense relative spacing corresponds to low numbers such 0, 1, 2, etc., open spacing to higher numbers 10, 11, 12.

Stub—That portion of a grinding wheel left after having been worn down to the discarding diameter for a particular operation or machine.

Surface Grinding—Grinding a plane surface.

Surface Grinding Machine—A machine for grinding plane surfaces.

Swing Frame Grinder—A grinding machine suspended by a chain at the center so that it may be turned and swung in any direction for the grinding of billets, large castings or other heavy work.

Table—That part of the grinding machine which directly or indirectly supports the work being ground.

Table Traverse — Reciprocating movement of the table of a grinding machine.

Tapered Wheel—A grinding wheel shaped similar to a straight wheel but having a taper from the hub of the wheel to the face and thus being thicker at the hub than at the face.

Treatment — A material impregnating an abrasive product aiming to improve its grinding action, often by reducing the tendency for loading in use.

Truing—A grinding wheel is trued in order to restore its cutting face to running true, so that it will produce perfectly round (or flat) and smooth work; or to alter the cutting face for grinding special contours.

Vitrified Bond — A bonding material of which the chief constituent is clay.

Washita Oilstones—A natural stone preferred by many to produce smooth, long-lasting edges.

Wheel Sleeves—A form of flange used on precision grinding machines where the wheel hole is larger than the machine order. Usually, the sleeve is so designed that the wheel and sleeve are assembled as one unit.

Wheel Speed—The speed at which a grinding wheel is revolving, measured either in revolutions or in surface feet per minute.

Wheel Traverse—The rate of movement of the wheel across the work.

Work—Used to designate the material being ground in a machine.

Work Speed—In cylindrical, centerless and internal grinding, the rate at which the work revolves, measured in either r.p.m. or s.f.p.m.; in surface grinding, the rate of table traverse measured in feet per minute.

GRINDING, BELT—Here an endless abrasive belt of any desired width runs over a backing or supporting plate and the work is pressed against the belt. This form of surface grinding has many uses and is very efficient, especially where removal of material rather than accuracy of dimensions is essential. Narrow flexible abrasive belts are also run over at some distance from each other and irregular work finished by pressing the parts against the belt.

GRINDING, CENTERLESS—Grinding cylindrical work which is not supported on centers. The work rests on a blade or support between two abrasive wheels, as shown. The front wheel takes the thrust and also regulates the rotation of the work. The regulating wheel usually has a rubber bond and gives a constant rotation to the work. It runs slower than the grinding wheel and determines the work speed, or speed at which the work turns. On long straight work the regulating wheel is set at a slight angle and feeds the work past the grind-

CENTERLESS GRINDING.

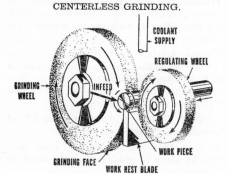

The infeed or wheel movement toward the work is indicated by the large arrow.

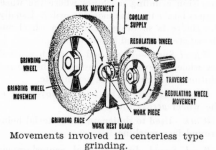

Movements involved in centerless type grinding.

ing wheel. Short pieces of the same diameter are also fed through in the same way. Work with varying diameters is fed down between the wheels from the top.

GRINDING, CYLINDRICAL — The grinding of round work held between centers or supported by suitable bearings, as rolls for calendaring paper or for rolling sheets of paper or metal. These vary in size from small, precision machines to those handling rolls of large diameter and long length.

GRINDING, DISK—Removing material from flat surfaces with abrasive paper or cloth, cemented or otherwise held against flat disks. In most cases the metal disks which support the abrasive disks have either concentric or spiral grooves cut in their face. This provides a sort of cushion and helps the escape of the particles removed in grinding.

GRINDING, ELECTROLYTIC—A method of removing stock from electrically conducting bodies such as metals or metal carbides. A metal disk cathode is revolved in close proximity to an anodic work piece while an electrolyte is applied to the disk and to the work piece the same as a coolant is applied to grinding wheel. It is especially suited for removing stock from large surfaces. Currents of 16 to 18 volts are used.

GRINDING, FORM—The removal of material to produce desired forms on the work instead of a straight cylindrical surface. The grinding wheel must be trimmed to the desired contour, either with a diamond tool or by crushing. This form of grinding requires a radial feed for the wheel, or a "plunge" cut and can be done in either a cylindrical grinder or a centerless type machine. Form grinding can also be done on surface type grinders where the work passes directly under the grinding wheel in a straight line. The illustration shows form grinding in a centerless type machine.

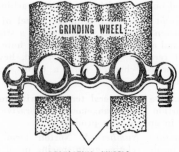

Form grinding (centerless profile (formed) grinding).

GRINDING, HOLLOW—A method of grinding external surfaces on pins or short shafts which cannot be reached by the usual methods. The inner surface of a ring wheel is used, the wheel entering the recess in which the pin is located. Similar to the way in which a hollow mill machines a pin that could not be turned by regular tools.

GRINDING, HORSE POWER REQUIRED— One authority states that for cast iron or soft steel about 10 horse power is required to remove one cubic inch per minute, with larger amounts in proportion.

GRINDING, INTERNAL — Removal of material from the inside of a bore by the use of abrasive wheels. In most machines the work is supported in some kind of a chuck, but in the Heald machine, cylindrical work is ground in a centerless device which supports and drives the work by rollers on the outside. Both the Bryant chucking type and the Heald machines are shown, on page 188.

GRINDER, INTERNAL—Grinding machine for finishing holes and internal surfaces. The work is usually held in chucks, but centerless grinders are used for this work.

GRINDING MACHINE—See *Grinder*.

GRINDING, MICRO-CENTRIC — A term coined by Cincinnati Grinders, Inc., for precision grinding of short work in a centerless type grinding machine. The work is supported on shoes and held against a driver plate by pressure rolls. It was developed for such work as the outside of roller bearing races.

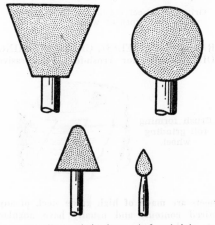

Grinding points (mounted points).

GRINDING POINTS—Small grinding wheels mounted on arbors which drive them. They are made in various shapes and sizes for die making and similar work. Some are molded on a small arbor and others have a small, threaded nut in the base which screws on the grinding spindle.

GRINDING ROOM EXHAUST SYSTEMS— See *Exhaust System for Grinding Rooms*.

GRINDING SCREW THREADS—Producing screw threads by grinding either as a finishing operation or by grinding from the solid, has become standard practice. Beginning with a thin grinding wheel shaped to grind a single thread, they now use wide wheels shaped to grind a number of threads, as shown. Wheels may be shaped to grind every thread or every other thread. Or they may be shaped to grind

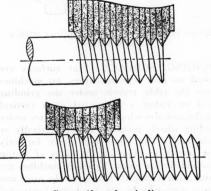

Screw thread grinding.

portions of each thread on different parts of the wheel face. This has been made possible by greatly improved grinding wheels and by development of diamond tools for dressing the wheels accurately. Much of this has been due to the Industrial Diamond Association of America, Inc.

GRINDING, SECTIONAL WHEELS—Sectional grinding wheels are made in a variety of ways. Some have plain radial segments held in a suitable frame or head. One special variety is also shown where the segments have contacts at varying distances from the center.

GRINDING, SOFT GRITS—Non-metallic particles, or grits, made by grinding shells from various kinds of nuts such as almonds, cherry pits, cocoanut, corn cobs, and walnuts of various kinds. Hulls from rice are also used in connection with the soft grits to give a satin finish on such metals as aluminum and brass. No particles of metal should be permitted to get into the soft grits. Air pressure of 90 pounds per square inch from a nozzle held 3 inches from the work has been used in making tests to determine the best soft grits to be used for various operations.

GRINDING, SPLINE—The finishing of splines or multiple keyways in shafting, by grinding with a wheel formed to the proper contour, as shown.

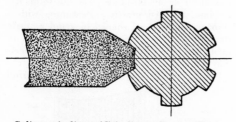

Spline grinding. (Grinding splines with a formed wheel.)

GRINDING, SURFACE — Flat surfaces are ground on disk type machines, on machines where the table travels under the grinding wheel on either a horizontal or a vertical spindle, and also where the table rotates under grinding wheels mounted either vertically or horizontally. The latter type were formerly used largely in grinding the sides of piston rings and similar work. Types of machines are shown, each having its advocates. In some machines, cup wheels are used on horizontal spindles, the work feeding past the wheel as

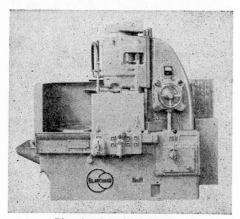

Blanchard surface grinder.

in the vertical type of machine.

GRINDING WHEEL—Wheel of abrasive material such as emery or artificially made particles such as alundum, carborundum and others.

GRINDING WHEEL BONDS—Most grinding wheels use a ceramic clay for bonding the grains to hold them together. Varying the elements composing the mixture affects the strength and the resistance to disintegration. The Grinding Wheel Manufacturers designate the bonds by the following letters: V—Vitrified; S—Silicate; E—Shellac or Elastic materials; R—Rubber; B—Resinoid substances, such as synthetic resins like Bakelite, and O—Oxychloride. Hardness, or grade, is the resistance of the grain in breaking loose from the bond. In diamond wheels a metal bond is preferred for grinding sapphire, glass and quartz, a resinoid bond for grinding carbide tools and a vitrified bond for uses between the two operations named.

GRINDING WHEEL CONTACT WITH THE WORK—The wheel contact depends on both the diameter of the grinding wheel and of the cylindrical work being ground. This is shown for outside and internal work, and for a flat surface. The area of contact affects the pressure on the work and the grade of grinding wheel best suited to it.

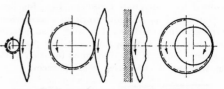

Grinding wheel contact with different types of work.

GRINDING WHEEL(S), CRUSH FORMING ROLLS — Rolls for crush-forming abrasive

Crush forming roll grinding wheel.

wheels are made of high grade steel, of any desired contour, and usually have angular slots as shown.

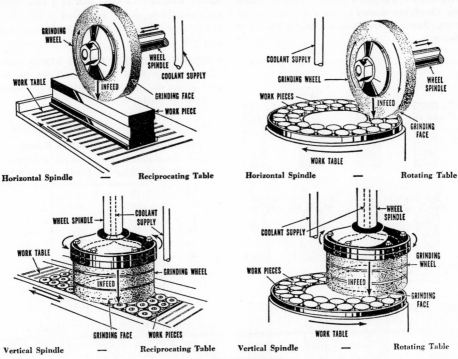

Horizontal Spindle — Reciprocating Table   Horizontal Spindle — Rotating Table

Vertical Spindle — Reciprocating Table   Vertical Spindle — Rotating Table

SURFACE GRINDING.
The infeed or movement of the grinding face of the wheel toward
the face of the work being ground is indicated by the large arrow.

GRINDING WHEEL DRESSER—A tool for
removing worn or glazed surfaces of grinding
wheels. It usually consists of a series of steel
disks that break or pry off small particles of

**GRINDING WHEEL(S),
DIAMOND** — Grinding
in which the abrasive is
a layer of small particles
of diamonds, held in a
suitable bond. For grind-
ing carbides, glass and
gems, speed of 4,200 to
5,000 surface feet per minute are suggested. Kero-
sene or some good solu-
ble oil is suggested.

$\frac{3}{4}$ to 1 in.

~Diamond layer

$\frac{1}{32}$ to $\frac{1}{8}$ in.

Diamond grinding wheels.

Plain cup

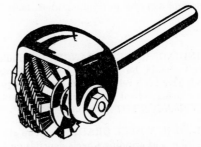

Grinding wheel dresser.

the wheel as it revolves. Small abrasive
wheels are also used. Diamond tools are generally used for finer finishing of the wheel
surface.

197

GRINDING WHEEL FACES—Faces of grinding wheels are shaped to suit a wide variety of work. Some of the standard wheel faces are shown.

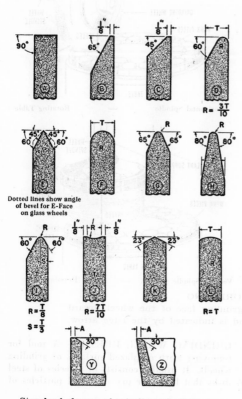

Dotted lines show angle of bevel for E-Face on glass wheels

$R = \frac{3T}{10}$

$R = \frac{T}{8}$ $S = \frac{T}{3}$

$R = \frac{7T}{10}$

$R = T$

Standard shapes of grinding wheel faces.

GRINDING WHEEL FLANGES—Grinding wheels should be mounted between flanges which have been relieved in the center to provide bearing only at the outer edges, as shown. See *Grinding Wheel Mounting*.

GRINDING WHEEL GRADINGS—The grade or hardness of grinding wheels depends on the bonding material used. The vitrified process makes open texture, free cutting wheels which are not affected by weather or oils. Large wheels may be made by the silicate process and have similar qualities to vitrified wheels.

Elastic wheels have some sort of a gum bond, such as rubber, shellac and other resins. They are more flexible and may be made as thin as 1/64 inch.

GRINDING WHEEL, GRAIN SIZES—The table shows grain sizes in general use, the figures giving the number of openings per lineal inch in the sorting screen.

Standard Grain Sizes for Aluminum Oxide and Silicon Carbide Grinding Wheels

Coarse	Medium	Fine	Very fine
10	30		
12	36	70	
14	..	80	220
16	46	90	240
20	..	100	280
24	54	120	320
..	60	150	400
..	..	180	500
..	..	...	600

GRINDING WHEEL HOODS—Hoods or casings for grinding wheels, to prevent pieces flying in case of breakage, are made in different forms—band type (formerly called protection band), cast hoods, drawn steel hoods and fabricated hoods. These are shown here.

GRINDING WHEEL(S) WITH INSERTED NUTS—Wheels of this type are for use on surface grinders where the grinding contact is with the side of the wheel, as in cup wheels. The nuts are imbedded in the wheels as shown. The wheels are drawn against the plate which supports them, which must be of a specified minimum thickness, as shown.

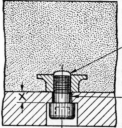

END OF SCREW MUST NOT TOUCH BOTTOM OF HOLE

HOLES LARGE ENOUGH SO THAT SCREWS WILL NOT BIND

Grinding wheels with inserted nuts.

198

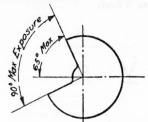

Bench and floor stands.

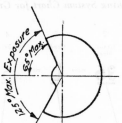

Where more wheel
exposure is needed.

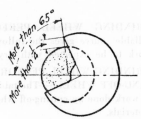

Cylindrical grinders.

Surface grinders and
cutting machines.

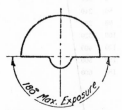

Swing-frame grinders.

For top grinding.

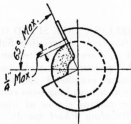

Hood moved to
limit opening.

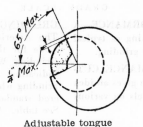

Adjustable tongue
to limit opening.

Hood opening too large
for smaller wheels.

GRINDING WHEEL HOODS.

GRINDING WHEEL MARKINGS—The standard method of marking grinding wheels, as adopted by the Grinding Wheel Manufacturers and by the American Standards Association, is as follows:

Each marking will consist of six parts, placed in the following sequence: 1. Abrasive type; 2. Grain size; 3. Grade; 4. Structure; 5. Bond type; 6. Manufacturer's record.

GRINDING WHEEL MOUNTING—The method of holding grinding wheels on the spindles which drive them. Proper flanges should be provided, with recessed centers so that they bear only on the outer diameters. A soft material, such as blotting paper, should be put between the flanges and the wheel, as shown.

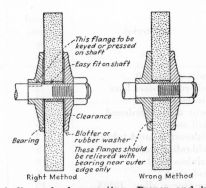

Grinding wheel mounting. Proper and improper methods of mounting wheels having small holes.

Standard Marking System Chart for Grinding Wheels

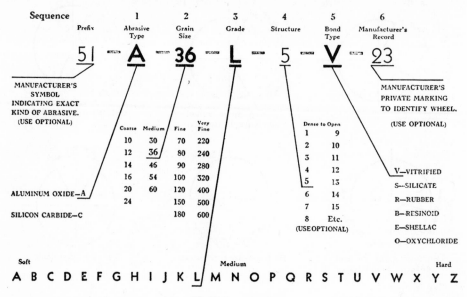

GRADE SCALE

GRINDING WHEEL PERFORMANCE—A reliable source gives the following as typical work to be expected with dry grinding.

GRINDING WHEEL PERFORMANCE, CUTTING-OFF WHEELS—The table gives an idea of work done by cutting-off wheels on various materials.

GRINDING WHEEL(S), SAFE SPEED OF— The American Standards Association Safety Code for the "Use, Care and Protection of Grinding Wheels" presents the table below indicating maximum peripheral speeds for grinding wheels which have long been considered standard for various classes of wheels. See table. Also *Grinding Wheel Speeds.*

Typical Dry Cutting Performances

Material	Wheel diam., in.	Bond	Time to cut 1 sq. in., sec.	Total area cut per wheel, sq. in.	Total life of wheel, min.
Twist drills, soft...........	12	Resinoid	2.27	88	$3\frac{1}{3}$
Cold-rolled steel bars	12	Resinoid	2.54	118	5
Miners' drill rod	12	Resinoid	2.34	153	$6\frac{1}{6}$
Twist drills, hardened	12	Resinoid	9.05	139	$9\frac{1}{3}$
Drill steel	16	Resinoid	2.34	385	15
High-carbon steel tubing....	12	Resinoid	3.70	486	30
Cold-rolled steel	16	Rubber	7.65	510	65
Stainless steel..............	16	Rubber	7.31	615	75
Tool steel.................	16	Rubber	7.89	659	$86\frac{2}{3}$
Manganese alloy, 1020X....	18	Rubber	19.97	531	$174\frac{3}{4}$
Manganese alloy, 1020X....	20	Rubber	15.25	707	180

Safe Operating Speeds of Grinding Wheels

The following table indicates maximum peripheral speeds for various types and grades of wheels. These speeds shall not be exceeded except upon the distinct recommendation of the grinding wheel manufacturer for each specific case, and then only if the user maintains his equipment in a condition satisfactory to the wheel manufacturer.

Types of Wheels	Vitrified and Silicate Bonds			Organic Bonds		
	Low Strength	Medium Strength	High Strength	Low Strength	Medium Strength	High Strength
	FPM	FPM	FPM	FPM	FPM	FPM
*Type 1—Straight Wheels (Including plate mounted and inserted nut wheels) *Type 4—Taper Wheels	5,500	6,000	6,500	6,500	8,000	9,500
*Types 5 and 7—Recessed Wheels	5,500	6,000	6,500	6,500	8,000	9,500
*Type 2—Cylinder Wheels (Including plate mounted and inserted nut wheels)	4,500	5,500	6,000	6,000	8,000	9,500
**Dovetail Wheels *Types 11 and 12—Dish and Flaring Cup Wheels Type 13—Saucer Wheels	4,500	5,500	6,000	6,000	8,000	9,500
*Type 6—Deep Recessed Cup Wheels	4,500	5,000	5,500	6,000	7,500	9,000
Cutting-off Wheels larger than 16″ diameter						7,500 to 14,000‡
Cutting-off Wheels 16″ and smaller						10,000 to 16,000‡
Thread Grinding Wheels	5,500 to 8,000‡	6,000 to 10,000‡	6,500 to 12,000‡			9,500 to 12,000‡
Automotive and Aircraft Crank Grinding	5,500	6,000 to 7,300	6,500 to 8,500‡			
Automotive and Aircraft Cam Grinding	5,500	6,000 to 8,000‡	6,500 to 8,500‡			
Diamond Wheels (all types)	Any Bond—Maximum 6,500 fpm					

NOTE: When wheels of unusual and extreme shapes such as deep cups with thin walls or backs, long drums or with large center holes are required, consult wheel manufacturer for speeds recommended.

NOTE: Maximum speeds indicated are based on the strength of the wheels and not on their cutting efficiency. Best speeds may sometimes be considerably lower.

*Standard Shapes.

**Non-Standard Shapes.

‡Depending on Stability and Design of Machine.

Reprinted from the "Safety Code for Use, Care and Protection of Abrasive Wheels."

GRINDING WHEEL(S), SECTIONAL—

Grinding wheels for heavy surface grinding which are made of sections rather than being in one piece. They are made in cup wheels of various types with different forms of sections or blocks. The spaces between the blocks or segments assist in the removal of chips and tend to prevent overheating of the work.

Sectional grinding wheels.

GRINDING WHEEL SHAPES—

There are a variety of grinding wheel shapes made to suit many different conditions. Standard types of wheels are shown.

The following cuts and classifications are copied from Simplified Practice Recommendations R45-47 of the National Bureau of Standards, Division of Simplified Practice.

Type No.

1	Wheels	Straight
2	"	Cylinder
4	"	Tapered two sides
5	"	Recessed one side
6	"	Straight cup
7	"	Recessed two sides
11	"	Flaring cup
12	"	Dish
13	"	Saucer
16	Cones	Curved side
17	"	Square tip
17R	"	Round tip
18	Plugs	Square end
18R	"	Round end
19	"	Conical end, square tip
19R	"	Conical end, round tip
20	Wheels	Relieved one side
21	"	Relieved two sides
22	"	Relieved one side, recessed other side

GRINDING WHEEL SHAPES.

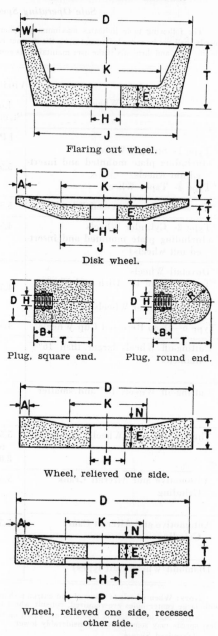

Flaring cut wheel.

Disk wheel.

Plug, square end.   Plug, round end.

Wheel, relieved one side.

Wheel, relieved one side, recessed other side.

The above shape types cover the vast majority of grinding wheels used. These type numbers, when used with dimensions corresponding to the applicable letter symbols, make it possible to describe completely and accurately the shape and size of any standard wheel without the necessity of submitting a drawing, thereby simplifying ordering and record keeping. See also page 199.

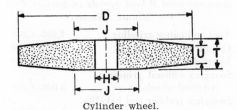

Straight wheel.

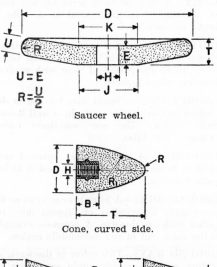

$$U = E$$
$$R = \frac{U}{2}$$

Saucer wheel.

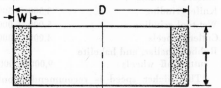

Cylinder wheel.

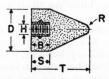

Cone, curved side.

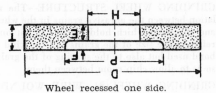

Wheel, tapered two sides.

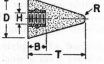

Cone, round tip.   Cone, square tip.

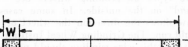

Wheel recessed one side.

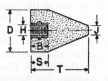

Plug, conical end, square tip.   Plug, conical end, round tip.

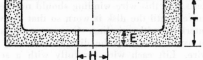

Straight cup wheel.

 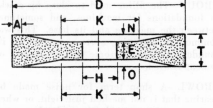

Wheel, relieved two sides.

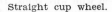 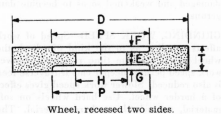

Wheel, recessed two sides.

GRINDING WHEEL SPEEDS—Surface speed of grinding wheels is very important. Too slow speed means a waste of both time and material. Too fast speed makes a hard grinding action and may cause breakage. The following speeds are suggested by the Norton Co. See also *Grinding Wheel Safe Speed.*

Recommended Wheel Speeds in Surface Feet Per Minute (Norton)

Tool and cutter grinding........4,500- 6,000
Cylindrical grinding 5,500- 6,500
Internal grinding 2,000- 6,000
Snagging offhand grinding
  (vitrified wheels) 5,000- 6,000
Snagging (rubber and bakelite
  (wheels) 7,000- 9,500
Surface grinding 4,000- 6,000
Knife grinding 3,500- 4,500
Wet tool grinding 5,000- 6,000
Cutlery wheels 4,000- 5,000
Rubber, shellac, and bakelite
  cutting-off wheels 9,000-16,000*

*This higher speed is recommended only where bearings, protection devices and machine rigidity are adequate.

GRINDING WHEEL STRUCTURE—The relation between the abrasive grains in the wheel and the bond which holds them. It not only refers to the size of the grains and the kind of bond used but also to the spacing of the grains so as to allow chip room between them.

GRINDING WHEEL(S), WIRE WOUND—Some types of grinding wheels are "wire wound" on the outside. In some cases an arrow shows the direction the wheel or disk should run. The Grinding Wheel Institute suggests that this wire winding should not be removed until the disk is worn so that the wire interferes with grinding. Care must be taken to avoid damaging the disk in removing the wire. Lift each wire carefully with a screw driver and cut with wire snips. Do not use a cold chisel and hammer, as the disk may be damaged and weakened so as to become dangerous.

GRINDING, WORK SPEED—Speed of work affects grinding as to the kind of wheel, the wheel speed and the time required. Slower work speed permits deeper cuts if traverse feed is also reduced. Slower work speed gives effect of a harder wheel. Use hard wheels on soft material, soft wheels on hard material. The

smaller the area of contact between work and wheel the harder the wheel should be.

GRINDSTONE—Wheel of sandstone formerly used for sharpening tools. Now almost entirely replaced by wheels of abrasive held in place by a bond.

GRIPE—A shop or local term for any kind of a clamp. Sometimes used to describe a brake of some kind.

GRIT—Particles of fine abrasives. Used interchangeably with "grain" in most cases. Grain seems to be the preferred term with modern grinding wheel makers.

GROBET FILES— Small files for use in die sinking and in similar work, by a well known Swiss maker. The are sometimes called "riffles." See *Files.*

GROMMET — A metal eyelet fastened into cloth or leather, generally to be used in lacing parts together.

GROUND JOINT—A joint between two metal parts made by grinding or lapping them together with an abrasive. A common example is the valve seat in any automobile engine.

GROUND WAYS—This refers to the ways, or sliding surfaces, which guide movement of tools or work, in any sort of machine tool, meaning that they are finished by grinding.

GROUP DRIVES — A method of supplying power to a group of machines from a single motor, as opposed to use of a motor on each machine. An advantage is that, as not all the machines are likely to be in use at the same time, a smaller total horse power will be sufficient. Also, the cost of one large motor is less than a number of small ones. The tendency, however, is all toward the individual drive because machines can be moved from place to place and any machine can be run without any of the others being used. These advantages offset the economies mentioned in most cases.

GROUT—The filling used to close up cracks in foundations for machines, and sometimes between the machine and its base. This was common in mounting a steam engine on its foundation. Usually some sort of mortar or cement is used.

GROWL—A shop term for noise made by gearing that is not meshed just right, or when teeth are not properly formed. **Numerous** other terms are used, depending on the locality.

GUDGEON—A projection or hub which may support another member inside or outside. Sometimes called a trunnion.

GUERIN FORMING PROCESS — A method of cutting and forming which only requires a die instead of a punch and die. The sheet metal is laid on the die and a thick, flat pad of rubber or other resilient material is laid on the sheet. Pressure on the back of the pad forces the sheet through the opening in the die and cuts the outline. Forming can also be done in the same way by using pads of proper size and shape. The process is very useful where only a few parts are needed, as in experimental airplane construction.

GUIDE LINER—A tool used in steam locomotive shops for lining up guides and crossheads.

GUIDE PULLEY—A loose pulley, or idler, for guiding a driving belt.

GUILLOTINE SHEARS—A special type of shearing machine for cutting up bars in steel mills.

GUN, GREASE—A device for forcing grease into bearings by pressure. They are cylinders filled with grease which is forced out by hand or air pressure.

GUN IRON—A fine grain iron low in sulphur.

GUN METAL—A bronze, usually 9 parts copper and one part tin. The name is also given to some strong mixtures of cast iron previously used in making cannon.

GUN, OIL—A device for forcing oil into bearings under pressure. It is practically a hand pump with the barrel filled with oil, which is forced into the bearings by hand pressure. There are also guns in which compressed air is used.

GUN TAP—A tap having a negative angle cutting point which forces the chips ahead of the tap. It does not require flutes as deep as standard taps except for bottoming taps. See *Taps*.

GUSSET—Usually a triangular piece which adds stiffness by being welded or riveted into an angle between two members.

GUTTER—The recess outside the flash line in forging dies.

GUY—A rope or cable fastened at or near the top of a pole or mast and anchored in the ground, to support the pole against side movement. Often called guy rope, or guy wire.

GYROL FLUID DRIVE—A hydraulic transmission with which a motor gets up to about 85 per cent of its power before starting the load. It gives a gradual but positive acceleration with no metal to metal contact in the mechanism, the shock being absorbed by a cushion of oil.

GYROSCOPE—A heavy wheel mounted in a cage or ring with the axis of the wheel free to turn in any direction. It may be made to revolve in a horizontal plane as though not affected by gravity. Used in many airplane instruments. Has been tried on board ship to counteract motion of waves, but did not prove practicable for that purpose.

H

HACK SAW—A saw for cutting metal or similar materials. The blades have teeth of varying pitch according to the work to be done. They are held in a frame for use either by hand or power.

Straight grip hack saw.

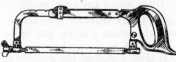

Easy grip hack saw.

HACK SAW BLADES—Saw blades used with a reciprocating motion to cut metal either by hand or power. The method of attacking the work, as well as the number of teeth per inch, are important. The illustrations show the former and the table suggests saws for different materials.

HALFMOON KEY—See *Key, Woodruff.*

HAFNIUM—See *Zirconium.*

HALF-NUT—A nut that is split lengthwise so as to be separated easily from its screw. Used in feeding mechanisms of various machines. Sometimes only half is used and rides on the screw feed. Generally both halves are used, being opened and closed by a cam.

HALF-SIDE MILLING CUTTERS—See under *Milling Cutters, Designation of.*

HAMILTON SCREW THREADS—See *Screw Threads, Watch and Instrument.*

HAMMER, AIR—A portable device using compressed air to operate a hammer or plunger which is aimed to strike rapid blows on rivet heads or other objects. When supplied with a chisel, the air hammer is used for chipping casting or other objects.

RIGHT   **WRONG**

Ample Chip Clearance   No Chip Clearance

Two Teeth or More in Contact   Teeth Straddle and Strip

Two Teeth or More on Metal   Teeth Too Coarse

Start Slowly   May Strip Teeth

Hacksaw blades. Hints for using power blades.

HAMMER, BLACKSMITH'S FLATTER — A flat-faced hammer used to smooth the surfaces of forgings after they have been hammered to shape. It is held on the work by the blacksmith and struck with a sledge by the helper.

HAMMER BLOW—A term describing a sudden blow, such as is caused by steam in improperly drained piping and similar noises. Also the blow caused by an unbalanced loco-

Speeds and Feeds for Power Hacksaw Blades

Material	High Speed and Tensile		
	Teeth per inch	Feed wt. lbs.	Strokes per min.
Aluminum	4-6	60	135
Brass Castings, Soft	4-6	60	135
Brass Castings, Hard	6-10	60	120
Bronze Castings	4-10	120	135
Cast Iron	4-10	120	120-135
C. R. Steel Bars	4-6	120	135
Copper Tubing	10	120	120
Copper Bar	4-6	120	120
Drill Rod	10	120	96-120
Forging Stock	4-6	120	90-120
High Speed Steels	6-10	120	90
Machine Steel	4-10	150	135
Manganese Bronze	6-10	60	90
Monel Metal	6-10	120	60-90
Nickel Steel	6-10	150	90
Pipe, Steel	10-14	120	120
Rails	6-10	120	135
Stainless Steel	6-10	120	60-90
Structural Steel	6-10	120	90-120
Tool Steels	6-10	120	90-120

Size of material to be cut should be taken into consideration. Thinner sections require finer teeth per inch.

motive driving wheel running on a railroad track.

HAMMER, BUMPING OR HORNING — A special hammer used in closing seams of sheet metal work, such as buckets or pipes.

HAMMER, DROP—A machine consisting of two uprights with a head, drop or "monkey," which falls by gravity and strikes hot metal held on an anvil or in a die. The head or drop is raised by a rope, a belt or a board held between rollers and released by the operator. This later is called a "board drop."

HAMMER, FLOGGING—A rather small, short handled hammer or sledge, used in chipping ingots or castings with a flogging chisel.

HAMMER FORGING—Any forging done with a hammer. See *Dies, Forging.*

HAMMER HARDENING — See *Hardening, Hammer.*

HAMMER, HELVE—A power hammer with an arm pivoted near the center. Power is applied at the back end with the hammer on the other end of the arm or beam. Such hammers are used in some comparatively light forging.

HAMMER, MACHINIST'S—Common types of machinist's hammers are shown, as well as a riveting hammer and an engineer's hammer. Special shaped heads are made for particular kinds of work.

DROP HAMMER.

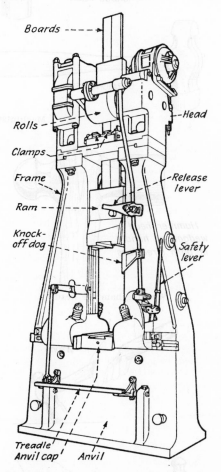

Motor drives through direct gearing to pair of lifting rolls in this board drop hammer. Other models use motor with V-belt drive or have pulleys for line drive. Large hammers use two pairs of lifting rolls.

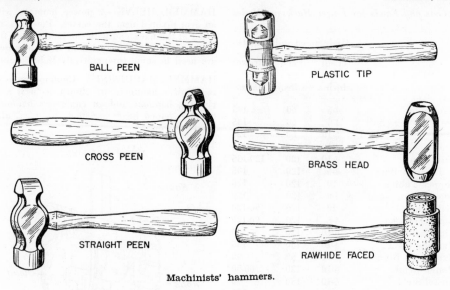

BALL PEEN

CROSS PEEN

STRAIGHT PEEN

PLASTIC TIP

BRASS HEAD

RAWHIDE FACED

Machinists' hammers.

Hammer head is wedged on handle in both directions

Wedging hammer head.

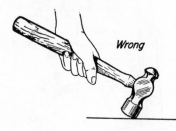

Wrong

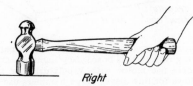

Right

Striking with hand hammer.

HAMMER, POWER—A forging hammer in which the hammer blow is mechanically controlled. Originally applied to steam hammers, the term now really includes all hammers in which power is applied in any way. A board drop hammer has boards attached to the hammer head for raising it to be dropped on the forging. The board is raised by electrically driven friction rollers in this case. Belts or ropes are also used on lighter hammers. A pneumatic hammer has an air compressor which supplies compressed air to the cylinder which forces the hammer head down on the work.

HAMMER, POWER DROP—A form of power drop used for sheet-metal work by the aircraft industry uses a rope to raise the hammer head. For this work the hammer head is much larger than for forging, and the drop is usually from a lower height.

HAMMER, RAISING—A local name for a hammer with a rounded face used to raise, or force up, the surface of sheet metal.

HAMMER, SET—A hammer, or set, with a face concaved to form the head of a rivet. If used by hand it is held by the smith and struck with a sledge by the helper. In machines it is one of the dies used in forming the head of a rivet. When used in riveting it is held over the plain end of the heated rivet and forms the head on that end.

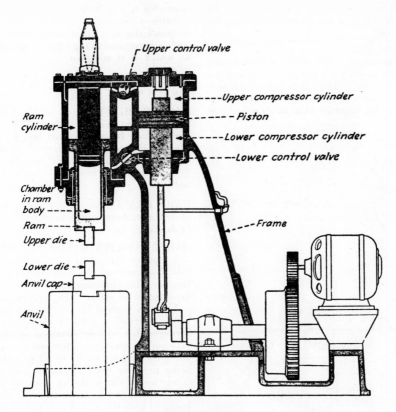

POWER HAMMER.

Pneumatic motor-driven hammers are powered by individual motors driving a
compressor piston which operates continuously when power is turned on. In this
design, air in the ram body is compressed on the upstroke to cushion upward
movement; expansion of this air helps drive ram down. Variations include
elimination of the ram chamber with pressure applied to entire top of ram
piston and a design in which piston is mounted at the center of the ram piston
rod with rod guided at both the top and bottom of the cylinder.

HAMMER, SLEDGE — A heavy hammer,
usually weighing from 5 to 14 pounds. Used
with both hands.

HAMMER, SOFT—A hammer with a head
made of the softer metals or of rawhide, rubber or plastic. Used when necessary to use a
hammer on a finished surface without bruising
it. The hammer shown has a divided head for
easy replacement of the soft faces.

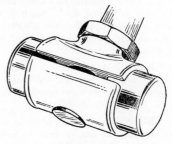

Soft hammer.

209

HAMMER, SPRING—A small hammer giving its blows by spring pressure when released by a foot treadle or lever. Used only in special, light work.

HAMMER, STEAM — A forging hammer in which the weight of the hammer head is augmented by power from a steam cylinder at the top of the frame. The admission of steam is controlled by the hammer-man. The steam also raises the hammer head to its upper position.

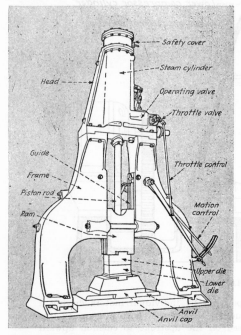

Steam hammer. An 8,000-lb. double-frame steam forging hammer. Design and method of operation are similar to the single-frame hammer.

HAMMER, TRIP—Similar to a helve hammer, but the arm is raised by a toothed wheel arrangement and tripped automatically when the tooth or arm passes the back end of the arm. Seldom used at present.

HAND MILLING MACHINE—A comparatively small milling machine in which the work feeding movements are hand operated, usually by levels. See *Milling Machine.*

HAND TIGHT—To assemble plain or threaded parts as much as can be done by hand, or without the aid of a wrench or tool.

HAND WHEELS, CLUTCHED—Hand wheels connected to the shafts which they operate by a clutch which can be thrown out at will, or automatically at a given point. When thrown out, no movement of the wheel affects the shaft on which it is mounted.

HANGER, POST—A hanger which is fastened to a post or wall.

HANGER, SHAFTING—A support for a line shaft or other shaft in a shop. This contains the bearings for the shafting and supports it whether idle or in use. Most common is the drop hanger, which hangs from the ceiling. The post hanger is supported on a post or side wall.

HARD BRASS—Brass which has not been annealed after being work hardened by rolling or drawing.

HARDENABILITY BANDS FOR H-STEELS —A method devised by the American Iron & Steel Institute and the Society of Automotive Engineers for obtaining two features necessary in selection of steels. They are based on an end-quench method by Jominy and Boeghold which provides a method of predicting the hardness that will be obtained at any point between the surface and the center of any size of round steel quenched in oil or water after being properly heated. Charts showing these bands have been made for more than 60 so-called H-steels and can be found in the handbooks of both the A. I. & S. I. and the S. A. E.

HARDENED AND GROUND WAYS—Ways, or sliding surfaces, which are hardened to increase their life and then ground for accuracy. In some cases the bed itself is hardened, in others separate steel strips are fastened to the bed.

HARDENING—A method of heat treating steel (or iron base alloys) by heating to a temperature within, or above, the critical range, holding at that temperature for a given time, and then cooling rapidly, usually by quenching in oil or water.

HARDENING, OIL—The hardening of steel by quenching in an oil bath. Cooling in oil is not as severe a shock to hot steel as water and is less likely to cause cracks or distortion, especially in intricate dies and varying sections of metal. The oil is usually circulated to secure even temperature throughout the bath and to prevent undue heating of the oil.

HARDENING, FLAMATIC — A method of flame hardening by special apparatus devised by the Cincinnati Milling Machine Co., in which the heat-treating cycle is controlled by a sensitive thermopile focussed directly on the work. This makes the actual temperature of the work itself the controlling factor in the heat treating cycle.

HARDIE—A blacksmith's cutting chisel which fits into a hole in the anvil and forms a lower cutter for cutting off work.

HARDENING, HAMMER — Hammering the surface of many metals hardens it by making the outer surface more dense. Some grades of brass can be made fairly hard and springy by this method. It is similar to work hardening of material by compressing the outer layer or skin. It is sometimes called "peening," although that is usually applied to the stretching or riveting over of the end of a piece.

HARDNESS AND TENSILE STRENGTH— The relation between hardness and tensile strength of steel is considered uniform enough to relate two characteristics in the following table. While hardness is usually given as a guide to cutting speed, some shops give the tensile strength instead.

HARDNESS, CLOUDBURST—A method devised by Edward G. Herbert, of England, using a shower of small, hard steel balls falling from a height of 3 to 4 meters at the rate of about 750,000 per minute. While they make no visible impression, they affect the surface so that hard and soft spots can be seen. The balls are from 3 to 5 millimeters in diameter. The method does not seem to have been used extensively.

HARDNESS NUMBERS — Numbers denoting the hardness of materials as tested by different methods. In the Shore scleroscope it is the height of rebound of a hardened steel ball on a scale divided into 100 parts. In the Brinell, Rockwell, Tukon and other machines it is based on measurement of indentations made in the surface being tested. Most tables of comparison are only approximate, but are convenient for comparison. The Brinell or BHN, and Rockwell systems, are best known.

HARDNESS OF MATERIALS—See *Hardness*, also see *Brinell Hardness Testing Machine, Rockwell Hardness Test, Sceleroscope* and *Moh's Scale of Hardness*.

HARDNESS TESTING MACHINES — See *Brinell Hardness Testing Machine, Knoop Indenter, Rockwell Hardness Test, Scleroscope* and *Tukon Test.*

HARD SOLDER—A solder made of copper and zinc, or copper and silver. It fuses only at a high heat and is stronger than soft solder. It is practically the same as brazing.

HARDSTEEL—A trade name for a very hard alloy which drills and cuts hardened steel.

HARVEY GRIP BOLTS—A type of railway track bolt with a thread of buttress form.

HATCHING OR CROSS-HATCHING — In mechanical drawings, the lines used to indicate a piece that is cut in section. The cross-hatching lines are usually drawn at 45 degrees with the base line of the drawing but can be at any other angle. Cross-hatching of adjacent parts is usually done at an opposite angle to avoid confusion. Modern drawing rooms space the lines by mechanical means. See *Drawings.*

HEAT, ATOMIC—The atomic heat of any substance is found by multiplying its atomic weight by its specific heat.

HEAT, IDENTIFYING—In order to keep a history of any batch of steel, each steel melt is given a number. This number is usually continued through all forging operations to maintain the identity of the melt.

HEAT TRANSFER—Heat is transferred or transmitted from one body to another in three ways; by conduction, convection or radiation. Conduction is the slow flow of heat from one molecule of the material to the next. Convection heat transfer is by eddy current or other actual movement of a gas or liquid. Radiation transfers heat electromagetic waves like those of light or radio.

HEAT TREATING BATHS—Instead of heating steel tools or other parts in an open fire or in a muffle furnace, some prefer to heat by immersion in baths of molten metals or salts of various kinds. As the melting points of these are known it is easy to keep the heat at a uniform temperature. Barium chloride baths have been largely used for this purpose. For aluminum some use sodium nitrate. The table gives the melting points of many of the materials used for this purpose.

Hardness Strength of Steel

The following table (prepared by Sir Robert Hadfield of the Research Laboratory, Hadfields, Ltd., Sheffield, England) represents the average of a large number of tests on all types of steel, and is intended as an approximate guide. Individual results vary considerably from the average. It also gives a comparison of Brinell ball and Scleroscope hardness numbers with their relations to the compression strength, also yield point and tenacity, of steel.

Zones of Hardness F to A	Approx. Scleroscope Hardness Number	Brinell Ball Hardness Number	Tensile Strength				Compression on Specimens .564″ Diam. and .70″ in Height		
			Yield Point		Maximum Stress		Elastic Limit and 25% Compression		Compression, Per Cent. (100 Tons per Sq. In.) (160 Kilograms) per Sq. M/M
			Tons per Sq. In.	Kilograms per Sq. M/M	Tons per Sq. In.	Kilograms per Sq. M/M	Tons per Sq. In.	Kilograms per Sq. M/M	
F		150	20	31	36	57	17	27	49.0
		175	26	41	41	65	19	30	40.0
	34	200	32	50	46	72	21	32	35.0
E	38	225	38	60	51	80	23	36	31.0
	42	250	44	69	56	88	26	41	27.9
	46	275	50	79	61	96	30	47	23.0
	50	300	56	88	66	104	34	54	19.0
D	54	325	61	96	71	112	38	60	15.2
	57	350	67	105	76	120	43	68	11.3
	61	375	73	115	81	128	49	77	8.0
	64	400	79	124	86	135	55	87	5.6
C	68	425	84	132	91	143	61	96	3.8
	71	450	90	142	96	151	67	105	2.4
	75	475	96	151	101	159	74	116	1.3
	78	500	102	161	106	167	81	127	0.6
B	80	525	107	169	111	175	87	137	0.23
	84	550	113	178	116	183	94	148	0.21
	86	575			121	190	101	159	0.20
	89	600			126	198	108	170	0.18
A	92	625*	Not determined		131	206	115	181	0.16
	95	650			136	214	122	192	0.14
	99	675			136	214	129	203	0.13
	101	700			141	222	136	214	0.12

* Glass scratching hardness commences here.

212

Conversion Table of Hardness Numerals

Moh	Duroscope	Scleroscope	Hebert Pendulum Time D	Hebert Pendulum Time S	Monotron Drop Hardness, Mm. Kgs.	Monotron Brinell, Diameter	Monotron Diameter Constant	Monotron Durometer	Rockwell 30-T	Rockwell 45-N	Rockwell 30-N	Rockwell 15-N	Rockwell ¼-Inch Ball E	Rockwell ⅛-Inch Ball B	Rockwell 60 Kilo-grams A	Rockwell 100 Kilo-grams D	Rockwell 150 Kilo-grams C	Brinell Tungsten Carbide Ball	Brinell Standard Ball	Brinell Diameter, Millimeters	Vickers or Firth
8.5		106	64	90		1200	130	28	…				…	…				872	780	2.20	1224
		102	59	85		1130	122	31	…				…	…				840	745	2.25	1116
		98	56	80		1030	111	32	…				…	…				812	712	2.30	1022
		94	53	76		956	103	34	…	72	82		…	…	84.5		65	794	682	2.35	941
8.0		91	52	72		894	96	37	…	71	81	92.5	…	…	83	73	64	760	653	2.40	868
		87	49	67		850	91	40	…	69	79	92	…	…	82.5	72	62	724	627	2.45	804
		84	47	63		804	91	43	…	66.5	77.5	91	…	…	81.5	71	60	682	601	2.50	746
		81	45	60	1400	767	82	45	…	64.5	76	90	…	…	80.5	70	58	646	578	2.55	694
		78	42	56	1300	727	78	46	…	62	74	89	…	…	79.5	68	56	614	555	2.60	650
	54	76	40	53	1225	690	74	48	…	60	72.5	88	…	…	78.5	67	54	578	534	2.65	606
	53	73	38	51	1160	660	71	49	…	57.5	70.5	87	…	…	77.5	65	52	555	514	2.70	587
	52	71	37	48	1095	630	68	50	…	55	69	85	…	…	76.5	64	50	525	495	2.75	551
	51	68	36	47	1050	610	66	51	…	54	67	84.5	…	…	76	63	49	514	477	2.80	525
7.0	50	66	35	44	1005	586	63	52	…	53	65.5	84	…	…	75	62	48	477	461	2.85	502
	49	64	34	41	950	548	61	53	…	51	64.5	83.5	…	…	74.5	61	46	460	444	2.90	474
	48	62	33	39	910	530	59	55	…	49.5	62.5	83	…	…	74	60	45	432	429	2.95	460
	47	61	32	37	880	510	57	56	…	47.5	62	81.5	…	…	73	59	43	418	415	3.00	435
	46	59	30	35	840	490	55	58	…	46.5	61	81	…	…	72.5	58	42	415	401	3.05	423
	45	57	30	34	810	471	53	59	…	45	60	80.5	…	…	72	57	41	401	388	3.10	401
6.5	45	56	29	33	780	462	51	60	…	44	59	80	…	…	71	56	40	388	375	3.15	390
	44	54	28	32	750	453	50	62	…	43	58	79.5	…	…	71	55	39	375	363	3.20	380
	44	53	27	30	725	433	48	63	…	41	56.5	79	…	…	70.5	54	38	364	352	3.25	361
	43	51	26	29	700	414	47	64	…	39.5	56	78	…	…	69.5	53	36	352	341	3.30	344
	42	50	25	28	675	408	45	66	…	38.5	54	77.5	…	…	69	52	35	341	331	3.35	334
	42	49	24	27	650	390	44	68	…	36	53	76.5	…	…	67.5	50	33	330	321	3.40	320
	41	47	24	26	630	380	42	69	…	36	52	76	…	…	67	50	32	321	311	3.45	311
6.0	41	46	23	24	610	370	41	70	…	34	51.5	75.5	…	…	66.5	49	31	311	302	3.50	303
	40	45	22	24	590	360	40	71	…	33	50.5	75	…	…	66	48	30	302	293	3.55	292
	40	44	22	23	570		39		…	31.5	50.5	74.5	…	…	65.5	47	29		285	3.60	285

HEAT TREATMENT—The heating and cooling of metal, without melting it, to secure qualities not present in the metal as it comes from the mill. All operations such as cyaniding, pack hardening and nitriding are different forms of heat treatment.

HEAT TREATMENTS—Operations or combinations of operations involving the heating and cooling of metals and alloys in a solid state. This does not include heating and cooling for such purposes as forging. Heat treatments include:

Quenching—Immersing to cool.

Hardening—Heating and quenching certain iron-base alloys from a temperature either within or above the critical-temperature range.

Annealing—Annealing is a heating and cooling operation of a material in the solid state. In annealing, the temperature of the operation and the rate of cooling depend upon the material being heat-treated and the purpose of the treatment. (Usually relatively slow cooling is implied.)

Certain specific heat-treatments coming under the comprehensive term "annealing" are:

Full Annealing — Heating iron-base alloys above the critical-temperature range, holding above that range for a proper period of time, followed by slow cooling through the range. The annealing temperature is generally about 100° F. (55° C.) above the upper limit of the critical-temperature range, and the time of holding is usually not less than 1 hour for each inch of section of the heaviest objects being treated. The objects being treated are ordinarily allowed to cool slowly in the furnace. They may, however, be removed from the furnace and cooled in some medium which will prolong the time of cooling as compared to unrestricted cooling in the air.

Process Annealing—Heating iron-base alloys to a temperature below or close to the lower limit of the critical range followed by cooling as desired. This heat treatment is commonly applied in the sheet and wire industries, and the temperatures generally used are from 1020 to 1200° F. (550 to 650° C.).

Normalizing—Heating iron-base alloys above the critical-temperature range, followed by cooling to below that range in still air at ordinary temperature.

Patenting—Heating iron-base alloys above the critical-temperature range followed by cooling to below that range in molten lead maintained at a temperature of about 700° F. (365° C.). Usually applied in the wire industry either as a finishing treatment or, especially in the case of eutectoid steel, as a treatment previous to further wire drawing. Its purpose is to produce a sorbitic structure.

Spheroidizing—Prolonged heating of iron-base alloys at a temperature in the neighborhood of, but generally slightly below, the critical-temperature range, usually followed by relatively slow cooling.

Tempering (also termed *Drawing*)—Reheating, after hardening to some temperature below the critical-temperature range, followed by any rate of cooling.

Malleablizing — Annealing operation with slow cooling whereby combined carbon in white cast iron is transformed to temper carbon, and in some cases the carbon is entirely removed from the iron.

Graphitizing—Annealing of cast iron whereby some or all of the combined carbon is transformed to free or uncombined carbon.

Carburizing (*Cementation*)—Adding carbon to iron-base alloys by heating the metal below its melting point in contact with carbonaceous material. ("Carbonizing" is an undesirable term.)

Case Hardening — Carburizing and subsequent hardening by suitable heat-treatment all or part of the surface portions of a piece of iron-base alloy.

Case—That portion of a carburized iron-base alloy article in which the carbon content has been substantially increased. (The terms "case" and "core" refer to both case hardening and carburizing.)

Cyaniding—Surface hardening of an iron-base alloy article or portion of it by heating at a suitable temperature in contact with a cyanide salt, followed by quenching.

HEAT TREATMENT, DRAWING BATHS—Baths containing salts of different kinds of which the melting point is known. Placing hardened steel in these baths and letting the parts remain until they are of the same temperature secures uniform tempers on the parts immersed in them. The materials used are given under *Heat Treating Baths*.

HEAT TREATING THERMOMETERS — Thermometers used in heat treating are calibrated as to accuracy by using the materials shown in the table.

Fixed Points for Thermometer Calibration Commonly Used in the Heat-Treating Department

Substance	Point	Temperature Thermo, °F.	Scale, °C.
Alcohol, ethyl	Boils	173.0	78.3
Aluminum (Al), pure metal	Melts	1218.0	658.7
Antimony (Sb), pure metal	Melts	1166.0	630.0
Barium (chloride) (BaCl$_2$) salt	Melts	1760.0	960.0
Benzene	Boils	176.0	80.0
Cadmium (Cd), pure metal	Melts	624.2	320.9
Cobalt (Co), pure metal	Melts	2696.0	1480.0
Copper (Cu), pure metal	Melts	1983.0	1083.0
Glycerine	Boils	554.0	290.0
Gold (Au), pure metal	Melts	1954.4	1063.0
Iron (Fe), pure metal	Melts	2912.0	1600.0
Lead (Pb), pure metal	Melts	620.0	327.0
Mercury (Hg), pure metal	Solidifies	173.0	78.5
Mercury (Hg), pure metal	Boils	675.0	357.3
Nickel (Ni), pure metal	Melts	2645.6	1452.0
Platinum (Pt), pure metal	Melts	3191.0	1755.0
Potassium nitrate (KNO$_3$) salt	Melts	642.0	337.0
Silver (Ag), pure metal	Melts	1769.0	960.5
Sodium chloride (NaCl) salt	Melts	1481.0	805.0
Sodium nitrate (NaNO$_4$) salt	Melts	593.6	312.0
Sodium sulphate (Na$_2$SO$_4$) salt	Melts	1623.2	884.0
Sulphur (S), amorphous	Boils	833.0	444.7
Tin (Sn), pure metal	Melts	450.0	232.0
Tungsten (W), pure metal	Melts	7052.0	3400.0
Water, distilled	Boils	212.0	100.0
Zinc (Zn), pure metal	Melts	786.2	419.0
Lead, 35% Tin, 65% }lowest melting alloy of these two metals	Melts	358.0	181.0
Sodium chloride, 45% Sodium sulphate, 55% } lowest melting mixture of these two salts	Melts	1154.0	623.0
Sodium nitrate, 50% Potassium nitrate, 50% }lowest melting mixture of these two salts	Melts	424.0	218.0

HEAT UNIT—The heat necessary to raise the temperature of one pound of water one degree F. from a standard temperature of 68 degrees F.

HEEL—In a tool, the surface opposite the cutting edge, or below the cutting edge. The surface on which a lathe tool rests when held in the tool post. See *Single-Point Tools.*

HEEL OR HOOK TOOL—An obsolete hand tool used for turning metal on lathes without a tool carriage or any sort of mechanical feed. A short projection on the end of the under side of a tool hooked over the tool rest and

took the thrust of the cut. The tool shank was long enough to go under the arm pit of the operator, and helped to control the feed of the cutting point as the tool was moved along the rest. It was made obsolete by the lathe carriage and feed.

HELI-ARC WELDING—Welding in which the arc is completely shielded or surrounded by helium gas to exclude air. See *Welding, Shielded Arc.*

HELICAL—Anything in the form of a helix, as a helical spring or screw thread.

HELICAL BROACHING—The broaching of helical splines or other surfaces. The teeth of the broach form a helix of the desired lead. Either the work or the broach turns as the broach passes through the hole.

HELICAL GEAR ANGLES—See *Gears, Helical Angles.*

HELICAL OR COIL SPRINGS—See *Springs, Helical or Coil.*

HELICAL-TOOTH MILLING CUTTER—See *Helical Milling Cutters* under *Milling Cutters, Terms Used for Teeth and Cutting Angles.*

HELIUM—A very light gas which is non-inflammable and highly desirable for dirigible balloons. It has about 8 per cent less lifting power than hydrogen.

HELIX—A line surrounding an axis and making an angle with it. The most common example is a screw thread. The particular angle is unimportant. Whether it is large or small it is still a helix. There is much confusion between helix and spiral and as to whether it is a *slow* or *fast* helix, or a *high* or *low* helix. Screw thread helix angles are measured from the axis. In screw threads we call a thread with a high lead, or that advances a nut rapidly, a *fast* thread. It is logical to call such a helix a *fast helix.*

HELIX ANGLE—In screw threads this is the angle between the helix and a line at *right angles to the axis of the screw.* In helical gearing it is the angle *between the gear teeth and the axis of the gear.* This difference causes confusion and it is hoped that the method of measuring the helix angle may be made the same for both. The terms *fast* and *slow* helix should also be standardized. This is now being called the "lead angle" by some engineers.

HELIX, FAST—A term used in connection with milling cutters to indicate a helix angle of more than 25 degrees with the axis of the cutter. The specified helix angles are over 25 degrees and not more than 45 degrees.

HELIX, LEAD OF—The lead of a helix is the pitch diameter $\times$ 3.1416 $\times$ the cotangent of the helix angle.

HELVE—Originally the handle of a heavy hammer or sledge. In power forging hammers the beam between the hammer head and the source of power. Helve power hammers were formerly used much more than at present, but they still find a place in some types of light forging work. See *Hammer, Helve.*

HEMATITE—An iron ore having a reddish color. It is sometimes known as *red ocher.* A natural oxide of iron of considerable value.

HIGH BRASS—A mixture containing about 65 parts copper and 35 parts zinc. Also called common or market brass.

HIGH HELIX—See *Helix, Fast.*

HIGH-LEAD BRONZE—A bearing metal with about 80 per cent copper, and 10 per cent each of lead and tin.

HIGH SPEED STEEL—A steel which retains its hardness at high temperature. These steels vary widely, as they may contain cobalt, tungsten, titanium, molybdenum, vanadium and other alloys.

HI-HELIX—A term sometimes applied to the helix angle of milling teeth with the axis of the milling center. It may be compared to a "fast" screw thread.

HINDLEY WORM—A worm shaped to conform with the curve of the worm gear with which it is to run. Frequently known as the "hour-glass" worm.

Designed many years ago and largely abandoned until the advent of the Cone worm gear, which has become very popular. It has been the subject of much argument for many years. See *Gears* and *Worm.*

HI-SHEAR RIVETS—See *Rivets, Hi-Shear.*

HOB—A type of milling center used in cutting teeth in gears. This is a continuous process which is largely used in gear production. The hob moves across the face of the gear blank, which is turned at the proper rate to produce the kind of teeth desired. The terms used for different parts of the hob are shown on illustration on next page.

HOB, IN-FEED—A hob designed to be fed radially or toward the center of a gear blank. The various parts are named on the illustration.

HOB, MULTI-THREAD—A gear cutting hob made with two or more threads or "starts." It divides the work among more teeth and, where feasible, reduces time required for hobbing gears.

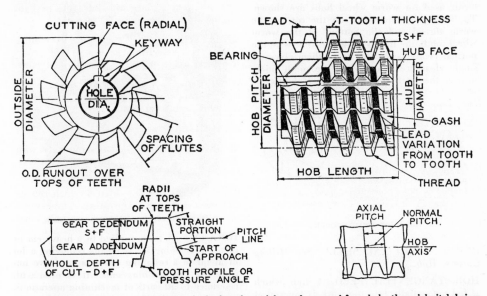

Illustration shows a right-hand, single thread, straight gash, ground form hob, the axial pitch being equal to the lead. In a multiple thread hob, the lead is equal to the axial pitch multiplied by the number of threads.

HOB. IDENTIFICATION OF TERMS.

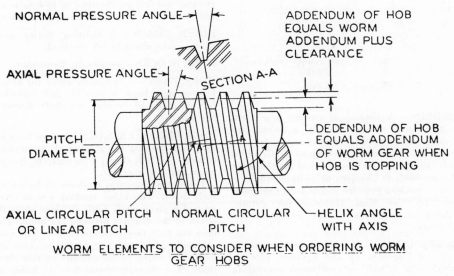

WORM ELEMENTS TO CONSIDER WHEN ORDERING WORM GEAR HOBS

IN-FEED HOB.

HOB(S) FOR WORM WHEELS—Standard terms used for worm wheel hobs are shown. To insure clearance between the top of the worm thread and the bottom of the worm wheel tooth, the hob is usually given twice the normal clearance for the teeth themselves. A single clearance is one-tenth the tooth thickness at the pitch line. See *Gear Hobbing.*

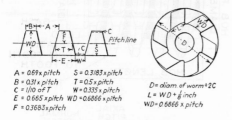

A = 0.69 × pitch   S = 0.3183 × pitch
B = 0.31 × pitch   T = 0.5 × pitch
C = 1/10 of T   W = 0.335 × pitch
E = 0.665 × pitch WD = 0.6866 × pitch
F = 0.3683 × pitch

D = diam. of worm + 2C
L = WD + ⅛ inch
WD = 0.6866 × pitch

Hobs for worm wheels.

HOB(S), SOLID AND SHELL—See *Milling Cutters, Hob.*

HOB, TANGENTIAL FEED—A hob which is fed tangentially into the work is tapered at end which starts into the work, as shown.

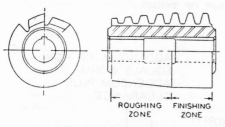

ROUGHING   FINISHING
ZONE   ZONE

Tangential feed hob.

HOBBING—A process of cutting gear teeth with a cutter which resembles a worm. See *Gears, Hobbing.* Claims are made for the origin of the process by George B. Grant in this country, but its first practical development was probably in Germany or Switzerland. It is now a standard practice and is both rapid and accurate. See *Gear Hobbing* for details. Should not be confused with *"hubbing."* See *Hubbing.*

HOBBING MACHINES—Machines for cutting gears and splines by the hobbing process, which uses a "hob" or continuous generating cutter instead of the single formed cutter. See *Gear Hobbing.* A Barber-Colman hobbing machine is shown here.

Barber-Colman hobbing machine.

HOGGING—A term applied to a heavy cut or to the tool doing it. It means removing a lot of metal in a roughing cut so as to leave but little for the finishing cuts. It is used with reference to all sorts of machining operations.

HOG NOSE TOOL—A single point tool with a round nose for lathe, boring mill, planer or shaper. Used mostly on heavy, roughing cuts.

HOIST—A device for lifting weights, usually by power. It can be operated by hand, by electric, internal combustion or hydraulic cylinders or motors, or compressed air motors.

HOIST, CHAIN—A hoisting device using chains and pulleys to lift the load.

HOKE BLOCKS—See *Blocks, Measuring.*

HOLE, BASIC—A system in which the hole is kept as near basic as possible and variations for fits made by varying the shaft diameter. See *Fits.*

HOLE CIRCLE LAYOUTS—A shop term for diagrams showing the spacing of any number of holes in a bolt circle, or at uniform distance from any given center.

There are numerous methods of laying out such holes. The older method was to space around a given circle with dividers set to the chord of the distance between the holes. This does not give very accurate results. The modern method is to use a jig boring machine and locate the holes by movements in two directions. The diagram shows how 13 holes are spaced around a circle one inch in diameter. For other diameters the figures shown are multiplied as necessary.

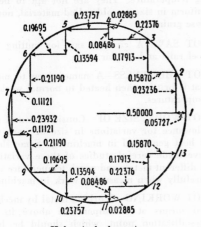

Hole circle layouts.

HOLLOW GRINDING—See *Grinding, Hollow.*

HOLLOW MILL—A cutter resembling a tube with teeth on the end or cutting edge. Usually refers to tools for screw machines. Some tools of similar construction are called "trepanning" tools.

Hollow mills and clamping collar.

HOLLOW-SPINDLE LATHE—A lathe having a hole through the spindle to permit passage of rods to be machined, through its center.

HONING—A form of finishing with abrasives, usually in the form of stones or sticks held in a special head. Largely a development of the automotive industry originally used almost exclusively for cylinders. The first use was for polishing the bore, with the abrasive stones floating rather than fixed, as at present. Modern honing heads expand the stones automatically until the desired size is reached. Usually from 0.002 to 0.003 inch is left for honing. The ratio of revolution to reciprocation is usually about 3 to 1—about 200 surface feet per minute for revolution and 65 to 70 feet for reciprocation. Roughing grit is from 80 to 150, finishing from 120 to 180. Using 600 grit gives mirror finish. Honing removes 0.002 inch in less than a minute as a rule. Similar to lapping.

HONING HEADS OR TOOLS—Skeleton framework for holding the abrasive stones used in honing. In some of these the honing stones are set out to larger diameters automatically. They start at the minimum size of the hole and feed out until the hole is of the desired size. The mechanism which feeds the honing stones out to their maximum diameter must be very delicate, as only .002 to .003 inch, or less, of material is removed by honing.

HONING MACHINES—Machines developed for finishing surfaces by honing. They are usually of the vertical spindle type, although special machines are made for honing the cylinder bores in engines having the cylinders in a V-shape, so that all cylinders can be honed at once. They vary in size from machines for small, short holes to those for honing the barrels of large field guns. These have strokes of over 20 feet and some of the machines are over 60 feet long, and hone diameters up to 12 inches.

HOODS FOR GRINDING WHEELS—Protective hoods are required by law to prevent accidents due to wheels bursting while in use. The types vary with the way in which the wheels are used. Hoods are made in different ways and of different materials. Many are cast iron, while others are made from steel plate and welded into the desired shapes. See *Grinding Wheel Hoods.*

HOOK BOLT—A bolt with a hook in place of the usual square or hexagonal head.

HOOK OF THREAD CHASERS—This refers to the shape of cutting edges which are ground with a "hook" or positive cutting angle, usually curved by the shape of the grinding wheel. The same term may be used in connection with other cutting tools. See *Dies.*

HOOK SPANNER WRENCH—A wrench which partly encircles a nut has holes or slots to engage the hook on the end of the wrench. The nut has no flat sides. See *Wrench.*

HOOK TAPS—See *Tap, Hook.*

HOOKE'S GEARING—An old name for helical and herringbone gears, presumably from some one who experimented with them many years ago. An old New England builder of engine lathes used them in back gearing by the middle of the 1800's, to secure a more constant pull on the work. As both of the back gears had the same angle, the end pressure against the bearings was objectionable. Opposite angles, or herringbone gears, obviate this objection.

HOPPER—In shop language, any receptacle into which blank or semi-finished work is placed to be fed to the machine for further work or for completion. Frequently the feeding mechanism is in the hopper itself.

HORN DIES—See *Dies, Horn.*

HORSEPOWER, ACTUAL — A mechanical horsepower is 33,000 pounds raised one foot high in one minute. Actual horsepower is the amount actually delivered to the machine being driven.

HORSEPOWER RATING, S.A.E.—An empirical or arbitrary rating for horsepower of internal combustion engines adopted by the Society of Automotive Engineers in the early days of the automobile. Although it bears little relation to the actual horsepower, it is largely used in determining license fees. The formula is: Square of the bore in inches $\times$ number of cylinders, divided by 2.5. By this formula a single 5-inch cylinder would be rated as $5 \times 5 \times 1$, or 25, divided by 2.5, or 10 horsepower.

HOSE COUPLINGS — Threaded connections between sections of fire and garden hose. Standardized to permit interchange of hose between localities. See *Screw Threads, Hose Coupling.*

HOT BED—The iron platform in a rolling mill on which bars or rails are placed after being rolled.

HOT-DIP PROCESS OF TINNING — Steel plates to be tinned are first pickled in a bath of 40 parts water and one part sulphuric acid, by volume. They are then washed clean and dipped in a flux made by dissolving zinc in hydrochloride acid, a saturated solution. The plates are then dipped in a bath of 80 parts lead and 20 parts tin, by weight, until thoroughly coated. The surplus metal is shaken off and the plates are thrown on a pile to cool.

HOT-ROLLED—Metals which have been finished to size by rolling at high heat, or forg-

ing temperature. They are not apt to be as uniform in size as cold rolled material, nor as close grained.

HOT SAW—A circular saw for cutting hot steel rails and similar parts.

HOT SHORTNESS—A name given to metal that is brittle when heated to normal working temperatures.

HOT WORK, SIZE OF—Consideration of and allowance for variations in size of work due to heat generated in machining. Some shops have made careful studies of these variations of different metals and watch temperature very carefully when measuring work in machine.

HOT WORKING—Working metal by mechanical means at a temperature above its recrystallization point, which should be high enough to prevent strain in hardening.

HOT WORKING STEEL—A designation of any steel useful in coming in contact with hot metals.

HOWL—A shop term for noise made by gearing at very high speed. Is also applied to any unusual noise made by gearing not in good adjustment. Shop noises vary from howls and squeals to growls.

HUB—A projection, or boss, on a casting or forging, and which is part of the body of the piece. It usually has a hole in it. Without a hole it is usually called a boss.

The name "hub" is also applied to a form forced into solid metal to make dies for plastics or other molds. It is also called a "force." Some call it a hob, the same as the cutting tool for gears, used on a hobbing machine. This dual use should be discontinued as it tends to cause confusion.

HUBBING—A method of forming desired depressions in a die by forcing a *hub,* or hardened steel form, into it under heavy pressure. It is largely used by silversmiths in making the dies for their product. It is also used in making dies for some plastic and other forms. This is frequently called "hobbing," which confuses it with the method used in cutting gear teeth. Hubbing is frequently done cold and a depth of one-half inch is common practice. Pressures average 100 tons to the square inch of area.

HUGHES OIL TOOL JOINT THREAD—See *Screw Threads, Hughes.*

HUNTING TOOTH—An extra tooth in a gear wheel to prevent the same teeth making contact at all times. This is an obsolete practice and could not be used where it is necessary to maintain an exact ratio between rotating parts.

HYDRAULICS—The science of liquid pressures and their applications. Common applications are in lifting jacks, hoists and presses for forming metals, hot or cold, and for riveting.

HYDRAULIC POWER PIPING — The Oil Gear Co. suggests forged steel, flareless, locking-shoulder fittings up to ¾ inch. For larger sizes use seamless steel tubing with forged steel screwed or socket welded hydraulic fittings. They should be specified as low carbon, low sulphur, cold drawn, seamless steel tubing with 1,200 deg. F. anneal and free of internal scale, draw marks or scratches. For pressures under 1,000 pounds and short pipe lines, copper tubes with extruded flanges can be used. The tables cover both kinds of pipe.

Seamless Steel Tubing for Fluid Power Systems

For Flareless Locking-Shoulder Fittings*

Pipe Size	O.D., in.	Wall Thickness for		
		1000 psi	1500 psi	3000 psi
⅛	¼	0.030	0.030	0.050
¼	⅜	0.035	0.035	0.060
⅜	½	0.050	0.050	0.080
½	⅝	0.050	0.050	0.095
¾	⅞	0.065	0.065	0.135
1	1⅛	0.065	0.080	0.160
1¼	1¼	0.065	0.095	0.195

For Screwed or Welded Fittings†

Pipe Size	O.D., in.	Wall Thickness	Pipe Size	O.D., in.	Wall Thickness
⅛	0.405	0.065	1½	1.900	0.219
¼	0.540	0.119	2	2.375	0.250
⅜	0.675	0.126	2½	2.875	0.313
½	0.840	0.147	3	3.500	0.375
¾	1.050	0.154	4	4.500	0.500
1	1.315	0.179	5	5.563	0.625
1¼	1.660	0.191	6	6.625	0.750

*Like Ermeta steel fittings—The Weatherhead Co., Cleveland.

†Capacity: ⅛- to 1-in. pipe sizes—to 4000 psi.; for 1¼- to 6-in. pipe sizes—to 3000 psi.

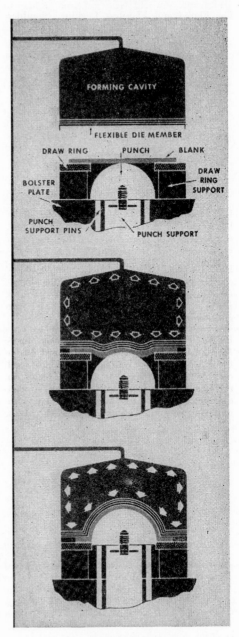

Hydroforming.

Copper Tubing

For Flared and Flareless Locking, Shoulder Fittings (Ferulok)

Pipe Size	O.D., in.	Wall for 500 psi.	Wall for 1000 psi.
⅛	¼	0.035	0.035
¼	⅜	0.050	0.050
⅜	½	0.065	0.065
½	⅝	0.065	0.065
¾	⅞	0.065	0.090
1	1⅛	0.065	0.110
1¼	1¼	0.065	0.120

HYDRAULIC RAM—A device whereby a large body of water with a low head, or fall, can force a small percentage of the water to a considerably higher point.

HYDRO-LAPPING — A mechanical process similar to machine lapping, except that bonded abrasive disks are used instead of cast iron plates with loose abrasives as in a lapping machine.

HYDROFORMING—A method of deep drawing by use of a punch working upward into a flexible die member, which acts as a universal die. As the punch moves up to pressure on the blank being formed is increased so that the metal is pressed against the punch with uniform pressure. The underside of the blank is held against the draw ring surrounding the punch to control metal flow. It might be called a development of the Guerin process. It eliminates the need for mating or female dies. See illustration page 221.

HYDROMETER—An instrument used in testing the density of solutions used in such operations as pickling. Also used in connection with batteries and anti-freeze solutions.

HYDRO-PNEUMATICS—The combined action of air and water, or oil, in hoists, presses or other appliances.

HYDRO-PNEUMATIC DIE CUSHION—A die cushion for press work in which both compressed air and hydraulics are combined to secure the desired cushioning effect.

HYDRO-PRESS—See *Press Hydro*.

HYDRO-PRESS DIE—See *Dies, Hydro-Press*.

HYDROSTATIC PRESSURE—Pressure built up in any hydraulic mechanism.

HYPER-EUTECTOID STEEL—Steel with *over* 0.80 per cent carbon. See *Eutectoid Steel*.

HYPER-MILLING—A name coined by the Firth-Sterling Co. to designate high-speed milling done with negative rake milling cutters.

HYPO-EUTECTOID STEEL—Steel with *less* than 0.80 per cent carbon. See *Eutectoid Steel*.

HYPOTENUSE — The longest side of any right angled triangle. It is always opposite the right angle and joins the ends of the two sides which form that angle.

I

I P M—Abbreviation for "inches per minute." Used in connection with the feed of cutting tools in some classes of machine tools.

I. S. A. SYSTEM OF FITS—A system developed by the International Standards Association, a federation of the national standardization associations of 21 countries, before World War II. It was studied by both the American Standards Association and the British Standards Institution but no definite steps were taken toward its adoption. Further consideration in the near future is doubtful.

I. S. A. TOLERANCE SYSTEM—A system of tolerances for different classes of fits between mating parts as adopted by the International Federation of National Standardizing Associations.

ICONEL—An alloy of 79 per cent nickel, 13 per cent chromium and 6 per cent iron.

IDEOGRAPH—A symbol or trade mark adopted by an individual, a company, or an oganization as a special designation, or a signature.

IDLER—A gear or pulley which does not transmit power. In pulleys it merely supports belts between driving and driven pulleys and sometimes holds the belt against a pulley to prevent slippage. In gearing it may reverse the direction of motion but in this case it does transmit power.

IMMUNIZE—To remove small particles of iron or grit from the surface of stainless steel by pickling in an acid solution. This prevents them from acting as points for the starting of rust.

IMPERIAL GALLON—The standard liquid measure for Great Britain and her colonies. Equal to 10 pounds of pure water at 62 deg. F. and to 1.2 United States gallons.

IMPERIAL WIRE GAGE—A gage for wire and small rods originating in England but which seems to have been superseded by the Birmingham and Stubs gages. Comparison can be made from the table of wire gages. See *Gage, Wire.*

IMPREGNATE—To force or induce particles of one substance to enter the pores of another substance. Wood can be impregnated with plastic or other liquid material, by enclosing both in a tank to which pressure is applied, as telephone poles and piles are impregnated with creosote to increase their resistance to moisture, insects and decay.

"IN" CUTTING—When a milling cutter contacts the work on its outer surface it is called "in" cutting. This is also called "climb" cutting and "down" cutting. The latter is only correct when the cutter contacts the *top* or largest dimension of the work first.

INCANDESCENT WELDING—Now called resistance welding.

INCH—The basic measurement in mechanics under the English and United States system. The inch is equivalent to 25.4 millimeters. See *Measurement, Inches and Metric.*

INCH-POUND—One pound raised one inch.

INCHES OF MERCURY—A method of measuring vacuum produced by condensers, as, 2.04 inches of mercury equal one pound per square inch pressure, at sea level. Or 29.9 inches of mercury equal 14.7 pounds pressure at sea level, and would be a perfect vacuum.

INCHES OF WATER—A method of measuring chimney draft, as, 27.6 inches of water equal one pound pressure per square inch. So 1.72 inches of water equal one ounce pressure and 12 inches of water equal 0.434 pounds pressure per square inch.

INCHING—Moving by slow and short intervals. Is applied to setting of machine cutting tools, moving them, or the work, very small distances until the right position is arrived at. Also called "jogging."

INCLINABLE PRESS—See *Press, Inclinable.*

INCLUSIONS—Impurities of any kind in cast, forged or rolled metals. These may be oxides, sulphides or silicates in the mechanical mixture.

INCREASE TWIST DRILL—A twist drill in which the helix angle of the flute increases from the point to the back to aid in the removal of chips.

INCREMENT—The amount of change in movement, size or weight. For example, most thermometers are graduated in increments of two degrees. Sometimes used to denote irregular spacing, as in the cutting of file teeth. This should be called "variable increment."

INDEX BASE—A term sometimes applied to a milling machine fixture or base, with two or more holding devices. While work is being machined in one fixture the other is reloaded. This reduces idle time to a minimum.

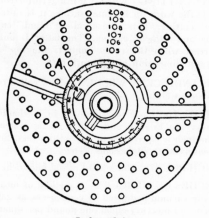

Index plate.

INDEX PLATE—A plate, usually a circular disk, having a series of holes spaced at desired intervals, for indexing or controlling the position of work to be drilled or milled in specified locations. In plain indexing the plate usually gives all the divisions needed. The index plate also forms a part of the more complicated indexing used in the different designs of special indexing heads made by different milling machine makers. The two arms of the sector are set to include the desired number of holes and moved around the plate after each indexing. This saves counting the number of holes for each division.

INDEXING—A method of securing the desired distance between drilled holes, spacing of gear teeth or similar work. It is usually rotary, but may be horizontal. The three methods used in milling are direct, compound and differential, the two latter being practically the same.

INDEXING, COMPOUND—Compound indexing consists of two separate, plain indexing operations, using a dividing head with an additional index pin which is only adjusted radially, to engage holes in the side index plate. The index crank is first rotated as usual for indexing a number of spaces in the side index plate. Then the index plate is rotated with the index crank engaged. The index plate is rotated by disengaging the plate stop and indexing, with respect to the fixed index pin, a number of holes on a different circle of holes in the same index plate. To *add* to the previous amount indexed, rotate the plate in the same direction as the rotation of the index crank. To *subtract* move in the opposite direction. The new types of dividing heads have rendered this method obsolete.

INDEXING, DIFFERENTIAL—Indexing with the index plate geared to the spindle, thus giving a differential movement that allows the indexing to be done with one circle of holes and the index crank turned in one direction, as in plain or direct indexing.

INDEXING FACE PLATE—A face plate with two parts, one of which can be moved on the other to facilitate cutting multiple screw threads. Instead of moving the tool into a new position, this allows the work to be turned to any position to give the right number of multiple threads. This is used on the engine or other screw cutting lathe, and differs from the index plate used on milling machines.

INDEXING, PLAIN—Using an index plate without gearing of any kind, to secure desired divisions on circular work, as in grinding, milling and planing. See *Indexing Face Plate*.

INDEXING ROTARY TABLE—A work table for drilling or milling machines which gives accurate spacing of holes or surfaces.

INDEXING, SIMPLE OR DIRECT—When the indexing plate corresponds to the number of spaces desired in the work, it is known as direct or simple indexing.

INDICATED HORSEPOWER—Power indicated by instruments for measuring the amount of power developed or transmitted. This usually refers to steam or internal combustion engines, the power being shown by pressures inside the cylinder, the area of the cylinder and the speed of the engine. Electrical horsepower is measured in kilowatts by a watt-meter.

INDICATING GAGE—See *Gage, Indicating.*

INDICATOR—Generally any tool which indicates concentricity of work in a lathe. They vary from the simple "wiggler" to elaborate dial indicators. When placed in contact with the work they indicate the amount by which the work is not concentric.

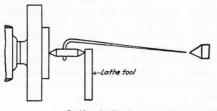

Lathe indicator.

INDICATOR, DIAL—An indicating device in which the readings are made on a dial resembling a watch. In addition to indicating movement of the pointer or feeler, this measures the variations. Most dial indicators are graduated in thousandths of an inch, but some read to ten-thousandths of an inch.

INDICATOR, LATHE TEST—An instrument with multiplying levers that show slight variations in the truth, or concentricity of revolving work. They are of many types, and are used in setting work true in a chuck or on a face plate.

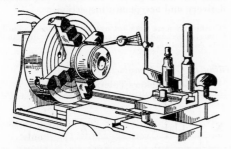

Lathe test indicator, as used on outside diameter.

INDIUM—Looks like silver but is soft and flexible. Melts at about 310° F. and boils at about 2460° F. By-product of zinc and lead production. Is used in bearings where a lead coated steel shell is plated with indium, and later diffused into the lead at high temperature. A solder containing indium will adhere to both glass and metal in limited temperature requirements.

INDUCTION BRAZING—The use of induction coils to heat the parts to be brazed. The coils are designed to distribute the heat where needed.

Induction heating.

INDUCTION HEATING— The use of an alternating current in a coil surrounding the work, which produces heat very rapidly. Low frequency current penetrates deeply and is used for hardening and for annealing. High frequency current does not penetrate as deeply and is used for brazing and soldering small parts. The action is shown herewith.

INERTIA—The tendency of a body at rest to resist motion, or of a body in motion to resist stoppage.

IN-FEED—When the tool or grinding wheel is fed radially against or into the work. Infeed is used in cutting off operations either by tool or grinding wheel. In centerless grinding in-feed refers to work which is fed vertically between the two wheels as disinguished from feeding parallel to the wheel spindles.

INFRINGEMENT—As applied to patents, use without permission of the inventor, or the owner of the patent during its life. An encroachment on the rights of others.

INGOT—The first casting of steel into shape for further processing. It is cast in a metal mold about 18½ by 21½ inches in cross section and about 36 inches long. The ingots go to the "blooming" mill where they are rolled in numerous passes to about 4 by 6 inches. These are called blooms. Blooms are still further reduced in cross section into "billets," although some billet mills reduce them from almost ingot size. Further reduction produces "bars," which may be made from 4 by 4 inch billets and reduced to any desired size.

INGOT IRON—An open hearth iron which is very low in carbon and manganese. It also has few impurities.

INHIBITORS—Colloid chemicals of organic origin which affect the action of acids in pickling solutions. Some are claimed to reverse the pickling process, causing the acid to dissolve the scale instead of attacking the metal. While this is not strictly true, as there must be some action on the metal to form hydrogen and remove the scale quickly, some inhibitors do reduce the action on the metal while allowing rapid action in the scale removing process. Sulphuric acid may be used at higher temperatures and in stronger solutions when a good inhibitor is used. This secures faster work and less trouble from objectionable fumes.

INJECTOR—A device for forcing water or liquids into cylinder or boiler against pressure. The injector for steam boilers uses steam pressure from the boiler itself, with nozzles of varying diameter to secure the necessary pressure. In diesel and other internal combustion engines the fuel is pumped into the cylinders at the correct interval, through small nozzles which spray it in the proper amount.

INKING IN—Covering pencil lines on a drawing with ink for a permanent record. Preliminary pencil marks are then erased.

INSERT NUT—See *Nut, Insert.*

INSERTED TOOTH MILLING CUTTERS—See *Inserted tooth cutter* under *Designation of Milling Cutters.*

INSPECTION BENCH—A bench with a smooth and level top, usually of cast iron, on which finished work can be inspected with surface gages and other instruments.

INSPECTION, FLUORESCENT PENETRANT—Flaws in non-magnetic materials cannot be detected by the magnetic method. A highly fluorescent substance is used, called zyglo, into which the material is dipped, or which is applied with a brush. The part is then washed and wiped, and a developer is applied to draw the penetrating material to the surface, where it can be seen in a black light.

INSPECTION GAGES—Any gage used in checking dimensions on work of any kind. It may be used by a workman, by a foreman, by a floor inspector or by those who finally inspect the product before it is shipped. In the same way many purchasers also have their own inspection service to avoid the cost of doing further work on pieces which do not meet specifications. See *Gages, Inspection.*

INSPECTION OF MACHINE PARTS, STANDARDIZING*—Lack of standard specifications for manufacturing limits of cylindrical parts, and permissible variations in sizes of limit gages used in inspection, cause unnecessary rejections and loss. Inspection is complicated by three phases, workshop inspection, delivery and acceptance inspection.

*Credit for these data belongs to Dr. John Gaillard, formerly mechanical engineer of the American Standards Association.

Table 1—Gagemakers Tolerances According to Gage Manufacturers Catalog

Nominal Gage Size—Inches   Gage Makers Tolerances—Inches

Above	Up to and including	Class XX Internal Gages only	Class X	Class Y	Class Z	Class ZZ Ring Gages only
0.029	0.825	0.00002	0.00004	0.00007	0.00010	0.00020
0.825	1.510	0.00003	0.00006	0.00009	0.00012	0.00024
1.510	2.510	0.00004	0.00008	0.00012	0.00016	0.00032
2.510	4.510	0.00005	0.00010	0.00015	0.00020	0.00040
4.510	6.510	0.00065	0.00013	0.00019	0.00025	0.00050
6.510	9.010	0.00008	0.00016	0.00024	0.00032	0.00064
9.010	12.010	0.00010	0.00020	0.00030	0.00040	0.00080

Table 2—Proposed Numerical Values of Gage Zone Limits for Delivery and Inspection-Acceptance Limits

Part Tolerance* (Inches)	Location of Zone Limits—(Inches)			
	a	b	c	d
0.0010	0.00005	0.00015	0.00005	0.00010
0.0012	0.00006	0.00018	0.00006	0.00012
0.0015	0.00008	0.00023	0.00008	0.00016
0.0020	0.00010	0.00030	0.00010	0.00020
0.0025	0.00013	0.00038	0.00013	0.00026
0.0030	0.00015	0.00045	0.00015	0.00030
0.0040	0.00020	0.00060	0.00020	0.00040
0.0050	0.00025	0.00075	0.00025	0.00050
0.0060	0.00030	0.00090	0.00030	0.00060
0.0080	0.00040	0.00120	0.00040	0.00080
0.0100 and above	0.00050	0.00150	0.00050	0.00100

*For a part tolerance lying between two values listed in this column, use the values a, b, c and d applying to the next smaller part tolerance listed.

The new American Standard "Limits and Fits for Engineering and Manufacturing, B 4.1 —1947" says "A part shall be acceptable if its actual size does not exceed the limits of size specified in numerical values on the drawing, in writing . . . It does not meet dimensional specifications if its actual size exceeds those limits."

This limit is the *nominal* size of the gage. Its *actual* size may differ slightly from the nominal for two reasons. 1—A new gage may vary within the gage makers' limits. 2—A gage, especially a Go gage, will wear from use.

Table 1 gives data from gage makers' catalogs. Some of these state that without special instructions, the tolerances on a working Go plug gage will be applied as a *plus* tolerance on the Go limit of the hole. The tolerance on the Not Go plug gage will be equally distributed on both sides of the Not Go limit of the hole. This is intended to keep as large a percentage as possible, of the tolerances shown in the drawing, for the shop.

For either *delivery* or *acceptance* inspection the main interest is in the width and location of the four gage zones. Delivery and acceptance can be harmonized by a standard system of gage zones based on the adoption of four gage zone limits which are inside the drawing limits.

The hole tolerance is the gage makers' maximum limit of the *acceptance* inspection Go plug gage. This is also the wear limit of the *delivery inspection gage.*

The maximum gage makers' limit of the *delivery* inspection Go plug gage is slightly larger. The maximum gage makers' limit of this gage is the Not Go limit of the hole. This is also the maximum gage makers' limit of the *delivery* inspection Not Go plug gage. Beyond this is the wear limit of the *delivery inspection* Not Go plug gage. Gage zone limits may be established in the same way inside the tolerance shown on the drawing, *for the shaft.*

This basic layout reserves, for each of the four gages involved, a zone of permissible variations in the size of the gage. Each gage zone may be designated by the gage zone limit which is located farthest inside the part tolerance.

Numerical values of gage zone limits are shown in Table 2. These are based on the following relationships between the a, b, c, and d, in Table 2 and the part of tolerance T on hole or shaft.

a 0.05 T Maximum value 0.0005 inch
b 0.15 T   "   "   0.0015   "
c 0.05 T   "   "   0.0005   "
d 0.10 T   "   "   0.0010   "

These values give an *acceptance* inspection gap of 90 per cent and *delivery* inspection gap of 75 per cent of the part tolerance for all part tolerances up to and including 0.0100 inch. In Fig. 2 there are the following choices:

Delivery Inspection Go Plug Gage	Gage Makers' Tolerance Inches	Gear Wear Allowance Inches
Class X	0.00006	0.00014
" Y	0.00009	0.00011
" Z	0.00012	0.00008

For a tolerance of 0.0020 inch *delivery* inspection Go gages, classes X, Y and Z can be used for nominal part sizes to, and including 4.500 inch. It also shows that in 8 cases with small tolerances on large parts, it will be necessary to use *delivery* inspection Go plug gages class X X. This class of gage has a very close gage makers' tolerance, and is used for setting plug or snap gages, rather than in regular inspection work.

Reducing gage makers' tolerances leaves more gage wear allowance. Using gages of hard alloy such as tungsten or boron carbide, the gage zone limits can be made closer to the corresponding parts limits and yet leave adequate gage wear life.

Dr. Gaillard proposes a system which utilizes the gage zone of the *delivery* inspection Go plug gage in Fig. 2. If Class X plug gages are ordered for workshop and delivery inspection, the gage makers' limits are 1.00030 and 1.00024 inch. The parts marker may decide that gages larger than 1.00015 shall be used for *shop* inspection and gages measuring 1.00015 or less for *delivery* inspection. This means all new gages go to the shop and that delivery inspection is done with worn gages.

INSPECTION, SUPERSONIC — The sending of supersonic impulses (inaudible high-frequency sound waves) into the material being tested and measuring the time required for these impulses to penetrate the material, be reflected from the opposite side of the defect, and return to the sending point. The sound waves are sent by a quartz crystal which is moved over the work surface. This is credited to the Sperry Gyroscope Co. and is known as the Reflectoscope.

INSTRUMENT SCREW THREADS— A series of screw threads adopted by makers of instruments and watches. They are of very fine pitch, running up to 256 threads per inch. See *Screw Threads, Watch and Instrument.*

INSULATORS — Materials which retard the flow of heat or electricity.

INTERCHANGEABLE ASSEMBLY—Assemblies which can be interchanged with similar assemblies as a whole but in which all parts may not interchange.

INTERCHANGEABLE PART—A part made with such limits of measurement as to interchange with similar or mating parts when the whole machine is assembled.

INTERCHANGEABILITY — The making of parts so nearly alike that they can be assembled without special fitting. The term is often used loosely, as much depends on the tolerances permitted on various parts. The closer the tolerance the more accuracy is necessary in the mating parts. For many wearing parts selective assembly is more economical. See *Selective Assembly.*

INTERDENTAL SPACE — A seldom used term for the space between two gear teeth.

INTERFERENCE BANDS—Light rays have a wave form of motion. When these rays are passed through a quartz optical flat and reflected back from the bottom surface of the flat and the surface of the part being examined some of these wave forms will coincide with the reflected wave form and amplify the intensity while others will interfere with the wave form, thereby blanking out the light. The interference occurs at one-half of the length of the light wave and causes a dark band to appear. As these interference bands occur at some multiple of one-half the wave length they can be used for determining lengths and flatness if the wave length of the light source being used is known.

A wave length is 11.6 millionths of an inch when a monochromatic light is used. Straight bands indicate a flat surface.

INTERFERENCE FITS—See under *Fits, Various Types and Systems.*

INTERFEROMETER—An optical instrument which uses light waves instead of merchanical means of measurement.

INTERLOCKING—The providing of mechanism which prevents movement except in prescribed sequence. In machines it prevents the movement of parts when there is danger of interference with other parts.

Interlocking Cutters, Milling Cutters under *Miscellaneous.*

INTERMITTENT MOTION—Any mechanical motion which is interrupted at intervals by any mechanical means. It may be done with levers or gearing. See *Gears, Intermittent.*

INTERNAL GEAR—A ring gear with the teeth on the inside surface. See *Gears, Internal.*

INTERPOLATION OF VALUES—Estimating the values of factors not given in a table. If the value given for 100 deg. Centigrade is 212 deg. F. and the value of 110 deg. Centigrade is 230 deg. F., we can interpolate between these values to find the equivalent of 105 deg. Centigrade. As the difference for the 10 deg. Centigrade is 18 deg. F., half this number will be the difference for 5 degrees, showing that 105 deg. Centigrade equals 221 deg. F. This makes it possible to condense many tables and still be able to find all the values needed.

INVENTORY—A list of equipment, tools, machinery, materials, etc., itemized to any extent necessary to show the amount on hand on a given date.

INVESTMENT CASTINGS—Castings made in molds from which the pattern has been melted out. Formerly called the "lost wax" process. A wax or soft plastic pattern is made. Special plaster is poured around this pattern, and the pattern is then melted out, or "lost." The process is used in making intricate shapes which could not be withdrawn from a sand or similar mold.

INVOLUTE CURVE—A curve formed by a point at the end of a cord unwinding from a drum. It is the most used form of gear tooth curve at present. See *Gearing* for illustrations.

INVOLUTE SERRATIONS — See *Serrations, Involute.*

INVOLUTOMETRY—The art of measuring and calculating involutes. The almost universal use of the involute curve in gear teeth has developed an intensive study of its characteristics, with at least one treatise on the subject.

IRIDIUM—A hard, heavy grayish-white metal. Sp. gr. 22.42. Melts at 4,260 deg. F.

IRON—A common metallic ore which is fused to drive off impurities. The base for all ferrous metals, such as steel.

IRON CEMENT—In common shop terms, a mixture of cast iron filings and an acid that will corrode them rapidly. Frequently used in patching cracks in castings or to fill low spots, but not where there is much stress on the cemented parts. There are commerical metal cements which are better.

IRON PYRITE—A common mineral sometimes called "fools gold" because of its color.

IRON SHOT—Irregular pieces of iron made by pouring molten metal into water. Used in tumbling barrels for cleaning castings.

IRON, WHITE—Cast iron which is hard and brittle and shows very little graphite when broken.

IRONING—The smoothing of wrinkles or undulations in sheet metal after pressing or drawing. It is sometimes done with a hammer but pressing or drawing is more satisfactory. Also a restriking or second operation in forging to secure a more perfect alinement of the parts of a forging. It is also sometimes used to secure a better surface.

ISINGLASS—Dried bladder of fish, a gelatin used in adhesives. Not the mineral "mica" which is sometimes called by that name.

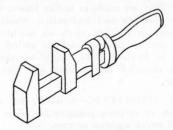

Isometric projection.

ISOMETRIC PROJECTION — A method of drawing which shows three sides of an object in one view. Plans and details drawn in this way are more easily understood than the three views in general use. Not a true perspective, but it enables various parts to be measured if desired. The horizontal lines are 30 degrees from a normal base line. Isometric drawings are particularly useful in assembling machine parts. See *Perspective, Isometric.*

ISOSCELES — A triangle having two equal sides and angles.

ISOTOPE—One of two or more elements having the same atomic number. Identical in chemical behavior. Distinguishable only by small differences in atomic weight.

IZOD TEST—A test with a standard notched bar supported at one end. Differs from the Charpy test, in which the bar is supported at both ends.

J

JACK—Any portable device used in lifting. They vary from the small automobile jack used in changing tires to large, hydraulically operated jacks used in heavy bridge construction. They are made to utilize levers, screws, compressed air and hydraulics. Small jacks are used in leveling work on machine tool beds, such as planers, and are called planer jacks or leveling jacks. Some are simply a screw threaded into a long nut. See *Jack, Planer*.

JACK, HYDRAULIC—A device for raising weights or exerting pressure by oil or other liquid under a piston or ram.

JACK, LEVELING — A small jack, usually operated by a screw, for leveling and holding work on planer beds and similar places. It is really an adjustable block when used in this way.

JACK, PLANER—A small device for regulating the height of work from the table of a planer or other machine tool, so named because it is used most often in planer work.

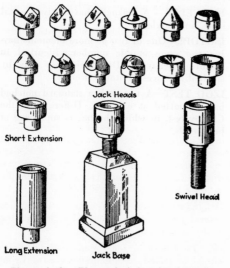

Jack Heads

Short Extension

Long Extension

Swivel Head

Jack Base

Planer jacks. Planer jack base and heads.

It is usually a small screw jack, as shown, but sometimes air or hydraulic cylinders are used to secure equal pressure at different points.

JACK, SCREW—A jack using screws for adjustment, or the screw itself, apart from the base. Also called screw jack.

JACK - IN - THE - BOX — A name sometimes given to a geared differential mechanism. See *Gearing, Differential*.

JACKSHAFT—An intermediate shaft between the prime mover and the machine which is to be driven. In automobile transmissions, the shaft betwen the main power drive and the driven member.

JAG—A term used variously to mean a small load; a projection; or a notch or barb.

JAG BOLT—See *Bolt, Jag*.

JAGGER — A shop term for a chisel with notched or toothed edges.

JAM NUT—A second nut forced or jammed against the main nut to prevent loosening. Sometimes called a lock nut. See *Nut, Jam*.

JAM PLATES—An old shop name for screw plates or dies. Dies were often made in an old file or other piece of steel before the days of die stocks and removable dies. In many cases the threads were literally "jammed" rather than cut.

JARNO TAPER—A system of machine tapers designed by Oscar J. Beale of the Brown & Sharpe Co. to simplify the designation of tapers, Jarno being his pen name for articles on machine shop work. The taper was 6/10 inch per foot or one inch in twenty, and the number gave the diameter of both the large and small ends. Multiplying the number of the taper by 8 gave the small diameter and multiplying by 10 gave the large diameter. It was a very simple system and was adopted by the Pratt & Whitney Co., the Norton Co. and others. It has now been abandoned to secure uniformity by use of the American Standards Association standard.

JAW CLUTCH—See *Clutch, Jaw*.

JAWS—Parts of chucks or other mechanisms for holding tools or work. Also any openings, such as the forks of a knuckle joint, or the pedestals of a locomotive frame which hold the driving and other boxes for the axles.

JET PUMP—See *Pump, Jet.*

JEWEL—A small bearing in watches, clocks and instruments of various kinds. Some are made of semi-precious stones or artificial substitutes. They reduce friction and carry a heavy load per square inch of projected area, because they have practically a point bearing.

JEWEL STONES—Stones used as bearings in watches and fine recording instruments range in size from 0.054 to 0.170 inch, varying by from 4 to 12 thousandths of an inch. Pallet stones for escapements vary from 0.0128 to 0.06168 inches in thickness.

JEWELS, INDUSTRIAL—Hard stones, such as rubies and sapphires, used for instrument bearings or for contact points in gages.

JEWELRY ALLOYS— Usually soft, light-colored alloys used in cheap jewelry and some plated ware.

JIG—A loosely used term to designate a device for holding work while different operations are performed, or for assembling various parts into a complete mechanism.

JIG BORER—A type of vertical spindle milling machine provided with accurate means of locating the work table under the spindle so as to secure the correct location. Two methods of location are used. One is a very accurate screw, sometimes with a device for compensating for any errors in the screw. Another uses standard length rods and size blocks, together with micrometers or indicators, to locate the work in two directions, at right angles to each other.

JIG-BORING—An operation in which a single point tool bores work accurately while it is located on a work table which can be located with precision, to bring any part of the work under the boring tool at the right distance from other holes. Its main feature is the accurate spacing of holes rapidly. Jig boring can be done on milling machines as well as on specially designed machines, which are called jig-borers. It usually means the work is done on this kind of a machine, but the term really means "precision boring."

Moore jig borer.

JIG BUSHING—A hardened steel guide for drills or other tools, set into jigs and fixtures. They are now standardized as to the main dimensions.

JIG, DRILL—A device for holding work so that all holes may be drilled in their correct positions. Holding devices for milling and planing are usually called *fixtures,* but many use the terms interchangeably. This is also true of fixtures made for assembling parts of various sizes, up to the wings and fuselages of larger airplanes.

JIG FEET—The points on which jigs or fixtures rest on the machine in which they are used.

JIG GRINDER—A machine for grinding the holes in jig and die work. It is usually vertical and has methods of locating the work similar to those used on jig borers, or jig boring machines. Some use an auxiliary grinding spindle in a jig borer.

JIG, STRING—A jig or fixture which holds several pieces to be machined at one setting of the machine or jig.

JIG, TUMBLE—A local name for a drill jig which is rolled or tumbled over to bring different surfaces under the drilling spindle.

Some may call it a box jig, or a roll-over jig, but the latter name is usually applied to jigs which are mounted in bearings and roll over to bring opposite sides of the work on top.

Jigs for milling connecting rods.

JIGGING MACHINE — A name sometimes given to a machine of the jig boring type.

JIG(S), — Many kinds of jigs are used to secure duplicate parts of machines, especially in mass production shops. They are called by various names, which usually indicate either their construction or their use. Some of the more common names are box, clamp, cradle, drilling, milling, pillar, roll-over or rotary, and turtle-back. A few are shown in outline.

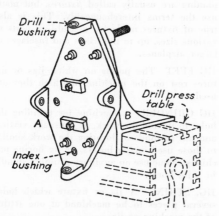

This type of rotary jig fastens to the drill press table. Body **A**, supported by angle plate **B**, rotates and is indexed by pin and bushings shown.

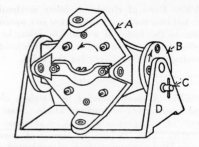

Double-acting rotary jig. Work clamped at **A** which revolves on **B**, and **B** also turns in **D**, located by index pin **C**. Good for large work.

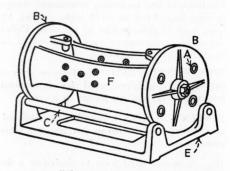

Cradle jig. This jig can also drill end holes when removed from cradle. Bushings are at **A** in the ends **B**. These ends roll on bars **C** which are held in base **E**. Cradle is removed for drilling end holes.

JIG(S), AIRCRAFT USAGE — Jigs or fixtures are to secure duplicate parts by guiding tools at work. Duplicate fixtures should produce duplicate work. Methods of insuring duplicate fixtures must check vital dimensions against wear and distortion. Dimensions can be transferred more accurately than they can be measured. Douglas Aircraft Co. defines *working jig* — for holding the piece being machined. *Master jig* fits into the working jig and checks the mating points. *Control master* fits into the master jig and checks mating points.

JIM CROW — One name for a machine for bending or straightening rails or other similar pieces.

JITNEYS — A shop term for shop trucks or inter-plant locomotives. Also called "bugs."

JO BLOCKS — See *Blocks, Measuring* and *Johansson* or *"Jo" Blocks.*

JOB EVALUATION—Determining the value of any worker in production. It can also be applied to the relative value of the part being made or the method used.

JOB SHOP—A shop which specializes in repairs to machines of various kinds. While such a shop sometimes takes contracts for a small number of pieces, it should not be confused with a "contract shop," the main work of which is the making of articles in large quantities, by contract.

JOGGING—A shop term for slow, intermittent movements, such as in setting a tool or bringing work into position. Similar to "inching."

JOHANSSON OR "JO" BLOCKS—Accurate gage blocks introduced into this country by Johansson, then taken over by Ford and now made by the Brown & Sharpe Co. There are several makers of similar blocks at present.

JOINTS USED IN ARC WELDING — See *Welding, Types of Joints.*

JOINT, UNIVERSAL — A shaft connection which allows movement in any direction within a limited angle, and still conveys a positive motion to the driven shaft. Many universal joints will function up to 45 degrees.

JOMINY TEST—A test used in comparing the hardenability of unknown steels. It is limited,

as it deals with the hardenability of the steel in its unquenched or partially quenched state. The Jominy sample is normalized and finish machined 1 inch in diameter and 3⅝ inches long, with a one-inch flange at one end, 1¼ inches in diameter. The sample is heated to proper temperature and cooled by water flowing *against the end of the piece only.* A flat surface is ground lengthwise 0.015 inch deep. Rockwell C readings are taken 1⁄16 inch apart for a distance of 2 inches, from the quenched end. A fixture is provided to hold the piece vertically by the flange, while the water plays against the lower end for about ten minutes. The test may be amplified in various ways.

JOURNAL—The part of a rotating shaft which is supported by a bearing. The name is sometimes erroneously applied to the bearing instead of the shaft.

JOURNAL BOX—The part of a bearing in which the shaft revolves.

JUMP THREAD—See *Screw Thread, Jump.*

JUMP WELD—The welding of parts to form a T. In other words, welding the edge of a plate against the flat surface of another plate.

JUNK RING—Usually means the metal ring used to retain the packing rings where the rings do not fit into the piston itself. Sometimes means the soft packing material used on some pistons.

K

KAMARSCH METAL—One of the many alloys used for bearing metals. It contains antimony, copper and tin.

KAOLIN—An aluminum silicate clay. Also called China clay.

KEEPER— Any piece of magnetic material placed across the poles of any magnet. This provides a free flow of magnetic lines across the poles and is supposed to reduce the loss of magnetism.

KENATRONS — Electronic tubes which produce high voltages for X-ray work.

KENNAMETAL—This, according to the makers, is a tungsten-tantalum carbide which uses cobalt as a binder in the sintering process.

KENTANIUM—A metal developed by Kennametal, Inc., for use at high temperatures. A tube with a wall thickness of only 0.0245 inch has been heated electrically to 1,800 deg. F. in 15 seconds, then cooled to 300 deg. F. by air blast in 30 seconds and subjected to a tensile stress of over 12,500 p.s.i. for 100 hours.

KERF—The slot cut by a saw in separating two pieces of material. The width of the cut made by the removal of the material.

KEROSENE—One of the products distilled from petroleum. A highly inflammable light oil used for lamps and stoves. Sometimes called "coal oil."

KEY—Primarily, a piece which prevents movement between two parts in one or more directions. It may be of any shape, but is usually square or rectangular. Frequently used to prevent pulleys from turning on shafting or locomotive driving wheels from turning on the axles. Keys are also used to prevent end or side motion in machine assemblies.

KEY, BARTH—A form of key designed by Carl Barth. It has a 45-degree angle in the hub. The object was to avoid concentrated stresses in the hub at the square corners of the ordinary key. The tendency of the angular sides to act as a wedge in splitting the hub

seemed to offset its advantages and it never became popular. The Lewis key is in distinct contrast to this.

KEY, CENTER—A name given to a flat piece of steel used for removing taper shank drills and other tools from drill spindles or similar work. It is more commonly called a *drift*.

KEY, DRAW—A flat tapered key for holding tapered shanks in their spindles. See *Key, Drift*.

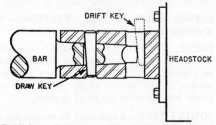

Drift key. Bar connection to the spindle.

KEY, DRIFT—A tapered key for forcing tapered shank tools out of a spindle, as shown. It is used in boring machines and drilling machines using tapered shank drills. The illustration also shows a draw key which is used to hold the tapered shank in place. Same as center key.

KEY FIT—See *Spline Fits*.

KEY, KENNEDY—A method of keying shafts designed by Julian Kennedy, of Pittsburgh, for use in such heavy work as rolling mill shafts. Two square keys are used, 90 degrees apart, and one-quarter the diameter of the shaft itself, where the diameter exceeds 6 inches. For smaller shafts but one key is used.

KEY, LEWIS—A key designed by Wilford Lewis to be subject only to compression and not to shearing stresses, as in most keys. It was however, in shear across its diagonal dimension. Never widely used.

KEY, NORDBERG—A key developed by the Nordberg Engineering Co. The large diameter

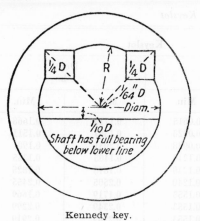

Kennedy key.

is about one-quarter the size of the shaft, up to 6 inches in diameter. Above this, the diameter is one-fifth the shaft diameter. It was Nordberg's practice to drill a small hole at A, right at the joint, then a large hole at B, but not to exceed the diameter of the key. This was to prevent the drill crowding into the softer metal of the cast iron hub. Then the hole was reamed with a taper of $\frac{1}{16}$ inch per foot and the key driven home.

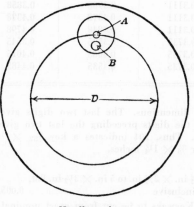

Nordberg key.

KEYSEAT—A slot or recess in a shaft, in a hub or in other parts, to receive the key which prevents motion. Same as keyway, and refers to straight keys and keyways.

KEYSEATER OR KEYSEATING MACHINE —Either a broaching machine designed for cutting keyways in the hubs of pulleys or gears, or a machine which mills keyseats in shafts or in hub bores. Some use a small end mill, while one design drives a small plain milling cutter held in a bar which goes into the bore of the pulley.

KEY, TAPER—A flat key which is not parallel on the upper and lower sides. Formerly rather widely used to draw pieces together (for example, a pulley on its shaft), when the keyway in the pulley was tapered at the same angle. The head, or projection on the end, facilitated drawing, or forcing the key out of the slot.

KEYWAY—Practically a keyseat, except that it is used to designate long slots in which sliding keys, or *feathers*, slide, as in some designs of lathe carriage feeds. The groove in both the shaft and in the piece which it connects may be called a keyway.

KEYWAYS, FOR GEAR HUBS—Keyways for gear hubs have been standardized by the American Gear Manufacturers Association to secure uniform practice in the industry. This standard is known as B 17.1 1943; its details are:

KEYSLOT—The recess cut for Woodruff keys. This is done by sinking a milling cutter of the right diameter and width into the shaft, as shown. These dimensions have been standardized as shown. See *Key, Woodruff*.

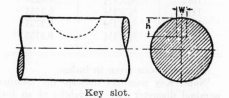

Key slot.

Depth of Keyways for Square Keys

The depth of keyways shall be one-half of the key height measured at the edge, according to Fig. 1 on page 237.

Fig. 1 and the table are also used for plain and gib head taper keys with the standard taper of $\frac{1}{8}$ in. per ft. where the depth shown is the deep end of the keyway.

Where the depth of keyway is measured on the centerline of the key instead of the vertical wall as recommended, use the formulae shown in Fig. 2 on page 237.

It is understood that these keys are to be cut from cold-finished stock and are to be used

235

Dimensions for Keyslot

Key[1] Number	Nominal Key Size A × B	Keyslot Width W Max.	Keyslot Width W Min.	Keyslot Depth h Max.	Keyslot Depth h Min.
204	1/16 × 1/2	0.0630	0.0615	0.1713	0.1668
304	3/32 × 1/2	0.0943	0.0928	0.1561	0.1511
305	3/32 × 5/8	0.0943	0.0928	0.2031	0.1981
404	1/8 × 1/2	0.1255	0.1240	0.1405	0.1355
405	1/8 × 5/8	0.1255	0.1240	0.1875	0.1825
406	1/8 × 3/4	0.1255	0.1240	0.2505	0.2455
505	5/32 × 5/8	0.1568	0.1553	0.1719	0.1669
506	5/32 × 3/4	0.1568	0.1553	0.2349	0.2299
507	5/32 × 7/8	0.1568	0.1553	0.2969	0.2919
606	3/16 × 3/4	0.1880	0.1863	0.2193	0.2143
607	3/16 × 7/8	0.1880	0.1863	0.2813	0.2763
608	3/16 × 1	0.1880	0.1863	0.3443	0.3393
609	3/16 × 1 1/8	0.1880	0.1863	0.3903	0.3853
807	1/4 × 7/8	0.2505	0.2487	0.2500	0.2450
808	1/4 × 1	0.2505	0.2487	0.3130	0.3080
809	1/4 × 1 1/8	0.2505	0.2487	0.3590	0.3540
810	1/4 × 1 1/4	0.2505	0.2487	0.4220	0.4170
811	1/4 × 1 3/8	0.2505	0.2487	0.4690	0.4640
812	1/4 × 1 1/2	0.2505	0.2487	0.5160	0.5110
1008	5/16 × 1	0.3130	0.3111	0.2818	0.2768
1009	5/16 × 1 1/8	0.3130	0.3111	0.3278	0.3228
1010	5/16 × 1 1/4	0.3130	0.3111	0.3908	0.3858
1011	5/16 × 1 3/8	0.3130	0.3111	0.4378	0.4328
1012	5/16 × 1 1/2	0.3130	0.3111	0.4848	0.4798
1210	3/8 × 1 1/4	0.3755	0.3735	0.3595	0.3545
1211	3/8 × 1 3/8	0.3755	0.3735	0.4065	0.4015
1212	3/8 × 1 1/2	0.3755	0.3735	0.4535	0.4485

All dimensions given in inches.

[1]Note: Key numbers indicate the nominal key dimensions. The last two digits give the nominal diameter (B) in eighths of an inch and the digits preceding the last two give the nominal width (A) in thirty-seconds of an inch. Thus, 204 indicates a key 2/32 × 4/8 or 1/16 × 1/2 inches; 1210 indicates a key 12/32 × 10/8 or 3/8 × 1 1/4 inches.

without machining, as this AGMA Standard is for general industrial practice. The keystock is to be cold-rolled steel 0.10 to 0.20 carbon.

Keystock to vary from the exact nominal size in width and thickness to a negative tolerance as follows:

3/32 in. sq. to 3/8 in. sq., inclusive ...... 0.002 in.
1/2 in. sq. to 3/4 in. sq., inclusive ...... 0.0025 in.
7/8 in. sq. to 1 1/2 in. × 1 in. flat, inclusive .... 0.003 in.
1 3/4 in. × 1 1/4 in. to 3 in. × 2 in. flat, inclusive .... 0.004 in.

3 1/2 in. × 2 1/2 in. to 5 in. × 3 1/2 in. flat, inclusive .... 0.005 in.

Keyways to be cut from exact nominal size to plus 0.002 in. in width, and depth shall be nominal to plus 1/64 in. for straight keys. For taper keys depth shall be nominal to 1/64 in. minus.

For heat-treated pinions the depth shall be 1/32 in. to 3/64 in. over nominal size with a minimum radius of 1/32 in. in corners of keyways.

For highly stressed or alternating loads encountered, it is recommended that the corners of the keyway be rounded to a minimum of $\frac{1}{32}$ in. radius and not over a maximum of 1/5 of the keyway depth. The edges of the keystock are to be rounded to correspond.

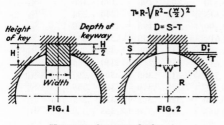

$$T = R - \sqrt{R^2 - \left(\tfrac{W}{2}\right)^2}$$

$$D = S - T$$

FIG. 1   FIG. 2

Keyways for gear hubs.

Keyways and Key Stocks for Holes in Gears

Diameter of Holes Inclusive, In.	Standard Keyways and Keys		
	Keyways		Key Stock
	Width	Depth	
$\frac{5}{16}$ to $\frac{7}{16}$	$\frac{3}{32}$	$\frac{3}{64}$	$\frac{3}{16} \times \frac{3}{32}$*
$\frac{1}{2}$ to $\frac{9}{16}$	$\frac{1}{8}$	$\frac{1}{16}$	$\frac{1}{8} \times \frac{1}{8}$
$\frac{5}{8}$ to $\frac{7}{8}$	$\frac{3}{16}$	$\frac{3}{32}$	$\frac{3}{32} \times \frac{3}{16}$
$\frac{15}{16}$ to $1\frac{1}{4}$	$\frac{1}{4}$	$\frac{1}{8}$	$\frac{1}{4} \times \frac{1}{4}$
$1\frac{5}{16}$ to $1\frac{3}{8}$	$\frac{5}{16}$	$\frac{5}{32}$	$\frac{5}{16} \times \frac{5}{16}$
$1\frac{7}{16}$ to $1\frac{3}{4}$	$\frac{3}{8}$	$\frac{3}{16}$	$\frac{3}{8} \times \frac{3}{8}$
$1\frac{13}{16}$ to $2\frac{1}{4}$	$\frac{1}{2}$	$\frac{1}{4}$	$\frac{1}{2} \times \frac{1}{2}$
$2\frac{5}{16}$ to $2\frac{3}{4}$	$\frac{5}{8}$	$\frac{5}{16}$	$\frac{5}{8} \times \frac{5}{8}$
$2\frac{13}{16}$ to $3\frac{1}{4}$	$\frac{3}{4}$	$\frac{3}{8}$	$\frac{3}{4} \times \frac{3}{4}$
$3\frac{5}{16}$ to $3\frac{3}{4}$	$\frac{7}{8}$	$\frac{7}{16}$	$\frac{7}{8} \times \frac{7}{8}$
$3\frac{13}{16}$ to $4\frac{1}{2}$	1	$\frac{1}{2}$	1×1
$4\frac{9}{16}$ to $5\frac{1}{2}$	$1\frac{1}{4}$	$\frac{7}{16}$	$1\frac{1}{4} \times \frac{7}{8}$
$5\frac{9}{16}$ to $6\frac{1}{2}$	$1\frac{1}{2}$	$\frac{1}{2}$	$1\frac{1}{2} \times 1$
$6\frac{9}{16}$ to $7\frac{1}{2}$	$1\frac{3}{4}$	$\frac{5}{8}$	$1\frac{3}{4} \times 1\frac{1}{4}$*
$7\frac{9}{16}$ to $8\frac{15}{16}$	2	$\frac{3}{4}$	$2 \times 1\frac{1}{2}$*
9 to $10\frac{15}{16}$	$2\frac{1}{2}$	$\frac{7}{8}$	$2\frac{1}{2} \times 1\frac{3}{4}$*
11 to $12\frac{15}{16}$	3	1	3×2 *
13 to $14\frac{15}{16}$	$3\frac{1}{2}$	$1\frac{1}{4}$	$3\frac{1}{2} \times 2\frac{1}{2}$*
15 to $17\frac{15}{16}$	4	$1\frac{1}{2}$	4×3 *
18 to $21\frac{15}{16}$	5	$1\frac{3}{4}$	$5 \times 3\frac{1}{2}$*

*Shaft sizes for these keys are not listed in American Standard B77.1—1943.

Diameter of Holes Inclusive, In.	Keyways		Key Stocks
	Width	Depth	
$\frac{1}{2}$ to $\frac{9}{16}$	$\frac{1}{8}$	$\frac{3}{64}$	$\frac{1}{8} \times \frac{3}{32}$
$\frac{5}{8}$ to $\frac{7}{8}$	$\frac{3}{16}$	$\frac{1}{16}$	$\frac{3}{16} \times \frac{1}{8}$
$\frac{13}{16}$ to $1\frac{1}{4}$	$\frac{1}{4}$	$\frac{3}{32}$	$\frac{1}{4} \times \frac{3}{16}$
$1\frac{5}{16}$ to $1\frac{3}{8}$	$\frac{5}{16}$	$\frac{1}{8}$	$\frac{5}{16} \times \frac{1}{4}$
$1\frac{13}{16}$ to $2\frac{1}{4}$	$\frac{3}{8}$	$\frac{1}{8}$	$\frac{3}{8} \times \frac{1}{4}$
$1\frac{7}{16}$ to $1\frac{3}{4}$	$\frac{1}{2}$	$\frac{3}{16}$	$\frac{1}{2} \times \frac{3}{8}$
$2\frac{5}{16}$ to $2\frac{3}{4}$	$\frac{5}{8}$	$\frac{7}{32}$	$\frac{5}{8} \times \frac{7}{16}$
$2\frac{13}{16}$ to $3\frac{1}{4}$	$\frac{3}{4}$	$\frac{1}{4}$	$\frac{3}{4} \times \frac{1}{2}$
$3\frac{5}{16}$ to $3\frac{3}{4}$	$\frac{7}{8}$	$\frac{5}{16}$	$\frac{7}{8} \times \frac{5}{8}$
$3\frac{13}{16}$ to $4\frac{1}{2}$	1	$\frac{3}{8}$	$1 \times \frac{3}{4}$

XX. It is recommended that these **alternates** be used only when conditions make it **undesirable** to use the sizes in the above table.

KEY, WOODRUFF—A semi-circular or half-round key resting in a circular groove cut in the shaft. Sometimes called a half-moon key. Largely used in machine building. See page 240.

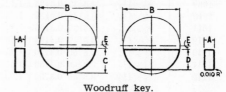

Woodruff key.

KICK PRESS—See *Press, Foot or Kick.*

KILLED ACID—Soldering acid in which zinc has been dissolved. It is said to be killed when it has dissolved all the zinc that it will absorb.

KILOGRAM—A thousand grams, which equals 2.2046 pounds. See *Metric System.*

KILOLITER — One thousand liters. Equals 264.2 gallons. See *Metric System.*

KILOMETER—One thousand meters. Equals 3,270.8336 feet or 0.62137 miles. See *Metric System.*

KILOWATT—One thousand watts, the unit of electrical power. Used in comparing electrical energy with mechanical horse power, one kilowatt is equal to 1.34 horse power, or 746 watts equals one horse power.

Dimensions for Woodruff Keys

Key[1] Number	Nominal Key Size A × B	Width of Key A Max.	Width of Key A Min.	Diam. of Key B Max.	Diam. of Key B Min.	Height of Key C Max.	Height of Key C Min.	Height of Key D Max.	Height of Key D Min.	Distance Below Center E
204	1⁄16 × 1⁄2	0.0635	0.0625	0.500	0.490	0.203	0.198	0.194	0.188	3⁄64
304	3⁄32 × 1⁄2	0.0948	0.0938	0.500	0.490	.203	.198	.194	.188	3⁄64
305	3⁄32 × 5⁄8	0.0948	0.0938	0.625	0.615	.250	.245	.240	.234	1⁄16
404	1⁄8 × 1⁄2	0.1260	0.1250	0.500	0.490	.203	.198	.194	.188	3⁄64
405	1⁄8 × 5⁄8	0.1260	0.1250	0.625	0.615	.250	.245	.240	.234	1⁄16
406	1⁄8 × 3⁄4	0.1260	0.1250	0.750	0.740	.313	.308	.303	.297	1⁄16
505	5⁄32 × 5⁄8	0.1573	0.1563	0.625	0.615	.250	.245	.240	.234	1⁄16
506	5⁄32 × 3⁄4	0.1573	0.1563	0.750	0.740	.313	.308	.303	.297	1⁄16
507	5⁄32 × 7⁄8	0.1573	0.1563	0.875	0.865	.375	.370	.365	.359	1⁄16
606	3⁄16 × 3⁄4	0.1885	0.1875	0.750	0.740	.313	.308	.303	.297	1⁄16
607	3⁄16 × 7⁄8	0.1885	0.1875	0.875	0.865	.375	.370	.365	.359	1⁄16
608	3⁄16 × 1	0.1885	0.1875	1.000	0.990	.438	.433	.428	.422	1⁄16
609	3⁄16 × 1 1⁄8	0.1885	0.1875	1.125	1.115	.484	.479	.475	.469	5⁄64
807	1⁄4 × 7⁄8	0.2510	0.2500	0.875	0.865	.375	.370	.365	.359	1⁄16
808	1⁄4 × 1	0.2510	0.2500	1.000	0.990	.438	.433	.428	.422	1⁄16
809	1⁄4 × 1 1⁄8	0.2510	0.2500	1.125	1.115	.484	.479	.475	.469	5⁄64
810	1⁄4 × 1 1⁄4	0.2510	0.2500	1.250	1.240	.547	.542	.537	.531	5⁄64
811	1⁄4 × 1 3⁄8	0.2510	0.2500	1.375	1.365	.594	.589	.584	.578	3⁄32
812	1⁄4 × 1 1⁄2	0.2510	0.2500	1.500	1.490	.641	.636	.631	.625	7⁄64
1008	5⁄16 × 1	0.3135	0.3125	1.000	0.990	.438	.433	.428	.422	1⁄16
1009	5⁄16 × 1 1⁄8	0.3135	0.3125	1.125	1.115	.484	.479	.475	.469	5⁄64
1010	5⁄16 × 1 1⁄4	0.3135	0.3125	1.250	1.240	.547	.542	.537	.531	5⁄64
1011	5⁄16 × 1 3⁄8	0.3135	0.3125	1.375	1.365	.594	.589	.584	.578	3⁄32
1012	5⁄16 × 1 1⁄2	0.3135	0.3125	1.500	1.490	.641	.636	.631	.625	7⁄64
1210	3⁄8 × 1 1⁄4	0.3760	0.3750	1.250	1.240	.547	.542	.537	.531	5⁄64
1211	3⁄8 × 1 3⁄8	0.3760	0.3750	1.375	1.365	.594	.589	.584	.578	3⁄32
1212	3⁄8 × 1 1⁄2	0.3760	0.3750	1.500	1.490	.641	.636	.631	.625	7⁄64

All dimensions given in inches.

[1]Note: Key numbers indicate the nominal key dimensions. The last two digits give the nominal diameter (B) in eighths of an inch and the digits preceding the last two give the nominal width (A) in thirty-seconds of an inch. Thus, 204 indicates a key 2⁄32 × 4⁄8 or 1⁄16 × 1⁄2 inches; 1210 indicates a key 12⁄32 × 10⁄8 or 3⁄8 × 1 1⁄4 inches.

KINEMATICS—The science or study of motion.

KINETIC—Movement, or what causes motion.

KINETIC ENERGY—The ability to perform work due to velocity. It is measured in foot pounds. The kinetic energy of a body is the amount of work it will do in coming to rest. In a drop hammer it is the weight of the drop, or "tup," times the distance it falls, in feet.

KINGPIN—A main pin holding a mechanism together, such as the pin which holds the steering spindle or knuckle in an automobile.

KIRKSITE—A metal with about 94 per cent of pure zinc. The remaining 6 per cent is aluminum, copper and magnesium. It is lighter than lead and melts at about 717 deg. F. Used in temporary dies in forming sheet aluminum parts.

KNEADING DIES—Dies which work against the surface of metal, such as type bars, and rock under pressure, "kneading" the metal into depressions cut in the dies. It is similar to coining except that in that operation the metal is forced into the depressions by pressure alone. It is used in shops making type bars for typewriters or calculating and adding machines.

KNEE—Usually means that part of a machine which projects from the base or pedestal.

KNEE ACTION—Movement of two members joined so as to resemble the action of a human knee. Similar to a toggle joint.

KNEE-JOINT—See *Knee Action.*

KNIFE EDGE—A sharp edge, usually hardened, which acts as a bearing for rolling contacts, as in a static balancing machine. The small contact reduces friction. The edge may sometimes be slightly rounded.

KNOCKOUT—Any piece used in removing or knocking out pieces, such as drill shanks out of adapters or drilling machine spindles. Also for knocking work out of a punch press die.

KNOOP INDENTER—A diamond ground to a pyramidal form as specified by the U. S. Bureau of Standards, to produce a diamond shape indentation with long and short diagonals of approximately 7 to 1 ratio. It is useful in testing thin or brittle materials, as the shape reduces the tendency to cracking. This indenter is used in the Tukon and other testers. It gives an impression approximately $\frac{1}{30}$ the depth of the long diagonal. Pressures as low as 10 grams can sometimes be used.

KNUCKLE OR KNUCKLE JOINT—A piece or a complete joint which permits motion in one plane, as the steering knuckle of an automobile. Movement similar to the knuckles of the hand.

KNURLING—The production of a roughened surface by contact with a wheel having a sharpened edge. It forces metal above the surface while making indentations below the surface. Some knurls have designs engraved on them for decorating brass and other soft materials. Knurling is frequently used to produce a roughened surface for holding parts which are forced together. The knurls make serrations or pointed projections on the shaft. Standard or preferred sizes are shown below.

Preferred Sizes for Cylindrical Type Knurls

Nominal Outside Diameter	Width of Face	Diameter of Hole	Number of Teeth for Standard Diametral Pitches N			
D	F	A	.64P	96P	128P	160P
½	³⁄₁₆	³⁄₁₆	32	48	64	80
⅝	¼	¼	40	60	80	100
¾	⅜	¼	48	72	96	120
⅞	⅜	¼	56	84	112	140

Additional Sizes for Bench and Engine Lathe Tool Holders

⅝	⁵⁄₁₆	⁷⁄₃₂	40	60	80	100
1	⅜	⁵⁄₁₆	64	96	128	160

L

LACE—See *Belt Lace, Lacing Belt.*

LACE LEATHER—Leather strips, usually oil-tanned and frequently of rawhide, used in lacing ends of flat belts together. Much less used than formerly, as cementing into endless belts is much more common except in small shops.

LACING BELTS—A method of fastening the ends of belting by use of narrow strips of leather, usually rawhide or semi-tanned leather. This was laced through holes punched in both ends of the belts. Fasteners of sheet metal and of wire were also used. Some belts were also cemented into endless strips, which is now being done in many cases. The lacing method enabled slack, due to the stretching of the belts, to be taken up.

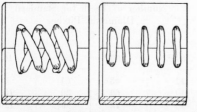

Belt lacings.

LACQUER—A finish harder than enamel, originated in the Far East. Not as elastic as enamel.

LAG—A slowing up of motion, intentional or otherwise. A dropping behind the regular rate of movement.

LAG SCREW—A wood screw with a square or hexagon head, usually the former. Used in bolting machines to the floor or to skids and for fastening hangers for shafting of all kinds to ceiling timbers. See *Screws, Wood.*

LAMINAR OIL FLOW—The layer of oil next to the bearing tends to cling to the bearing surface. The other layers between the bearing and the shaft slip over each other, similar to a deck of cards. This internal "shear" is known as fluid friction.

LAMINATION—One of a number of thin plates or sheets used in building up shims, cores of electrical apparatus or for other purposes.

LAMP SOCKET SCREW THREADS — See *Screw Threads, Electric Lamp Sockets.*

LAMPBLACK—A powdery soot obtained from burning oil, coal tar or resin. Used in making rubber tires, paints, pencils and carbon paper.

LAND—This term formerly applied to all metal left between the grooves or flutes of drills, reamers and taps. Later definitions restrict the term to portions of this metal.

LANTERN GEAR OR PINION—A gear built up by bars or rods between two flanges or disks, the bars acting as gear teeth. Largely used in mill work when the gearing was made of wood. Sometimes found in old clock mechanisms, made of brass disks and steel pins.

LAP—The term is applied in several ways. Among them are seams which lap over each other; the distance a valve must move before opening its port, when valve is central on its seat, and to a tool used in lapping holes or other surfaces by use of fine abrasives. See also *Lapping.*

LAP JOINT—A bolted, riveted or welded joint in which two plates lap over each other to permit double thickness at this point. In welding, it is usual to make a welded seam at both edges of the plate. See *Riveting* and *Welding.*

LAP, LEAD—A bar or piece of lead which carries abrasive pressed into its surface. Lead laps are usually round for finishing holes which have been bored and perhaps ground.

LAP, SURFACE—A flat plate, usually of cast iron, which has been machined as nearly flat as possible, and with fine abrasive rolled into its surface. It is used in finishing flat surface joints where as perfect a fit as possible is necessary. The grooves are to receive the fine particles removed by the abrasive. Now nearly obsolete.

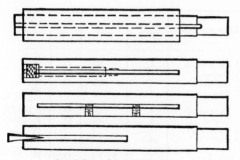

Lead lap. Laps for holes.

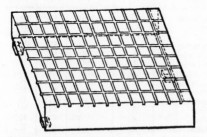

Surface lap. Lapping plate for flat work.

LAP WELD—See *Weld, Lap.*

LAPPING—A method of finishing surfaces of any kind with very fine abrasives. It is a form of grinding. Usually the abrasive is rolled or pressed into the surface of the lap which may be of copper, lead, cast iron or close grained wood. The lap is then applied to the surface in various ways to secure the finish desired. Recommendations for lapping materials for different uses are given on page 242.

LATENT HEAT—The amount of heat which disappears when some change, other than temperature, takes place. This is seen in the decalescence point of steel. See *Decalescence.*

LATEX—A milky juice from the rubber tree. Used in making natural rubber.

LATHE—A machine tool for turning, cutting off, boring, facing or cutting threads in, or on, metal work of any kind. It is the basic machine tool of the small shop. See various types of lathes which follow.

LATHE ANGLE PLATE—An angle plate made for use on the face plate of a lathe. It

is very useful in holding work at unusual angles. See *Angle Plate, Lathe.*

LATHE APRON—The front of the tool carriage which contains the gearing and other mechanism which controls the feeds.

LATHE, AUTOMATIC—A lathe in which the various movements of the tool are controlled by automatic mechanism of various kinds. In a fully automatic machine, the stock is also fed through the spindle without attention of the operator.

LATHE, BENCH (HAND) — A small lathe with short legs for mounting on a bench. Used for turning with hand tools unless a slide rest is used. See *Slide Rest.* When mounted on legs reaching to the floor it is usually called a "hand" lathe. Some bench lathes are also made with screw cutting and power feed. Sometimes called "precision" bench lathes.

LATHE, BLANCHARD—Supposed to be the first machine designed for turning irregular shapes such as gun stocks, for which it was originally made. The tool movement is controlled by a master pattern set parallel with the work to be turned. First used to turn stocks for rifles at the Springfield Armory, Springfield, Mass. The first machine is still in the museum at the armory. Modifications of the machine use rotary cutters and are largely used for turning shoemakers' lasts.

LATHE, CAPSTAN — A British term for a turret lathe.

South Bend engine lathe.

LATHE, ENGINE—The most common form of lathe in a metal working shop, as it is geared for cutting screw threads with a single pointed tool as well as drilling, boring, facing and cutting off work. It is the basic machine

Lapping Recommendations

Uses	Compounds	Abrasive	Approx. grit	Vehicle	Solvent
Locomotive bootlegs and headers........	R7 ex. coarse	C.	50	G.	W.
Large steel valves.....................	R7 coarse	C.	90	G.	W.
Large steel valves, coarse gears (hard)....	R7 medium	C.	150	G.	W.
Small steel valves, fine gears (hard)......	R7 fine	C.	220	G.	W.
Spiral bevel gears—truck and bus........	R1 ex. coarse	C.	120	O.	K.
Spiral bevel gears—truck and bus........	R1 coarse	C.	150	O.	K.
Spiral bevel gears—automobile..........	R1 medium	C.	F	O.	K.
Hypoid gears—large....................	R1 fine	C.	FF	O.	K.
Hypoid gears and steel parts and use on Bethel-Player lapping machine........	R1 ex. fine	C.	FFFF	O.	K.
Truing rubber reclaiming rolls...........	RR1 special	C.	60	G.	K.
Spur gears (Red Wing lapper).. {fast cut	R8 medium	C.	150	G.	K.
{finish	R8 fine	C.	220	G.	K.
Large cast-steel or cast-iron gears........ {	W7 coarse	A.	90	G.	W.
{	W4 coarse	A.	90	G.	K.
{	W5 coarse	A.	90	G.	W.
Medium-size cast-steel or cast-iron gears and ball bearings.................... {	W7 medium	A.	150	G.	W.
{	W4 medium	A.	150	G.	K.
{	W5 medium	A.	150	G.	K.
{	W9 medium	A.	150	S.O.	W.
Small cast-steel or cast-iron gears and ball bearings.......................... {	W7 fine	A.	F	G.	W.
{	W4 fine	A.	F	G.	K.
{	W5 fine	A.	F	G.	K.
Aircraft engine cranks......... {fast cut	W40 medium	A.	F	S.O.	W.
{finish	W40 fine	A.	FFF	S.O.	W.
All large reduction gears (soft action)... {	G7 coarse	G.	150	G.	W.
{	G4 coarse	G.	150	G.	K.
All medium size reduction gears (soft action).................................. {	G7 medium	G.	220	G.	W.
{	G4 medium	G.	220	G.	K.
All fine reduction gears and nonferrous valves................................ {	G7 fine	G.	FF	G.	W.
{	G4 fine	G.	FF	G.	K.
Machine bearings............. ⎫ Molds........................ ⎪ General tool-room work....... ⎬ General use on Bethel-Player ⎪ lapping machine........... ⎭	H40 coarse	A.	220	S.O.	W.
	H41 coarse	A.	220	O.	K.
	H440 coarse	A.	220	G.	W.
	H40 medium	A.	320	S.O.	W.
	H41 medium	A.	320	O.	K.
	H440 medium	A.	400	G.	W.
	H40 fine	A.	800	S.O.	W.
	H41 fine	A.	800	O.	K.
	H440 fine	A.	600	G.	W.
	H400 fine	A.	800	S.O.	W.
	R440 fine	C.	600	G.	W.
High finish on Bethel-Player machine....	A41 medium	A.	600	O.	K.
Coarse polishing.....................	H46 coarse	A.	220	P.	W.
General polishing....................	H46 medium	A.	400	P.	W
Fine polishing.......................	H46 fine	A.	800	P.	W.
Extremely fine and soft lapping.........	H440 ex. fine	A.	1000	G.	W.
Extremely fine and medium-soft lapping..	W440 ex. fine	A.	1000	G.	W.

NOTE: All 400 series compounds are chemically pure and precision controlled. C.—Silicon carbide. A.—Aluminum oxide. G.—Garnet. G.—Grease. O.—Oil. S.O.—Soluble oil. P.—Paste. W.—Water K.—Kerosene.

tool in the small shop. A small engine lathe is shown on page 241. The motor drives a cone pulley in the base which is belted to the cone of the spindle. Many large engine lathes have an all-geared head and many special features.

LATHE, EXTENSION—A lathe in which the bed can be lengthened by moving the upper part along the base or lower bed. When the bed is lengthened a gap is formed near the headstock to swing large diameter work.

LATHE, FOX—A brass workers' lathe having a "fox" or chasing bar for cutting screw threads. The bar has a leader that acts as a nut on a leader of the desired pitch (or half the pitch if the leader is geared down) and carries the chasing tool along at the proper rate. It sometimes has a turret on the back head.

LATHE, GAP—A lathe having a U-shaped gap in the bed near the headstocks to permit swinging large diameter work.

LATHE, GUN—A lathe designed for boring and turning big guns. Usually a long lathe with feeds for the boring heads as well as for turning the outside of the gun.

LATHE, INGOT—A lathe designed for turning and cutting off ends of steel ingots.

LATHE OPERATIONS—While many kinds of operations can be performed on an engine lathe, the nine illustrations show those most commonly found in the average shop, on the type of engine lathe illustrated.

LATHE, PATTERN-MAKERS'—A wood working lathe in which the work is turned with a handtool or chisel and which has no power feed. Many pattern-makers' lathes carry a large face-plate at the back end of the spindle, sometimes extending almost to the floor. A portable tool rest which stands on the floor is used when turning large work.

LATHE, PIT—A lathe with a headstock on one side of a pit and a tailstock on the opposite side. The work swings in the pit and is machined by tools held in a tool carriage across the pit at the outside of the work. These lathes were formerly used in turning large fly-wheels which are now turned on vertical boring mills. Some of these lathes turned fly-wheels over 30 feet in diameter. It is doubtful if any are still in use or in existence.

LATHE, POLISHING—Not a lathe in the usual sense, but a head with a spindle carrying polishing wheels.

LATHE, PRECISION—A name usually applied to bench lathes for small and very accurate work. The same designation might apply to modern tool-makers' lathes except that they are usually mounted on their own legs.

LATHE, PROJECTILE—Heavy lathe designed for turning and machining projectiles. While this work can be done on any lathe of sufficient capacity, these lathes are designed especially for this work.

LATHE, PULLEY—Designed for turning pulleys with either a straight face or a crowned face, as desired. With the growing use of electric motor drive on each machine, the use of pulleys has greatly decreased and these special lathes are seldom seen.

LATHE, RING TURRET—A turret lathe designed by Foster some years ago in which the tools were held in a ring turret which encircled the bed. It was mounted on a carriage which fed the tools to the work. The ring turret moved around the saddle, under the bed, to bring new tools in position. It never became popular.

LATHE, ROLL TURNING—A heavy duty lathe for turning rolls for steel rolling mills and paper mills. On these lathes the tools are fed directly into the work in what is known as a "plunge cut."

LATHE, SCREW CUTTING—An engine lathe with a lead screw so that any thread for which gears are available can be chased with a single point tool.

LATHE, SEMI-AUTOMATIC—A lathe in which a sequence of machining operations is

Jones and Lamson semi-automatic lathe.

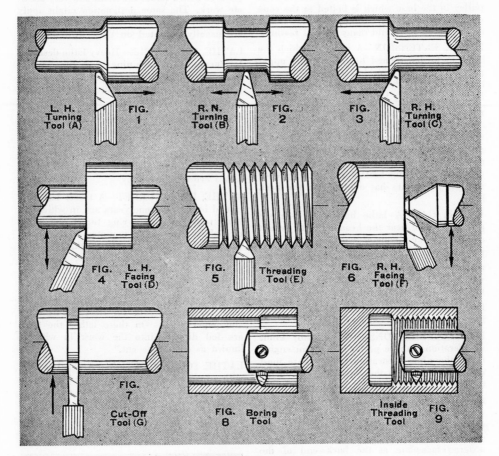

Nine common lathe operations.

performed without effort on the part of the operator. It is only necessary to remove the finished work and replace it with a piece not yet machined. Many call these automatic machines, but the term is not strictly correct.

LATHE, SHAFTING—A lathe designed for turning long lengths of shafting. It has simply a feed for the tool carriage but no screw cutting lead screw.

LATHE, SPEED—A small lathe with no back gearing, and on which turning is done with a slide rest rather than tool carriage with power feed. They are useful for many light operations and are frequently used for wood turning, as well as for metal. They differ, however, from a pattern-makers' lathe.

LATHE, SPINNING—A lathe designed for forming sheet metal into various hollow shapes as the metal is revolved in the lathe. The forming is done by forcing the sheet metal against a form of some kind, usually with a single round ended tool, as the metal revolves. Where only a few parts are needed, this is

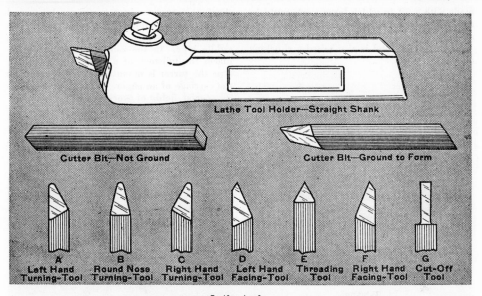

Lathe Tool Holder—Straight Shank

Cutter Bit—Not Ground   Cutter Bit—Ground to Form

A	B	C	D	E	F	G
Left Hand Turning-Tool	Round Nose Turning-Tool	Right Hand Turning-Tool	Left Hand Facing-Tool	Threading Tool	Right Hand Facing-Tool	Cut-Off Tool

Lathe tools.

Jones and Lamson ram type turret lathe.

generally cheaper than making even the most inexpensive dies.

LATHE, SWIVEL-HEAD—A lathe in which the head can be swung at an angle with the bed for boring taper holes. It is only used in special work.

LATHE, "T"—A type of engine lathe where the bed is at right angles to the spindle and used largely for facing work held on the face plate or in a chuck. Boring and turning is done with a tool carrying rest in line with the lathe spindle. Very old lathes of this type were

245

made with a pit in which large work could be handled. The work shown is 48 inches in diameter, 10 inches wide and 2 inches thick. It swings 60 inches and is also called a chucking lathe.

T-lathe.

LATHE TOOLS—Although many types and shapes of tools are used on engine lathes, the seven simple shapes shown will handle nearly all work found in the average shop. Those shown include both solid tools and tool bits used in a tool holder. The solid tools are formed from carbon or high speed steel, while the tool bits are likely to be of high speed steel or carbide, thus saving material. Many lathe tools have a small carbide tip on the cutting edge, but there is a tendency to use solid bits with cutting edges on the end. This reduces the loss by grinding and gives a long lasting tool. See illustration, page 245.

LATHE TOOLS, DIAMOND POINT—A solid tool with one end forged into a sort of projecting neck, turned nearly vertical. The upper or cutting surface was diamond shaped. It was a standard tool for many years but has been largely replaced by a tip of special alloy brazed or clamped to a holder. The diamond shape is now seldom seen in production turning.

LATHE, TURRET—A lathe having a multiple tool holder, which revolves on the tail or back carriage and presents new tools to the work for different operations. Many have automatic devices for turning the turret and for feeding the tools into the work. Unless they also handle the stock or work in and out of the

chuck they are semi-automatic machines and are not fully automatic. Turret lathes are made in two types, called the ram and the saddle type. In the ram type the turret replaces the tailstock of a lathe. In the saddle type the turret is mounted on what would be the carriage of an engine lathe. Each type has its special fields of work.

LATHE, TURRET, ELECTRO-CYCLE—A type of semi-automatic turret lathe built by the Warner & Swasey Co. in which the cycles, after the work is put in the chuck, are auto-

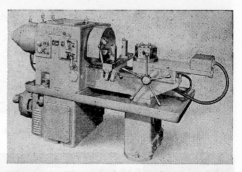

Warner and Swasey electro-cycle turret lathe.

matically controlled by electrical devices mounted on the turret slide. This controls the speed for different operations as well as the feed and the turning of the turret.

LATHE, VERTICAL—Name given to a type of vertical boring mill with a side head in addition to the usual cross rail and the tool heads which it carries. The name originated with the Bullard Co. See *Boring and Turning Mill.*

LATHE, WATCHMAKERS'—A very small bench lathe for jewelers and watchmakers.

LATHE, WHEEL—A class of lathe designed for turning locomotive driving wheels, when steam was the motive power. Some of these lathes could turn a wheel 90 inches in diameter. A caliper attachment is used to assist in getting both wheels of the same diameter. The passing of the steam locomotive makes these large lathes unnecessary. See page 247.

LAYING-OUT BENCH—A metal bench or plate having a level top, on which work can be laid out for future machining operations. Both this and the inspection bench are sometimes called "leveling benches."

Niles wheel lathe.

LAYOUT—In designing, the drawing which shows the general picture of the machine or plant. In shop work, lines drawn on the material to be machined to show what metal is to be cut away, what holes are to be drilled, etc.

LAYOUT FLUID—A fluid to be brushed on a metal surface so that marks made in laying out and design of work can be plainly seen. Some of these have largely replaced the use of "Prussian blue," which was formerly used for the same purpose.

LAYOUT PLATE—See *Plate, Layout.*

LEAD—A heavy, but soft, blue-gray metal. Sp. gr. 11.38. Melts at 621 deg. F. Has many uses both by itself and as an alloy.

LEAD—The advance made by a nut with one turn of the screw. With a single thread the lead and pitch are the same, but with a double thread the lead is twice as much as the pitch. Triple and quadruple threads reduce the pitch to one-third and one-quarter of the lead. In steam engine work it refers to the valve opening when the crank is on center.

LEAD ANGLE—A new name for the helix of screw threads. It is the angle of the thread at the pitch diameter to a line at *right angles* to the *axis* of the screw. In steam engine parlance, it is the angle made by the crank with relation to the cylinder axis, when the valve opens to admit steam to the cylinder.

LEAD BATH—One method of heating small tools for hardening consists of a container with molten lead into which the tool is dipped until it is heated to the temperature of the bath itself. Immersion in the lead prevents oxidization of the surface of the tool, as takes place in an open fire, the exposure being limited to the passage from the lead bath to the quenching tank.

LEAD BURNING—An incorrect term used for many years to describe joining lead surfaces by fusion or welding. No flux is used, but the parts to be joined must be perfectly cleaned either by shaving or by using a wire brush. The joint is sometimes made by fusing with hot lead or by a sort of soldering iron. Later practice is to use a small welding torch.

LEAD CAST OR PROOF—A sample casting made by pouring lead into a forging or other die to check the dimensions.

LEAD ERROR—A variation in the distance between the threads of any screw. In a screw with lead errors the load is not evenly distributed between all the threads as only two threads bear on each other. The load is taken by one side of one thread and by the other side of the second thread. Lead error affects the accuracy of the movement of parts affected by the screw.

LEAD SCREW—The screw which moves or "leads" the carriage of a screw cutting lathe.

LEADED BRASS—A standard grade of brass with about 65 per cent copper, a little lead and the rest zinc.

LEAF METAL—Metal in thin sheets or leaves, such as gold leaf or foil. See *Gold Leaf.*

LEAF SPRING—See under *Springs.*

LECTRO-ETCH—A process of etching where the action of the acid is accelerated by an electric current. The surrounding metal must be protected as in plain acid etching.

LEFT-HAND MOTION—Rotation opposite to the hands of a clock.

LEFT-HAND SPIRAL ON BEVEL GEARS—Left hand teeth incline away from the axis in a counter-clockwise direction when seen from the face of the gear. The mating gear is of the opposite "hand."

LEG VISE—A bench vise with a leg or strut reaching to the floor. This is seldom seen now.

LEHR—An oven used for annealing. The term is not in general use.

LENS, OBJECTIVE—The lens in a microscope which is nearest the object being examined.

LET-IN—Shop language for work where one piece is recessed into another.

LEVEL—An instrument to show when any surface is level, usually by means of a bubble in a horizontal glass tube. A piece of work is said to be level when it is checked by one of these instruments. The liquid in the tube is usually alcohol.

LEVEL, QUARTERING—A tool used in railroad shops to see if crank pins are 90 degrees apart.

LEVELING WAYS—The leveling of the ways or bed bearing surfaces, as in a planer. A precision level is used in connection with suitable

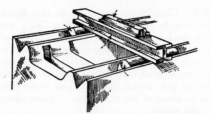

Leveling ways. Two round bars, a straight test bar, and an accurate level planer bed alignment.

bars or blocks which rest on the ways of the machine.

LEVERAGE—Mechanical advantage due to use of levers, so that a small force moving through a large distance exerts greater power through the shorter distance.

LEVERS—Arms pivoted or bearing on points called fulcrums. There are three classes of levers, as shown. The first has the fulcrum, or bearing point, between the power and the weight; the second has the weight between

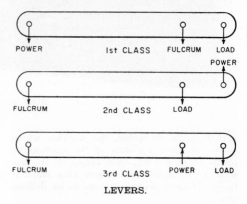

LEVERS.

the power and the fulcrum; the third has the power between the weight and the fulcrum. Two or more levers may be used together, making compound levers. They are used in nearly every type of machine. A wheel, pulley or gear may be called continuous levers, with the axis as the pivot. Levers which do not move may be called *beams.*

LEVERS, COMPOUND—Any combination of levers by which the force applied moves through a greater distance as compared with the movement of the working end of the last lever. In cutting nippers with compound levers, the advantage is found by dividing the movement of the handles where power is applied by the movement of the cutting jaws. This is true no matter what the combination of levers or toggles. This does not consider any power lost by friction in the joints.

LEWIS—A device made in three sections, two of which act as dovetails or tenons, that fit into dovetailed mortises, larger at the bottom than at the top. The loose central piece holds the others against the angular undercuts. Used largely in lifting stone without the use of slings.

LEWIS GEAR TOOTH FORMULA—See *Gearing, Lewis Gear Tooth Formula.*

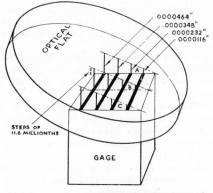

Light-wave band. Bands locate steps of
11.6 millionths.

LIGHT WAVE BANDS — Bands produced when monochromatic light is reflected by the surface being tested. Monochromatic light is transmitted through a vertical ground diffusing glass and is reflected downward to the surface being inspected by a 45-degree inclined reflector glass. The light is then reflected by

Wave bands on worn gage anvil.

the surfaces being tested and the optical flat and through the inclined reflector glass. It is then again reflected to the observer by a 45-degree mirror above.

With the correct monochromatic light, the wave bands measure 0.0000116 inch per dark band. This gives results correct to less than a millionth of an inch.

Conversion Table of Interference Bands to Micro-Inches

For a Monochromatic Light Having an Interference Band of 11.6 Millionths of an Inch

No. of Bands	Equivalent in Micro-Inches	No. of Bands	Equivalent in Micro-Inches
1/10	1.2	6	69.6
2/10	2.3	7	81.2
1/4	2.9	8	92.8
3/10	3.5	9	104
4/10	4.6	10	116
1/2	5.8	12	139
6/10	7.0	14	162
7/10	8.1	16	186
3/4	8.7	18	209
8/10	9.3	20	232
9/10	10.4	22	255
1	11.6	24	278
2	23.2	26	302
3	34.8	28	325
4	46.4	30	348.
5	58.0		

Van Keuren light-wave equipment.

LIGHT WAVE EQUIPMENT—A typical light wave equipment is that made by Van Keuren who are among the pioneers in this field. It consists of 4 double surface fused quartz optical flats, and a special monochromatic light source, i.e., a light with only one wave length and color. Such equipment detects worn spots in anvils of micrometers, and in gage blocks, which shows what correction is necessary to make them reliable instruments again.

LIGNE—A watchmakers' measurement, which is 0.0888 inch. See *Watchmakers' Measure-*

249

ments. The button industry also uses the term *ligne* as a measurement, but their ligne is 0.025 inch.

LIGNUM VITAE—A very hard wood found in the Caribbean countries. Formerly used for some bearings, especially shaft bearings of propellers of steamships.

LIMESTONE — Any rock containing lime. Used in smelting iron ores.

LIMIT—Maximum and minimum dimensions. This should not be confused with tolerance, allowance or clearance. See *Tolerance, Allowance* and *Clearance.*

LIMITS AND FITS FOR ENGINEERING AND MANUFACTURING, AMERICAN STANDARDS—

Scope—This standard gives definitions of terms applying to fits between plain (non-threaded) parts and makes recommendations concerning the procedure of specifying such fits, including the choice of the basic size of the parts and their tolerance; the allowance of the fit; the use of the basic hole or the basic shaft system and recommended fits for general engineering purposes.

Application of Standard—The recommendations made in this standard apply particularly to fits between cylindrical parts, briefly designated as "holes" and "shafts," where the term "size" refers to the diameter of the mating parts. The data may also be applied to fits between mating parts other than cylindrical, in which case the "size" refers to a length, width or other dimension instead of a diameter.

DEFINITIONS

Dimension—The specified value of a diameter, length, angle or other geometrical characteristic of a part.

Nominal Size—The size used for the purpose of general identification.

Basic Size—The theoretical size from which the limits for that dimension are derived by the application of the allowance and the tolerance.

Design Size—The size in relation to which the limits of tolerance for that dimension are assigned.

Actual Size—The measured size of that dimension on an individual part.

Limits of Size—The maximum and minimum sizes permissible for a specified dimension.

Tolerance—The total permissible variation in size. The difference between the high and low limit of size.

Bilateral Tolerance System—A system in which the tolerance is given in both directions.

Unilateral Tolerance System—A system in which the tolerance is given in one direction only; plus for the hole and minus for the shaft. See *Bilateral Tolerance.*

Fit—The relationship existing between two mating parts with respect to the amount of clearance or interference when they are assembled.

Allowance—A prescribed difference in dimensions of mating parts. It is a minimum clearance (positive allowance) or a maximum interference (negative allowance) between mating parts.

Clearance Fit—A fit between mating parts having limits of size so that there is always a clearance when assembled.

Interference Fit—A fit where there is always interference between parts in assembly.

Transition Fit—A fit which may have either a clearance or an interference between mating parts.

Basic Hole System—A system in which the minimum limit of each hole is basic. The desired fit is obtained by varying the allowance of the shaft and the tolerance of the mating parts.

Basic Shaft System—A system in which the maximum limit of each shaft size is basic. The desired fit is obtained by varying the allowance of the hole and the tolerance of the mating parts.

PREFERRED BASIC SIZES

Basic Sizes Four Inches and Below: It is recommended that in specifying fits, the basic sizes of the mating parts be chosen from the table.

	0.0100	5/16	0.3125	1 7/8	1.8750
	0.0125	3/8	0.3750	2	2.0000
1/64	0.01562	7/16	0.4375	2 1/8	2.1250
	0.0200	1/2	0.5000	2 1/4	2.2500
	0.0250	9/16	0.5625	2 3/8	2.3750
1/32	0.03125	5/8	0.6250	2 1/2	2.5000
	0.0400	11/16	0.6875	2 5/8	2.6250
	0.0500	3/4	0.7500	2 3/4	2.7500
1/16	0.0625	7/8	0.8750	2 7/8	2.8750
	0.0800	1	1.0000	3	3.0000
3/32	0.09375	1 1/8	1.1250	3 1/4	3.2500
	0.1000	1 1/4	1.2500	3 1/2	3.5000
1/8	0.1250	1 3/8	1.3750	3 3/4	3.7500
5/32	0.15625	1 1/2	1.5000	4	4.0000
3/16	0.1875	1 5/8	1.6250		
1/4	0.2500	1 3/4	1.7500		

All dimensions are given in inches.

Diameters Above Four Inches: Diameters larger than 4 in. are usually adopted on the basis of engineering considerations. Therefore, no preferred sizes in this larger range are given in the table.

ACCEPTANCE OF PARTS

Acceptability: A part shall be acceptable if its actual size does not exceed the limits of size specified in numerical values on the drawing or in writing. It does not meet dimensional specifications if its actual size exceeds those limits.

Reference Temperature: The actual size of a part shall be considered to be that size which the part has when it is measured at the international Standard Reference Temperature of 68 deg. F. (20 deg. C.).

Tolerance and Allowances—Choice of Values: It is recommended that in specifying fits, the tolerances and allowances be chosen from the values in the table, the values in heavy type being preferred.

Basic Hole and Basic Shaft Systems—Choice Between Two Systems: A cylindrical fit shall be specified in such a manner that it will be identified as belonging to either the basic hole system or the basic shaft system. The decision whether a fit shall be specified in the basic hole system or basic shaft system must be made after due consideration of a number of factors concerning the design of the product to which the part belongs and the methods by which the part is to be manufactured.

Tolerances and Allowances:

0.00015	0.0008	0.0030	0.0150
0.0003	0.0015	0.0060	0.0250
0.0001	0.0006	0.0025	**0.0100**
0.0004	**0.0020**	0.0080	**0.0300**
0.0005			

All dimensions are given in inches. *The values indicated in heavy type are the preferred values.

LIMIT GAGE—A gage with both "go" and "not go" dimensions.

LIMITORQUE—A device which shuts off power when a motor is overloaded, and before any damage can occur. See *Wrench, Torque.*

LINE ASSEMBLY—Continuous assembly of parts from a production line, or from a storage or parts supply, usually the former.

LINE PRODUCTION—A method of manufacturing where the machine tools and other equipment are arranged by sequence of operations instead of by grouping machines of the same kind into departments.

LINE SHAFTING—The main shafting in a shop with belt driven machines. Belts from the line shaft drive pulleys on the countershafts over each machine.

LINEAR EXPANSION—Expansion in a lengthwise direction.

LINER—A piece for separating parts of mechanisms by a desired distance. Sometimes called a *shim* when separating parts of a bearing. Liners are also used to give better bearing surfaces and to enable replacement when worn. Diesel and other engine cylinders usually have liners in which the pistons travel.

LINK—A part which connects other parts of a mechanism. In railroad practice a link is part of a valve gear in which a link block slides to give a different cut-off of steam entering the cylinders of steam locomotives.

LINK BELTING—A power transmitting device composed of a series of short links. Usually applied to metal links, but they have been made of leather. These link chains run over toothed sprocket wheels and give a positive drive. They are sometimes called a chain belt. They are made with open links and also of links of different forms, among them being the "silent chain." See *Belt, Link.*

LINK CHAIN SPROCKETS—See under *Sprockets.*

LINK MOTION—Refers particularly to a mechanism still used on steam locomotives for controlling the slide or piston valve which admitted steam to the cylinder. It provided a simple and efficient way of regulating the entry and exhaust of steam to and from the cylinders. It consisted of a curved link moved by two eccentric rods providing different lengths of stroke to the valve, according to the position of the link block in the link. This was originally between the driving wheels. When locomotives became so large that the valve motion had to be moved outside the wheels, the link motion gave way to the Walschaerts valve gear and other devices outside of the wheels.

LIP—A sharp cutting edge of a tool or a projection from the body of the piece. Lip angle is the angle of the cutting edge.

LIP DRILL—A name given a type of flat drill with the lip of the cutting edges curved forward to meet the metal at an acute angle.

LIQUATE—A seldom used term for separation of one metal from another by heat.

LIQUEFY—To melt or become liquid.

LIQUID HONING—A name given to a process of finishing metals by forcing a stream of liquid, in which is suspended a very fine abrasive, against the surfaces to be finished. It is sometimes called a "vapor blast."

LITHARGE—A yellow powder used in making glass and in pottery. Also used as a filler in rubber compounds and in pipe joints. It is made by roasting lead in open air. It fuses and solidifies into reddish-brown scales.

LITHIUM—The lightest metal, being half the density of water. Melts about 365° F. Boils about 2500° F. Sometimes used as an alloy in lead, copper, aluminum and magnesium. Used in the German "Bahn" lead base bearing alloy which remains hard at comparatively high temperatures.

LIVE CENTER—A lathe or grinder center in the spindle which revolves with the work. On heavy work this prevents wear of the center hole which suppports the work. Ball or roller bearing centers may be used in either the headstock or tailstock of the machines.

LIVE SPINDLE—The spindle of any machine which revolves with the tool or the work.

LIVE STEAM—Steam direct from a boiler, used either to drive some mechanism or for processing of some kind. It differs from exhaust steam in being hotter and also in having less moisture.

LOBE—Usually applied to a projection on a revolving body, such as a cam. It could refer to the high spots on a straight cam. It usually means the rise due a larger diameter or a high spot, which actuates a lever, roller or pin and gives it the desired movement.

LOCAL INTERCHANGEABILITY—Interchangeability of parts made in the same factory but not necessarily with those made elsewhere.

LOCK BOLT—See *Bolt, Lock.*

LOCK NUTS—See *Nut, Lock.*

LOCK WASHER—See *Washer, Lock.*

LOCKER—In shop terms, a closet for keeping workers' clothes away from the dirt and dust of the shop, or for other purposes.

LOCOMOTIVE AXLES, MOUNTING PRESSURE FOR—The Association of American Railroads recommends the following pressures for mounting locomotive and car axles.

Mounting Pressures for Engine Truck Axles
Tons Pressure

Nominal Wheel Seat Dia. Inches	Cast Iron Centers or Chilled Cast Iron Wheels		Cast Steel or Wrot. Iron Centers or Wrot. Steel Wheels	
	Min.	Max.	Min.	Max.
4	25	40	40	55
4½	30	45	45	60
5⅛	30	55	50	70
5¾	35	60	55	75
6	35	60	60	90
6¼	40	65	70	100
6½	40	**65**	70	100
7	45	70	75	110
7⅝	50	75	80	120
8⅛	50	75	85	130
8½	55	80	90	140
9			100	150
9½			105	160

LOCOMOTIVE CRANE—See under *Crane.*

LOCOMOTIVE REPAIRS, STANDARDS—There were five classes of standard repairs designated by the Association of American Railroads. The almost universal abandonment of the steam locomotive now makes these obsolete.

LOCOMOTIVE TIRES, SHRINKAGE ALLOWANCE FOR—See *Shrinkage Allowance for Locomotive Tires.*

LOGARITHM—The exponent of the power to which the base number must be raised to produce a given number. In decimal calculations the base is 10. The logarithm of 100 is 2 because 10 must be squared, or raised to the second power, to equal 100. The logarithm of 1,000 is 3, because 10 must be multiplied by itself twice to equal 1,000. The system is used by engineers for involved computations; tables are available giving the logarithms of different numbers. Logarithms are rarely used in machine shop calculations.

LOGARITHMIC PAPER—Special section lined paper on which the lines are spaced in *one* direction in logarithmic progression instead of at regular intervals as with regular

Mounting Pressures for Driving and Trailing Axles and Crank Pins

Tons Pressure

Diameter of Fit Inches	Cast Iron Centers			Cast Steel Centers or Wrought Steel Wheels		
	Min.	Preferred	Max.	Min.	Preferred	Max.
4	35	40	45	55	60	65
4½	40	45	50	60	68	75
5	45	50	55	65	75	85
5½	50	55	60	75	83	90
6	55	60	65	80	90	100
6½	60	65	70	90	98	110
7	65	70	75	95	105	115
7½	70	75	80	100	113	125
8	70	80	90	110	120	130
8½	75	85	95	115	128	140
9	80	90	100	120	135	150
9½	85	95	105	130	143	160
10	90	100	110	135	150	165
10½	95	105	115	140	158	175
11	100	110	120	150	165	180
11½	105	115	125	155	173	190
12	110	120	130	160	180	200
12½				170	188	205
13				175	195	215
13½				185	203	225
14				190	210	230
14½				195	217	240
15				200	225	250

cross-section paper. It is used in laying out curves showing the performance of cutting tools or other data resulting from tests of various kinds. See *Log-Log Paper.*

LOG-LOG PAPER—Another specially ruled paper with the lines logarithmically spaced in *both* directions. A paper used largely in cutting tool tests has a cycle of 1 to 10 every 2¾ inches of the paper, as this seems to meet the requirements of many tests. Where a curve of such tests on ordinary cross-section paper would be a parabolic curve, it becomes a straight line on the log-log paper, which is preferred for this work.

LOK-THREAD — See *Screw Threads, Lok-Thread.*

LONGITUDINAL RIVETING — Lengthwise seams of boilers or tanks, or other riveted structures.

LOOSE PULLEY—See *Pulley, Loose.*

LOST MOTION—Looseness between mating parts which allows movement between parts supposed to move in unison. This may delay action of the machine until the parts again come into contact.

LOST-WAX PROCESS— See *Investment Castings.*

LOUVERS—Slots or openings in the case or cover of any mechanism, or in the wall or ceiling of a building to permit ventilation.

LOW-ALLOY STEELS—Steels with little alloy to reduce cost and save critical material.

LOEWENHERZ (GERMAN) THREAD—See *Screw Threads, Loewenherz-German.*

LUBRICANT—Any oil, grease or other material which helps to reduce friction between moving parts.

LUBRICATION, SPLASH — Where moving parts are enclosed in an oil-tight case and dip or splash in the oil as they revolve.

253

LUCITE—A methyl-methacrylate resin that is transparent like glass. It can be readily machined and has many special uses.

LUG—Any projection from a casting or forging, frequently of irregular shape. Sometimes provided as a tong-hold on forgings or for fastening places on castings. Also applied to stampings.

LUTES—Materials which are somewhat adhesive. Used in making sewer pipe and similar joints; in filling cracks in fire brick linings, and to seal openings in crucibles and boxes used in heat treating steel. They exclude air and prevent oxidization. Various kinds of clay are used for the purpose.

M

MACHINE BOLT—A square or hexagonal headed bolt, used with a nut, to hold parts of machines together. Special machine bolts may have round or other shaped heads. See *Bolts, Machine*.

MACHINE CYCLES—These refer to machines provided with mechanisms that control their operation in performing definite pieces of work. The operation shown is on a Brown & Sharpe milling machine. The horizontal arrows indicate movement of the table and the vertical arrows the vertical movement of the spindle of a manufacturing type milling machine. The solid lines show rapid traverse and the dotted lines the time in the cut. The cycles in this case are mechanically controlled. Some machines use electrical controls.

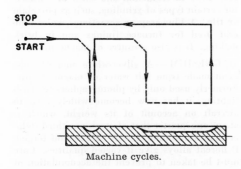

Machine cycles.

MACHINE DRILLING—Drilling by power rather than by hand.

MACHINE FORGING—Forging by pressure rather than by impact, or hammer blows. It involves the use of upsetting or forging machines instead of any type of forging hammer. See *Forgings*.

MACHINE MOLDED—Any casting in which the mold has been rammed by, or prepared by machine instead of by hand.

MACHINE SCREW—A screw used in holding machine parts together. The largest size is ¼ inch in diameter, sizes above that being called bolts. They differ from wood screws both in the shape of the point and in the thread. See *Screw, Machine*.

MACHINE SCREW TAP—A tap for threading holes for machine screws. See *Tapping, Machine Screw*.

MACHINE SHOP—A shop equipped with machine tools for building or repairing machinery or mechanical devices. It may be for manufacturing some special machine, or for repairs only. The latter is frequently called a job shop.

MACHINE TAP—Any tap to be used in a machine. See *Tapping*.

MACHINE TENDER—One who simply puts work in a machine and removes it when it is finished. The term implies that he or she is not capable of setting the machine up on a new job, setting the tools and getting the job started. Same as a machine operator. Usually called an "operator."

MACHINE TOOL—The name given to any machine of that class, which taken as a group, can build other machines. This includes such machines as the lathe, drilling machine, planer, milling machine, grinding machine, etc. No other class of machines can be used to build other machines. Because of this, machine tools are known as the "master tools of industry."

MACHINE TOOL ELECTRICAL STANDARDS—See *Electrical Standards for Machine Tools*.

MACHINEABILITY—Relative ease or difficulty in cutting. There are no definite standards, although hardness is an important factor and is the one usually considered. In most metals Brinell hardness, known as B.H.N., is used as indicating machineability. Some use Rockwell hardness and others the tensile strength of the material. On some metals, such as manganese alloys, hardness is not a good test of machineability. These metals are relatively soft and flow easily under impact, but resist the cutting action of most tools. Latest tests indicate that micro-structure of the material is a better guide than hardness.

MACHINERY, METAL FORMING—See *Metal Forming Machinery*.

MACHINERY STEEL—A very indefinite term for mild steel which does not have enough carbon content to harden when heated and cooled rapidly. It can be given a hard surface by introducing carbon into the surface by various means such as carburizing, pack-hardening, cyaniding, etc.

MACHINING OPERATIONS—Fundamental machining operations are illustrated and named. These will help to distinguish between the uses of the various types of machine tools on the next page.

MACHINIST—Literally, a man or woman operating a machine. In common usage, a person who is capable of setting up a machine and doing accurate and intricate work on the average machine tool. This originally meant *all* machine tools, but the increase in kinds of machine tools, and the special purposes for which some are made, makes it unlikely that many, even skilled men, can be familiar with them all. The term is used to distinguish a man trained on many machines from one who is simply skilled on a certain machine tool, like an "operator."

MACROSTRUCTURE—The internal condition of metals, as shown by their surfaces which have been machined and acid etched. Examination of these surfaces, preferably with a microscope, shows details of the structure. See *Microstructure*.

MACRO-TESTING—The testing of materials under heavy pressures, as distinguished from light load testing, called micro-testing. See *Tukon Tester*. Pressures from 3,600 to 50,000 grams come in this classification.

MAGAZINE—A storage place for parts to be fed to a machine for some machining operation.

MAGNAFLUX—Magnetized steel, and similar materials, develops fields which attract magnetic particles. Both direct and alternating current can be used. Direct current is commonly used, because it shows cracks below the surface more distinctly than alternating current, which is largely for surface defects. Two methods are used, wet and dry. In the wet method, fine particles of magnetic materials are mixed with a light oil and the parts usually dipped in the bath, which is very sensitive to small surface cracks. The dry method is more sensitive to sub-surface cracks. Here magnetic powder is dusted over the surface. In both methods the magnetic particles form each side of the crack, and indicate its location.

MAGNAGLO—An inspection method using a paste suspended in oil with the parts inspected by the wet method. The parts are examined in a darkened enclosure under near-ultraviolet or "black" light. Flaws show as bright greenish-yellow lines of fluorescence.

MAGNE-GAGE—A device which operates on the principle of breaking the magnetic attraction between a calibrated magnet and the magnetic coating, or magnetic-base material. A graduated dial actuates a torsion spring attached to a horizontal lever arm supporting the magnet. Dial readings are averaged and when compared with a calibrated curve, they indicate the thickness of the coating. It is said to be accurate within plus or minus 10 per cent for coatings thicker than 0.002 inch.

MAGNESITE—A material used as a bond in abrasive wheels. It is also known as oxychloride. Used in segmental and solid disc wheels for certain types of grinding, such as porcelain or tile. A blue-gray or sometimes white mineral used for furnace linings and in brick making. It is also a source of magnesium.

MAGNESIUM—A silver-white metallic element made from salt water or magnesite ore. Formerly used only by photographers for flash lighting, it has now become widely used in aircraft on account of its weight, which is about one-quarter that of steel, one-third lighter than aluminum. It can be cast and forged. Different alloys give it varied qualities. Care must be taken to prevent the accumulation of fine dust or small chips on account of fire hazard. It melts at about 1,200 deg. F., weighs 0.063 lbs. per cu. in., or 109 lbs. per cu. ft. Its symbol is Mg.

MAGNET—A piece of steel which has been magnetized so as to have a north and a south polarity. Their shop use is usually in separating iron and steel chips from brass and other non-magnetic metals. They are essential parts of many types of electrical mechanisms. A more recent shop use is in a magnetic chuck which requires no outside electrical connections.

MAGNET STEELS—Steels which retain magnetism after being in a magnetic field.

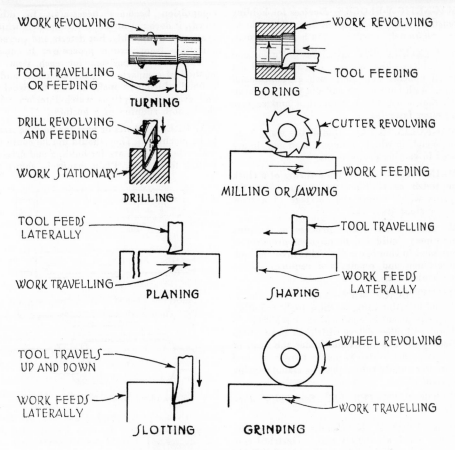

Typical machining operations.

MAGNETIC ANALYSIS COMPARATOR —
This is somewhat similar to the cyclograph, but operates at a lower frequency range. Two coils are used, one for the standard and one for the piece being tested. The part to be tested is placed vertically in the proper coil. The pattern made by the oscilloscope shows whether the piece is up to standard or not. It indicates chemical composition, heat treatment, hardness and structure, size and shape, mechanical processing and internal stresses. Insertion of material in the coil causes distortion of the sine wave of voltage in the secondary. Comparing this distortion with a standard pattern shows the condition of the test piece. It is made by the Magnetic Analysis Corp.

MAGNETIC CHUCK—See *Chuck, Magnetic.*

MAGNETIC CLUTCH — See *Clutch, Magnetic.*

MAGNETIC DIES—See *Dies, Magnetic.*

MAGNETIC DRAIN PLUG—A drain plug with a permanent magnet for use in a crank case or gear case. It attracts and holds fine chips of steel or iron and keeps them from being circulated between wearing surfaces.

MAGNETIC SUPERHARDENING—A method discovered by Edward G. Herbert of England. By placing a piece of hardened steel across the poles of a powerful electro-magnet, tapping it slightly and turning the piece to different angles, it is made extra hard. This seems to be experimental only, to date.

MAGNETIC V-BLOCKS—Devices for holding magnetic metals for machining. The blocks are, alternately, north and south pole magnets.

MAGNETIZED DIE HOLDERS—Punch and die holders which are magnetized to hold flat metal punches and dies, such as Continental dies. With both punch and die properly located, they are held by magnetism and require no other fastenings.

MAGNOLIA METAL—One of the many bearing metals in which antimony, lead and tin are used in varying proportions.

MAINSPRING—The driving spring of a clock or watch or similar mechanism. Also the spring which moves the carriage of a typewriter along its track.

MAINTENANCE—The process of keeping machinery, buildings, or physical property of any kind in running order. This involves both adjustment and repairs and requires skilled mechanics.

MAINTENANCE MAN—A mechanic who is skilled in maintaining machine tools and other shop equipment in good order, to avoid breakdowns and other delays which cut production. Many years ago this came under the head of millwrighting, which is now generally applied to power supply rather than to manufacturing equipment.

MAJOR DIAMETER FIT—See *Spline Fits, Major Diameter.*

MAKE-AND-BREAK—Usually applied to any device which alternately makes electrical contact and breaks it at desired intervals. Early ignition systems for internal combustion engines were of this type.

MALE—A term universally applied to any part which fits into another, such as the shaft on which a pulley or gear hub fits. A plug gage is a male gage.

MALLEABILIZING—See under *Heat Treatments.*

MALLEABLE BRASS—See *Muntz Metal.*

MALLEABLE IRON—White cast iron that has had a long heat treatment which makes it tough enough to bend without breaking.

MANAGEMENT BY EXCEPTION—A method of industrial management by the late Chester B. Lord. It may be described as a method which only *directs* when matters are going satisfactorily, but which *compels* when

compulsion becomes necessary. In other words, it does not interfere with matters which are running smoothly, but detects and corrects variations from regular procedure. It entails a basis for comparison, for each item; a method of comparing related elements; and a method which will make it easy to visualize and evaluate exceptions which interfere with the smooth running of a business.

MANDRELS—Shafts or bars for holding *work* to be machined. They should not be confused with arbors, which are for holding and driving cutting tools only. Plain mandrels, shown at

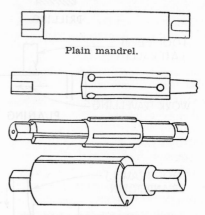

Plain mandrel.

Expanding mandrel—three types.

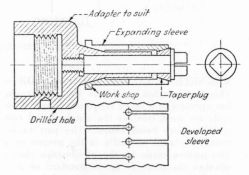

Another type of expanding mandrel.

the top, have a taper of about 0.010 inch per foot and are forced into the work. The next has a sleeve which can be expanded inside the work with the taper shaft in the center. The third has blades which slide in tapered grooves. Another type of expanding mandrel is also shown.

MANGANESE—A metal used in many alloys of steel. The proportion of manganese varies from 0.30 to 1.90 per cent in ordinary steel. Special steels may have as high as 14 per cent of manganese. It adds strength to all steels. It also makes them more difficult to cut with a tool.

MANGANESE ALUMINUM—Aluminum alloyed with manganese, which adds to its strength and stiffness.

MANGANESE BRONZE—An alloy of copper, tin and ferro-manganese. It resists corrosive action of sea water and adds to the ductility of the alloy.

MANGANESE STEELS—Steels with from 10 to 15 per cent manganese. High manganese steels can only be machined with super high speed steel or carbide tools, or by abrasives. They are, however, not hard by Brinell or other tests and are quite malleable.

MANIFOLD—Any fitting which connects several openings together, as the exhaust manifold of an automobile engine.

MANOMETER—A gage used in measurement of pressure of air or gases.

MARKET BRASS—See *High Brass* under *Brass, Alloys for Different Uses.*

MARKING MACHINE—A machine for stamping or rolling trade marks, patent numbers or trade names on cutlery, gun barrels or other metal products.

MASTER CHUCK—See *Chuck, Master.*

MASTER DISKS—See *Gages, Master Disk.*

MASTER GAGE BLOCKS—Extremely accurate gage blocks, to be used only in checking gage blocks and instruments used in production and in inspection.

MASTER GEAR STANDARDS—See *Gears, Master.*

MASTER PLATE—A steel plate serving as a model or pattern, by which holes in jigs, fixtures and other tools can be accurately located. The illustration shows the piece to be bored dowelled to the master plate, which is mounted on the face plate of a lathe. The master plate has as many holes as there are to be bored in the work and guides the tool to secure the correct location. The plate is located on a center plug in the lathe spindle. After a hole is bored the plate is shifted and re-centered for the next hole. This is a very

accurate method, but has been made unnecessary by the jig boring machine.

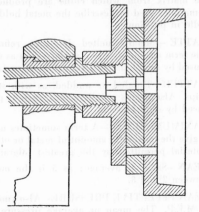

Master plate.

MASTER TAP—A standard tap used to make dies, or that is kept as a standard.

MASTER TOOLING—A general term which includes tools, jigs and fixtures used to secure duplication of parts in manufacturing. Various names are used by different concerns. These are collected under *Tool Master, Match Plate* and *Control Master.*

MATCH PLATE—A tool used to locate and coordinate a group of holes in production tooling, for the purpose of effecting interchangeability of two or more production parts to facilitate their assembly. (North American Aircraft Co.) Other aircraft companies use the following names: Consolidated—master plate; Vultee—transfer plate; Lockheed—transfer plate, master drill plate; Northrop—master plate, master plate template; Ryan—master drill plate.

Also a plate used in foundry work having one-half of the pattern in matching position, on each side. Both cope and drag (the two parts of the flask) can be rammed at the same time. On removing the match plate, both halves of the mold are ready to be put together, for pouring.

MATCHED SET STEELS—A term coined by the Carpenter Steel Co. for steels selected to match, or meet, different conditions of use for best results. For most purposes suitable steels harden satisfactorily in water by normal methods. But if wear or toughness is required, other methods of hardening, including oil baths, may be necessary.

MATRIX—This usually refers to the depression or cavity in which parts are formed, as the matrix from which coins are produced. Sometimes used to describe the metal holding a die in position.

MATTE — Metal smelted but not refined. The term also applies to a surface such as that caused by sand blasting. Not a smooth surface.

MATTED—Tangled or wadded, as with steel chips. Also means a dull surface, such as produced by sand blasting.

MAXIMUM METAL—A term sometimes used to give the maximum amount of metal or other material permitted by the greatest tolerance.

MEAN—Same as average; as 5 is the mean between 2 and 8.

MEAN EFFECTIVE PRESSURE—Also known as M.E.P. The mean or average pressure in gas or steam engine cylinders during the stroke of the piston.

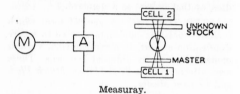

Measuray.

MEASURAY—A gaging instrument made by the Sheffield Corp. which checks the thickness of hot or cold sheets or strips of many materials instantly. It is based on the absorption effects of X-rays as they pass through the materials being measured.

When the X-rays pass through the master of known thickness, some of the X-rays are absorbed. The balance passes into the pickup cell where a small current is allowed to flow. Similarly, when the beam of X-rays passes through the material of unknown thickness, part of the X-rays are absorbed and the balance goes into the pickup cell and causes a small current to flow.

The outputs from both pickup cells are bucked against each other, then passed through an amplifier so that any difference is registered on the meter. If both master and unknown are of same thickness (absorb equal amounts of X-rays), then the current generated in each cell is the same. Therefore, the meter would read zero. If the unknown absorbs less than the master then more current is generated in cell 2 than in cell 1 and the

difference between the two registers on the meter. This reading is in terms of percentage thickness variation in relation to the master.

The X-ray method of determining thickness is confined to those materials that are homogenous. For example, steel which is made up of iron, silicon, carbon and other elements, is almost homogenous. So is brass made of copper and zinc. Paper, on the other hand, is not homogenous and cannot be tested by this method.

MEASUREMENT, BASIC HOLE AND BASIC SHAFT SYSTEMS—See *Tolerances and Allowances*.

MEASUREMENT CONVERSION TABLE—A table which makes it easy to calculate areas or circumferences of various shaped objects from dimensions which are easily accessible. This is known as mensuration, or the measurement of surfaces and solids. The table follows:

Mensuration Formulas

Area of section of square of flat bar or rectangle or parallelogram—width × thickness or length × breadth.

Area of triangle—half base × perpendicular height.

Area of circle—square of the diameter × .7854.

Area of circle sector—number of degrees in arc × square of radius × .008727.

Area of circle segment—area of sector with same arc minus area of triangle formed by radii of the arc and chord of the segment.

Area of equal circle—area of square × 1.273.

Area of sphere (ball)—square of diameter × 3.14159; or area of its great circle × 4.

Area of trapezoid—half the sum of the two parallel sides × the perpendicular distance between them.

Regular polygon—half the perimeter × the perpendicular distance from the center to any one side.

Area of octagon—square of diameter of inscribed circle (distance across flats) × .828.

Area of hexagon—square of diameter of inscribed circle (distance across flats) × .866 or one side × 2.598.

Area of ellipse—product of axes × .7854.

Area of cylinder—length × circumference of body plus area of both ends.

Circumference of circle—diameter of circle × 3.14159.

Circumference of circumscribing circle—side of square × 4.443.

Circumference of equal circle—side of square × 3.545.

Diameter of circle—circumference of circle × .31831.

Diameter of circumscribing circle — side of square × 1.1142.

Diameter of equal circle—side of square × 1.128.

Diameter across flats in hexagon — diameter across corners divided by 1.156.

Diameter across flats in octagon — diameter across corners divided by 1.082.

Side of inscribed square—diameter of circumscribing circle × .7071 or circumference of circle × .2251.

Side of an equal square—diameter × .8862; or circumference × .2821.

Volume of prism—area of base × perpendicular height.

Volume of wedge—length of edge plus twice length of base × one-sixth of the product of the height of the wedge and the breadth of its base.

Volume of cylinder—area of base × perpendicular height.

Volume of cone—area of base × one-third of perpendicular height.

Volume of parallelogram (square or rectangular)—area of cross section × length.

Volume of sphere (ball)—cube of diameter × .5236.

Specific gravity of steel (carbon)— (approx.) 7.85.

Specific gravity of gray cast iron— (approx.) 7.22.

Specific gravity of white cast iron— (approx.) 7.65.

Specific gravity of high speed steel— 8.45 to 8.75.

1 cubic inch of cast iron weighs— (approx.) 0.26 lb.

1 cubic inch of wrought iron weighs— (approx.) 0.28 lb.

1 cubic inch of steel (carbon) weighs— (approx.) 0.283 lb.

Weight per foot of square or flat section (steel—area × 3.4.

Weight per foot of round section (steel)— square of the number of ¼ inches in the diameter divided by 6.

Weight per foot of octagon (steel)—weight per foot of same size Round Bar × 1.0547.

Weight per foot of hexagon (steel)—weight per foot of same size Round Bar 1.1026.

MEASUREMENT, INCHES AND METRIC—
Translation from inches to metric equivalents for sizes up to one inch is made easy by the table. Larger dimensions present no difficulty. See *Decimal Equivalents*.

MEASUREMENT PRESSURE FOR SCREW THREADS—
One pound pressure is recommended for threads of 24 per inch and finer and 2½ pounds for threads coarser than 24 per inch.

MEASUREMENT, SCREW THREAD, SUPER-MIKE—
A type of bench micrometer designed for measuring screw threads by use of standard wires. The wires are suspended by threads, in the thread angles. They are free to float and square themselves with both the anvil faces and the helix of the screw being measured. One anvil moves in and out as with any micrometer. The other anvil is set to resist only predetermined pressures so as to secure uniform measurements. One pound pressure is recommended for threads of 24 inch and finer and 2½ pounds for threads coarser than 24 per inch.

MEASUREMENT TEMPERATURES—
Standard temperature for all measurements is 68 deg. F. This was formerly 70 deg. F. in the United States and Great Britain, but was changed to make it even with 20 deg. Centigrade. Gage blocks will expand approximately 7 millionths of an inch per inch of length with a temperature rise of 1 degree. When the work expands at the same rate, there is no difficulty; in all cases both work and gage should be at the same temperature.

MEASURING AND GAGING —
These terms are often confused. While they may at times mean the same thing, this is only when the gaging is done by measuring instruments. Gaging usually means determining whether the work is within prescribed limits but without determining its exact size. Gages are not usually adjustable except by the gage inspector. Some cannot be adjusted at all. Measuring shows the size of the piece. Gaging only shows whether it is within prescribed limits.

MEASURING HELICAL GEARS WITH WIRES—
A method of determining pitch diameter of gears. Wires of proper diameter are held in place between the teeth of the gears between parallels. Meaurement is taken over parallels and their thickness subtracted from the total. See *Gears, Measuring with Wires*.

MEASURING MACHINE—
Practically, a large bench micrometer caliper of any desired form to measure such work as taps, drills, reamers and gages. Some are now made to utilize light

waves instead of mechanical methods and can measure in millionths of an inch.

MEASURING WITH LIGHT WAVE BANDS
—Using an optical flat on a gage block or other flat surface, the shape and number of light wave bands seen indicate the flatness of the surface. When a series of bands are seen between two nearly flat surfaces, there is a wedge of air between them. The slope of this wedge is at right angles to the bands. If the bands curve around the thin part of the air wedge the surface is convex. If they curve around the thick part of the air wedge the surface is concave. The bands show steps of 11.6 millionths of an inch vertical distance between the optical flat and the surface being tested. These interference bands are due to the light waves being reflected from test surface. They either interfere with, or reinforce, the light waves reflected from the gage block. The illustration on page 251 shows that the gage is flat. If the bands curved the distance of one space, the error would be 11.6 millionths of an inch. See *Light Wave Bands.*

MECHANIC—A skilled worker with tools of any kind. Usually applied to the metal working trades.

MECHANICAL DRAWINGS—See *Drawings, Mechanical.*

MECHANICAL EQUIVALENT OF HEAT—The number of foot-pounds of mechanical energy contained in one heat unit, as these are convertible. The accepted equivalent is that one heat unit equals 778 foot pounds, or, 778 pounds falling one foot will generate one heat unit.

MECHANICAL MOVEMENT — Any arrangement of mechanical elements, such as cranks, levers, cams or gears, to secure desired movements in mechanisms of any kind.

MECHANICAL TUBING—See *Tubing, Mechanical.*

MECHANICS—The theory of machines and of dealing with the action of forces on matter.

MEEHANITE—A processed cast iron of great uniformity. A very reliable material for railroad castings and similar parts. Can be heat treated to 450 Brinell hardness.

MELTING POINTS OF SOLIDS—The temperature at which solids become liquid. The Bureau of Standards gives the melting points shown under *Metals, Properties of.*

MERCASTING—Castings made by a method similar to the lost wax process, but using solidified, or frozen, mercury as the pattern. A new development which has promise for larger castings than the wax process. As mercury does not solidify above 39.7 deg. below zero F., the material must be kept below that point during its use as a pattern. This belongs in the "investment" casting group.

MERCOID SWITCHES—Electric switches in which mercury forms one contact instead of having two metal contacts. They are silent in operation, as there is no spring needed to break the contact suddenly. Sometimes called mercury switches.

MERCURY—The only metal which is liquid at ordinary temperatures. Sp. gr. 13.596. Solidifies or freezes at -39.7 deg. F. Also called quicksilver.

MERIT RATING—The measurement of the qualities of a worker of any kind to determine his or her value in terms of payment. Practically the same as "job evaluation."

MESH—A term describing the contacting of gears with each other, or between a gear and a rack.

Also used to refer to the space between wires in fencing or the size of holes used in screens to sort material into different sizes.

METAL FLOW—Usually refers to the flow of cold metal sheets or plates under pressure, as in dies for forming such parts as automobile bodies or fenders. Also refers to the flow of heated metals, as in forging. The line of flow is especially important in metals of a fibrous nature. See *Forgings, Grain Flow.*

METAL FORMING, AIRCRAFT PRACTICE—The large number of sheet metal parts used in modern aircraft has led to development of special methods for cutting and forming them. The main machines used in this work are shown herewith.

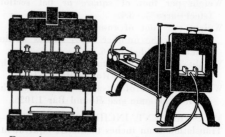

Deep draw press.   Draw bench.

Contouring rolls.

Drop hammer.

Punch press.

Power brake.

Shrinking machine.

Spinning lathe.

Flanging machine.

Corrugating and forming rolls.

Hydro-press for forming.

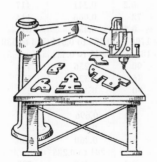

Router.

Special router.

Stretcher press.

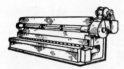

Straight free edge shearer.

Saw.

Rotary shearer.

METAL FORMING MACHINERY.

METAL, PACKFONG—An old Chinese alloy of copper and zinc, now little used. The copper was a little more than half the mixture.

METAL SPRAYING—Metal, usually in the form of wire, is fed through a device which melts it and also blows it on the surface to be coated, as with spray painting. If metal is to be coated, the surface must be roughened so that a mechanical bond can be formed with the spray coating. This is done in various ways. Satisfactory results can be obtained by this method in building up worn parts. See *Sprayed Metal, Preparations for.*

METALLIC ARC WELDING—See *Welding, Arc.*

METALLIC IRON—Iron after it has been removed from the ore.

METALLIZING—The modern term for covering metals or other materials with a metal spray. See *Metal Spraying.*

METALLIZED WOOD—Wood with the cells filled with molten metal that melts below the scorching temperature of the wood.

METALLOID—A non-metallic substance such as carbon, boron, phosphorous, etc. They com-

METALS, PROPERTIES OF—

Properties of Metals

Metal	Melting Point, °F.	Weight, Cubic Inches	Weight, Cubic Feet	Specific Gravity or density		Chemical Symbol
				g/cm³	Degrees F.	
Aluminum	1220 ± 0.2	0.0975	168.5	2.702	68	Al
Antimony	1166.9 ± 0.2	0.241	417	6.684	68	Sb
Beryllium	2336 ± 72	0.066	114	1.83	68	Be
Bismuth	520.3 ± 0.2	0.354	611	9.80	68	Bi
Brass cast (20 to 36 Zn)	1850 to 1706	0.303 to 0.311	523 to 538	8.39 to 8.63	68	
Bronze	1535 to 1832	0.315 to 0.321	545 to 554	8.74 to 8.89	68	
Chromium	3272 ± 90	0.256	443	7.1	68	Cr
Cobalt	2714 ± 36	0.321	555	8.9	68	Co
Columbium	3632 ± 90	0.309	534	8.57	68	Cb
Copper	1981.4 ± 0.2	0.322	556	8.92	68	Cu
Gold	1954.4 ± 0.2	0.696	1,203	19.3	68	Au
Iridium	4449 ± 5	0.808	1,397	22.4	68	Ir
Iron, cast	2795 ± 5	0.260	456	7.22	68	Fe
Iron, wrought	2786	0.281 to 0.285	486 to 493	7.80 to 7.90	68	
Lead	621.3 ± 0.2	0.409	707	11.34	68	Pb
Magnesium	1202 ± 4	0.063	109	1.74	68	Mg
Manganese	2300 ± 36	0.260	449	7.2	68	Mn
Mercury	−37.97 ± 0.04	0.512	885	14.19	102	Hg
Nickel	2651 ± 2	0.321	555	8.90	68	Ni
Molybdenum	4757 ± 90	0.365	630	10.11	68	Mo
Platinum	3224 ± 2	0.774	1,338	21.45	68	Pt
Silver	1760.9 ± 0.0	0.379	655	10.5	68	Ag
Steel, cast ⎱ Steel, rolled ⎰	2714 to 2768	0.274 to 0.281	474 to 486	7.60 to 7.80	68	
Tantalum	5432 ± 180	0.598	1,033	16.57	68	Ta
Tin	449.4 ± 0.2	0.264	456	7.31	68	Sn
Tungsten	6170 ± 36.	0.696	1,203	19.3	68	W
Vanadium	3155 ± 90	0.215	372	5.96	68	V
Zinc	787.1 ± 0.2	0.258	445	7.140	68	Zn

[1]Cubic foot of water at 32° F. = 62.3565 pounds; weight per cubic inch = 0.036086 pound.

bine with metals, however, and effect changes in its quality.

METALS, SYMBOLS FOR—Some of the more common of these are:

Al........... Aluminum
Fe........... Iron
Mm-Cu....... Manganese-Copper
P-Cu........ Phosphor-Copper
P-Sm........ Phosphor-Tin
Sb.......... Antimony
Su-Cu....... Silicone-Copper

METALS FOR DIE-CASTING—See *Die-Casting Alloys.*

METALS, PROPERTIES OF—Average melting points, weight per cubic inch and foot, specific gravity or density at various temperatures and the chemical symbols are given by the Bureau of Standards. See table.

METCALF DRESSER FOR ABRASIVE WHEELS—This device uses an abrasive wheel to dress the face of grinding wheels. The dressing wheel is mounted on a spindle with a handle at each end and held against the revolving wheel.

METER—A measuring device.

Also the basis of the metric system, devised in France following the French revolution. It was designed to be one ten-millionth (1/10,000,000) of the distance from the equator to the pole, but is not. It is considered as 39.37 inches. See *Metric System.*

METRIC GEARS—See *Gears, Module* or *Metric.*

METRIC SYSTEM—A system of weights and measures devised in France after the French revolution, in which length, weight and cubic capacity are definitely related. The meter is the unit of length, the gram the unit of weight and the liter the unit of capacity. The gram is the weight of 1 cubic centimeter of distilled water at a temperature of 39.2 deg. F. The kilogram is the weight of one liter of water, and the ton the weight of one cubic meter of water, all under the same conditions. Metric units are shown in the tables, and the method of converting some of them to our own system, in the conversion tables which follow. The convenience of being able definitely to relate one unit of measurement to others, as well as the advantage of the decimal system, have led to its adoption in nearly all scientific and laboratory work. All fine mechanical work in this country is also done

by use of decimals of an inch, some of these measurements reaching into the millionths.

Inch—Millimeter Conversion Tables
Table 1—Inches to Millimeters
(Basis: 1 inch = 25.4 millimeter)

In.	Mm.	In.	Mm.	In.	Mm.	In.	Mm.
1	25.4	26	660.4	51	1295.4	76	1930.4
2	50.8	27	685.8	52	1320.8	77	1955.8
3	76.2	28	711.2	53	1346.2	78	1981.2
4	101.6	29	736.6	54	1371.6	79	2006.6
5	127.0	30	762.0	55	1397.0	80	2032.0
6	152.4	31	787.4	56	1422.4	81	2057.4
7	177.8	32	812.8	57	1447.8	82	2082.8
8	203.2	33	838.2	58	1473.2	83	2108.2
9	228.6	34	863.6	59	1498.6	84	2133.6
10	254.0	35	889.0	60	1524.0	85	2159.0
11	279.4	36	914.4	61	1549.4	86	2184.4
12	304.8	37	939.8	62	1574.8	87	2209.8
13	330.2	38	965.2	63	1600.2	88	2235.2
14	355.6	39	990.6	64	1625.6	89	2260.6
15	381.0	40	1016.0	65	1651.0	90	2286.0
16	406.4	41	1041.4	66	1676.4	91	2311.4
17	431.8	42	1066.8	67	1701.8	92	2336.8
18	457.2	43	1092.2	68	1727.2	93	2362.2
19	482.6	44	1117.6	69	1752.6	94	2387.6
20	508.0	45	1143.0	70	1778.0	95	2413.0
21	533.4	46	1168.4	71	1803.4	96	2438.4
22	558.8	47	1193.8	72	1828.8	97	2463.8
23	584.2	48	1219.2	73	1854.2	98	2489.2
24	609.6	49	1244.6	74	1879.6	99	2514.6
25	635.0	50	1270.0	75	1905.0	100	2540.0

Note: The above table is exact.

Table 2—Millimeters to Inches.
(Basis: 1 inch = 25.4 millimeters)

Mm.	In.	Mm.	In.	Mm.	In.
1	0.039370	16	0.629921	31	1.220472
2	0.078740	17	0.669291	32	1.259843
3	0.118110	18	0.708661	33	1.299213
4	0.157480	19	0.748031	34	1.338583
5	0.196850	20	0.787402	35	1.377953
6	0.236220	21	0.826772	36	1.417323
7	0.275591	22	0.866142	37	1.456693
8	0.314961	23	0.905512	38	1.496063
9	0.354331	24	0.944882	39	1.535433
10	0.393701	25	0.984252	40	1.574803
11	0.433071	26	1.023622	41	1.614173
12	0.472441	27	1.062992	42	1.653543
13	0.511811	28	1.102362	43	1.692913
14	0.551181	29	1.141732	44	1.732283
15	0.590551	30	1.181102	45	1.771654

(Continued on following page.)

265

Table 2—Millimeters in Inches
(Continued from previous page.)

Mm.	In.	Mm.	In.	Mm.	In.
46	1.811024	65	2.559055	84	3.307087
47	1.850394	66	2.598425	85	3.346457
48	1.889764	67	2.637795	86	3.385827
49	1.929134	68	2.677165	87	3.425197
50	1.968504	69	2.716535	88	3.464567
51	2.007874	70	2.755906	89	3.503937
52	2.047244	71	2.795276	90	3.543307
53	2.086614	72	2.834646	91	3.582677
54	2.125984	73	2.874016	92	3.622047
55	2.165354	74	2.913386	93	3.661417
56	2.204724	75	2.952756	94	3.700787
57	2.244094	76	2.992126	95	3.740157
58	2.283465	77	3.031496	96	3.779528
59	2.322835	78	3.070866	97	3.818898
60	2.362205	79	3.110236	98	3.858268
61	2.401575	80	3.149606	99	3.897638
62	2.440945	81	3.188976	100	3.937008
63	2.480315	82	3.228346		
64	2.519685	83	3.267717		

Note: The above table is approximate:
$1/25.4 = 0.039370078740 +$
(See also Table 3 on page 267.)

METRIC THREADS—Screw threads in which the pitch or lead is measured in metric units. See *Screw Threads, Comparing English and Metric.*

MICA—A mineral which can be split into very thin layers or sheets. It is semi-transparent and was largely used in stove doors. It is a good insulator and is largely used in electrical apparatus. Sometimes erroneously called isinglass.

MICRO-CENTRIC GRINDING—See *Grinding, Micro-Centric.*

MICRO-FINISH—Another name for superfinish, or fine honing. This usually removes from 0.0003 to 0.0005 inch. Special honing stones are used for this work. Blind holes are honed with specially shaped stones having more surface at the lower end of the hole.

MICROFLAT—Trade name for a machine for accurate finishing of recessed surfaces.

MICROHARDNESS TESTING—A term referring to the testing of thin materials or parts of small diameter. It is used in determining hardness variations in small areas of superficially hardened surfaces. Micro-indentation is really a more accurate term, as it uses minute indentations.

MICRO-INCH—One millionth of an inch. It is written, 0.000001 inch. Should not be confused with "micron," which is one-millionth of a *meter.* The micro-inch is largely used in measuring imperfections of surface finishes.

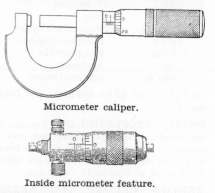

Micrometer caliper.

Inside micrometer feature.

MICROMETER-CALIPER—Usually a U-shaped frame with an anvil on one side and a 40-pitch screw on the other. The thimble or sleeve around the screw has 25 divisions, which makes each division read one one-thousandth of an inch. Micrometers are also made to read to ten-thousands of an inch. A very common form of measuring instrument in a machine shop. They are also made for inside measurements.

MICROMETER, LIGHT WAVE—A bench micrometer utilizing the accuracy of light waves to secure extremely accurate measurements. This has a ½-inch screw with 40 threads per inch and spring tension nut which eliminates backlash. The light wave indicator is enclosed. The wheel is 8 inches in diameter, which makes the 0.0001-inch graduations approximately 1/10 of an inch apart. The vernier on the side reads to 0.00001 inch. These are tool room or inspection department machines.

Van Keuren light wave micrometer.

Table 3—Common Fractions of an Inch to Millimeters*
(Basis: 1 inch = 25.4 millimeter)

2nds	4ths	8ths	16ths	32nds	64ths	Decimal Inch	Milli-meter
					1	0.015625	0.396875
				1		0.031250	0.793750
					3	0.046875	1.190625
			1			0.062500	1.587500
					5	0.078125	1.984375
				3		0.093750	2.381250
					7	0.109375	2.778125
		1				0.125000	3.175000
					9	0.140625	3.571875
				5		0.156250	3.968750
					11	0.171875	4.365625
			3			0.187500	4.762500
					13	0.203125	5.159375
				7		0.218750	5.556250
					15	0.234375	5.953125
	1					0.250000	6.350000
					17	0.265625	6.746875
				9		0.281250	7.143750
					19	0.296875	7.540625
			5			0.312500	7.937500
					21	0.328125	8.334375
				11		0.343750	8.731250
					23	0.359375	9.128125
		3				0.375000	9.525000
					25	0.390625	9.921875
				13		0.406250	10.318750
					27	0.421875	10.715625
			7			0.437500	11.112500
					29	0.453125	11.509375
				15		0.468750	11.906250
					31	0.484375	12.303125
1						0.500000	12.700000
					33	0.515625	13.096875
				17		0.531250	13.493750
					35	0.546875	13.890625
		9				0.562500	14.287500
					37	0.578125	14.684375
				19		0.593750	15.081250
					39	0.609375	15.478125
			5			0.625000	15.875000
					41	0.640625	16.271875
				21		0.656250	16.668750
					43	0.671875	17.065625
			11			0.687500	17.462500
					45	0.703125	17.859375
				23		0.718750	18.256250
					47	0.734375	18.653125
	3					0.750000	19.050000
					49	0.765625	19.446875
				25		0.781250	19.843750
					51	0.796875	20.240625
			13			0.812500	20.637500
					53	0.828125	21.034375
				27		0.843750	21.431250
					55	0.859375	21.828125
		7				0.875000	22.225000
					57	0.890625	22.621875
				29		0.906250	23.018750
					59	0.921875	23.415625
			15			0.937500	23.812500
					61	0.953125	24.209375
				31		0.968750	24.606250
					63	0.984375	25.003125
2	4	8	16	32	64	1.000000	25.400000

Note: the above table is exact; all figures beyond the six places given are zeros.

*The basis of 1 in. = 25.4 mm. is proposed by the American Standards Association and leading manufacturers instead of the present ratio of 1 in. = 25.40005 mm. The difference is two millionths of an inch.

MICROMETERS, RATCHET—Micrometers in which the barrel has an extension containing a ratchet device to prevent undue pressure being applied to the screw. The ratchet slips when the desired pressure has been applied so that each measurement is presumably made with the force applied to the part being measured.

MICRON — One millionth of a meter, or 0.00003937 inch. Should not be confused with "micro-inch."

MICRON EQUIVALENTS — 1 micron = 1/1,000,000 meter, or 1/1,000 millimeter. 1 micron = 1/25,000 inch. 5 microns = 2,500 mesh. 10 microns = 1,250 mesh. 20 microns = 625 mesh. 30 microns = 400 mesh. 45 microns = 300 mesh. 62 microns = 200 mesh.

MICRO-NUTS OR COLLARS—Nuts or collars having graduations by which they can be used to adjust tools or other parts within fine limits.

MICROSTRUCTURE—The structure of any material, especially metals, as seen through a microscope. See *Macrostructure*.

MICRO-TESTING—The testing of materials using very light pressures. In the Tukon tester this is considered as being pressures of from 10 grams to 3,600 grams.

MILD STEEL—A low carbon steel which can be welded but not hardened.

MILE—A distance of 5,280 feet or 1,760 yards, used for all distance measurements in the United States. A nautical mile is 6,080 feet and is sometimes called a "knot." Strictly speaking, the knot is a measure of speed rather than a distance.

MILL FILE—A flat file used in lathe work and draw-filing. It is usually thinner than a regular file. See under *Files, Types of*.

MILL, HOLLOW—See *Hollow Mill*.

MILLED SCREW—A screw with a head knurled to afford a grip for the fingers. It does not usually refer to the manner in which the thread is cut.

MILLIMETER—One-thousandth of a meter. See *Metric System*.

MILLIMETER CONVERSION TABLES—See *Metric System*.

MILLING—The cutting of metal by means of a rotating cutter with teeth on its periphery or face, or both. The work is usually moved past the cutter as it revolves. The work usually moves in a flat plane, but it may revolve or the cutter may move around or past the work. Hobbing is one form of milling. Some of the more common types of milling operations are shown on page 273.

MILLING, ABBREVIATIONS OF TERMS USED IN TESTS—The following abbreviations and terms were established by Prof. O. W. Boston, University of Michigan, and used on all reports on milling emanating from the research laboratory at that institution.

hp (horsepower) within a sentence and in formulas within a sentence.

Hp (horsepower) at the beginning of a sentence, or in formulas beginning a sentence, or when used as a heading in tables

kw = kilowatt
kw_g = gross kw to motor
kw_t = tare kw to motor
kw_n = net kw to motor ($kw_g - kw_t$)
hp_g = gross hp to motor ($hp_n + hp_t$)
hp_t = tare hp to motor
hp_n = net hp to motor ($hp_g - hp_t$)
hp_c = net hp at cutter
　　　　($hp_n \times$ mechanical efficiency)
hp_c/cu. in. per min. = unit net hp at the cutter
hp_n/cu. in. per min. = unit net hp to motor
hp_g/cu. in. per min. = unit gross hp to motor
cu. in. per min./hp_c = cubic in. per minute
　　　　per net hp at the cutter
in. = inch, e.g., 4-in.
in. = inch in tabular form where space conditions necessitate
eff_m = mechanical efficiency (hp_c/hp_n)
eff_o = over-all efficiency (hp_c/hp_g)

MILLING ATTACHMENT, ROTARY—An attachment for the table with a rotary base which can be rotated either by hand or power for milling radial surfaces. The attachment shown, on a Brown & Sharpe machine, is power driven by two universal joints. This also shows a vertical spindle attachment driven from the main spindle of the machine.

Brown and Sharpe rotary milling attachment.

MILLING, CHIP THICKNESS—Chip thickness in milling operations is usually measured by the "feed-per-tooth" instead of in inches-per-minute. With a symmetrical chip, as shown at the left, the chip thickness equals the feed per tooth. When the teeth have a chamfer or radius the chip thickness averages less than the feed per tooth, as shown.

MILLING CUTTERS—Rotary cutting tools with one or more teeth on their periphery, or end, or both. They are classified in several different ways, by: (1) The method of pro-

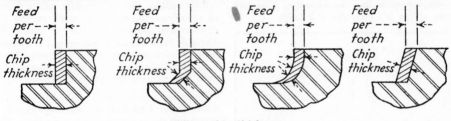

Milling chip thickness.

viding relief back of the cutting edge; (2) the method of mounting the cutter in the milling machine; (3) by the type of teeth used, integral or inserted; and (4) by the material used in the cutting edges. Class (1) includes profile, shaped profile and formed cutters. Both profile and shaped profile cutters are relieved or backed off just behind the cutting edge to make a narrow land. They are sharpened by grinding this land, which reduces the cutter diameter at each grind. In the formed cutter the relief is eccentric and maintains the same outline when the cutter is ground on the *face* of the tooth although the diameter decreases.

Cutters are mounted in three ways. They may have a shank which fits the machine spindle, they are mounted on arbors or they may be attached directly to the spindle of the machine as in facing cutters.

Cutters also have teeth integral with the body or inserted into or clamped to it. The first may be either of the same material as the body or may have special cutting materials brazed to the body. The second have separate teeth or cutters, which are held to the cutter body by various means.

Cutters are also classified by the kind of material used in the cutting edges, such as carbon steel, high speed steels, cast alloys such as Stellite, or any of the sintered carbides now being so widely used.

General Classification of Milling Cutters

Solid Cutters—Made of one piece of cutting material, such as high speed steel.

Tipped Solid Cutters—Similar to solid cutters, but with special cutting materials joined to the cutting edges of the teeth.

Inserted Tooth Cutters — Cutters having teeth of any material separate from the body but held by special clamps. They may or may not be adjustable.

Profile Type Milling Cutters include plain milling cutters, heavy duty plain cutters, helical cutters, alternate gash cutters, side milling cutters, half-side milling cutters, staggered tooth side milling cutters, herringbone type cutters, channeling cutters, interlocking side milling cutters, slitting saws, screw slotting cutters, key-seat cutters, T-slot cutters, end mills, die-sinking and engraving cutters, taper cutters, shell end mills and inserted blade end mills.

Shaped Profile Cutters include single angle cutters, single thread milling cutters, and special profile form cutters.

Formed Milling Cutters include convex and concave cutters, corner rounding cutters, sprocket wheel cutters, spline cutters, involute gear cutters, gear tooth stocking (or roughing) cutters, multiple thread mills, hacksaw and band saw cutters, and hobs for gear cutting.

Inserted Tooth Cutters: While many plain milling and slabbing cutters are made with inserted teeth, the great majority are used in face milling operations.

The various types of cutters are shown on the following pages.

MILLING CUTTERS, CLEARANCE DROP— Clearance for the cutting edges of milling cutters and reamers can be secured by off-setting the cutter or reamer with regard to the center of the grinding wheel spindle. The method, and the amount of off-set necessary to secure different clearance angles, are shown in the accompanying tables.

MILLING CUTTERS, CONTOUR GROUND —Milling cutters sharpened by grinding on the formed contour instead of on the face. This is not as easy as face grinding but it does not weaken the cutter teeth.

MILLING CUTTERS, COARSE TEETH— A relative term to distinguish modern cutters from those originally made with finely spaced teeth. A rough rule for a coarse toothed cutter is one for each inch in diameter, plus two teeth, giving a 6-inch cutter 8 teeth.

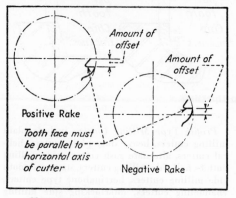

Clearance drop of milling centers.
Milling Cutters

Plain milling cutter (slabbing mill): Cutter of plain cylindrical form having teeth on the circumferential surface only. Teeth may be either straight or helical.

Side milling cutters (straddle mill): Cutter of cylindrical form, having teeth on the circumferential surface and also on both sides. The side teeth extend a portion of the distance from the circumference toward the axis. These cutters are frequently used in pairs for milling both ends of work to a given dimension.

Half-side milling cutter: Cutter of cylindrical form having teeth on the circumferential surface and teeth on one side only. The side teeth extend a portion of the distance from circumference toward the axis. These cutters are frequently used in pairs for milling both ends of work to a given dimension.

Interlocking side-milling cutter: Similar in design to a side-milling cutter except made in a *unit* of two or more interlocking sections for the purpose of milling slots to exact width. Maintained at constant width by use of thin shims or collars between inner hubs.

NOTE: Side teeth extending from circumference a short distance toward axis are for chip clearance only but are not ground for cutting purposes. Used for obtaining exact width of

Clearance Drop of Milling Cutters
Amount to Offset Cutters

Cutter Diameter Inches	Rake Angle, Deg.				
	5°	7°	10°	12°	15°
¼	.011	.023	.022	.026	.032
⅜	.016	..023	.033	.039	.049
½	.022	.030	.043	.052	.065
⅝	.027	.038	.054	.065	.081
¾	.033	.046	.065	.078	.097
⅞	.038	.053	.076	.091	.113
1	.044	.061	.087	.104	.129
⅛	.049	.069	.098	.117	.146
¼	.054	.076	.109	.130	.162
1⅜	.060	.084	.119	.143	.178
1½	.065	.091	.130	.156	.194
1¾	.076	.107	.152	,182	.226
2	.087	.122	.174	.208	.259
2¼	.098	.137	.195	,234	.291
2½	.110	.152	.217	.260	.324
3	.131	.182	.261	.312	.388
4	.174	.244	.347	.416	.518
5	.218	.305	.434	.520	.647
6	.261	.366	.521	.624	.776
8	.349	.487	.695	.832	1.035
10	.436	.609	.868	1.040	1.295

Courtesy National Twist Drill & Tool Co.

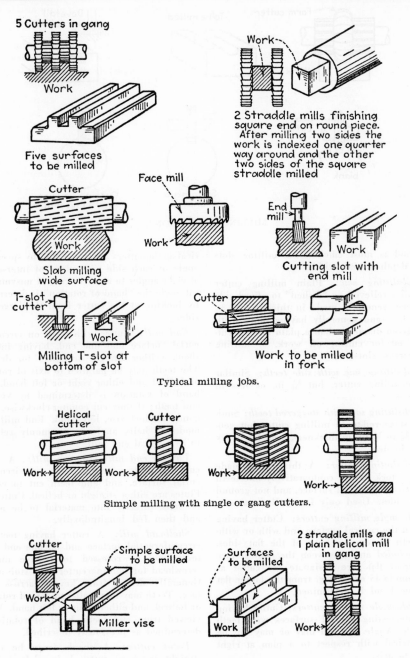

5 Cutters in gang

Work

Five surfaces to be milled

2 Straddle mills finishing square end on round piece. After milling two sides the work is indexed one quarter way around and the other two sides of the square straddle milled

Cutter

Work

Slab milling wide surface

Face mill

Work

Cutting slot with end mill

End mill

Work

T-slot cutter

Work

Milling T-slot at bottom of slot

Cutter

Work to be milled in fork

Typical milling jobs.

Helical cutter

Cutter

Work→   Work→

Work→

Work→

Simple milling with single or gang cutters.

Cutter

Work→

Simple surface to be milled

Miller vise

Surfaces to be milled

Work→

2 straddle mills and 1 plain helical mill in gang

Work→

Two simple milling jobs.

271

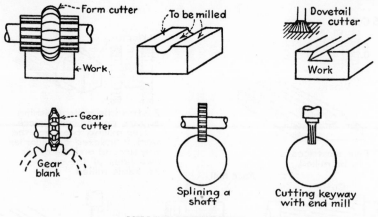

MILLING OPERATIONS.

slots and is most efficient for milling slots where depth exceeds width.

Metal-slitting saw: Plain milling cutter with sides relieved or "dished" to afford side clearance, generally made in thickness of $\frac{3}{16}$ in. or less, and generally having more teeth for a given diameter than a plain milling cutter. Used for cutting off work, or milling very narrow slots.

Metal-slitting saw with side teeth: Similar to side-milling cutter, but $\frac{3}{16}$ in. or less in thickness.

Metal-slitting saw with staggered teeth: Similar to staggered-tooth milling cutter but generally $\frac{3}{8}$ to $\frac{3}{16}$ in. in thickness, used for heavy sawing in steel.

Screw-slotting cutter: A thin cutter made of sheet stock having comparatively fine teeth on its circumferential surface, and not ground on the sides. Used only for shallow cuts.

Single-angle milling cutters: Cutter having teeth on the conical surface and with or without teeth on one or both of the flat sides. The *included* angle between the conical face and larger flat face designate the cutter as for example 45 or 60 deg. from the larger flat side, the hand is determined.

Double-angle milling cutters: Cutter having two intersecting conical surfaces with teeth on both. Angle of teeth may or may not be symmetrical with respect to a plan at right angles to axis.

NOTE: Symmetrical-angle cutters are designated by included angle of teeth. Unsymmet-rical-angle cutters are designated by specifying angle of each side with plane of intersection at right angles to axis. In case of unsymmetrical angle the "hand of rotation" is determined by looking at the cutter from the larger flat side.

End mill: Cutter with teeth on circumferential surface and one end, having integral shank (either straight or taper) for driving. The teeth may be paralled to axis of rotation or helical and either right or left hand. The hand of rotation is determined by viewing end teeth; if they cut counter-clockwise, right hand; if clockwise, left hand. End mill with moderate helix angle is commonly referred to as a spiral end mill.

Two-lip end mill (slotting mill): A shank cutter with two cutting teeth on circumferential surface, and end teeth cut to center. Flutes are either straight or helical. Cutter can be sunk directly into material to be milled and then fed longitudinally.

Shell-end mill: A cutter having teeth on circumferential surface and on one end. The tooth end is recessed to receive nut or screwhead for holding cutter on a stub arbor. Generally driven from keyslot across back face. Teeth may be parallel to axis of rotation, or helical, and either right or left hand. When viewed from end teeth, hand of rotation is determined as previously described.

T-slot cutter: A shank (may be either straight or taper) cutter designed for milling T slots having teeth on circumferential surface and both sides.

MILLING CUTTER

Circular Clearance Drop on Milling Cutters and Reamers

The clearance drop (see sketch) is a convenient means of determining whether cutters are ground with the correct clearance angle, because the drop is easily measured with a dial indicator.

Diam. In.	Width of Land	Clearance Angle—Deg. 2°	3°	4°	5°	6°	7°	8°	9°	10°	11°	12°	13°	14°
1/8	1/64	.0000	.0000	.0000	.0000	.0000	.0000	.0002	.0005	.0008	.0010	.0015	.0017	.0020
3/16	1/64	.0000	.0000	.0000	.0000	.0004	.0006	.0010	.0012	.0014	.0017	.0020	.0023	.0026
1/4	1/64	.0000	.0000	.0001	.0004	.0007	.0009	.0012	.0015	.0018	.0020	.0023	.0026	.0029
5/16	1/64	.0000	.0000	.0003	.0006	.0009	.0011	.0014	.0017	.0021	.0022	.0025	.0028	.0031
3/8	1/64	.0000	.0002	.0004	.0007	.0010	.0013	.0015	.0018	.0030	.0024	.0026	.0030	.0032
1/2	1/32	.0000	.0000	.0002	.0008	.0013	.0020	.0024	.0030	.0035	.0041	.0047	.0052	.0058
5/8	1/32	.0000	.0001	.0006	.0012	.0017	.0023	.0031	.0036	.0039	.0045	.0050	.0056	.0062
3/4	1/32	.0000	.0003	.0009	.0014	.0020	.0025	.0033	.0038	.0042	.0048	.0053	.0059	.0065
7/8	1/32	.0000	.0005	.0011	.0016	.0022	.0027	.0034	.0040	.0044	.0050	.0055	.0061	.0067
1	1/32	.0001	.0007	.0012	.0018	.0023	.0029	.0036	.0042	.0045	.0051	.0057	.0062	.0068
1 1/4	1/32	.0003	.0008	.0014	.0020	.0025	.0032	.0038	.0044	.0047	.0053	.0059	.0065	.0070
1 1/2	1/32	.0004	.0010	.0015	.0021	.0026	.0033	.0038	.0045	.0049	.0054	.0060	.0066	.0072
1 3/4	1/32	.0005	.0011	.0016	.0022	.0027	.0034	.0039	.0045	.0050	.0055	.0061	.0067	.0072
2	1/32	.0006	.0012	.0017	.0023	.0028	.0035	.0039	.0045	.0050	.0056	.0062	.0067	.0073
2 1/4	1/32	.0007	.0012	.0017	.0023	.0029	.0035	.0040	.0046	.0051	.0056	.0062	.0068	.0074
2 1/2	1/32	.0007	.0012	.0018	.0023	.0029	.0035	.0041	.0046	.0051	.0056	.0062	.0068	.0074
2 3/4	1/32	.0008	.0013	.0018	.0024	.0030	.0035	.0041	.0046	.0051	.0057	.0063	.0069	.0074
3	1/32	.0008	.0013	.0019	.0024	.0030	.0035	.0059	.0068	.0051	.0057	.0063	.0069	.0074
3 1/2	3/64	.0010	.0018	.0026	.0035	.0043	.0051	.0059	.0068	.0076	.0085	.0093	.0102	.0111
4	3/64	.0010	.0018	.0027	.0035	.0043	.0051	.0060	.0069	.0076	.0086	.0094	.0103	.0111
4 1/2	3/64	.0011	.0019	.0028	.0036	.0044	.0052	.0059	.0068	.0077	.0087	.0095	.0104	.0112
5	3/64	.0012	.0020	.0029	.0037	.0045	.0053	.0061	.0070	.0078	.0088	.0096	.0105	.0113
6	1/16	.0014	.0025	.0036	.0048	.0060	.0070	.0082	.0092	.0104	.0115	.0127	.0138	.0150
8	1/16	.0015	.0027	.0038	.0050	.0061	.0072	.0084	.0094	.0106	.0118	.0129	.0140	.0152
10	1/16	.0017	.0028	.0040	.0052	.0063	.0075	.0086	.0097	.0108	0.210	.0132	.0143	.0154
12	1/16	.0019	.0031	.0042	.0054	.0065	.0077	.0088	.0100	.0111	.0123	.0134	.0146	.0157

Courtesy National Twist Drill & Tool Co.

Hob: Formed milling cutters, the teeth of which lie in a helical path about the circumferential surface of the cutter. Generally used for spur and helical gears, worm wheels, sprocket teeth, ratchets, spline shafts, square driven shafts, etc.

Helical mill: Helical mills are of the profile type. They may be either hole or shank style. While most slab mills and shank end mills have their peripheral teeth at a slight helix angle, the name "helical mill" is used to designate a high (45 deg. or greater) helix angle of tooth. Used for slab milling or for profiling, such as cam milling and for elongating slots.

Inserted-tooth cutter: Cutter in which teeth are inserted and secured by various methods in a body of less expensive material, the object being economy in first cost and also in maintenance because of opportunity of tooth replacement.

Intermittent-tooth-type cutter: Formed cutter having a tooth contour of fine points such as a thread-milling cutter or hacksaw-milling cutter in which succeeding lands around the cutter carry alternately only half the necessary cutting points so staggered as to complete the full required pitch on the finished work. These cutters may be of the shank or arbor type.

Inserted-tooth-facing cutter: A cutter adapted to be attached directly to spindle end, or stub arbor, and having inserted teeth cutting on circumferential surface and one end, similar to side mill.

MILLING CUTTERS, DESIGNATION OF VARIOUS ANGLES AND ABBREVIATIONS USED IN DESCRIBING CUTTERS—

n (number of teeth in cutter)
N (rpm) = revolutions per minute
V = cutting speed in fpm (feet per minute)
f = feed per tooth per revolution in inches
f^1 = feed per cutter revolution in inches
F = feed in inches per minute
d = depth of cut in inches
w = width of cut in inches
D = diam. in inches
diam. = diameter
psi = pounds per square inch
fpm = feet per minute
FPM (as heading in tables)
rpm = revolutions per minute
RPM (as heading in tables)
high-speed steel tools

cast non-ferrous tools
sintered-carbide tools
sintered-carbide tipped tools

MILLING CUTTERS, FORM RELIEVED—
Milling cutters sharpened by grinding on the face of the teeth, as shown. The easiest method of sharpening but the teeth become weaker with each sharpening. See *Milling Cutters, Contour Ground*.

Hob for gears or splines.

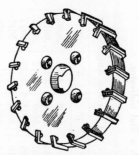

Inserted-tooth facing cutter.

Helical-tooth shell mill.

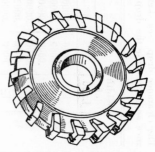

Inserted-tooth milling cutter.

274

MILLING CUTTERS, FEED OF—

CLASSIFICATION BASED ON RELIEF OF CUTTER TEETH—

Profile Relieved Cutters—Those which are relieved and sharpened by grinding a narrow land (commonly known as clearance) back of the cutting edge. They are sharpened by grinding the teeth on the periphery of the cutting edges. They may produce flat, curved, or irregular surfaces, these being called profile type form cutters.

Form Relieved Cutters—Those on which a curved relief back of the cutting edge is produced by a cam actuated tool or grinding wheel. These cutters are sharpened by grinding the faces of the teeth.

Classification of Milling Cutters Based on Relief of Teeth

Shaped Profile Cutters: Milling cutters made to be sharpened in the same manner as profile cutters, but with cutting edges of irregular or curved shape.

Form Relieved Cutters: Cutters on which the eccentric relief back of the cutting edge is of the same contour as the cutting edge. These cutters are sharpened by grinding the *face* of the tooth. So long as the face is maintained in its original plane with respect to axis of rotation, the tooth contour will remain unchanged. Formed cutters are usually of curved irregular outline.

Classification Based on Purpose or Use— Milling cutters are sometimes described by terms which refer to their use or the purpose for which they are made. By way of illustration, there are:

T-Slot Cutters, specifically used to finish the "head space" of a T-slot.

Woodruff Keyseat Cutters, the purpose of which is the machining of seats for Woodruff keys.

Gear Milling Cutters, designed to produce properly shaped teeth on gears.

Corner Rounding Cutters, intended for rounding the edges of a workpiece.

Single and Multiple Thread Milling Cutters, used to produce screw threads, one thread at a time or a number of threads, respectively.

CLASSIFICATION BASED ON METHOD OF MOUNTING—Milling cutters may also be described using terms relating to the manner of mounting them on the milling machine. The three types are as follows:

Arbor Cutter: intended for mounting on a machine arbor and usually being driven by a key.

Shank Cutter: having one or more straight or tapered extensions for the purpose of mounting and driving.

Facing Cutter: with provision for mounting directly on the milling machine spindle nose, stub arbor or adapter.

Screw-slotting cutter.

Single-angle cutter.

Double-angle cutter.

Shell-end mill.

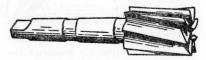

End mill with helical teeth.

Two-lip end mill.

T-slot cutter.

(Continued on pages 276 and 277)

Cutter for square
keyseats or slots.

Hollow mill.

Shaped profile cutter with
inserted teeth.

Plain milling
cutters.

Side or straddle
milling cutter.

Half-side cutter.

Cutter for Woodruff keyseat.

Slitting saw with side teeth.

Interlocking cutters.

Staggered-tooth milling
cutters.

Metal-slitting saw.

Slitting saw with
staggered teeth.

Single formed gear-
tooth cutter.

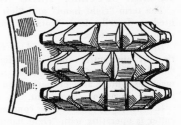

Multiple gear-tooth cutters.

Roughing or "stocking"
cutter with teeth grooved
to break up chips.

Single-sprocket
tooth cutter.

Double-sprocket
tooth cutter.

Half-round grooving
cutter.

Half-concave
cutter.

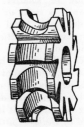

Concave half-round
cutter.

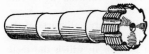

Solid and shell hobs for
fine threads.

Alternate-staggered-
tooth double-angle
cutter.

Double-spline
cutter.

Single-spline
cutter.

277

MILLING CUTTERS, "HAND" OF—

The term "right hand" and "left hand" are used to describe both "rotation" and "helix" of milling cutters.

Hand of Rotation or Hand of Cut—Direction of any cutters may be referred to as "hand of rotation" when viewed towards the machine spindle as a properly mounted cutter revolves so as to make a cut.

If this rotary motion is counterclockwise, cutter is operating with "right hand rotation." If this rotary motion is clockwise, cutter is operating with "left hand rotation."

NOTES: Exceptional cases in determination of hand of rotation:

To determine hand of rotation of a single milling cutter, view it from the side of larger diameter and decide whether it is right or left hand.

To determine hand of rotation of an unsymmetrical double angle milling cutter, view it from the side having the smaller acute angle included between a plane perpendicular to the axis and the cutting edge, and decide whether it is right or left hand.

To determine hand of rotation of a single corner rounding milling cutter, view it from the side of smaller diameter and decide whether it is right or left hand.

To determine hand of rotation of a single corner rounding milling cutter, view it from the side of smaller diameter and decide whether right or left hand.

Hand of rotation of unsymmetrical cutters must be clearly stated or shown on sketches.

To determine hand of rotation of a half side milling cutter, view it from the side tooth side.

Hand of Helix—Cutters with teeth in planes parallel to the cutter axis are described as having "straight teeth." Cutters with every other tooth of opposite (right and left) helix are called "alternate helical tooth cutters." When helix is in one direction only, cutters are described as being right or left hand helix.

A cutter viewed from one end, with flutes that twist away from the observer in a clockwise direction, has right hand helix, whereas;

A cutter with flutes that twist away in a counter-clockwise direction has left hand helix.

MILLING CUTTERS, "HAND" OF HELIX OR SPIRAL—

Right and left hand helical or spiral cutters are designated according to the direction of the helix with relation to the axis of the cutter. The "hand" of the helix is the same as for screw threads. The direction of

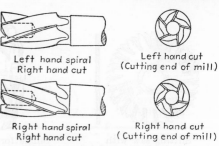

Left hand spiral
Right hand cut

Left hand cut
(Cutting end of mill)

Right hand spiral
Right hand cut

Right hand cut
(Cutting end of mill)

Hand of milling cutters.

cutting may be either right or left, as shown. The upper cutter, with a left hand helix and a right hand cut, has a negative rake on the cutting edges.

MILLING CUTTERS, HELICAL, CLEARANCE ANGLE—

No matter what the helix angle, or whether the teeth are right or left hand, the effective clearance angle is measured in the direction of cutter rotation and not normal to a tangent of the cutting edge. See illustration.

MILLING CUTTERS, METHOD OF MOUNTING—

Arbor cutters: A cutter with hole for mounting on arbor. The most common type have a straight hole and keyway in same. Sometimes keyway is across one end as in shell end mills. Frequently, the hole is tapered. Cutters are also made with threaded holes.

Right- and left-hand cutters: The "hand of rotation" of any cutter may be determined by looking at the cutter end of spindle. If the cutter rotates counterclockwise, it is right hand; if it rotates clockwise, it is left hand.

Shank cutters: A cutter having either a straight- or taper-shank integral with the cutter.

Facing cutter: A cutter designed to be attached directly to spindle end or stub arbor.

MILLING CUTTERS, MISCELLANEOUS—

Axis—Line about which cutter rotates.

"Backed-Off"—Describing form relieved cutters whose relief is produced by a cam actuated flat form tool.

Body—(1) In solid cutters—all parts of the cutters exclusive of the teeth; (1) In inserted tooth cutters—the portion in which the teeth are secured by means of wedges, screws, etc.; (3) In tipped solid cutters—the portion to which the hard alloys are joined.

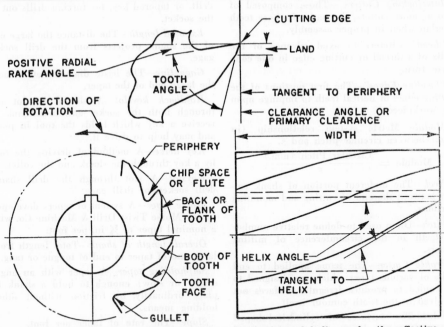

Clearance angle of helical milling cutters. Regardless of helix angle, the effective clearance angle is measurable in the direction of cutter rotation rather than normal to a tangent of the cutting edge.

Channeling Cutters—Used to mill relatively wide elongated slots. (Usually of the inserted tooth type).

"Climb Milling—Cutter is so rotated relative to the direction of table movement that the chip becomes thinner toward the surface machined.

"Conventional" Milling—Cutter is so rotated that the direction of cutting is away from the machined surface.

"Concave"—(1) Descriptive of the curved inward side surfaces of saws, etc., which provide the side relief; (2) Description of tooth shape on concave cutters.

"Dish"—Either straight or concave side relief.

"Down" Milling—Same as climb milling.

"Drag" Ends—The trailing ends of helical teeth are called "drag" ends.

Duplex—Compound cutters of two parts.

End—(See *Side*) Sides of end mills are called ends; the shank or mounting end and the cutting or toothed end.

Face — The outer circumferential toothed surface of milling cutters.

Facing—As applied to the application of a cutter, the production of a plain flat surface is described.

Flatted—Round shanks provided with a flat spot suitable for a set screw bearing are described as "flatted."

"Gang" Cutters—Two or more separate cutters so assembled as to jointly mill a workpiece.

Gash—See "Stocking."

Generate—To produce gear teeth with a hob type milling cutter which cuts in a geared relation to the workpiece. The teeth are not the shape of the space between gear teeth but are so designed as to progressively machine the desired shape.

Ground Form and Unground Form—Form relieved milling cutters may have this relief finished by grinding or simply by the use of a flat form tool. The former are called "ground form cutters," the latter "unground form cutters."

Hub—The center hole boss provided on some milling cutters.

279

Interlocking Cutters — Those composed of two or more cutters, the path of whose teeth overlap when in proper assembly.

"Lead" — Refers to axial advance of the helix of a thread or cutting edge in one complete turn.

"Leading Edges" — The first portions of the cutting edges of helical teeth to impinge upon the workpiece.

Module — Metric system relationship (in mm.) between circular pitch and π.

$$\text{Module} = \frac{\text{Circular Pitch (mm.)}}{\pi}$$

Neck — The undercut portion of shank cutters between the end of cutting and mounting portions.

Pitch — Often used to define relative number of teeth in the circumference of milling cutters.

Profile Cutter — The name applied to end mills of various types which are designed to be guided to produce irregular surfaces not involved in the tooth contour itself.

Side — The surfaces of cylindrical-shaped cutters perpendicular to the cutter's axis of rotation.

Shank — The elongated round or tapered mounting portion of end mills.

Slotting Cutter — One with side relieved teeth suitable for milling relatively narrow elongated recesses in a workpiece.

"Step" Cutter — Inserted tooth end mill, hard alloy tipped or otherwise, with several blades adjustable axially and radially so that the unit becomes a mutiple "fly cutter," each blade cutting its own separate path.

Stocking — Preliminary milling operation to remove excess metal prior to finishing operation.

MILLING CUTTERS, NOMENCLATURE—

Basic size — The theoretical or nominal standard size from which all variations are made.

Brown & Sharpe taper — A system of tapers developed by the Brown & Sharpe Manufacturing Company with a nominal taper of $\frac{1}{2}$ in. to the foot.

Drift or drift key — A flat bar with one end tapered, for forcing the drill out of its socket.

Drift keyslot — A slot through the socket at the small end of the tapered hole to receive a drift, or tapered key, for forcing drills out of the socket.

Exposed length — The distance the large end of the shank projects from the drill socket gage.

Gage line — The basic diameter at or near the large end of the taper.

Holdback keyslot — A slotted keyslot cut through both the socket and tool shank to receive a key which holds the tool in place and may help to drive it.

Key drive — A method of driving the tool by a key through the shank and the collet.

Keyslot — A slot through the drill shank, drill socket, or drill gage.

Morse taper — A system of tapers developed by the Morse Twist Drill & Machine Co. with a nominal taper of $\frac{5}{8}$ in. per foot.

Overall length of shank — Total length from large end of taper to end of tongue or tang.

Self-holding taper — A taper with an angle small (or slow) enough to hold a shank in place ordinarily by friction without other holding means.

Slope — The rate of taper per foot.

Slow taper — See self-holding taper.

Tang — The flattened end of a drill shank. Also called tongue.

Tang drive — The method of driving a tool by a tongue or tang on the end of the shank.

Taper per foot — The difference in diameter between two points 12 in. apart measured on the axis.

Tolerances — The permissible variation from basic dimension.

Tongue — See tang.

Tongue drive — See tang drive.

Straddle Cutters — Cutters mounted on one arbor, used to mill both ends of a workpiece simultaneously.

Tang — The flat end portion of a shank which mates into a driving socket portion of similar width, thus providing the milling cutter with a positive drive.

"Topping" and "Non-Topping" — Refers to that provision or lack of it in form relieved cutters which, when present, enables the cutter to finish machine the top surfaces of the work, e.g., gear teeth and threads.

Web — That portion of the cutter body between the cutting or fluted portion and the hub.

MILLING CUTTERS, RAKE ANGLES—The
angle between the cutting edge and the center
of rotation. The illustrations show positive,
neutral and negative rake angles, for both
radial and axial rakes.

MILLING CUTTERS, T-SLOT—Dimensions
of cutters for milling T-slots have been standardized to agree with standards for T-bolts, as
shown. See *T-Bolts.*

MILLING CUTTERS, TERMS USED FOR TEETH AND CUTTING ANGLES—

Chip space is that space between the back
of one tooth and the face of the next.

Clearance angle is the angle between the
margin and the tangent at the cutting edge.

Cutting edge or lip of the profile is formed
by the intersection of face and margin.

Depth of tooth is measured from the cutting
edge to the center of the gullet circle.

Gullet is the circular fillet joining the face

of one tooth with the back of the next.

Lip angle is the angle measured in a plane
at right angles to the cutting edge between
the face and margin.

Margin is that surface back of the cutting
edge ground to produce the clearance angle.

Rake angle is the angle measured between
the face of the tooth and a radial line in a
diametral plane. If the cutting edge is ahead
of the bottom of the face, the rake is positive.

Secondary clearance or relief is the angle
between the margin continued and the back
of the tooth below the margin. The secondary
clearance may be produced by a continuous
curve from the land to the bottom of the tooth
or by one or more straight lines.

Thickness of the base of tooth is the length
of the chord connecting the face of one tooth
with its back, as measured along a circle
passing through the center of the gullet areas.

Tooth face is that surface on which the chip
impinges as it is cut from the work.

NOTE: "Land" is applied to drills, etc., and
has no clearance.

Helical Milling Cutters:

Helical mills are similar to plain mills, except that the cutting edges, instead of being
straight elements of the outside cylinder, form
helices in the surface.

The helix angle is measured between a tangent of the helix and a line parallel to the
axis of the cutter. A straight-tooth cutter has
zero helix.

Helical mills with small helix angles are
called slow helical mills, while those with
large helix angles (above 45 deg.) are called
fast helical mills.

Side-Cutting Milling Cutters:

Side-cutting milling cutters have cutting
edges as well as on the outer edges of each
tooth.

Radial undercut or face clearance is the
angle between the side-cutting edge of the
tooth and the diametral plane. It eliminates
dragging of the inner ends of the side-cutting
or radial teeth.

Half-Side, End Mills, and Face-Milling Cutters:

Face clearance is the angle betwen the flank
of the cutter tooth and a line at right angles
to the axis of the cutter.

Rake is the angle between the tooth or blade
face and a line parallel to the axis of the
cutter.

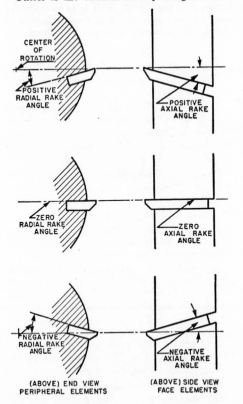

CENTER OF ROTATION

POSITIVE RADIAL RAKE ANGLE

POSITIVE AXIAL RAKE ANGLE

ZERO RADIAL RAKE ANGLE

ZERO AXIAL RAKE ANGLE

NEGATIVE RADIAL RAKE ANGLE

NEGATIVE AXIAL RAKE ANGLE

(ABOVE) END VIEW PERIPHERAL ELEMENTS

(ABOVE) SIDE VIEW FACE ELEMENTS

Peripheral and face elements of rake angles.

Dimensions of T-Slot Milling Cutters

Width of Throat [1],[2]		Thickness of Cutter (H)		Diameter of Cutters (A)		Diameter of Neck[2]	Length of Neck
Standard	Nominal Bolt Size	Maximum	Minimum (Worn)	Maximum	Minimum (Worn)		
9/32	1/4	15/64	13/64	9/16	1/2	17/64	3/8
11/32	5/16	17/64	15/64	21/32	19/32	21/64	7/16
7/16	3/8	21/64	19/64	25/32	23/32	13/32	9/16
9/16	1/2	25/64	23/64	31/32	29/32	17/32	11/16
11/16	5/8	31/64	29/64	1 1/4	1 3/16	21/32	7/8
13/16	3/4	5/8	19/32	1 15/32	1 3/8	25/32	1 1/16
1 1/16	1	53/64	25/32	1 27/32	1 3/4	1 1/32	1 1/4
1 5/16	1 1/4	1 3/32	1 1/32	2 7/32	2 1/8	1 9/32	1 9/16
1 9/16	1 1/2	1 11/32	1 9/32	2 23/32	2 9/16	1 17/32	1 15/16

All dimensions in inches.

[1]The "width of throat" given in the above tables corresponds to that given for T-slots.

[2]In addition to the "width of throat" given above, a secondary standard is recognized, having the "width of throat" the same as the nominal diameter of the T-bolt. This is to provide for the use, during the transition period, of this standard on many machine tools where it is already established. If the narrower throat is used, the diameter of neck "D" should be reduced accordingly.

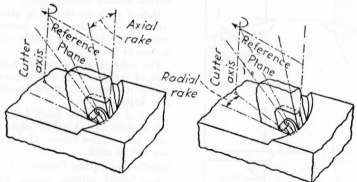

Axial rake.   Radial rake.

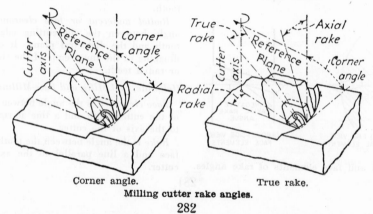

Corner angle.   True rake.

Milling cutter rake angles.

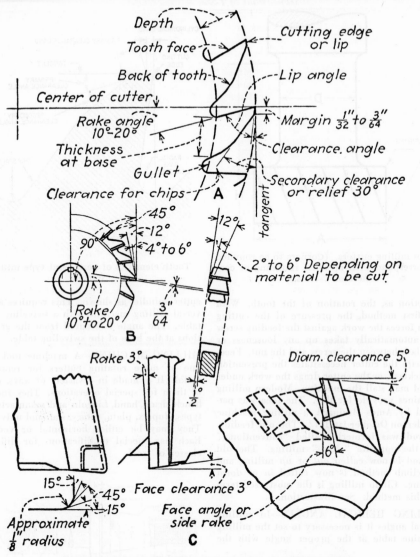

Terms used for teeth and cutting angles of milling cutters.

Side rake or face angle is the angle between the face of the tool and a radial line measured in a plane, perpendicular to the axis of the cutter.

MILLING CUTTERS, TOOTH ELEMENTS— The tooth elements of a peripheral type milling cutter are shown. These include radial rake angle, cutting edge, cylindrical land, primary clearance land, primary and secondary clearance angles and chip space.

MILLING, DIRECTION OF FEED—There are two different methods of feeding the work to peripheral milling cutters. The older method was to feed opposite or against the rotation of the cutting teeth. Where possible, it is now considered best to feed with, or in the same

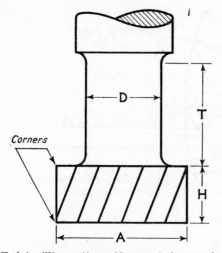

T-slot milling cutters. (Corners to be rounded to correspond with optional rounding of corners of T-slots.)

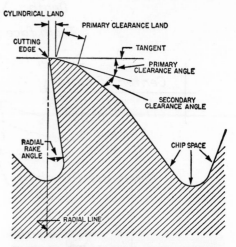

Tooth elements of peripheral type milling cutter.

direction as, the rotation of the tooth. With the first method, the pressure of the cutting tooth forces the work against the feeding screw and automatically takes up any looseness or backlash between the screw and the nut. Feeding *with* the cutter necessitates the prevention of backlash, or the cutter drags the work under it and may stall the machine. Modern milling machines provide for this. The idea was patented by Amos Brainard, a milling machine builder, on October 1st, 1872. The old feeding method was formerly called "conventional" and the opposite "climb" milling. The old method is now called *out* or *up* milling and the climb method is now called *in* or *down* milling. Climb milling is the most used term for this method. See illustration.

MILLING HELICAL ANGLES—In milling helical angles it is necessary to set the milling machine table at the proper angle with the

cutter spindle, as shown. This requires a universal milling machine with a swiveling work table. The angle is secured from the graduations at the base of the swiveling table.

MILLING MACHINE—A machine tool with one or more rotating cutters for removing metal. It is made in a variety of ways, many of them for special operations. They include bench, drum, hand, Lincoln and manufacturing types, duplex, plain, rotary, slab and universal. They may be either horizontal or vertical. Each has special qualifications for different classes of work.

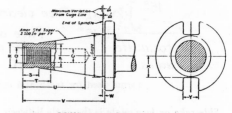

Milling machine arbors.

MILLING MACHINE ARBORS, STANDARD—Standardized arbors will now fit all makes of milling machines, the essential dimensions being given below.

Approved by A. S. A., November, 1943; reaffirmed by A. S. A. June 10, 1949.

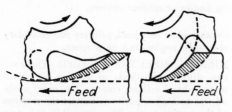

Direction of milling feed. Left, out or up cutting; right, climb or in cutting.

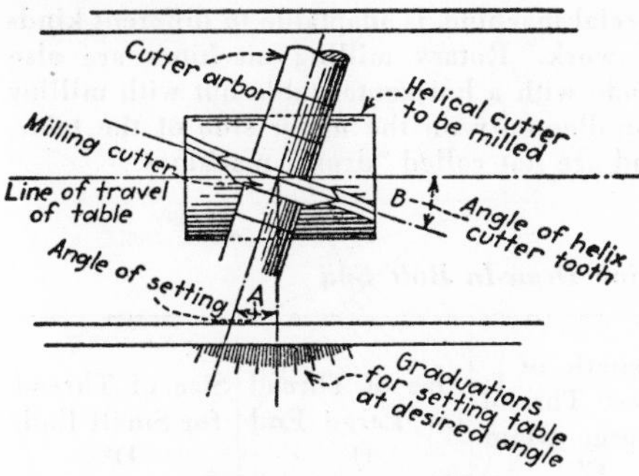

Milling helical angles.

MILLING MACHINE, BED TYPE—A manufacturing milling machine developed from the Lincoln type.

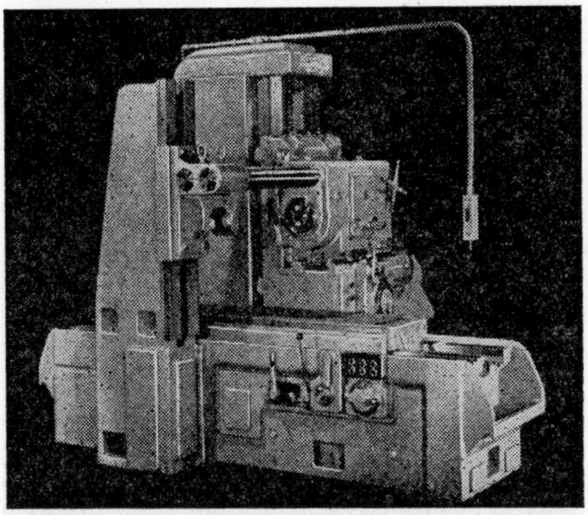

Kearney and Trecker bed type milling machine.

MILLING MACHINE, BRIGGS—A type of manufacturing milling machine developed about 1914 by Arthur Briggs for typewriter and similar work. Has been largely replaced by later types.

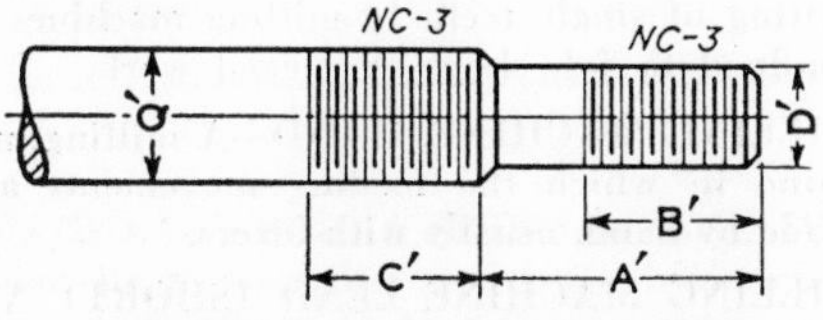

Milling machine draw-in bolt.

MILLING MACHINE DRAW-IN BOLT—The bolt used to draw milling machine cutter arbors into the spindle and hold them securely while at work. Even with slow, or self-holding tapers, cutter arbors sometimes worked loose; it is necessary to hold them firmly with

Essential Dimensions for Ends of Milling Machine Arbor and Adapter

Size Number	Gage Diameter of Taper	Drill Clearance for Draw-In Bolt	Diameter of Neck	Size of Thread for Draw-In Bolt	Plot-Diameter	Length of Pilot	Length of Perfect Threads	Depth of Clearance Hole	Distance from Rear of Flange to End of Arbor	Clearance of Flange from Gage Diameter	Depth of Driving Slot	Width of Driving Slot
	N	O	P	Q	R	S	T	U	V	W	X	Y
30	1¼	27/64	41/64	½-13	0.675 0.673	13/16	1	2	2¾	1/16	0.064 0.625	0.630 0.640
40	1¾	17/32	15/16	5/8-11	0.987 0.985	1	1⅛	1 15/16	3¾	1/16	0.890 0.875	0.630 0.640
50	2¾	⅞	1½	1-8	1.549 0.547	1	1¾	3½	5⅛	⅛	1.390 1.375	1.008 1.018
60	4¼	1 7/64	2 9/32	1¼-7	2.361 2.359	1¾	2¼	4¼	8 5/16	⅛	2.400 2.390	1.008 1.018

All dimensions are given in inches.

the new "self-releasing" taper 3½ inches per foot. The standard draw-in bolt has two threaded diameters and is patented, but is in general use, through license. Approved by A. S. A. November, 1943; reaffirmed June 10, 1949.

special machine, is adaptable to different kinds of work. Rotary milling machines are also made with a horizontal table but with milling spindles only on the upper side of the table, and are not called "drum" machines.

Dimensions of Milling Machine Draw-In Bolt End

Size Number	Length of Small End A′	Length of Perfect Thread at Small end B′	Length of Perfect Thread on Large Diam. C′	Size of Thread for Large End Q′	Size of Thread for Small End D′
30	1 1/16	3/4	3/4	1/2—13	3/8—16
40	11/16	11/16	1 1/8	5/8—11	1/2—13
50	1 1/2	1 1/4	1 3/8	1—8	5/8—11
60	1 3/8	1 3/8	2	1 1/4—7	1—8

All dimensions are given in inches.

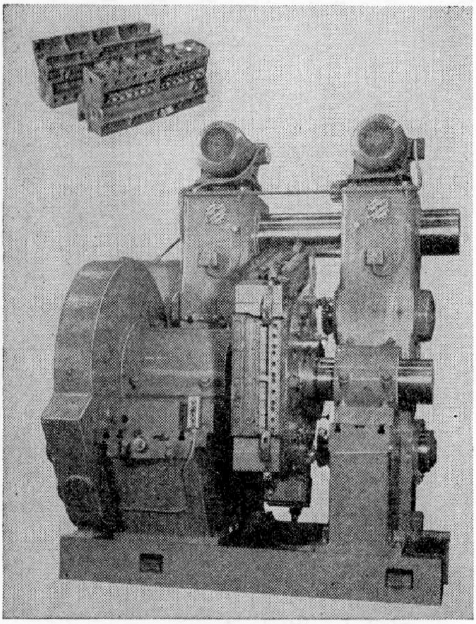

Davis and Thompson drum type rotary milling machine.

MILLING MACHINE, DRUM—A type of milling machine in which the work to be milled rotates between milling cutters, while held on a kind of drum, as shown. Developed by the Davis & Thompson Co. for milling automobile cylinder blocks and other parts. It is made in various forms, and, while a somewhat

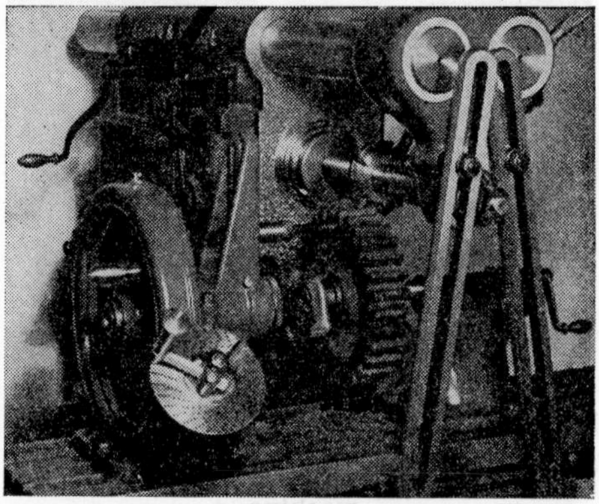

Brown and Sharpe gear cutting on milling machine.

MILLING MACHINE, GEAR CUTTING—A milling machine having suitable indexing mechanism, as shown, for cutting gears one tooth at a time. Since gear shaping and gear hobbing have become standard practice, the cutting of single teeth in milling machines is confined to job shops or special work.

MILLING MACHINE, HAND—A milling machine in which the feeding movements are made by hand, usually with levers.

MILLING MACHINE LEAD (SHORT) ATTACHMENT—The Brown & Sharpe attachment shown is for securing very short leads in milling helical cuts on a machine. As shown, the leads can be reduced to 1/800th of the

Brown and Sharpe short lead milling
attachment.

MILLING MACHINE, LINCOLN—An early
type of milling machine designed for duplicating parts of guns and sewing machines. It
originated in New England. Modern manufacturing millers are based on this design.

normal, giving leads as low as 0.0125 inch per
revolution. Primarily useful in tool room and
experimental work.

Brown and Sharpe manufacturing milling
machine.

Nichols hand milling machine.

Cincinnati plain milling machine.

MILLING MACHINE, MANUFACTURING—
A development of the Lincoln type milling machine. Also known as the "bed" type and "plain" milling machine.

MILLING MACHINE, PLAIN — A pedestal type milling machine similar to the universal miller except that the table does not swivel on the knee so that the table only feeds at right angles to the spindle.

MILLING MACHINE, PLANETARY—A milling machine, usually horizontal, with the spindle mounted eccentrically in a drum which revolves and carries the milling cutter in a circular path. The path or orbit of the spindle can be adjusted to any desired radius. It has many interesting applications. The work usually remains stationary but can be fed longitudinally.

MILLING MACHINE, RAM TYPE—A pedestal type milling machine in which the cutter spindle is mounted in a ram at the top of the column. This ram is adjustable to move spindle across the table and to permit the spindle to be horizontal, vertical or at any desired angle, as in the Van Norman machine.

MILLING MACHINE, ROTARY—This has a horizontal rotary table to which the work is fastened and which revolves it beneath one or more vertical cutter heads. Differs from the drum type, which has horizontal spindles. Resembles a vertical boring mill in appearance.

MILLING MACHINE SLOTTING ATTACH-MENT—An attachment where the rotation of a milling machine spindle gives a reciprocating motion to a slotting head. Especially useful in tool room work for occasional jobs. As shown, a keyway is being cut in a large milling cutter.

MILLING MACHINE SPINDLE N O S E, STANDARD — Milling machine spindles now have a standard taper of $3\frac{1}{2}$ inches per foot and other holding and driving dimensions have also been standardized. Some formerly used Brown & Sharpe tapers, others the Morse taper and a few the Jarno taper, so that tools were not interchangeable. Other dimensions are also standardized. Approved by A. S. A. in November, 1943; reaffirmed June 10, 1949.

MILLING MACHINE TAPERS—See *Tapers, Milling Machine.*

MILLING MACHINE, UNIVERSAL—A column type milling machine with work table which swings in the horizontal plane and feeds arranged so that all classes of plane, circular, helical and index or other milling may be done. Equipped with index centers, chuck, etc.

Van Norman ram type milling machine

PLANETARY MILLING.

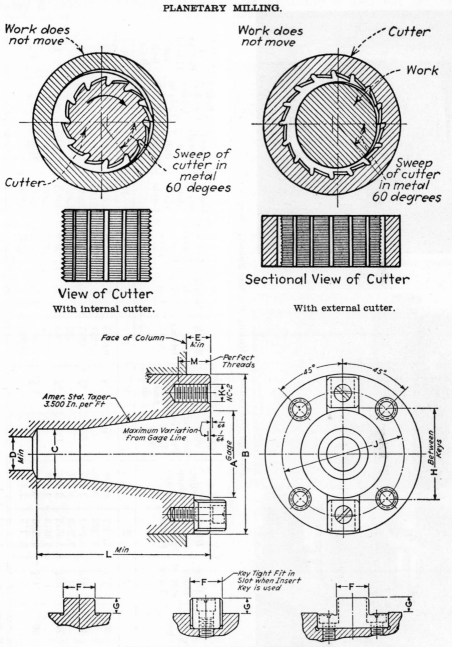

Work does not move

Cutter

Sweep of cutter in metal 60 degees

Cutter

View of Cutter
With internal cutter.

Work does not move

Cutter

Work

Sweep of cutter in metal 60 degrees

Sectional View of Cutter
With external cutter.

Face of Column

E Min

M

Perfect Threads

Amer. Std. Taper
3.500 In. per Ft

K NC-2

Maximum Variation from Gage Line

1/64
1/64

A Gage

B

D Min

C

45°   45°

J

H Between Keys

L Min

F

G

F

Key Tight Fit in Slot when Insert Key is used

G

F

G

SELECTIVE TYPES OF DRIVE KEY CONSTRUCTION

Milling machine spindle nose.

289

MILLING MACHINE

Kearney and Trecker universal milling machine.

Brown and Sharpe slotting attachment.

Essential Dimensions of Milling Machine Spindle Nose

Size Number	Gage Diameter of Taper	Diameter of Spindle Flange	Pilot Diameter	Clearance Hole for Draw-in Bolt, Min	Minimum Dimension Spindle, End to Column	Width of Driving Key	Height of Driving Key	Distance Between Driving Keys	Diameter of Bolt Hole Circle	Size of Threads for Bolt Holes	Full Depth of Arbor Hole in Spindle, Min	Depth of Perfect Thread for Bolt Hole
	A	B	C	D	E	F	G	H	J	K	L	M
30	1¼	2.7493 2.7488	0.692 0.685	21/32	½	0.6255 0.6252	5/16	1.315 1.285	2.130 2.120	⅜-16	2⅞	⅝
40	1¾	3.4993 3.4988	1.005 0.997	21/32	⅝	0.6255 0.6252	5/16	1.819 1.807	2.630 2.620	½-13	3⅞	1 13/16
50	2¾	5.0618 5.0613	1.568 1.559	1 1/16	¾	1.0006 1.0002	½	2.819 2.807	4.005 3.995	⅝-11	5½	1
60	4¼	8.7180 8.7175	2.381 2.371	1⅜	1½	1.000 0.999	½	4.819 4.807	7.005 6.995	¾-10	8⅝	1¼

All dimensions are given in inches.

Becker, Reed, and Prentice vertical milling machine.

MILLING MACHINE, VERTICAL—A milling machine with a vertical spindle adapted for end or face milling. The table feeding mechanism is the same as on plain, horizontal milling machines.

MILLING, STRADDLE—Using two or more cutters spaced desired distances apart, to mill certain parts of the work and not the entire surface. This may be for cutting channels at given distances apart or it may be milling the sides of parts which project above the body of the work. See *Milling.*

MINIMUM METAL—The smallest size which will be passed by the tolerances permitted.

MINOR DIAMETER FIT—See *Spline Fits, Minor Diameter.*

MIST COOLING—The cooling of tools and work by a rapidly moving mixture of air and coolant. This has been previously mixed up in either a venturi mixer, or some kind of mixing valve, such as a simple T-connection into which air and coolant are forced under pressure. The "wetness" of the mixture is varied to suit the work being done. It may range from a very light fog, which scarcely showns the liquid, to a heavy spray, the latter being used on some planer jobs. Air pressures may vary from 5 to 50 or even 60 pounds per square inch, which of course changes the velocity with which the mixture comes out of the discharge nozzle.

MITER—An angle of 45 degrees, or the joint formed by two pieces each having a 45-degree angle. Also spelled *mitre.*

MITER BEVEL GEARS—Gears which drive shafts at right angles to each other.

MITER GEARS OR WHEELS — An older name for bevel gears. Usually applied to gears with a 45-degree angle. See *Gears, Bevel.*

MODIFIED SQUARE SCREW THREAD—See *Screw Threads, Modified Square.*

MODIFIED THREADS—Screw threads which have been changed or "modified' from their original or standard form. See *Screw Threads.*

MODULE OR METRIC SYSTEM OF GEARING—See *Gears, Module or Metric.*

MINUTES OF ARC—These are 1/60 of each of the 360 degrees in a complete circle. As it is frequently necessary to convert minutes of arc into decimals of a degree, a table is given on page 292 which does this without any calculation.

MODULUS OF ELASTICITY—The ratio of stress to the corresponding strain imposed within the limit of elasticity of a piece. The stress in pounds per square inch is divided by the amount of elongation, measured in fractions of an inch, for each inch of the original gage length of the specimen used.

MOHS' SCALE OF HARDNESS—This classifies *natural* materials on the basis of resistance to being scratched. It was established in 1818. The numbers are arbitrary. As no material is hard enough to scratch a diamond, this was called No. 10. As sapphire (corundum) could be scratched by a diamond, this was called No. 9, topaz became No. 8, quartz No. 7, etc. As the Bureau of Standards has developed equipment showing that the diamond is at least *three times* as hard as the next hardest material, the scale has no very definite meaning. The old belief that the sapphire was almost as hard as the diamond, is not true. See *table of comparisons of various hardness scales* on page 295.

MOLD—A form or matrix used to form molten or powdered material into any desired shape. Either the molten metal or the powdered material may be forced into the mold, or poured in by hand. When used in forging or stamping, a "mold" is usually called a *die.*

Minutes of Arc

Min. of Arc	Decimal of a Degree	Min. of Arc	Decimal of a Degree	Min. of Arc	Decimal of a Degree	Min. of Arc	Decimal of a Degree	Min. of Arc	Decimal of a Degree	Min. of Arc	Decimal of a Degree
¼	0.00416	10¼	0.17083	20¼	0.33750	30¼	0.50416	40¼	0.67083	50¼	0.83750
½	0.00833	10½	0.17500	20½	0.34166	30½	0.50833	40½	0.67500	50½	0.84166
¾	0.01250	10¾	0.17916	20¾	0.34583	30¾	0.51250	40¾	0.67916	50¾	0.84583
1	0.01666	11	0.18333	21	0.35000	31	0.51666	41	0.68333	51	0.85000
1¼	0.02083	11¼	0.18750	21¼	0.35416	31¼	0.52083	41¼	0.68750	51¼	0.85416
1½	0.02500	11½	0.19166	21½	0.35833	31½	0.52500	41½	0.69166	51½	0.85833
1¾	0.02916	11¾	0.19583	21¾	0.36250	31¾	0.52916	41¾	0.69583	51¾	0.86250
2	0.03333	12	0.20000	22	0.36666	32	0.53333	42	0.70000	52	0.86666
2¼	0.03750	12¼	0.20416	22¼	0.37083	32¼	0.53750	42¼	0.70416	52¼	0.87083
2½	0.04166	12½	0.20833	22½	0.37500	32½	0.54166	42½	0.70833	52½	0.87500
2¾	0.04583	12¾	0.21250	22¾	0.37916	32¾	0.54583	42¾	0.71250	52¾	0.87916
3	0.05000	13	0.21666	23	0.38333	33	0.55000	43	0.71666	53	0.88333
3¼	0.05416	13¼	0.22083	23¼	0.38750	33¼	0.55416	43¼	0.72083	53¼	0.88750
3½	0.05833	13½	0.22500	23½	0.39166	33½	0.55833	43½	0.72500	53½	0.89166
3¾	0.06250	13¾	0.22916	23¾	0.39583	33¾	0.56250	43¾	0.72916	53¾	0.89583
4	0.06666	14	0.23333	24	0.40000	34	0.56666	44	0.73333	54	0.90000
4¼	0.07083	14¼	0.23750	24¼	0.40416	34¼	0.57083	44¼	0.73750	54¼	0.90416
4½	0.07500	14½	0.24166	24½	0.40833	34½	0.57500	44½	0.74166	54½	0.90833
4¾	0.07916	14¾	0.24583	24¾	0.41250	34¾	0.57916	44¾	0.74583	54¾	0.91250
5	0.08333	15	0.25000	25	0.41666	35	0.58333	45	0.75000	55	0.91666
5¼	0.08750	15¼	0.25416	25¼	0.42083	35¼	0.58750	45¼	0.75416	55¼	0.92083
5½	0.09166	15½	0.25833	25½	0.42500	35½	0.59166	45½	0.75833	55½	0.92500
5¾	0.09583	15¾	0.26250	25¾	0.42916	35¾	0.59583	45¾	0.76250	55¾	0.92916
6	0.10000	16	0.26666	26	0.43333	36	0.60000	46	0.76666	56	0.93333
6¼	0.10416	16¼	0.27083	26¼	0.43750	36¼	0.60416	46¼	0.77083	56¼	0.93750
6½	0.10833	16½	0.27500	26½	0.44166	36½	0.60833	46½	0.77500	56½	0.94166
6¾	0.11250	16¾	0.27916	26¾	0.44583	36¾	0.61250	46¾	0.77916	56¾	0.94583
7	0.11666	17	0.28333	27	0.45000	37	0.61666	47	0.78333	57	0.95000
7¼	0.12083	17¼	0.28750	27¼	0.45416	37¼	0.62083	47¼	0.78750	57¼	0.95416
7½	0.12500	17½	0.29166	27½	0.45833	37½	0.62500	47½	0.79166	57½	0.95833
7¾	0.12916	17¾	0.29583	27¾	0.46250	37¾	0.62916	47¾	0.79583	57¾	0.96250
8	0.13333	18	0.30000	28	0.46666	38	0.63333	48	0.80000	58	0.96666
8¼	0.13750	18¼	0.30416	28¼	0.47083	38¼	0.63750	48¼	0.80416	58¼	0.97083
8½	0.14166	18½	0.30833	28½	0.47500	38½	0.64166	48½	0.80833	58½	0.97500
8¾	0.14583	18¾	0.31250	28¾	0.47916	38¾	0.64583	48¾	0.81250	58¾	0.97916
9	0.15000	19	0.31666	29	0.48333	39	0.65000	49	0.81666	59	0.98333
9¼	0.15416	19¼	0.32083	29¼	0.48750	39¼	0.65416	49¼	0.82083	59¼	0.98750
9½	0.15833	19½	0.32500	29½	0.49166	39½	0.65833	49½	0.82500	59½	0.99166
9¾	0.16250	19¾	0.32916	29¾	0.49583	39¾	0.66250	49¾	0.82916	59¾	0.99583
10	0.16666	20	0.33333	30	0.50000	40	0.66666	50	0.83333	60	1.00000

MOLD BOARD—The board used in a foundry to hold sand in the flask while the mold is being made. Also called a follow board.

MOLD LOFT—A large floor area on which plans for ships and large airplanes are laid out to full size.

MOLD STEEL—Steels used for making molds for die-casting or for plastics.

MOLDING MACHINE—Any mechanical device for preparing sand molds for castings. Also applies to machines for making plastic products in molds of various kinds. See *Sand Slinger.*

Mohs' Scale of Hardness

Mohs' Hardness Scale	Mineral	Carborundum Number	Indentation Number	Rockwell Hardness
1	Talc	1		
2	Gypsum	2	32	
3	Calcite	3	135	74 RB
4	Fluorite	4	163	84 RB
5	Apatite	5	360-430	39-45 R_c
6	Feldspar	6	560	56 R_c ⎱ Range of
7	Quartz	7	710-790	61-56 R_c ⎰ Steel Tools
8	Topaz	8	1250	72 R_c
9	Sapphire	9	1445	75 R_c
.	Fused Alumina	10	1635	77 R_c
.	Tungsten Carbide	12	1850	80 R_c
.	Silicon-Carbide	14	2150	84 R_c
.	Boron Carbide (Norton)	19.7	2250	85 R_c
.	Carbonado	36.4	8200	
.	Congo (Gray)	37.8	8275	
.	Congo (Yellow)	41.0	8450	
10	Brazil Ballas	42.0	8500	

MOLECULE—A unit used by scientists in describing matter of different kinds. Supposed to be the smallest portion of matter which retains its identity.

MOLYBDENUM—A heavy, silvery metal. Sp. gr. 10.2. Melts at 4,750 deg. F. Softer than tungsten and can be drawn into wire. Used mostly as an alloy, for hardening and heat resistance. It also increases ultimate strength, hardness and toughness, as well as resistance to chemical action.

MOLYBDENUM CAST IRON— Cast iron with a small percentage of molybdenum, which increases its strength and hardness.

MOLYBDENUM STEEL OR MOLY-STEEL—Steel hardened by a small amount of molybdenum. It also increases the strength of the steel. It replaces tungsten in some cases.

MOMENTUM—The energy stored in any moving body. It depends on the weight and the velocity at which it is moving.

MONEL—The original Monel metal was two-thirds nickel and one-third copper. "K" Monel is 66 per cent nickel, 29 per cent copper and 2.75 per cent aluminum. "R" Monel is 67 per cent nickel, 30 per cent copper and 0.035 per cent sulphur. It is rust resisting.

MONGREL THREAD—A thread which is not standard in pitch or form. Frequently called a "bastard" thread. The same terms are also applied to other machine elements which are not standard.

MONITOR—A revolving turret which holds a variety of tools with which different operations are performed. Sometimes used to describe a turret lathe, which the British call a capstan lathe. The resemblance to the Ericsson gunboat "Monitor" of 1864 accounts for the name.

MONKEY WRENCH—See *Wrench*. There are numerous stories as to the origin of the name.

MONOCHROMATIC LIGHT—A light with only one wave length and one color. This is necessary in making fine measurements by use of light waves which can detect errors in flat surfaces in millionths of an inch. Used in inspecting fine measuring instruments, gage blocks and precision work where flat surfaces are involved. Tests can be made without the flat surface being tested being in actual contact with the optical flat. Contact can be prevented by using small strips of very thin paper of equal thicknesses between the flat and the gage block surface. With a good light the separation may be as much as 0.005 inch, meaning that this is the thickness of paper which can be used. Thinner paper is desirable but not necessary. See *Light Wave Bands*.

MONOTRON HARDNESS TESTING MACHINE—A machine registering the load required to produce a definite penetration of the metal being tested. It uses a diamond ball of ¾ of a millimeter (0.029527) inch, which penetrates to a depth of 0.0018 inch. The pressure required for this penetration is read on a scale which converts it directly into Brinell numbers.

MORSE TAPER — Used largely for drill shanks. Nominally ⅝ inch taper per foot. See *Tapers, Standard.*

MORTISE—A cavity cut to receive the end of another piece. The part fitting into the mortise is called a "tenon."

MOTTLED IRON—A cast iron between gray iron and white iron.

MOUNTING PRESSURE FOR LOCOMOTIVE AXLES — See *Locomotive Axles, Mounting Pressure for.*

MOUSING HOOK—A hook with a keeper or latch which prevents it from coming unhooked accidentally.

MOVE-MEN—Men whose duty it is to move material from department to department in a shop of any kind.

MOVE TICKET — The ticket or instruction card used to direct the movement of material, rough or finished, from one department to another.

MUCK BAR—Iron bars which have only been rolled once. The name is also applied to the bar used by puddlers in making wrought iron.

MUD DRUM—A drum or container below a steam boiler to hold any sediment that may collect.

MUFF—A short hollow cylinder, such as is used in connecting steel mill rolls with the shafts which drive them. The muffs are ribbed or corrugated, similar to having splines, for securing a positive drive. The term is also used for other parts of similar shape.

MUFFLE—Applied to a furnace, a baffle which prevents direct heat from coming in contact with the metal to be heated. Sometimes used to describe a pulley block with several pulleys or sheaves. See *Furnace, Muffle.*

MULE PULLEY, OR MULEY—See *Pulley, Muley.*

MULEY BELT AND PULLEYS—An arrangement of pulleys and belts to drive at right or other angles from the source of power. Performs the function of bevel gears. See *Pulley, Muley.*

MULEY SHAFT—See *Shaft, Muley.*

MULLAR—A little used term for a die used for stamping or embossing in relief.

MULTAUMATIC BORING AND TURNING MACHINE—A special type of automatic vertical boring machine built by the Bullard Co.

Bullard multaumatic boring mill.

MULTICHECK GAGES—See *Gages, Multi-Check.*

MULTIPLE SPINDLE DRILLING MACHINES — See *Drilling Machines, Multiple Spindle.*

MULTIPLE THREAD HOBS—See *Hobs, Multi-Thread.*

MULTIPLE TOOLING—The use of more than one tool at the same time on machining a piece of work. It is usually applied to use of a number of tools, as shown, in turning the bevel gear blank on the end of a shaft. The various operations are indicated by different diameters and surfaces on the piece in the lathe.

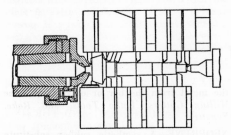

Multiple tooling. Tools for roughing a bevel stem pinion.

MULTI-ROLL BEARING—Another name for needle bearing. See *Needle Bearing.*

MULTI-START SCREW THREADS— See *Screw Threads, Multiple or Multi-Start.*

MUNTZ METAL—A ductile alloy of 60 parts copper and 40 parts zinc. It can be forged hot. Named for its inventor, Muntz, of Birmingham, England. See under *Brass, Alloys for Different Uses.*

MURIATIC ACID—The same as hydrochloric acid. Used in dissolving or cutting zinc and for use as a soldering acid. It is now largely replaced for this purpose by various soldering pastes, some of these being incorporated with the soldering wire itself.

MUSHET STEEL—An air-hardening steel for cutting tools. It does not lose hardness at moderate heats from contact with the work. Said to contain about 9 per cent tungsten and 2 per cent manganese. It was probably the first of the steel alloys which replaced carbon steel tools for machining work.

MUSHROOM HEAD—A shop term for any enlarged end or head, as on cold chisels. Continued blows of a chipping hammer rivet over the ends of chisels until they resemble mushrooms.

MUSIC WIRE—High quality steel wire first developed for musical instruments. Now largely used for springs. Sometimes called piano wire. See *Gages, Wire.*

MUTILATED GEAR—See *Gears, Intermittent.*

N

N. E. M. A.—Abbreviation for National Electrical Manufacturers Association. The N.E.M.A. has adopted several standards in connection with motor sizes and powers which have been of great assistance to designers of machine tools and other machines which are electrically driven. They enable machine builders to use different makes of motors and know they will fit standard mountings.

N. E. STEELS—See *Steel, National Emergency*.

NACELLE—The structure which holds engines of an airplane to the wings.

NAVE—Another name for the hub, or center of a wheel having spokes.

NAVY CASTING ALLOYS—Navy specifications for castings in which bronze plays a part have been revised under dates of 1945 to 1948. They include bronze, aluminum bronze, aluminum-manganese, bronze bearings, bronze ornamental castings, and bronze hydraulic (ounce metal). See *Ounce Metal* and *Manganese Bronze*.

NEAT'S FOOT OIL—An oil secured from boiling the feet of cattle. Formerly used in dressing or softening leather for belting.

NECK—Generally a reduced diameter, as between the shank and flutes of a reamer, or tap. Sometimes used in connection with a smaller diameter at the end of a piece of work.

NECKING TOOL—A tool for turning a neck or groove in any piece of work.

NEEDLE BEARING—A type of roller bearing in which a large number of small diameter rollers are used. The name probably originated because the rollers resemble knitting needles. See *Ball and Roller Bearings*.

NEEDLE FILE—See *Files, Needle*.

NEEDLE VALVE—See *Valve, Needle*.

NEGATIVE ALLOWANCE—See *Allowance, Negative*.

NEGATIVE RAKE—As applied to cutting tools, a cutting angle of more than 90 degrees. The opposite of a cutting angle which shears the metal from the bar or other work. See *Milling Cutters, Lathe Tools*, and *Rake, Negative*.

NEOPRENE—A synthetic rubber substitute which has many advantages for use in mechanical mechanisms, as it resists oils and chemicals.

NEST—This generally refers to a number of holes or pins grouped together in a jig or die. Sometimes used to describe the guide that places work in contact position.

NEST FOR PRESS WORK—In second operation work, the blank is fed into an opening in the die face to locate it for the second stroke of the press.

NEUTRAL AXIS—The point or plane of any body at which pressures are equalized and there is no tension or compression. Usually refers to beams of various kinds.

NEUTRAL BATHS—Baths such as barium salts, for heating steel, in which the surface of the steel is not affected as by carburizing or decarburizing. The same is true of a lead bath.

NEUTRAL ZONE—The minimum clearance space intended between mating parts. An intentional or permissible difference in size of mating parts.

NEUTRALIZE—To overcome action in any direction. In chemistry, to cause it to become inactive.

NEUTRON — An uncharged particle having neither a positive nor a negative charge. Of nearly the same mass as a proton. See *Proton*.

NEWHALL SYSTEM OF GAGING—A British method which was widely used before adoption of their present standards. It was based on a "uniform standard hole" from which all interchangeability measurements were taken.

NIB—A railroad term for a depression used on leaf springs. See *Springs, Nibbed*.

NIBBED—A term sometimes used to describe anything with a point.

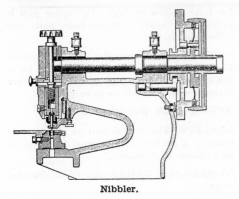

Nibbler.

NIBBLER — Usually called a nibbling machine. Really a form of slotting machine using a narrow chisel as a cutting tool and used to outline metal plates to any desired shape. It cuts, or "nibbles," small chips as the material is fed under the chisel and guided to cut the outline wanted.

NICK—Any kind of notch or indentation in the edge or surface of a piece of work. Usually refers to a V-shaped notch rather than one with a rounded bottom.

NICKEL—A silver-white metal largely used as an alloy in steel, bronze, brass and cast iron. Sp. gr. 8.84. Melts at 2,646 deg. F. It strengthens steel and adds to its ability to resist shock and attack by acids.

NICKEL-CHROMIUM ALLOYS—Metals for heat resistance wires in electric apparatus. The alloys also resist acids.

NICKEL-CHROMIUM STEELS — Steels alloyed with nickel and chromium for toughness and uniform hardening qualities. Various alloys of nickel-cobalt, nickel-copper and nickel-molybdenum and steel.

NICKEL-SILVER—An alloy of copper, nickel and zinc, much like German silver.

NICKEL STEELS—Steels with nickel as the main alloy.

NICKEL SULPHATE—A salt used in nickel plating baths.

NIPPERS—One method of describing small cutting pliers. Sometimes used in connection with fingers for feeding or holding sheets in place.

NIPPLE—Usually refers to a short piece of threaded pipe used to connect two fittings close to each other. Some nipples, such as those used in some steam radiators, are not threaded but are a force fit into the radiator sections. They may be slightly tapered.

NIPPLE HOLDER—A device for holding nipples while they are being machined.

NISILOY—An alloy containing approximately 60 per cent nickel, 30 per cent silicon and the rest iron. It melts at 1,800 deg. F. and diffuses through melted iron. It is said to minimize local hard areas, insure solid castings and facilitate machining gray cast iron in which it is used.

NITER—See *Potassium Nitrate*.

NITER-BLUING STEEL—A method of producing a blue surface on steel. Mix 10 parts of saltpeter (niter) and one part of black oxide of manganese, by weight, and heat to 800 or 850 deg. F. in a cast iron pot. The parts to be blued must be chemically clean. Using a wire basket, they are dipped in the heated solution for from 5 to 10 minutes, then quenched in warm water, from 125 to 150 deg. F. They are usually then covered with oil, such as raw linseed, and allowed to drain. The depth of color depends on the length of time they remain in the bath.

NITRIC ACID—An acid used widely in etching and in pickling metals. Also called aqua fortis.

NITRIDING — A surface hardening process used on ferrous metals by heating the metal in contact with ammonia gas or other nitrogenous material.

NITRO-GLYCERINE — An explosive compound which detonates, or explodes, by shock or concussion.

NOMENCLATURE—Names or classifications of objects or processes used in any industry. A standard nomenclature is very important, in order that everyone in an industry knows exactly what is meant by different names and terms used.

NOMINAL SIZE—The designated size, such as a 1-inch bolt, but which may vary somewhat according to permissible variations allowed in actual use.

NONAGON—A figure with nine equal sides and nine angles of 40 degrees each.

NON-FERROUS METALS—Metals or alloys without an appreciable amount of iron. Generally applies to aluminum, brass, copper, and similar metals or alloys.

NONMAGNETIC STEELS—Steels with such alloys as manganese or nickel in sufficient quantity to render the steel non-magnetic. See *Steel, Nonmagnetic.*

NON-METALLIC PLANER WAYS—Bearing strips, usually of plastic material, fastened to the planer table, to present a non-metallic surface to the planer bed ways. Used to prevent distortion due to heat generated between metal surfaces at high speed.

NON-SHRINKING STEELS — A group of steels made with alloys which tend to prevent deformation while being heat treated. They are used for accurate dies and gages.

NORBIDE—A boron carbide, an artificial material made by the Norton Co. Said to be the hardest material yet produced for commercial use. It is used as an abrasive and is also molded to be used for blast nozzles and for gages. It shows long life when subjected to extreme conditions.

NORDBERG KEY—See *Key, Nordberg.*

NORMALIZING — The heating of steel to about 100 deg. F. above the critical range. It is then held at this temperature for a given time and cooled, in still air, below the critical range. This brings the structure of the material back to normal after it has been disturbed by either hot or cold working and improves the grain structure.

NORMAL PLANE — In screw threads and helical gears normal plane refers to a line at right angles to the helix.

NORTON QUICK CHANGE FEED BOX—Refers to the gear feed box designed many years ago by W. P. Norton for the Hendey lathe. It pioneered the use of this type of feed mechanism for the lathe and other machine tools.

NOSE—In shop work, the term is applied to the cutting end of tools or other articles. Also applied to the threaded end of spindles of lathes and other machines. A "hog-nosed" drill or lathe tool make good examples of the use of the term.

NOTCHING DIE—See *Dies, Notching.*

NOWEL—Generally the lower part of a foundry flask, or drag. Sometimes used in connection with the core or inner part of a mold

for large hollow castings. The upper part is called the "cope." Intermediate parts are called cheeks.

NOZZLE—A nose or outlet tube for controlling flow of liquids or gases. This may be at the end of a hose or pipe or in any chamber through which liquids or gases pass.

NUB—A small projection or knob.

NUCLEUS—The central part of an atom. It contains a positive charge equal to the negative charge of electrons.

NUMBER SIZE DRILLS—See *Drills, Number Sizes.*

NUT—The internally threaded piece used on the threaded end of a bolt. The term is also applied to other internally threaded parts, but not to tapered holes in machines or other parts.

NUT, ACORN—See *Nut, Crown.*

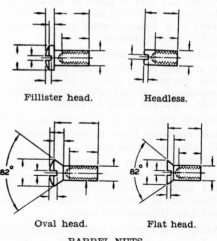

Fillister head.   Headless.

Oval head.   Flat head.

BARREL NUTS.

NUT, BARREL—An internally threaded screw having a slotted head. It differs from a sleeve nut only in that the hole does not go through the screw head. Barrel nuts range from 0.112 inch to 5/16 inch, inclusive.

NUT, CASTLE OR CASTELLATED—A nut with slots across the outer end to receive a cotter or other pin, which is also passed through the end of the bolt, to prevent turning under vibration. It necessitates tightening the nut until the slots match the hole in the bolt. See illustrations.

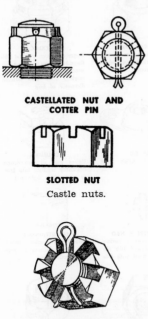

CASTELLATED NUT AND COTTER PIN

SLOTTED NUT

Castle nuts.

Cooke-Micro Slotted Nut.
This is a special design of castellated nut, the slots being arranged so that there are 14 to 22 locking positions.

NUT, CLINCH—A nut which is inserted in the work and clinched or fastened in place by swaging or peening. It then acts as a tapped hole in which a bolt can be threaded. Sometimes a clinch nut has a locking washer or other device and does not require a lock washer in addition.

NUT, COLD PUNCHED — A nut punched cold, from bar stock. The hole is usually reamed to size before tapping.

NUT, CROWN—A nut which is closed over the end of the bolt as protection against damage and also to give a finished appearance. Sometimes called an acorn nut.

NUT, ELASTIC—A nut with some means of gripping the thread on the bolt to prevent loosening under vibration. They are largely replacing the lock nut.

NUT, HALF—A nut that is split lengthwise so that one or both halves can be engaged

with a screw, as desired. In screw cutting lathes, the two halves of the nut are controlled by a cam from the outside of the apron so that the nut can be closed on the lead screw, or released from it, at will. When the nut is released, the carriage can be moved independently of the lead screw. When closed on the lead screw, the carriage is moved by the gearing which determines the pitch or the number of threads per inch that are to be cut.

NUT, HOT PRESSED—A nut formed from heated bars in a forging machine.

NUT, INSERT—A nut or threaded piece to be inserted in other parts, such as in plastic or other cast or formed materials. They save tapping the material itself and frequently save money, as well as providing a stronger thread.

Lock jam nut.

NUT, JAM—A thin nut to be tightened or "jammed" on top of the regular nut to prevent its coming loose through vibration. Same as lock nut. Lock washers and locking nuts have largely replaced the old jam or lock nut. Sometimes used under the regular nut as shown.

NUT, LOCK—A term originally applied to a second nut which was screwed against the first, or main nut, to prevent its jarring loose. The lock nut was usually half the thickness of the regular nut. Some contended that the thin nut should be put in place first. There are many types of lock nut, most of them patented before being put on the market. Most of them attempt to impose extra friction on the thread by various methods to prevent loosening. Lock washers are used for the same purpose and probably more extensively than lock nuts. Illustration on page 300. See also *Washer, Lock*.

NUT, MACHINE—A nut drilled and tapped in a machine.

NUT MACHINE — A machine for cutting, drilling and tapping nuts from a bar or rod.

SECURITY
Elliptical alloy-steel retainer grips bolt threads

NATIONAL
Tightening develops a spring or flexing action to provide locking

AN-COR-LOX
Soft metallic collar flattens against work, forcing edges into bolt thread

FLEXLOC
Segments press against bolt threads because inner diameter of upper part is slightly less than outside diameter of bolt

ANCO
Pin impinges against bolt to hold nut in place

SIMLOK
Snap ring engages serrations in bolt thread to hold nut in place

CAMLOC
Fiber collar grips bolt thread

COLUMBIA
Upper part of two-section assembly wedges into lower part when tightened

PINNACLE
Metal diaphragm provides spring locking action

SEALTITE
Threads in section above slot are deformed to provide friction grip

PALNUT TYPE 6 NAO
Top portion exerts spring pressure for added grip. No other nut is used with this type

SELF-RETAINING
Threads in section above slot are deformed to provide friction grip

PALNUT
Single-thread lock nut applied and tightened after regular nut is in place

ESNA
Fiber collar grips bolt threads. Also available with metallic collar in place of fiber for high-temperature applications

MARSDEN
Segments are forced inward against bolt threads when pressure is applied against recessed bearing surface

AEROTIGHT
Upper part of nut is slotted and turned in to provide spring grip

FIBER
Fiber collar grips bolt threads

NUTT SHELL
Conventional nut pressed into light metal shell with fiber collar, which grips bolt threads

DRAKE
Consists of two separate mating parts

UNBRAKO
Fiber plugs pass through nut and press against threads of bolt

STOVER
Upper part of conventional nut is deformed to elliptical shape that provides spring grip against bolt threads

HUGLOCK
Upper threads press inward against bolt

BOOTS
Threads of two sections are normally out of phase. Tightening sets up compressive force to provide holding

LAMSON
Raised crown is distorted and heat-treated to give spring grip on bolt thread

Examples of typical lock nuts.

NUT, SLEEVE—An internally threaded screw in which the thread is tapped clear through the screw head. Similar to a barrel nut.

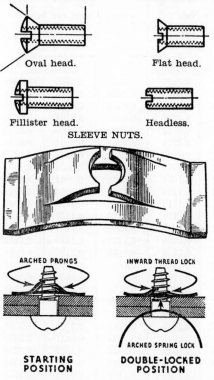

Oval head.   Flat head.

Fillister head.   Headless.

SLEEVE NUTS.

ARCHED PRONGS   INWARD THREAD LOCK

ARCHED SPRING LOCK

STARTING POSITION   **DOUBLE-LOCKED POSITION**

Standard flat-type speed nut. When tightened, the prongs press against the stud and the strip acts as an arched spring lock.

NUT, SPEED — A patented type of nut punched from a metal strip with prongs which engage the threads of a screw. When drawn tight, it exerts pressure on the screw and the friction tends to prevent it from jarring loose.

NUT TAPPING MACHINE—A machine especially for tapping nuts which, in most cases, does not reverse the tap. Special taps permit the nuts to feed over the shank, giving continuous production.

NUT, 12 POINTED—A new type of nut with two shallow V grooves cut in each flat of the sides of a hexagon nut. This forms 12 sides with equal angles and the 12 points distribute the load in tightening with a socket wrench so that a thinner nut and thinner wrench can be used than with a hexagon nut. This makes smaller clearances possible on bolted parts.

NUT, WING—A nut with wings or ears for tightening with fingers.

NUT, WRENCHING—A nut made by the Allen Mfg. Co. for use with their hollow head screws. The nut is round but knurled on the outside. It is drawn into a round, counterbored hole by the screw, the knurled outside locking it in place.

NUTS AND SCREWS, GAGES FOR—Gages for nuts and screws under one inch for coarse, fine and extrafine, and for two classes of fits. See table page 302.

Gages for Nuts and Screws

Size	Symbol	Basic Pitch Dia.	Plug Gages for Nuts			Ring Gages for Screws		
			Go	Not Go		Go	Not Go	
			Class	Class		Class	Class	
			2 & 3	2	3	2 & 3	2	3
0-80	NF	0.0519	0.0519	0.0536	0.0532	0.0519	0.0502	0.0506
1-64	NC	0.0629	0.0629	0.0648	0.0643	0.0629	0.0610	0.0516
1-72	NF	0.0640	0.0640	0.0658	0.0653	0.0640	0.0622	0.0627
2-56	NC	0.0744	0.0744	0.0764	0.0759	0.0744	0.0724	0.0729
2-64	NF	0.0759	0.0759	0.0778	0.0773	0.0759	0.0740	0.0745
3-48	NC	0.0855	0.0855	0.0877	0.0871	0.0855	0.0833	0.0839
3-56	NF	0.0874	0.0874	0.0894	0.0889	0.0874	0.0854	0.0859
4-40	NC	0.0958	0.0953	0.0982	0.0975	0.0958	0.0934	0.0941
4-48	NF	0.0985	0.0985	0.1007	0.1001	0.0985	0.0963	0.0969
5-40	NC	0.1088	0.1088	0.1112	0.1105	0.1088	0.1064	0.1071
5-44	NF	0.1102	0.1102	0.1125	0.1118	0.1102	0.1079	0.1086
6-32	NC	0.1177	0.1177	0.1204	0.1196	0.1177	0.1150	0.1158
6-40	NF	0.1218	0.1218	0.1242	0.1235	0.1218	0.1194	0.1201
8-32	NC	0.1437	0.1437	0.1464	0.1456	0.1437	0.1410	0.1418
8-36	NF	0.1460	0.1460	0.1485	0.1478	0.1460	0.1435	0.1605
10-24	NC	0.1629	0.1629	0.1662	0.1653	0.1629	0.1596	0.1442
10-32	NF	0.1697	0.1697	0.1724	0.1716	0.1697	0.1670	0.1678
¼-20	NC	0.2175	0.2175	0.2211	0.2201	0.2175	0.2139	0.2149
¼-28	NF	0.2268	0.2268	0.2299	0.2290	0.2268	0.2237	0.2246
¼-32	NEF	0.2297	0.2297	0.2329	0.2319	0.2297	0.2265	0.2275
⁵⁄₁₆-18	NC	0.2764	0.2764	0.2805	0.2794	0.2764	0.2723	0.2734
⁵⁄₁₆-24	NF	0.2854	0.2854	0.2287	0.2878	0.2854	0.2821	0.2830
⁵⁄₁₆-32	NEF	0.2922	0.2922	0.2955	0.2945	0.2922	0.2889	0.2899
⅜-16	NC	0.3344	0.3344	0.3389	0.3376	0.3344	0.3299	0.3312
⅜-24	NF	0.3479	0.3479	0.3512	0.3503	0.3479	0.3512	0.3455
⅜-32	NEF	0.3547	0.3547	0.3581	0.3571	0.3547	0.3512	0.3523
⁷⁄₁₆-14	NC	0.3911	0.3911	0.3960	0.3947	0.3911	0.3862	0.3875
⁷⁄₁₆-20	NF	0.4050	0.4050	0.4086	0.4076	0.4050	0.4014	0.4024
⁷⁄₁₆-28	NEF	0.4143	0.4143	0.4179	0.4168	0.4143	0.4107	0.4118
½-13	NC	0.4500	0.4500	0.4552	0.4537	0.4500	0.4448	0.4463
½-20	NF	0.4675	0.4675	0.4711	0.4701	0.4675	0.4639	0.4649
½-28	NEF	0.4768	0.4768	0.4805	0.4794	0.4768	0.4731	0.4742
⁹⁄₁₆-12	NC	0.5084	0.5084	0.5140	0.5124	0.5084	0.5028	0.5044
⁹⁄₁₆-18	NF	0.5264	0.5264	0.5305	0.5294	0.5264	0.5223	0.5234
⁹⁄₁₆-24	NEF	0.5354	0.5354	0.5394	0.5382	0.5354	0.5314	0.5326
⅝-11	NC	0.5660	0.5660	0.5719	0.5702	0.5660	0.5601	0.5618
⅝-18	NF	0.5889	0.5889	0.5930	0.5919	0.5889	0.5848	0.5859
⅝-24	NEF	0.5979	0.5979	0.6020	0.6008	0.5979	0.5938	0.5950
¾-10	NC	0.6850	0.6850	0.6914	0.6895	0.6850	0.6786	0.6805
¾-16	NF	0.7094	0.7094	0.7139	0.7126	0.7094	0.7049	0.7062
¾-20	NEF	0.7175	0.7175	0.7221	0.7207	0.7175	0.7129	0.7143
1¹³⁄₁₆-20	NEF	0.7800	0.7800	0.7846	0.7832	0.7800	0.7754	0.7768
⅞- 9	NC	0.8028	0.8028	0.8098	0.8077	0.8028	0.7958	0.7979
⅞-14	NF	0.8286	0.8286	0.8335	0.8322	0.8286	0.8237	0.8250

O

O. D.—Common abbreviation for "outside diameter."

OBJECTIVE—In optical instruments, such as the microscope, the lens by which an image of the object is seen.

OBLIQUE—A line or surface is said to be oblique when it is at an angle with a horizontal or a vertical line.

OBLIQUE ANGLE—See *Angle, Oblique.*

OBLONG—A figure which is longer in one direction than the other. While the term is usually applied to a rectangle, some also use it as describing an oval.

OBSOLESCENCE—Decrease in value of a machine or tool because of newer designs being more efficient or productive, rather than from age or wear in the machine itself. This might apply to perishable tools as well as to machine tools.

OBTUSE ANGLE—See *Angle, Obtuse.*

OCTAGON—A figure with 8 equal sides and 8 equal angles of 45 degrees. One side = the long diameter $\times$ 0.382 or the short diameter $\times$ 0.415.

OCTAGON BAR STOCK—Steel or other bars having 8 equal sides. Used in some places in making objects requiring this shape to avoid milling flat surfaces.

OCTANE—A measure of the volatility and compression qualities of gasoline. High-octane gasoline possesses high anti-knock qualities for use in high compression engines.

ODD PITCH—Pitches of either screw threads or gears which are not standard.

ODONTOGRAPH — A device developed by George B. Grant many years ago, for laying out the curves of gear teeth.

OFF-CENTER DRILLING—See *Drilling, Off-Center.*

OGEE—A reversed curve or an S shape. Used in describing curves and moldings.

OIL BATHS—See *Baths, Quenching.*

OIL, CUTTING—Oil used in machining metals. Such oils vary widely in quality and characteristics, many being made by mixing different ingredients. They both cool and lubricate the tool as it cuts. There are also many cutting lubricants in which oil plays only a small part, if any, See *Cutting Fluid* and *Coolants.*

OIL CUP—A cup-like device for holding oil and feeding it to a bearing as needed. It is usually screwed into place in the bearing cap, over the shaft. See *Oiling Devices.*

OIL DIES—See *Dies, Fluid.*

OIL GROOVE—A groove or passageway in a bearing for oil to reach all parts of the bearing.

OIL GROOVER—A machine for cutting oil grooves. These grooves are cut straight or in varying patterns of curves.

OIL GUN—See *Gun, Oil.*

OIL HARDENING—See *Hardening, Oil.*

OILING DEVICES—The mechanical arrangements for furnishing a steady supply of oil to bearings and other parts of machinery. They vary widely, from plain gravity feed oilers, such as oil cups, to devices where pumps supply predetermined amounts of oil. Wick oilers feed by capillary attraction. Ring rollers dip in oil and carry it up into the bearing. Grease cups are either screw or spring operated and grease guns use either manual, air or power pressure to force grease to bearings.

OLEIC ACID—An acid which helps in drilling hard materials, such as drill rods. It comes in two grades, "pure" and "technical grade." The latter is less expensive and is said to work just as well.

OLIVER—A power hammer of the helve type, now probably obsolete. The hammer head was sometimes attached to a long beam similar to the handle of a heavy sledge hammer, but was sometimes spring mounted.

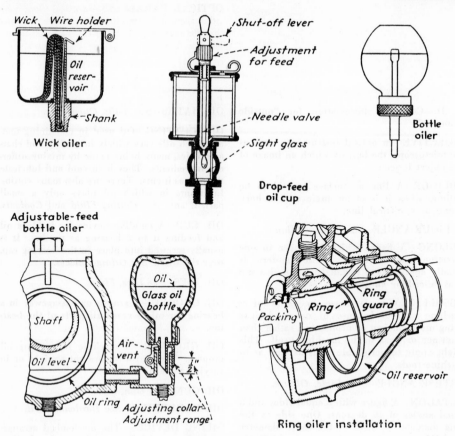

OILING DEVICES.

OLSEN TEST—A test to determine the deep drawing properties of sheet metal, somewhat similar to "Erichsen Values." It is a cupping test simulating deep drawing and continues until the sample is fractured. The drawing properties are judged by the depth, the location of the break and the surface after the break. The test was devised for use on the Olsen testing machine.

ONE PITCH THREADS—See *Screw Threads, 8, 12 and 16 Pitch.*

OPEN CIRCUIT SYSTEM—An ignition or other electric system in which the circuit remains open except when closed instantaneously to perform its duty.

OPEN END WRENCH—See *Wrench.*

OPEN HEARTH STEEL—Steel made in an open furnace instead of in a converter, as with Bessemer steel. It uses cast iron and scrap steel as a suitable flux. The slag that forms on top of the molten metal acts as a purifier by contact with the molten mass.

OPTICAL FLAT—A glass plate or disk with a surface as nearly a perfect flat as possible. It is used in fine measurements to show, by light wave bands, the accuracy of work. A wave band is 11.6 millionths of an inch wide. A good working "flat" should be accurate within 5 millionths of an inch. A master or reference flat should be accurate within half that amount. Optical flats are also made of alloy tool steel, hardened and seasoned and guaranteed accurate within 10-millionths of an inch. They are used for testing the accuracy of gage blocks and other measuring devices.

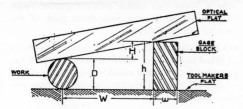

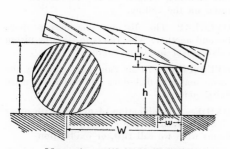

Measuring with optical flats.

OPTICAL FLATS, MEASURING WITH—

With a glass optical flat and a standard gage block it is possible to measure diameters or heights of other pieces very accurately. Illustrations show how the gage block, optical flat and work are placed. With the parts in position, read the number of bands across the face of the gage block and put this number in the first formula below. The result will be very accurate. See *Light Wave Bands.*

General Formula for Measuring Dimensions with Optical Flat and Gage Blocks.

D = dimension to be measured
h = height of gage blocks
H = difference between height of gage blocks and dimension to be measured
W = distance between points where optical flat contacts work and gage blocks respectively
w = width of gage blocks
N = number of bands across gage block face

then $H = 11.6 \times N \times \dfrac{W}{w}$ (in microinches or millionths of an inch)

and D = h − H (blocks higher than work)
or D = h + H (blocks lower than work).

OPTICAL GLASS — Refined glass, usually made from flint glass or from rock crystals, for use in microscopes, telescopes, binoculars, transits and similar instruments.

OPTICAL PARALLELS — Optical flats with sides accurately parallel, for use in checking the flatness and parallelism of micrometer anvil and screw or similar instruments.

OPTICAL PROJECTION—This refers to systems used in inspection instruments known as "comparators." Both direct and indirect lighting are used, and also what is known as surface projection. Modern instruments do not require that rooms be darkened. See *Comparator.*

ORDINATES—In charts made on cross-sectioned paper, ordinates are the vertical lines and horizontal lines are the abscissa.

OSCILLATE—To move back and forth like a clock pendulum. "Oscillate" is applied to swinging objects rather than to those which travel back and forth in a straight line, such as the ram of a shaper or the crosshead of a steam engine. In those cases the parts are said to reciprocate.

OSCILLATING ENGINE—Usually, a steam engine in which the cylinder swings, or oscillates, on trunnions or projections from the side of the cylinder, as the front end of the connecting rod follows the crank pin in its circular path. In most steam engines the connecting rod swings on, or oscillates on, a pin in the cross head, which moves in a straight line. Here the cylinder is stationary.

OSCILLOGRAPH—An instrument which permits a study of oscillating or moving parts while in motion. It is equivalent to a "slow motion" camera which gives an opportunity of studying distortions or vibrations of parts in any mechanism to which it can be applied. Records of the results can be made in some cases. An earlier machine for this purpose was the stroboscope.

OSMIUM—A rare, heavy metal. Sp. gr. 22.50. Melts at 4,890 deg. F. Alloyed with iridium for pen tips.

OUNCE-INCHES—A term used in connection with balancing rotating parts in balancing machines. It refers to the excess weight in ounces, at a given distance from the center of rotation, which causes the unbalance. Values are frequently given in "ounce-inches, squared," or multiplied by themselves.

OUNCE METAL—An old Navy term supposed to have originated from early foundry practice of adding 1 ounce each of lead, tin and zinc to each pound of copper melted. The present Navy specifications for bronze, hydraulic (ounce metal) castings is approximately 5 parts each of lead, tin and zinc to 85 parts copper.

OUTBOARD BEARING—A bearing or support at the outer end of a shaft.

OUTBOARD SUPPORT — Any bearing or brace outside the body of a machine or other mechanism, to prevent or lessen deflection of parts.

OVAL — Any rounded shape which is not round. The term is usually applied to what might be called a flattened circle. The curvature does not have to be uniform; an egg is an oval.

OVAL CHUCK—A lathe chuck used in turning oval shapes. See *Chuck, Oval*.

OVATE—See *Oval*.

OVER-ARM—An arm which acts as a support from a position above the spindle or other part supported. A common example is in the horizontal milling machine.

OVER-DRIVE — Any device which increases the speed of the driven member beyond the normal. In automobiles it reduces the revolutions of the engine for the same rate of speed and of course reduces the power delivered at the wheels in the same proportion. Sometimes used on machine tools to give extra high speed for special operations, as in drilling.

OVERHANG—The unsupported portion of a beam or other portion of a machine, or of a building outside the line of the walls.

OVERHAUL—A common term used to describe a more or less extensive repair on any piece of machinery.

OVERHEAD—A term usually applied to the operating costs of any business aside from both labor and material. It includes rent, taxes, insurance, interest on investment, clerical hire, stationery, supervision and similar expenses. It is now common practice to consider machine overhead as separate from labor in operating it. Interest on the investment in a machine, plus the cost of keeping it in repair, and the laying aside of a fund for its replacement when it is either worn out or obsolete, make up machine overhead. Some include the power cost of operating, while others lump this under general power costs. "Overhead" is a very important part of the cost of doing business.

OVERHEAD ENGINE—A term sometimes applied to steam or other engines in which the cylinder is above the crankshaft. This includes nearly all vertical engines, which are now seldom seen.

OVERHEAD WORK—This usually refers to line shafting, hangers or any mechanisms located on the ceiling.

OVERLAP—The distance one part projects beyond another. Also refers to slide or piston valve travel in steam engines.

OVERSPRAY—In air gun spray painting, the waste material that does not reach the work being painted.

OXIDE—A combination of oxygen with other elements, such as iron or steel. In that case it forms what we call rust, or oxidization.

OXIDIZING FLAME — Any flame in which there is an excess of oxygen. In cutting steel with an oxy-acetylene torch, the supply of acetylene is reduced when the metal becomes heated, and only oxygen is supplied. This oxidizes the metal touched by the flame and it disintegrates rather than melts.

OXY-ACETYLENE TORCH—A device which combines oxygen and acetylene in desired proportions for melting and heating many metals. Used largely in welding and cutting steels. In cutting steel the acetylene is turned off after the desired heat has been reached and only the oxygen used to produce the necessary heat for cutting. It really melts the steel where the stream of oxygen hits the hot metal.

OXYGEN—The most abundant gaseous element in nature. It is colorless, tasteless and odorless. It forms about 21 per cent of the air, by volume and is necessary in combustion. Combined with acetylene it produces a very hot flame used in various operations, such as welding. See *Oxy-Acetylene Torch*.

OXY-HYDROGEN TORCH—A torch similar to an oxy-acetylene torch, but which uses oxygen and hydrogen, from separate tanks, as with the oxy-acetylene torch. An extremely hot flame is produced by using two parts of hydrogen to one part of oxygen. It is said to be hot enough to consume or disintegrate a diamond.

P

P S I—Abbreviation for "pounds per square inch." Refers to pressures of some kind such as hydraulic, steam, air or pressure applied by mechanical means.

PACK-HARDEN—To impart carbon into the surface of low carbon steel by packing it in a metal box, surrounded by ground bone, charcoal or other material which contains carbon. Special pack hardening materials have been developed for this purpose. The container is sealed by "luting" with clay and placed in a furnace for a long period. The steel absorbs carbon from the material which surrounds it and acquires a "case" of varying depths, depending on the time it remains in the furnace. It is a modern method of case-hardening or carburizing. Not being in contact with the flame it is not discolored by it. Luting refers to a mixture of fire clay and water filling the cracks between the container, or box, and the cover which goes inside near the top, over the parts being pack-hardened. It keeps the gases away from the work in the box.

PACKAGED POWER—A trade name for a motor and reducing gear enclosed in one base, or package.

PACKED BIT—See *Boring Heads, Packed Bit.*

PACKFONG METAL—See *Metal, Packfong.*

PACKING RING—A ring for sealing spaces between parts to prevent leakage of gases or liquids. The packing rings in a piston in an automobile engine prevent leakage of burning gases past the piston as it travels in the cylinder.

PAD FORM DIES—The pads used in the Guerin process. See *Guerin Forming Process.*

PALLADIUM — Resembles platinum, but is rare and lighter. Sp. gr. 12.16. Melts at 2,820 deg. F. Resists corrosion.

PALLET—A term sometimes used to describe a pawl or detent or "click" which regulates the movement of a ratchet wheel, as in a watch or clock movement.

PALLETS.

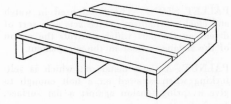

Flush pallet, 2-way, single face.

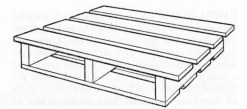

Single-wing pallet, 2-way, double face.

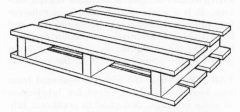

Double-wing pallet, 2-way, double face.

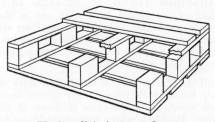

Flush pallet, 4-way or 8-way.

PALLETS — Platforms for supporting work pieces of various kinds for transport in the shop, or for storage between manufacture and

307

assembly. They are designed to be lifted and carried by shop trucks provided with forks which can reach under the platform or between its two faces. The four standard types of wooden pallets adopted by the National Wooden Pallet Mfrs. Association are shown. Projecting boards are called wings. They are made single and double face with one design permitting handling from any side.

PALLET STONE—The jewel used in watch and clock mechanisms which acts as a sort of detent on the part which controls the action of the balance wheel in the escapement.

PALNUT—A sheet metal nut which is self-locking when screwed on a bolt enough to give a spring tension against a flat surface. See *Nuts*.

PAN HEAD RIVET—See *Rivet*.

PANTAGRAPH—A combination of parallel bars or levers used to enlarge or reduce drawings from one scale to another. There are four light but rigid bars or arms, pivoted to form a parallelogram with a tracing point and a pencil point for tracing and reproducing the desired outlines to different scales. Practically all engraving machines have modifications of the pantagraph as part of the design.

PARABOLA—A special form of curved surface. It is a conic section used as a reflector for projecting light, as in headlights and flood lights. A geometric projection designed to utilize the maximum brilliancy of a lamp placed in the proper position in the reflector.

PARAFFIN OIL—Oil which is squeezed from wax bearing distillates. Used for lubrication of some bearings. Not good in crankcase lubrication.

PARAFORM TEETH IN MILLING CUTTERS—These cutters have teeth cut in the form of a parabola, hence the name. They are supposed to shear the metal with a curve having less frictional resistance and so taking less power. They are not widely used.

PARALLEL—As used in the shop, a block or strip having both sides equally distant from each other, or of the same thickness at all points. Used in blocking up work and locating it so that holes and machined surfaces will be at right angles. Two straight lines equidistant from each other at all points are said to be parallel.

PARALLEL MOTION—A combination of levers so pivoted to each other as to give parallel motion. Used in engraving machines for enlarging or reducing movement between the guide, or master, and the work being done. Also used in drawing board instruments and formerly for taking indicator cards from steam and other reciprocating engines.

PARBUCKLE—A little used term for a double sling used in hoisting or handling round objects with a crane or derrick. Also used in working a large round object up an inclined plane.

PARENT METAL—The main metal, being considered as the metal welded rather than the metal used in welding rods.

PARIS OR FRENCH INCH—The Paris inch is 12 lignes, which is 1.0656 U. S. inches. The Paris foot has 12 Paris inches or 12.7872 U. S. inches.

PARKER-KALON SCREWS—See *Screw, Parker-Kalon*.

PARKERIZING—A method of treating metal surfaces to prevent corrosion.

PARKINSON DRILL—A twist drill with a point designed by Ray W. Parkinson, of Columbus, Ohio. The point has a double angle, plus a 45-degree chamfer at the outer edge and a small slot across the web of the drill.

PARROT BILL NIPPERS—See *Wire Cutter, Parrot Bill*.

PARTING SAND—A dry sand used to surface the two parts of a mold to prevent adherence between the sand of the two parts. The sand must be non-adhesive, as it must prevent sticking and damaging the surface of either half of the mold.

PARTING TOOL—The tool used in cutting pieces from the end of a bar, really a cutting-off tool. It must be relieved on the sides to prevent undue friction by contact with the sides of the cut. Cutting-off tools are somewhat standardized.

PASSIVATION—A process of surface treatment for neutralizing stainless steels. An oxydizing solution, such as nitric acid, is applied to the surface. This strengthens the normal protective film which helps in resisting corrosion. It also removes any foreign substance which might cause local corrosion.

PATCH, SOFT—Soft putty-like material held in position by metal plates, to stop small leaks in boilers and other vessels. The plates are usually riveted in position. Since the use of torch and arc welding became common it offers a better and more lasting repair than the soft patch.

PATINA — The film which accumulates on bronze surfaces by long exposure to air or by application of special acids.

PATTERN—A wooden or metal model of the part to be cast in metal. It is used in making the impression in the sand mold into which the metal will be poured. Patterns are made enough larger than the dimensions of the casting desired to allow for shrinkage of the metal in cooling. Pattern-makers use a "shrink-rule" which shows the allowance to be made for the shrinkage of different metals.

PATTERN-MAKERS' LATHE — See *Lathe, Pattern-Makers'*.

PAWL—A hinged piece which drops into a ratchet or gear and prevents it from running backward. Also used to turn a ratchet or gear wheel in one direction but to prevent movement in the other. Frequently called a detent or dog. See *Ratchet*.

PEDAL — A foot operated lever, or crank. When used on a lever it produces a straight line motion, and when on a crank, a rotary motion, as on a bicycle. While generally used to denote the part touched by the foot, it may include the whole lever, as in the pedal or "kick" press used in small printing operations.

PEEN—The end of a hammer opposite the face which is generally used. Also the act of hammering over the end of a rivet or other piece of metal, to enlarge it and prevent its withdrawal.

PEENING—The stretching of metal by hammering or rolling the surface. The small end of a machinist's hammer, called the "peen," is often used for this operation. Curved bars or strips can be straightened by peening on the concave side.

PEG TOOTH—A gear tooth which has been broken and repaired by drilling holes in the gear rim and inserting pegs or rods which are then filed to approximate the original gear tooth shape. It might also refer to special gears in which the teeth consist of round pegs or pins.

PENDULUM—Any body suspended from a fixed point and which swings freely in both directions, as the pendulum of a clock. The same term has been applied to foot or kick presses where the foot lever swings back and forth, but by foot power. In a free swinging pendulum, as in a clock, the rate of swing depends entirely on the length of the pendulum. A pendulum approximately 36 inches long will swing one beat to a second.

PENETRATION—The entering of one body into another. The amount of penetration is used to determine hardness of materials, in both the Brinell and Rockwell hardness tests. See *Brinell Hardness Testing Machine* and *Rockwell Hardness Test*.

PENETRON—A device in which gamma rays are used to measure the thickness of the walls of pipes or tubes from one side without affecting the material. The head is a steel tube containing radium salts and a shield which directs the gamma rays into the part to be tested at an angle. It also has a detector unit and a pre-amplifier. The gamma rays may pass through the metal, or be scattered in all directions. The back scattered rays are picked up by the detector and set off current discharges or pulses which are measured, and denote the thickness of the wall.

PENTAGON—A five-sided figure with equal sides and equal angles. See *Polygon*.

PERCUSSION—A blow or shock, as in striking an anvil with a hammer. Trip hammers are percussion machines. Usually applied to tools or machines which give a series of blows in rapid succession, as air or electric hammers.

PERCUSSION PRESS—See *Press, Percussion*.

PERIMETER—The outside boundary of any figure, as the rim of a pulley. The perimeter of a circle is always 3.1416 times the diameter.

PERIPHERAL SPEED—The speed of the outside of a revolving body, as a pulley. It is this speed which affects the power transmitted by belting, per inch of belt width.

PERISHABLE TOOLS — Tools which wear out in use and have to be replaced frequently, such as drills, taps, files, abrasive wheels and the like. Some class these as "small tools." This term should not be applied to small machine tools, for while they do wear out, become obsolete and require replacement, they really are capital goods. See *Expendable Tools.*

PERMANENT SET—The deformation which takes place when any substance is stressed beyond its elastic limit. Up to that point the piece will return to its original shape. This is why most designers consider the elastic limit as more important than the breaking point, or ultimate strength.

PERMEABILITY ALLOYS—Alloys which are more magnetic than iron. Made under different trade names.

PERPETUAL MOTION—The continuance of motion, after it has once started, without the assistance of outside energy. A dream of many inventors, but a *mechanical* impossibility, as friction alone defeats the idea. Atomic chemists tell of fissionable material reproducing itself as it is used, but it seems unlikely that power can be produced, used and at the same time continue to produce more power.

PERSIAN DRILL—A name sometimes applied to the type of hand or breast drill which drives the spindle by moving a nut with a fast thread, up and down. It is also called a Yankee drill in some places.

PERSPECTIVE, CAVALIER—A method of making perspective projection drawings in which the base line is horizontal and the projected lines are at 45 degrees to the base. It is seldom used and is much less useful than isometric projection.

PERSPECTIVE DRAWINGS—Drawings which show the effect of distance as well as the front, top or side views shown in the usual mechanical drawing. They give a much better idea of the appearance of the work than the regular three view type, but drawings in true perspective are seldom used in the shop. Isometric drawings are, however, being used in shops and tend to avoid errors caused by misunderstanding of the regular type of shop drawings. Isometric drawings are especially useful in assembly drawings. See *Perspective, Isometric.*

PERSPECTIVE, ISOMETRIC—A modified form of perspective drawing well suited to mechanical work. The base lines are 30 degrees from the horizontal and can be measured the same as regular drawings. An isometric drawing gives the views usually secured by three different views in ordinary drawings. By using specially ruled isometric

paper, many drawings can be made freehand. See *Isometric Projection.*

PETCOCK—A small cock, or plug valve, used for draining surplus water or emptying small amounts of liquid, as in automobile radiators.

PETROLEUM—Mineral oil or earth oil. High in carbon. Refined into kerosene and gasoline.

PETTICOAT PIPE—A conical pipe used in the front ends of steam locomotives to direct the blast of the cylinder exhaust up into the smoke stack.

PEWTER—Tin-lead alloys used for dishes and ornamental objects. Proportions vary from 70 parts tin and 30 parts lead to 90 parts tin and 10 parts lead. Some has been made with tin and antimony.

PHENOL—Commonly called carbolic acid. It is obtained from coal tar and usually comes in the form of white crystals. Phenolic base compounds are thermo-setting, not softening when heated after being formed.

PHENOL-FORMALDEHYDE RESIN—A transparent, brittle resin used in plastics. Soluble in alcohol but not in water.

PHENOLIC GEARS—See *Gears, Phenolic.*

PHILLIPS SCREW HEADS—Screw heads with cross slots at right angles, which do not extend to the edge of the head. They are used in both machine and wood screws. See *Screws.*

PHONO-BRONZE—Phono bronzes are alloys, high in copper, containing small amounts of tin, approximately 1¼ per cent, and fluxed with silicon. Their outstanding properties are in their ability to be hot-worked, and to be strengthened by cold work to a high degree without losing their toughness or becoming brittle. They do not season-crack. Consisting largely of copper, they maintain the latter's resistance to corrosion, and most of its electrical conductivity; unlike copper, which normally contains considerable cuprous oxide, the phono alloys are deoxidized, and are consequently tougher. These alloys are available in the form of rod, sheet, tube, and wire, for uses where high strength, toughness, resistance to corrosion and wear, hardness, and high electrical conductivity are needed. They can be machined, drawn, cupped, upset, hot- and cold-forged, soldered, brazed, and electroplated. Phono alloys can be hot-rolled and hot forged with ease at temperatures from 1,290 to 1,470 deg. F. The results are moderately soft, very tough, and ductile materials. They can be cold-rolled, or drawn without intermediate anneals. While not "free-cutting," phono alloys can be machined when tools with sufficient clearance and rake are used.

PHONOMETER—An instrument for measuring sounds, especially as to intensity, or frequency. Many gears for automobiles and other high class machinery are now tested for noise before being assembled into the machines, by devices having different names.

PHOSPHOR BRONZE—Any bronze to which phosphorous has been added. A standard alloy is 80 per cent copper, 10 per cent tin, 10 per cent lead and 0.25 per cent phosphorous.

PHOSPHOR COPPER—An alloy of copper and phosphorous used for de-oxidizing brass and bronze alloys.

PHOSPHOROUS — A non-metallic element, usually considered as an impurity in steel, where it varies from a mere trace to 0.10 per cent. It has a bad effect on the steel.

PHOTO-MICROGRAPH—Photographs of microscopic objects, greatly enlarged for study. Sections of steel and other metals are studied in this way to detect flaws and to see the arrangement of the grains. Their use has made it possible greatly to improve the quality of steels and other materials.

PIANO HINGE — A continuous hinge the whole length of the movable part. It originated in the piano business to distribute the weight of the lid and permit the use of light metal and small diameter pins or rods.

PIANO WIRE—See *Music Wire*.

PICKLE—To clean castings or other parts in an acid bath. Or the bath itself is called a pickle. Either sulphuric or nitric acids are used, usually in much diluted form.

PICKLING—Removing scale from castings or forgings by dipping in sulphuric or other acid, preferably heated to 180 or 190 deg. F. Dipping tanks with mechanisms which raise and lower the work in and out of the bath 20 or 30 times a minute speed the process by keeping the bath agitated, well mixed and by introducing air into the bath with the work. Some of the principles of pickling are:

1. Steam and air as aids to scale removal are cheaper than acid.

2. A fresh solution will pickle clean; an old solution will leave stains.

3. With almost no exceptions, the fastest pickling is the best pickling.

Common solutions are: One part sulphuric acid to 8 or 10 parts water for iron and steel; for brass, one part nitric acid to 5 parts water.

PICKLING ACIDS—Acids used to remove scale or impurities from casting or sheet metals. Sulphuric acid and water is a common solution. The strength varies from 5 to 10 parts water to one of acid.

PICKLING SOLUTIONS — Solutions for cleaning, pickling and passivating are given as follows:

Sulphuric acid is 1.83 sp. gr., nitric acid is 38° Be, hydrofluoric acid 40%, hydrochloric acid 20° Be, all acids in parts by volume unless noted.

Solution "A"—For general pickling and cleaning of stainless steel: sulphuric acid 10, rock salt ¼ lb/gal sol, water, to make 100 parts. Used at 160-180 F.

Solution "B"—For additional pickling and cleaning stainless steel: nitric acid 10, water, to make 100. Whitens surface, may react with mild steel to produce poisonous fumes.

Solution "C"—To remove scale softened by "A": Nitric acid 10, hydrofluoric acid 2, water, to make 100. *Handle acids with care.*

Solution "D"—To passivate stainless steel, seldom required, mix: Nitric acid 10-20, water, to make 100. Use at 120-140 F for 15 min.

Solution "E"—Second choice to passivate stainless steel: Nitric acid 1, sodium or potassium dichromate 1, water 200. Use at 125-150 F for 15-30 min.

Solution "F"—Paste for pickling nickel and Monel: Lampblack 1 lb, Fuller's earth 10 lb, hydrochloric acid 3 gal, nitric acid ½ pt. Use at 70 to 100 F, 20-60 min for Monel, and 2-4 hr or longer for nickel. Apply with whitewash brush.

Solution "G"—(Step 1) Paste pickle for Inconel: Lampblack 1 lb, Fuller's earth 10 lb, cupric chloride 2 lb, hydrochloric acid 3 gal. Use at 70-100 F for 1-3 hr. Apply with whitewash brush.

Solution "H"—(Step 2) Paste pickle for Inconel: Lampblack 1 lb, Fuller's earth 10 lb, nitric acid 2¾ gal, hydrochloric acid ¼ gal. Use at 70-100 F for 15-60 min. Apply with whitewash brush.

Solution "I"—Paste to remove imbedded iron from nickel, Monel and Inconel: Lampblack 1 lb, Fuller's earth 10 lb, hydrochloric acid 1½ gal, water 1½ gal. Mix to creamy paste in glass or ceramic jar. Use at room temp for at least 1 hr. Apply with brush. Follow with hot-water rinse.

Solution "J"—Liquid to remove imbedded iron from nickel, Monel and Inconel: Hydrochloric acid ¼ pt, ferric chloride 1½ oz, water 1 gal. Use cold, for not more than 1 hr. Rinse as with Solution "I."

PICK-OFF GEAR—See *Gear, Pick-Off.*

PIECE WORK—A method of payment where a worker receives a fixed sum per piece produced. It is a simple system and has some advantages, depending on the work being done and the production methods. It involves the problems of time lost through bad castings, broken tools or machines, or lack of material supply. It is always a temptation to cut piece rates when men earn more than an average wage, even though this gives more production on the investment in machine equipment. Where work moves along a production line at a fixed rate, the rate must be set by the slowest worker and piece work is of no help in spurring production. For this reason few large plants use piece work where they have mechanized production lines.

PIG BED—The sand bed in which pig iron is cast as it comes from the smelter. The bed carries molds of the pigs to be cast with channels running to each mold. The whole thing is frequently referred to as the "sow and pigs."

PIG IRON—Iron which has been poured into the molds in the pig bed which is near the smelter. The term "pig" is used for some other metals such as pig lead or tin. While solder is frequently cast in this way the pieces are comparatively small and called bars instead of pigs in most cases. Pig iron contains about 92 per cent iron and from 3.5 to 4 per cent carbon, with some silicon, manganese, phosphorous, sulphur and other impurities.

PILLAR FILE—See *Files, Types of.*

PILLOW BLOCK—A shaft bearing resting on some sort of foundation. This may be masonry or the bed of a machine.

PILOT—A guide on the end of a boring bar, reamer or other tool. It pilots or steers the tool to keep it in alinement.

PILOT DRILL—A drill to remove part of the metal before the regular sized drill is used. In some cases the diameter is but slightly larger than the *web* of the drill which follows, in others it may leave but little work to be done by the second or following drill, or drills.

PILOT ORDER OR PILOT LOT—Usually a comparatively small order which is put through a plant to test the tooling and the method to be used. This experience often shows where changes may be necessary for satisfactory production or product.

PILOT PLANT—An experimental plant or factory in which new operations are tried or new products produced.

PILOT WHEEL—A wheel, or a few spokes, by which some part of a machine is operated. In turret lathes, the pilot wheel moves the turret slide. In British practice this is called a capstan, from its resemblance to the capstan used on shipboard for raising the anchor.

PIN, COLLAR—A pin with a collar to limit its position. Usually driven into part of a machine to carry a roll, lever or gear. Similar to a collar stud except that it has no thread. Frequently has a cotter pin hole in the outer end. Also known as a "fulcrum pin."

PIN, DOWEL—A pin or plain stud fastened in one piece to locate it in proper position on a mating part. They are used in patterns and in many places as a simple means of securing accurate mating of parts. In wooden patterns, the mating holes frequently have a metal bushing to match the pin and prevent inaccuracies due to wear of the wood itself. The ends of the dowel pins are either beveled or rounded to make it easy to enter them in the holes.

PIN, TAPER—Standard taper pins have a taper of ¼ inch to the foot and are made from ¾ to 6 or more inches long. Special reamers are made so that each size overlaps the other so that there is no break in the holes reamed by them. Lengths are also standardized. See table.

PIN METAL—An alloy of copper and zinc with about 62 per cent copper and 38 per cent zinc.

PINCERS—A name frequently used in place of pliers. It is applied to many types of hand tools of this variety, although some define pincers as having jaws at right angles to the handles.

PIPE THREADING TOOLS

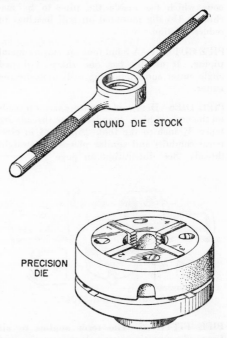

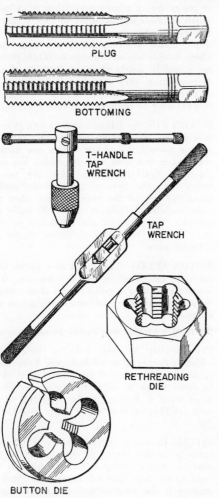

PLUG

BOTTOMING

T-HANDLE
TAP
WRENCH

TAP
WRENCH

ROUND DIE STOCK

PRECISION
DIE

RETHREADING
DIE

BUTTON DIE

PINCH BAR—Any bar used to move heavy weights by prying under the object and moving it a short distance at a time. Same as crow-bar in many cases. In others it may have a projection on one side, known as a heel, which acts as a pivot.

PING—A sharp sound made in internal combustion engines when the spark is advanced too far for the speed at which the engine is running. It is also frequently due to carbon accumulation in the cylinder head or to too high compression for the type of fuel being used.

PINION—A small gear, especially when used with a larger gear. See *Gears*.

PINNING—A shop term for scratches left by a file due to chips being allowed to remain between the file teeth. It also refers to the fastening of two or more pieces by the use of pins.

PINS, COTTER—See *Cotter Pins*.

PINS, MACHINE—Machine pins are straight with ends perfectly square, beveled (or chamfered) or rounded, and with heads and a hole for cotter pins drilled at the plain end. They may be ground, soft or hardened. The headed pins are called clevis pins and standard sizes run from $\frac{3}{16}$ to 1 inch diameter.

PINTLE—An old term for a projection or post, to carry a pivoted part of a mechanical device. Really a small short shaft extending out from a main shaft to form a bearing.

PIPE—A tube for conveying air, gases or liquids. Also a cavity formed in ingots, forgings or castings by contraction during the solidification of the last portions of the liquid metal. The "pipe" is caused by the outer surface cooling before the center which continues to contract and causes the "pipe."

313

PIPE CENTER—A lathe center having a large cone which fits inside the pipe to be machined. Usually mounted on ball bearings to reduce friction.

PIPE CUTTER—A hand tool for cutting metal piping. It usually has one sharp V-shaped angle cutter and supporting rolls opposite the cutter.

PIPE DIES—Dies used in cutting screw threads on the ends of pipe. Standard pipe threads are taper, ¾ inch to the foot. Pipe used in electrical conduits and similar places has straight threads. See illustration on page 313.

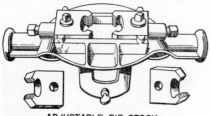

ADJUSTABLE DIE STOCK

PIPE FITTINGS—The term applies to all forms of connecting parts which join pieces of pipe together.

PIPE LINE COLORS—Painting pipe lines with distinctive colors to show the purposes for which they are used is common practice in many plants and on board ship. These colors are standardized for regular uses, but many plants have special colors for special materials or uses. The DuPont Co. uses the colors shown herewith.

Application	*Color*
Steam	Orange
Gases	Yellow
Water	Green
Solvents	Blue
Electrical conduit	Black
Process materials	Gray
Extra-valuable materials	Purple

PIPE REAMERS—See *Reamer.*

PIPE TAPS—See *Taps.*

PIPE TONGS—See *Wrench.*

PIPE THREADS—Screw threads used in connecting pipes. See *Pipe Dies* and *Screw Threads, Pipe.*

PIPE WRENCH—See *Wrench.*

PISTON—Every reciprocating engine, motor or pump has a piston moving in a cylinder which confines the pressure so that it can be exerted against the head of the piston, in single acting engines, or against both sides where double action is secured. While pistons are round in nearly all cases, because of ease in machining, they may be of any form. In some cases where the piston is a rod working in a cylinder or chamber it is called a plunger.

PISTON RINGS—Rings which fit into grooves in a piston and prevent passage of steam, air or gas around the piston. They are usually made of a cast iron mixture which has considerable flexibility. The rings are turned larger than the bore of the cylinder and a piece cut out of the ring so that when the ends are closed together they will enter the cylinder. Some rings are refinished to size after closing, to secure a better fit in the cylinder bore.

PISTON SPEED—The speed of a piston in a cylinder, measured in feet per minute. It is found by multiplying the length of the stroke in *feet* by twice the number of revolutions per minute.

PISTON VALVE—See *Valve, Piston.*

PIT—Usually a small hole or indentation which is deeper than its diameter. Frequently caused by the action of acids or of sand blast. In some shops it refers to the pit in which large work is lowered to be operated on by such machine tools as radial drills. See *Lathe, Pit.*

PITCH—In screw threads, pitch is the distance from the center of one thread to the next. In single thread screws the pitch is the same as the *lead,* but not otherwise. Pitch in gearing is the relation between the diameter and the number of teeth. See *Pitch Diameter.*

PITCH ANGLE OF GEARS—See *Gears, Pitch Angle.*

PITCH, CHORDAL—See *Gear Nomenclature.*

PITCH, CIRCULAR—See *Gear Nomenclature.*

PITCH DIAMETER—In a screw thread, the diameter at the center of the thread depth, not considering clearance. In gears, it is the diameter at the point where the gear teeth contact. This may be in the center of the teeth, without clearance, or it may be moved in or out according to the design of the gear teeth. See *Gear Nomenclature* and *Screw Threads.*

PITCH, DIAMETRAL—In gearing, it is the number of teeth per inch of diameter of the gear. See *Gear Nomenclature.*

PITCH LINE—See *Gear Nomenclature.*

PITMAN—A connecting rod between moving parts. More commonly used in connection with woodworking or agricultural implements.

PIVOT—A point, pin or rod about which a lever moves. For example, the pin connecting the jaws of pliers or tongs, the knife edge bearing for a beam scale, or the axis on which any lever moves.

PLAIN INDEXING—See *Indexing, Plain.*

PLAIN MILLING CUTTERS — See *Milling Cutters.*

PLANCHET—A blank piece of metal punched out of a sheet or strip before other work is done on it. Usually applied to the blanks from which coins are made.

PLANER—A machine for producing flat surfaces. In metal working, a stationary tool is held on a cross rail while the table moves the work under it. In woodworking, the tool is a set of revolving knives under which the work passes. There are several types of planers for different kinds of work, some of which are shown. The two main types are double housing and open-side. There are several methods

of driving the table, direct gearing being most common, but both worm and hydraulic drives are used.

PLANER CENTERS — Indexing centers for holding work which must be indexed into different positions. Similar to milling machine plain index centers.

PLANER, DOUBLE HOUSING — A metal planer in which there is an upright, or housing, on each side of the table, which limits the size of the work. This is the most common type.

PLANER DRIVES—Three kinds of planer drives are now in use for moving the table on the bed or ways. Spur or helical gearing,

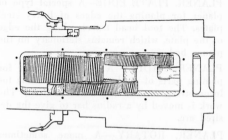

Planer drives. Helical gearing used in Gray planer.

Gray double housing worm drive planer.

working on a rack under the table, is most common. The Sellers, or worm drive is very old and usually satisfactory. The latest drive is an hydraulic cylinder mechanism fastened to the under side of the planer table.

PLANER, HYDRAULIC — Any planer in which the table is moved by an hydraulic cylinder instead of by the usual method of gearing.

PLANER JACKS—See *Jack, Planer.*

PLANER, OPEN SIDE—A planer with one housing which supports the overhanging arm that takes the place of the cross rail on the standard type of planer. Useful in planing work too wide to go between the uprights, or housing, of the standard planer.

PLANER, PLATE EDGE—A special type of planer for planing the edges of heavy steel plates, The tool head travels along the edge of the plate, which remains stationary on the planer bed.

PLANER, RADIUS—A planer designed for planing parts of circles, such as the links for locomotives or stationary valve motions. The work is moved by a radius bar to give the desired arc.

PLANER, ROTARY — A name sometimes given to a type of milling machine with a milling cutter on a large horizontal spindle. The work moves past the cutter on a bed, as in a planer.

PLANER, SCREW—A type of planer in which the table was driven by a screw under the table. Only used in special types of work, such as armor plate.

PLANER, SELLERS TYPE—A type of planer drive developed over 60 years ago in which the table was driven by a worm meshing into a rack under the planer table. The worm sets at an angle that corresponds with the lead of the worm. It produced a very steady motion, but it largely gave way to the use of straight faced gears and then to helical or herringbone gears.

PLANER STOP—See *Stops, Planer.*

PLANER, TRAVELING HEAD—A planer in which the work is stationary and the planer tool moves over it. Seldom used in the United States except in planing armor plate. It is really a shaper, except that, instead of the usual shaper ram, the tools are carried in a bridge-like structure which travels over the work.

PLANER, WALL—A planer with guides on the wall on which the tool head travels. There were few of these in this country and they are now extinct.

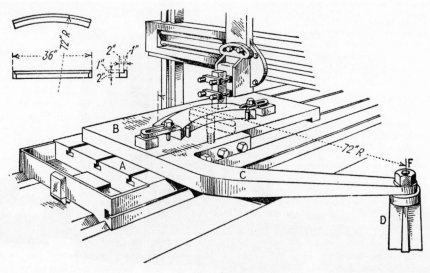

Radius planer

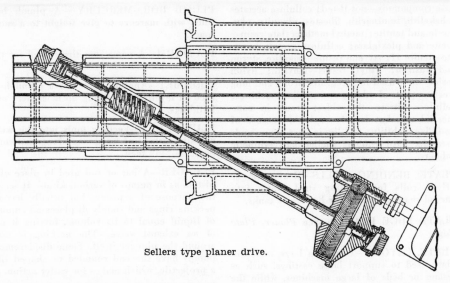

Sellers type planer drive.

PLANER WAYS—The guides which support the planer table and keep it in proper alinement. The term applies to both the planer bed and planer table. Non-metallic strips to form the bearing of the table were developed by the Gray Co. and have proved very successful in reducing friction and wear. They also prevent distortion from heat in high speed planing and insure more accurate work.

PLANET GEAR—Any gear which travels around another gear, as in a planetary gear transmission, or an epicycle train of gears. The central gear is known as the "sun" gear and the mechanism is frequently called "sun and planet" gearing.

PLANETARY GEARS—A combination of gears in which small "planet" gears revolve inside an internal gear. Used for securing reduced speeds in gear transmissions of different kinds. See *Gears, Planetary*.

PLANIMETER—An instrument which measures the area of a chart or diagram of any kind by tracing around its outer edge. It was largely used in checking the performance of steam engines by means of diagrams to show the steam pressure at different parts of the stroke.

PLANISH—The finishing of a flat metallic surface, like sheet steel, by a light hammering action. Russia sheet iron, very popular in early locomotive practice for boiler covering,

was said to be planished by placing powdered charcoal between sheets of iron and hammering them. This gave a sort of mottled surface which was fairly hard and which resisted corrosion more than plain sheet iron.

PLANISHING—The finishing of sheet metal by hammering with smooth faced hammers or their equivalents.

PLASTIC BRONZE—Bronze bearing metals which are soft enough to fit themselves to the shaft and form a good bearing.

PLASTICS—A class of non-metallic, synthetic materials which can be easily formed into many shapes. Many are entirely synthetic, while others use natural materials as a base. Celluloid and bakelite were among the early plastics. There are two general types, thermosetting and thermo-plastic. The first can be molded or shaped and after being heated will retain the shape on cooling. The others will soften whenever heat is applied. They are frequently used as binders for particles or sheets of other materials. Used with fabrics, they make excellent gears and other mechanical accessories. See various plastics under their trade names.

PLASTICS, MOLDING—Plastics suitable or adapted to being formed by molding in dies. The Boonton Molding Co. lists them as follows: Phenolic base compounds—bakelite, durez, durite, indur, makalot and resinox; urea

317

base compounds—not listed; cellulose acetates —bakelith, luminarith, fibestos, nixonite, plastacele and tentite; methyl-methacrylate resin— lucite and plexiglass; cellulose acetate butryate—tenite 11; styrene resins—bakelite, styron and lustron; vinyl resins—vinylite; nylon resins—now used for accurate, strong and long wearing parts of adding and similar machines; cellulose nitrate—the oldest group in commercial use, but largely replaced because of its inflammability; and lignin base compounds —casein, hard rubber, shellac and synthetic rubbers.

PLATE BENDING ROLLS—Heavy, power driven rolls for bending steel plates into curved shapes, such as for boilers or tanks.

PLATE EDGE PLANER—See *Planer, Plate Edge.*

PLATE, LAYOUT—Usually a large cast iron plate used to support large castings, such as frames or beds of large machines, while the different bearings and other surfaces are being laid out as a guide in machining.

PLATEN—The work holding table of various machines, such as milling machines, planers or drilling machines, as well as printing presses. Usually called a table.

PLATES, STEEL—Sheet steel thicker than No. 5 (0.2145 inch) is known as steel *plate*. Thinner than this is known as *sheets.*

PLATING SCREW THREADS — See *Screw Threads, Plating.*

PLATINUM — A heavy, rather rare metal which is very ductile and resists most acids. Sp. gr. 21.40. Melts at 3,190 deg. F.

PLEXI-GLASS — An acrylic, synthetic resin that is as transparent as glass. It is made from coal, petroleum and water. A very useful member of the plastic family, resembling lucite in appearance and being practically identical.

PLUG TAP—See *Tap, Plug.*

PLUMB BOB—A very old device of a heavy weight with a point in line with its point of suspension. Suspended from a tripod or other support it hangs vertically and indicates or makes a straight line which is at exact right angles to the earth. Used by carpenters, surveyors and machine erectors to secure proper alinement for buildings, bridges, roads and machinery.

PLUMB BOB, MERCURY — A plumb bob filled with mercury to give weight to a small space.

PLUMBUM—A name sometimes used for the metal, lead.

PLUMMET—Another name for a plumb-bob, used in leveling and lining up machinery and buildings.

PLUNGE CUT—Feeding tools into the work radially instead of traversing along the work. Same as "in" feed.

PLUNGER—A bar or rod used in place of a piston, as in pumps of various kinds. It serves the purpose of a piston, but usually has no packing rings and simply displaces an amount of liquid equal to its volume, forcing it out of an exhaust valve. The packing is used around the plunger itself. Some displacement pumps have the end rounded or shaped like a projectile, which makes for easier action.

PLY—Generally used in connection with materials composed of several layers. Heavy belting is usually two-ply, or double, and fabric and wooden materials are built of up several layers. By crossing the grains of thin sheets of wood and cementing with modern plastics, splitting and warping is reduced to a minimum.

POINT ANGLE—See under *Drills Twist, Names of Parts.*

POLARISCOPE—An instrument for use in examining materials under polarized light.

POLARITY—Pertaining to the north and south pole attraction in magnetic fields. In a compass needle one end points north and the other south. In electromagnets or in electrical fields of motors and generators or other devices, magnetic poles are created by passage of electric current through the windings.

POLE OR SPRING POLE LATHE—A primitive type of lathe in which the work is revolved on two dead centers by a cord wound around the work. The upper end of the cord is fastened to the top of a long, springy pole and the lower end is pulled down by the operator's foot, either in a loop or with a treadle. Pulling the cord down turns the work against the tool. The spring in the pole returns the cord and reverses the work. There are still a few in existence in the Kentucky hills and elsewhere.

POLISHING—The finishing of metal surfaces with fine abrasives, either on wheels or on flexible belts to reach hard-to-get-at places. Polishing is frequently confused with buffing. See *Buffing.*

POLISHING OPERATIONS—Polishing operations are usually divided into three classes: roughing, dry fining, and finishing or oiling. Abrasives used for roughing usually run from Nos. 20 to 80; for dry fining, from Nos. 90 to 120; and for finishing from 150 to XF. For both roughing out and dry fining, polishing wheels should be used dry. For finishing, wheels are first worn down a little and then oil, beeswax, tallow, and similar substances are used on the wheel. This, together with the abrasive, brings up a fine finish.

Speed of Buffing Wheels

Material	Feet per Minute
Wood, leather covered	7,000
Walrus	8,000
Rag Wheels	7,000
Hair-brush wheels	12,000
Ohio grindstone	2,500
Huron grindstone	3,500

POLISHING WHEEL—A wheel made of varying materials and having the edge coated with an abrasive. Frequently confused with a buffing wheel, which is usually made up of layers of fabric, sewed together and used for finishing surfaces of brass and the softer metals.

POLYGON—A figure having more than four sides and angles is usually considered as a polygon. Strictly speaking, a polygon may also be a triangle or a square.

POLYSTYRENE—A synthetic resin used in plastics. It is tough and strong at low temperatures, and a good insulator. Used in injection molding.

PONY PLANER—A small planer operated by a crank, the stroke of the table being adjusted by changing the position of the driving crank pin. Similar to a shaper, except that the crank drives the work table instead of the tool. Another name for a small crank-planer.

POP VALVE—See *Valve, Pop.*

POPPET VALVE—See *Valve, Poppet.*

PORT—A passageway for flow of air, gas or liquid. It is frequently cored into a cylinder

Laying Out Regular Polygons

The cut-and-try method is to draw a circle and space it off, but it saves time to know what spacing to use or how large a circle to make to get the desired number of holes at a given distance apart.

Table of Regular Polygons

Number of Sides	Name of Figure	Diameter of circle that will just enclose when side is 1	Diameter of circle that will just go inside when side is 1	Length of side where diameter of enclosure circle equals 1	Length of side where inside circle equals 1	Angle formed by lines drawn form center to corners	Angle formed by outer sides of figures	To find area of figure multiply side by itself and by number in this column
3	Triangle	1.1546	.5774	.866	1.732	120°	60°	.4330
4	Square	1.4142	1.	.7071	1.	90	90	1.
5	Pentagon	1.7012	1.3764	.5878	.7265	72	108	1.7204
6	Hexagon	2.	1.732	.5	.5774	60	120	2.5980
7	Heptagon	2.3048	2.0766	.4338	.4815	51°-26′	128¼⁄₇	3.6339
8	Octagon	2.6132	2.4142	.3827	.4142	45	135	4.8284
9	Nonagon	2.9238	2.7474	.342	.3639	40	140	6.1818
10	Decagon	3.236	3.0776	.309	.3247	36	144	7.6942
11	Undecagon	3.5494	3.4056	.2817	.2936	32°-43	147³⁄₁₁	9.3656
12	Dodecagon	3.8638	3.732	.2588	.2679	30	150	11.1961

casting in steam engines, but internal combustion engines usually have them outside in what is called a "manifold."

PORTER-BAR—This may be either a bar for handling heavy forgings or a bar which has the end forged into shape for any purpose.

POSITIONERS—A term used to describe devices made for holding work to be welded by gas or electric arc. They are usually provided with means of tilting or swinging, or both, so as to bring different parts of the work within easy reach of the welder.

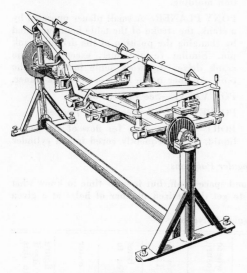

Positioner.

POST DRILL—Any drilling machine attached to a post or column instead of having a base of its own. Blacksmith's drills are frequently of this type.

POT CHUCK—A hollow sleeve fastened to a lathe spindle for holding special shapes in the lathe. See *Chucks.*

POT METAL—A name sometimes given to an alloy, usually of lead and copper, and used in casting or rolling large pans.

POTASSIUM—A white metal that is lighter than water and that oxidizes in air. It is kept in ether or kerosene, and is soluble in acids and in alcohol. Sp. gr. 0.859. Melts at 150 deg. F.

POTASSIUM CYANIDE—Crystals used in carburizing or surface hardening steel. Also used for electroplating. Very poisonous. Sp. gr. 1.52. Melts at 1,500 deg. F. See *Sodium Cyanide.*

POTASSIUM NITRATE—Sometimes called nitre or saltpeter. Used in bluing steel and in tempering baths. Melts at 482 deg. F.

POUNDAL—A term seldom used in the shop, based on a unit of force derived from the pound, the foot and the second of time. The force which moves a weight of one pound one foot in one second.

POWER OF A NUMBER—The number found by multiplying a number by itself one or more times. The second power of 2 is 4; the 5th power of 2 is 32. The second power is called the "square" and the third power the "cube" of a number.

PRECIPITATION HARDENING—A term describing the process of hardening an alloy by heating so as to allow a structural constituent of the alloy to be precipitated into a solid mass.

PRECISION DRILLING MACHINE—A small drilling machine built especially for small, precision drilling. They have hand feed and sometimes drill holes as small as 0.003 inch in diameter. Sometimes called sensitive drilling machines.

PREFERRED DRILL SIZES—See *Drills, Preferred Sizes.*

PREFERRED NUMBERS—A system designed to bring about standardization in the selection of numbers designating sizes or capacities of machines or of the tools used in them. A study of the old wire gages shows the confusion arising when numbers are selected without any system in the steps between sizes. The electrical industry early in its life, abandoned the numbered wire gages and adopted the "mil," of 1/1,000th of an inch, as a base, and their sizes cannot be mistaken. In practice they select the wire nearest to the one desired. Nor do all designers adhere to the theoretical preferred numbers.

PRELOADED BEARINGS—This refers to ball and roller bearings which are assembled under pressure so that there should be no further deflection when the bearing is under load.

PRESS, ARBOR—A small press for forcing mandrels into work. So-called when work holding shafts were called arbors instead of mandrels. Arbors are seldom forced into place.

PRESS, BLANKING—A press for punching blanks from a sheet of metal. It is usually a first operation press, the blanks being formed later in other presses.

PRESS BRAKE—See *Brake* and *Metal Forming Machines.*

PRESS, BROACHING—A press for forcing push broaches through holes in metal work.

PRESS, CABBAGING—A press for compressing sheet metal scrap into convenient form for handling and remelting. Sometimes called a baling press.

PRESS, COINING—A press for making coins or medals from planchets or disks, previously blanked on another press. Is usually a double acting press.

PRESS, DEEP DRAW—A press designed for making deep impressions or forms by a controlled drawing action. Automobile fenders and cartridge cases are examples of deep drawing.

PRESS, DOUBLE ACTING—A double acting press has two rams, one inside the other, each driven by an independent cam, so that one follows the other. In this way the press performs two operations at one stroke.

PRESS, DRAWING AND FORMING—A press for drawing and forming sheet metal into hollow or tubular form, and to other shapes, as in making cartridge cases, automobile fenders and similar work.

PRESS FIT—See *Fit, Press or Force.*

PRESS, FLANGING—A press, usually double acting hydraulic, for making flanges on boiler plate and similar work. Some exert pressures up to 300 tons per square inch.

PRESS, FOOT OR KICK—A type of punch press operated by the foot. A lever comes down from the press nearly to the floor and is operated with a swinging motion of the foot. The increased leverage afforded by the lever makes it easy to operate and it is very fast, when run by a skilled operator.

PRESS, FORCING—A press for forcing one piece into another, such as rod brasses into a connecting rod or wheels on axles. These are usually called wheel presses. Arbor presses are also forcing presses, but should be called mandrel presses.

PRESS, FORGING—A press for forging hot metals by continuous pressure rather than by blows. See *Forgings.*

PRESS, HORNING—A press for closing side seams on tinware made from rolled up sheets.

PRESS, HYDRAULIC—A machine, operated by hydraulic pressure, for forming metal in, or over dies.

PRESS, HYDRO—A press operated by hydraulic pressure.

PRESS, INCLINABLE—A punch press in which the upper part, containing the punch and die, can be inclined relative to the base. In many kinds of work this permits the blanks that have been punched to slide out of the die into a receptacle behind the press, and saves rehandling.

PRESS, PENDULUM—A foot press having a pendulum like lever for applying power to the ram. Same as kick press.

PRESS, PERCUSSION—A name given to a screw press with a heavy flywheel at the upper end of the screw which builds up momentum as it turns and strikes a heavy blow on the work at the end of its travel. Designed for cold forming of work but not used as much as formerly.

PRESS, PNEUMATIC—A press in which pressure is applied by compressed air. The type shown is frequently used in assembling machine parts which are a press fit. Illustration on page 322.

PRESS, SCREW—A punch or forming press operated by a screw instead of the more common levers and toggles. It is preferred by some for operations where it seems necessary to give the metal time to flow. It permits watching the action of metal sheets in trying out new dies, but is not commonly used in production.

PRESS, STRAIGHT SIDED—A press made with straight sides to secure maximum strength for heavy pressures without frame distortion.

PRESS, STRETCHING—A press in which the sheet of metal is held at the end or sides and stretched to desired curves or shapes by a form forced up against the sheet. See *Metal Forming Machines.*

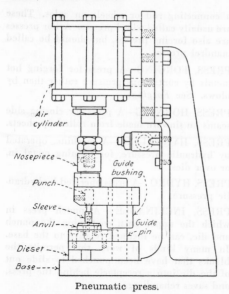

Pneumatic press.

PRESS, TRIPLE ACTION — A press with three distinct actions. Only used on special work.

PRESSURE, ABSOLUTE—Pressure from absolute zero. At sea level the absolute pressure is 14.7 pounds per square inch more than is shown on a steam or other pressure gage. If the gage shows 70 pounds, the absolute pressure is 84.7 pounds. This decreases as we rise above sea level.

PRESSURE ANGLES OF GEARS—See under *Gearing Nomenclature*.

PRESSURE USED IN MEASURING — As nothing is free from distortion under sufficient pressure, the pressure used in accurate measuring is important. In a light wave micrometer the pressure can be determined by noting the position of the wave bands, between zero and 2½ pounds pressure. The measuring pressure should be selected to suit the material being measured. Van Keuren, an authority on light wave measurement, suggests 1 to 2 ounces for rubber, 1 pound for gages and precision parts and for screw threads of 20 pitch and finer. For coarser threads he suggests 2½ pounds pressure.

PRICK PUNCH—See *Center Punch*.

PRIME MOVER—Usually considered to refer to the source of power, as a steam or internal combustion engine, or a turbine which gets its power from a water fall. It does not regularly apply to an electric motor, as the current which operates it comes from a generator which is in turn driven by some kind of engine, or water power. A locomotive is a prime mover whether it is powered by a steam or diesel engine. Strictly speaking, an electric locomotive does not come under this heading.

PRIME NUMBER—A number which cannot be divided evenly by any number but itself, as 3, 5, 7. Nine is not a prime number as it is divisible by 3, nor is 21, as it is divisible by 3 and 7.

PRITCHEL—An uncommon name used by some blacksmiths for a tool used to punch or to enlarge holes already punched, in forgings. Also applied to the round hole sometimes seen in anvils for holding the tool itself.

PROBOLOG — An instrument for recording the internal defects of tubes made of non-magnetic materials from 1 to 12 inches outside diameter. It detects pin-holes, cracks, corrosion and erosion pits, as well as differences in the chemical composition of the tubes. It is especially useful in oil-refinery work.

PRODUCER GAS—Any combustible gas made for use in internal combustion engines or for light and heat.

PROFILE—A special outline, as in cutters made to produce given shapes. Profiling is the cutting of given outlines either in sheet metal or in a solid mass of metal, as in dies for various purposes. Special machines for doing this work are called profilers.

PROFILE MILLING CUTTERS—See *Milling Cutters*.

PROFILING—Forming a desired contour, usually on a flat surface, as in blanking or forming dies. It is done with an end mill, usually in a vertical spindle machine of the milling type, the spindle being guided from a master form, to cut the desired contour. It should not be confused with *form* turning or milling, or with other machining with a formed tool. See *Duplicating Machine*.

PROFILOMETER — An instrument which measures and records the depth and frequency of serrations, scratches or other imperfections on a finished surface. The roughness is measured in micro-inches or millionths of an inch.

These variations are given in R.M.S. units. See *Root, Mean Square*.

PROJECTED AREA—A term applied to bearings which means the diameter of the shaft multiplied by the length of the bearing. This is much less than the actual bearing surface in contact with the shaft if it is in contact on its full circumference. Many bearings, as in railroad car axles, do not surround the axle, but only bear on a small portion of it. Here the projected area is simply the width of the bearing multiplied by its length, regardless of the axle diameter.

PROJECTION, CAVALIER—Similar to isometric projection except that base lines are horizontal and projection lines are at 45 degrees. See *Isometric Projection*.

PRONG DIES—See *Dies, Prong or Spring*.

PRONY BRAKE—A mechanical device for absorbing and measuring power produced by an engine or motor of any kind. It is usually a friction device in which power absorbed is measured by pull at the end of a lever against a known resistance, as special spring devices. In other cases, hydraulic mechanisms absorb and measure the power put into the service.

PROTEIN PLASTICS — Molding materials made from animal or vegetable products, such as soy beans.

PROTON—Nucleus of the atom of the light isotope of hydrogen. It has a positive charge of one elementary unit.

PROTRACTOR—A tool used by both draftsmen and tool makers in laying out and measuring angles. They are made in numerous forms to suit different requirements.

PROTRACTOR, BEVEL—A protractor combined with an adjustable bevel so that angles can be accurately laid out and read.

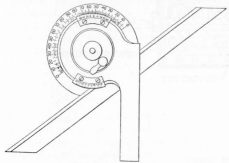

Bevel protractor.

PRUSSIAN BLUE—A substance for coating metals to make it easy to lay out work with a scriber or other tool. See *Layout Fluid*.

PUDDLING—The converting of cast iron into steel by frequent stirring of the molten mass in a furnace. This liberates many impurities and produces a much better metal.

PUG— A blast furnace name for the wad of fire clay used in stopping the tap, or outlet hole in the furnace.

PULL BROACH—See *Broach, Pull*.

PULL END—A term used to designate the end of a pull broach which connects it to the power head of the machine.

PULL PIN—A means of locking or unlocking two parts of machinery. Sometimes used on gears which slide in and out of mesh. At other times, operates a sliding key which engages any desired gear of a number held on a stud or shaft.

PULLEY—A wheel which is mounted on a shaft and has a flat, or slightly crowned rim, to carry flat belts used in driving machinery of various kinds. Pulleys are also made with either half round or V- shaped grooves in the rim to receive round or V-belts. Some have been made with holes in the rim to permit the escape of air drawn in under the belt.

PULLEY BLOCKS—See *Blocks, Hoisting*.

PULLEY, CHAIN—A pulley with depressions in its rim to receive a chain as used in a hoist.

PULLEY, EXPANDING—A special type of pulley in which the diameter can be expanded or increased to a limited extent. Formerly used in some special constructions to secure changes of speed. The arms were lengthened and the rim left with gaps in the circumference or supplementary pieces introduced. This has been replaced by various speed changing devices.

PULLEY, GALLOWS OR GUIDE—A loose pulley mounted in a movable frame and used to guide or tighten belts.

PULLEY, IDLER—A pulley which helps support a belt but does not drive any machinery. Generally used on the outside of the belt to support a long belt from undue sag between pulleys or to increase the arc of contact with the smaller pulley. In the latter case it is really a belt-tightener.

PULLEY, LOOSE—A pulley running loose on a shaft and doing no work. In belt driven machines a loose pulley was provided for the driving belt when the machine was idle. This might be on the machine itself or on the countershaft over the machine. To start the machine the belt was shifted from the loose pulley to the tight pulley. In machines with a reverse motion there was a loose pulley for both the forward and the reversing belt.

PULLEY, MULEY—A pulley used in guiding belts between the driving and driven pulleys, when they are not parallel. Muley pulleys are often used in driving shafting at right angles to the shaft of the driving pulley. They must be carefully lined up and any turning of the driving pulley in the wrong direction will throw the belt off. See Belt, Muley.

PULLEY, PERFORATED — A pulley with holes in the rim to allow the escape of air between pulley and belt. Practically obsolete.

PULLEY, SPLIT—A pulley made in halves so as to be clamped on a shaft instead of being forced on the end. It makes changing pulleys much simpler.

PULLEY, STEPPED—A pulley having various diameters, or "steps." Usually called a cone

pulley, although each step is of uniform diameter.

PULLEY, TIGHT—The pulley that drives the machine when the belt is shifted on to it.

PULLEY, V-BELT—A pulley with grooves in its rim to drive V-belts. Sometimes called a sheave.

PULLEY, VARIABLE SPEED—Pulleys which provide means for driving or being driven by V-belts at different distances from the center. The Lovejoy pulley shown is usually mounted on the shaft of a motor mounted on a movable base so that the center distance between the motor and the driven mechanism can be varied. As shown, the belt is at the large diameter of the driving pulley and drives at maximum speed. Moving the motor away from the driven member forces the V-belt down between the sides of the pulley and decreases the diameter of the driving pulley. The spring maintains proper contact for the belt at the various diameters.

PULSATOR—Any device that pulses or beats or throbs when at work, as a pump of the diaphragm type of the hydraulic ram.

PUMICE—A porous volcanic rock or glass, used for polishing.

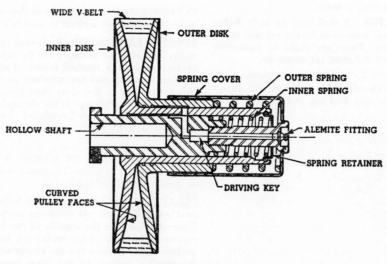

Variable speed pulley.

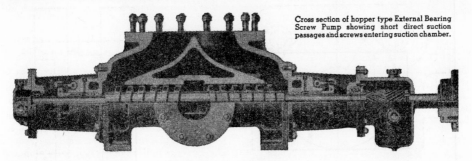

Cross section of hopper type External Bearing Screw Pump showing short direct suction passages and screws entering suction chamber.

Screw pump.

PUMP, JET—A pump in which the fluid moved is propelled by a jet of air, gas or steam.

PUMP, SCREW—A type of pump in which the material being moved is acted on by a form of screw instead of pistons. The Quimby pump shown uses two screws, each with a right and left hand thread. The screws are a threaded type which mesh into each other as shown. They are used in handling heavy viscous materials.

PUMP, VACUUM—A pump for removing air pressure to permit normal pressure of the atmosphere to draw water or air into a chamber. In a vacuum cleaner, removal of pressure in the dirt tube draws dirt from the floor into the cleaner bag. In condensing steam engines it reduces back pressure on the piston and adds to the effective power which can be delivered. In pumps it allows water or air to be forced up into the pump. Also called suction pump.

PUNCH AND DIE SETS—A punch and die set is an assembly consisting of an upper member called the punch holder. The lower surface of the punch holder and the upper surface of the die holder are those on which the punch and die details of a finished punch press tool are mounted. In use, the die holder is clamped to the bed or bolster plate of the punch press, while the punch holder shank is clamped in the clamping hole in the punch press ram. The tool is actuated by the reciprocating motion of the ram. The mating guide posts and bushings of an assembled die set assist in maintaining tool alinement during die setting and the operation of the tool in the punch press. The size of punch and die set is gen-erally designated by its available die area.

Die sets are made both with round posts at the back and also at diagonal corners, in the rectangular series, and are also made round. Bushings are round and have circular oil grooves for lubricating the pins. The "die area" is the surface of the die-holder that may be utilized for mounting tool members in a punch and die set. Die sets were formerly called "sub-press dies." Die sets have been standardized by the A. S. A. as to die area, thickness, guide posts and bushings and tolerances, parallelism of top and bottom face, squareness of guide posts, guide bushings and other essential dimensions. A typical backpost set is shown with dimensions of small and large size. See *Die Sets.*

PUNCH, BELT—A hollow round or elliptical punch for making holes for belt lacings.

PUNCH, CENTER—A hand tool with a sharp point, to mark desired points in laying out work or for starting a drill in the right place. Various types of punches are shown.

PUNCH, CENTER SPACING—Two center punches set at any desired distance apart, or adjustable as to distance, for making punch marks at equal distances apart, or a single punch with a guide member that enters the hole already punched.

PUNCH, HAND—Hand tools for forcing pins out of holes or for aligning the holes in two parts. Illustrations page 327.

PUNCH PRESS—Machines in which a ram moves a punch or die to punch holes in stock. A die supports the stock while it is being punched. The presses used in some automobile plants punch the whole top at one operation.

325

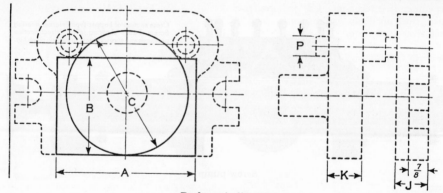

Back-post die set.

Dimensions of Back-Post Die Sets

Die Area			Thickness				Min. Guide-post Diam.
Right to Left	Front to Back	Diam-eter	Die Holder		Punch Holder		
			J		K		
A	B	C	From	To	From	To	P
3	3	3	1	1¼	1	..	¾
4	4	4	1⅜	1¾	1¼	..	1
4	6	..	1½	2¾	1¼	2¼	1
20	5	..	1¾	2½	1½	2	1½
22	12	..	2	3	1½	2	1½
25	14	..	1¾	3	1½	2¼	1½

All dimensions are given in inches.

MATERIAL: This standard does not specify the material for the punch holder or die holder. They are generally made from cast iron, semi-steel, or steel plate and should be free from dirt, slag, and detrimental blow holes and be sufficiently thick to permit machining of outer scale to provide uniform structures as to the finish of the surface on which the punches and dies are mounted. The material should be of sufficient hardness to stand up on service and have good machining qualities.

NOTE: A and B dimensions may be plus or minus ½ in. during a five-year transition period, so that suppliers may use present patterns.

PUNCH PRESS DIE—See *Die, Punch Press.*

PUNCH PRESS DIES, EDGE TRIMMING— Dies which trim the edges of shells that have been drawn in a previous operation. The illustrations show two methods of trimming drawings of this kind.

PUNCH PRESS SCRAP—The waste of material made necessary by leaving enough material between punchings to hold the sheet or strip together while it is being fed through the press. In many cases it is necessary to run the strip through more than once, offsetting it

to utilize as much of the material as possible, as shown. In some cases it is possible to secure a minimum waste by reversing the strip as in the double-pass layout shown. The width of the retaining strips, as A, depends on the kind of material as well as its thickness, approximately ⅛ inch in many cases.

PUNCH, SHOULDER—A punch with a shoulder or collar at the upper end which holds it in the punch plate when it is withdrawn from the work, as shown. This makes it easily replaceable when necessary to remove it for sharpening. It is recommended for holes from $\frac{3}{16}$ to $\frac{1}{2}$ inch in diameter but can be used in larger sizes if desired.

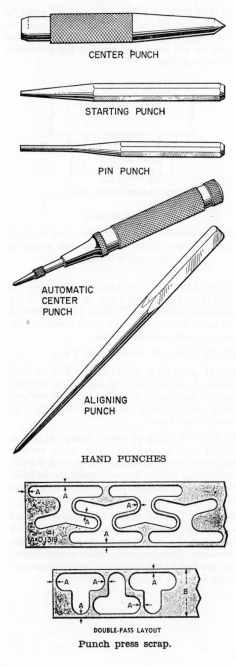

CENTER PUNCH

STARTING PUNCH

PIN PUNCH

AUTOMATIC CENTER PUNCH

ALIGNING PUNCH

HAND PUNCHES

A = 0.319

DOUBLE-PASS LAYOUT

Punch press scrap.

EDGE-TRIMMING METHODS

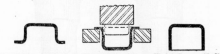

Partly Drawn Shell   Flange Trim Die   Finish Drawn Shell

Fig. 1.—FLANGE TRIM AND FINISH DRAW. This method is satisfactory for most shells, particularly diameters greater than 2 in. Only one additional die— a trimming die—is required.

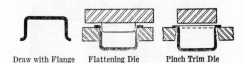

Draw with Flange   Flattening Die   Pinch Trim Die

Fig. 2—PINCH TRIM DIE. This method will produce a shell with uniform height, but the inside edge is considerably rounded. The flange must be flattened to a sharp corner, which will require one or two dies.

Edge trimming punch press dies.

PUNCHES, PLAIN AND SPIRAL POINTED

—The entire surface of the plain punch contacts the metal at once, while the spiral, or

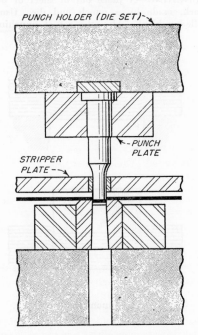

PUNCH HOLDER (DIE SET)

PUNCH PLATE

STRIPPER PLATE

Shoulder punch. A shoulder punch is the most efficient type for holes from $\frac{3}{16}$ to $\frac{1}{2}$ in. diameter.

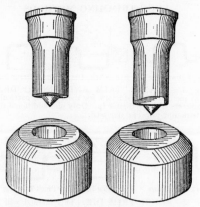

Plain and spiral pointed punch dies.

helical, point has a shearing action and requires less power.

PUNCHES, SOFT METAL—For short runs in forming soft metal, lead with from 6 to 10 per cent of antimony is sometimes used successfully. See *Kirksite* and *Cerro Metals*.

PUNCHING—A piece out of sheet or other stock, made by a punch and die. Usually called a blank. Also, the act of punching a

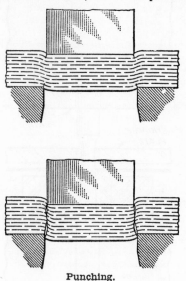

Punching.

piece out of sheet or other stock. Illustration shows how metal is sheared from the surrounding plate.

PUNCHING, S T E P—Arranging multiple punches so all do not contact the work at the same time, as shown. This divides the load on the press and reduces the maximum power required.

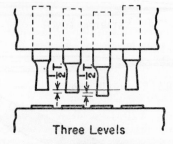

Three Levels

Step punching. By stepping punches one-half the thickness of the metal required, punching pressure is reduced.

PURCHASE—A mechanical advantage, as with levers or pinch bars, in moving heavy materials, where a small effort, moving through a longer distance, moves a much greater resistance a much shorter distance.

PUSH BROACH—See *Broach, Push.*

PUSH BUTTON CONTROL—The use of motors, controlled by push buttons, to perform various movements of the machine. It replaces hand movements of tables and other parts of modern machines.

PUTTY—Whiting or other chalky substances mixed with linseed oil. Also made from a variety of other substances. It is used for filling cracks, usually in wood work, or in holding panes of glass in their forms. It hardens when the oil evaporates, or dries out.

PYROMETER—A device for measuring, and sometimes recording, temperatures in much higher ranges than can be done with a thermometer. There are many types of pyrometers designed and built for special applications and some for very high temperatures.

Q

QUADRANGLE—Any plane having four sides and four angles. The term is used whether the angles are all right angles or not.

QUADRANT—Really a quarter of a circle, but the term is also applied to any segment of a circle. In steam locomotives, it is the notched curved bar which locates the reversing lever in any desired position. Also used in connection with the throttle valve. In lathes with change gears on the outside it is the plate at the end of the lathe carrying the change gears.

QUADRATE—Any surface with four right angles and resembling a square.

QUADRILATERAL—A figure or space having four sides and four angles. Usually applied to a rectangular figure having four equal angles.

QUARTERING—Laying out in quarters. In steam locomotive practice it is locating the crankpins on opposite driving wheels at exactly 90 degrees apart. This is done by use of "quartering levels." An arm has a fork at one end and a level at 45 degrees at the other end. With the fork against the crankpin and the bubble in the center, the edge of the level should cut the center of the axle. Without moving the wheels, this test is reversed on the other crankpin and if the result is the same the wheels are at 90 degrees or at "quarters."

QUARTERING MACHINE—A machine tool used in railway shops for boring the crankpin holes in both driving wheels mounted on the same axle at 90 degrees from each other.

QUARTER-TURN BELTS—Belts used in driving shafting at 90-degree angles. The pulleys must be so placed that the center of the driven pulley face is in line with the outside of rim of the driving pulley. See *Belts, Quarter-Turn.*

QUARTZ, FUSED—Clear fused quartz is made by melting natural quartz crystals in an electric furnace and casting into ingots or molds. It is then ground to desired shapes, such as for optical flats. It is very transparent and has fine wearing qualities. Expansion and contraction from changes in temperature are less than in any other known substance, nor does age seem to cause changes. As it does not begin to soften under 3,000 deg. F., the strain point is 1,958 deg. F., and it resists abrasion and thermal shock, it is ideal for optical flats. It is much harder than glass; and its coefficient of expansion is approximately one-third of a millionth of an inch per degree F. It is very stable in every way.

QUENCH—The cooling of heated materials in water or other liquid. In air hardening steels the air blast may be called an air quench.

QUICK CHANGE GEARING—Gearing so arranged that different ratios of speed between the driver and driven shafts can be secured without removing and replacing gears, as in the old screw cutting lathe. Sellers, Norton and Norris were early designers of gearing devices, known as "gear boxes," which could engage different sets of gears without removing any of them. The automobile transmission and nearly all machine tools now have devices of this kind for changing both speeds and feeds.

QUICK RETURN—Devices which save time by returning a reciprocating tool or work holder at a faster rate than the cutting stroke. There are several methods of securing this result with combinations of levers, with cams and with gearing at different speeds. The best examples are seen on shapers and slotters, while planers have a different method of returning the table at a much higher speed than the cutting stroke. One favorite method with modern planers is to use an electric motor which reverses instantly and drives at a very high rate on the return stroke.

QUICKSILVER—Same as mercury. See *Mercury.*

QUILL—A hollow shaft or sleeve surrounding another shaft. Used in some types of clutches to carry the clutch fingers. Frequently used to carry members moving at different rates of speed or in opposite directions. In some farm machinery, a quill is the bearing in the wheel which revolves on a stationary shaft. One well known machine tool builder calls a short boring bar a quill.

QUILL GEAR—See *Gears, Quill.*

QUOTA—A share or proportion of work or of any commodity, assigned to different groups or persons.

329

R

R P M—Abbreviation for "revolutions per minute." Largely used in connection with engines or motors of various kinds, and in connection with drilling and boring. Cutting speeds are usually given in surface feet per minute, abbreviated as S F P M.

R. W. M. A. ALLOYS—See *Alloys, R. W. M. A.*

RABBET—The term is sometimes applied to a complete joint where a slot and tongue fit together, and sometimes only to the groove. Very similar to tenon and mortise, except that rabbet usually refers to a slot or groove only, the length of tongue width. These are carpentry, rather than machine shop terms.

RABBLER—An unusual name for a scraping tool used in smoothing the surface of metal parts.

RACE—In bearings, a rounded channel or groove in which the balls of a ball bearing run. With roller bearings, the race is usually flat, at an angle for tapered roller bearings. A few bearings are made in which the rollers are somewhat barrel shaped, with raceways to conform to the contour of the rollers. Race could also be applied to any channel in which rollers of any kind run. See *Ball and Roller Bearings.* A motor or machine is said to "race" when it exceeds normal speed.

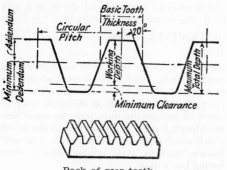

Rack of gear teeth.

RACK—Usually a straight bar having gear teeth cut on one or more surfaces. Fastened to a machine, as a lathe, it provides means by which a gear attached to the carriage can move the carriage along the bed. In some mechanisms the rack moves and rotates one or more gears. Frequently mechanisms have the rack teeth cut on two or more surfaces of the bar. Where the involute tooth is used in the gearing the rack teeth can have straight sides at the proper angle. With cycloidal form gear teeth it is necessary to have rack teeth of the same curve. Racks can also be segments of a circle, usually of large radius. See *Gearing Rack, Basic for.*

RADIAL DRILL—See *Drilling Machine, Radial.*

RADIAL FEED—See *Feed, Radial.*

RADIAL RAKE—The rake of cutter teeth to the radius. See *Milling Cutters, Rake Angles.*

RADIAN—The angle measured by an arc which is equal to the radius. Also the arc of a circle which equals the circle's radius.

RADIO-ACTIVE METALS—Metals which emit radiations that penetrate objects that are opaque to ordinary light. They also give out light, as in luminous paints. Radium is the most radio-active material.

RADIOGRAPHS—Photographs made by passing X-rays through solids. These show changes in the density of the object and reveal cracks and other defects.

RADIOGRAPHY—As applied in the shop, this is the use of X-ray apparatus in examination of metals for flaws, as in castings or in welded joints.

RADIUM—A radio-active element discovered by Curie in 1898.

RADIUS—The distance from the center of a circle to its outside, or curved, edge (perimeter). See *Angle Constants.*

RADIUS BENDS—Making bends to a given radius or angle, within tolerances. When accuracy is required, several conditions must be considered, mainly the springback of the metal used. This depends on the thickness and hardness of the metal. There seems to be no dependable rule, owing to the many variables involved, so that trial and error is the general rule.

RADIUS DRESSER—A device for shaping and dressing the face of a grinding wheel to any desired radius.

RAG WHEEL—This usually refers to a buffing wheel made of layers of cloth sewed together. In some sections, a sprocket wheel, made for use in a chain drive, is called a rag wheel.

RAIL STEEL—See *Steel Products, Rail.*

RAIL TRAIN—A set, or train, of rolls in a steel mill used in forming rough stock, or blooms, into railway rails.

RAISING HAMMER—See *Hammer, Raising.*

RAKE—Usually applied to the angle at the top of a tooth of milling cutters or to the cutting surface of other metal cutting tools. In turning or boring, the angle made by the cutting face of the tool with a line from the center of the work, when the cutting edge is level with the same center. When the cutting edge makes an acute or shearing angle with the work, it is called positive rake. If the cutting edge is level with the center, it has a neutral angle. When the cutting end of the tool or tooth makes an obtuse angle, the tool has a negative rake. This is used for heavy cutting with some tools such as carbide, to protect the cutting edge. It is also used for intermittent or "jump cuts." The illustrations make the different angles clear. See *Lathe Tools* and *Milling Cutters, Rake Angles.*

RAKE, NEGATIVE—In cutting tools, such as lathes and planers and milling cutters, cutting angles which *do not* give a shearing action to the tool.

RAKE OF MILLING CUTTER—The true rake of a milling cutter tooth is a combination of the axial rake and the radial rake. It requires a careful study of the diagram to see the different phases of the problem. See *Milling Cutters, Rake Angles.*

RAM—This may refer to any moving part with a reciprocating action, such as the ram of a shaper or slotting machine. It is also sometimes applied to the reciprocating plunger of a pump, although plunger is the usual term used. In the foundry, the molder rams the

sand to compress it. A hydraulic ram, however, has no moving parts except the valves which control the flow of water. It pumps but a small percentage of the water flowing through it.

RAMMER—A hand tool used in foundry work to ram, or pack, sand around the pattern in a mold. Rammers are also made to be driven by compressed air and save the labor of hand work.

RAM-TYPE MILLING MACHINE—See *Milling Machine, Ram Type.*

RASP—A very coarse file, generally for use on wood. The teeth are raised individually with a rounded, pointed chisel, instead of extending across the width of the file as on files to be used for metal.

RATCHET—Usually a wheel having teeth with unequal angles, as a buttress thread. The term is also applied to the complete mechanism of a ratchet wheel and a pawl, or detent, which drops into the teeth and moves the wheel or prevents its motion. A ratchet wheel may also be called a detent wheel, although the term detent usually applies to the pawl which fits into the teeth of the wheel.

RATCHET DRILL—A device for turning a drill when obstructions prevent a complete revolution of the handle. A pawl in the handle contacts a ratchet wheel in the barrel so that it can be turned one or more teeth at a time.

RATIO OR PROPORTION—A most useful method of calculation in all mechanical work. The relation between objects of the same kind. For example, two gears of 24 teeth each, running together, will both run at the same speed. But a 24-tooth gear running with a 48-tooth gear has a 2 to 1 ratio, meaning that one is twice the diameter of the other or has twice the number of teeth, and that the smaller will turn twice as fast as the other. The same is true with pulleys and belting or with levers. The relation, or ratio between the driving and driven gears or pulleys, or between the two ends of the lever, determines the relative speed movement and power of each. The ratio of 2 to 1 is the same as 48 to 24. Ratios are often written as $2:1 = 48:24$.

RAWHIDE GEARS—See *Gears, Rawhide.*

REAMER—Tool used for enlarging holes previously formed by drilling or boring. Standard terminology follows below. Trade usage perpetuates the incorrect use of the

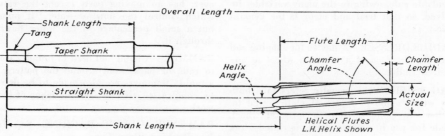

CHUCKING REAMER, STRAIGHT AND TAPER SHANK

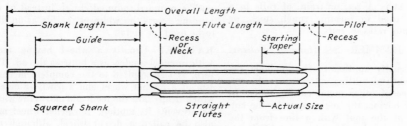

HAND REAMER, PILOT AND GUIDE

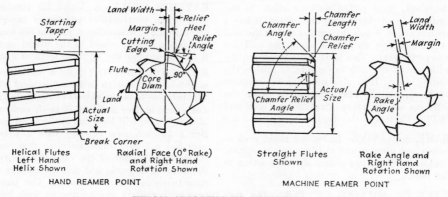

HAND REAMER POINT   MACHINE REAMER POINT

TERMS APPLYING TO REAMERS.

term "spiral" in connection with reamer flutes, except in the newer types of taper pin reamers. The illustrations show the names of the parts of reamers, including the cutting edges. Most types of reamers are made with either straight or helical flutes. Many types are made with either straight or taper shanks. It should be noted that the helix angle is measured from the reamer axis.

REAMER, AMERICAN STANDARD TERMINOLOGY AND DEFINITIONS—

Lengths (All measured parallel to the axis): (a) *Overall Length*—The extreme length of complete tool from end to end, but not including expansion screws.

(b) *Flute Length*—The cutting length of the flutes.

332

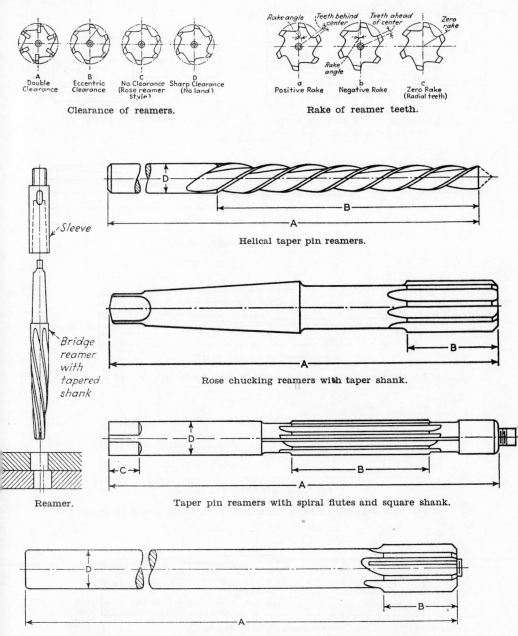

Clearance of reamers.

Rake of reamer teeth.

Helical taper pin reamers.

Rose chucking reamers with taper shank.

Reamer.

Taper pin reamers with spiral flutes and square shank.

Expansion chucking reamers with straight flutes and squared shank.

(Continued on next page)

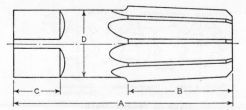

Taper pipe reamers with straight flutes
and squared shank.

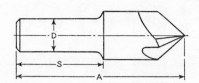

Center reamers, with straight shank.

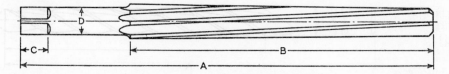

Center reamers, with straight shank.

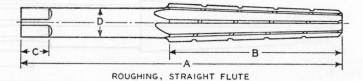

ROUGHING, STRAIGHT FLUTE

Morse taper reamers, roughing, with straight flutes and squared shank.

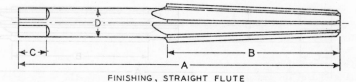

FINISHING, STRAIGHT FLUTE

Morse taper reamers, finishing, with straight flutes and squared shank.

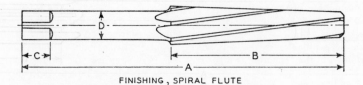

FINISHING, SPIRAL FLUTE

Morse taper reamer, finishing, with spiral flutes and squared shank.

334

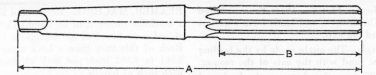

Machine (jobbers) reamers with straight flutes and taper shank.

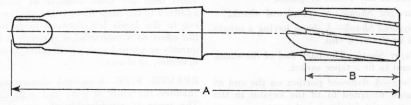

Fluted chucking reamers with spiral flutes and taper shank.

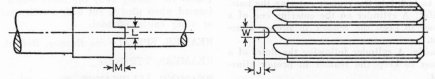

Driving slots and lugs for shell reamers and shell reamer arbors.

(c) *Shank Length*—The length from the end of the shank to the recess or to the flutes.

(d) *Recess Length*—The length of the section between the shank and the flutes.

Size: The diameter measured across two margins, at the cutting edge, on a diametral line.

(a) *Nominal Size*—The designated size.

(b) *Actual Size*—The actual measured size, usually slightly larger than the nominal size to allow for wear.

Chamfer: The conical shaped portion at the front or entering end of the reamer.

(a) *Chamfer Length*—Distance measured parallel to the axis from the greatest to the smallest diameter of the chamfer.

(b) *Chamfer Angle*—The angle between the axis and a continuation of the cutting edge of the chamfer.

(c) *Chamfer Relief Angle*—The angle between a plane perpendicular to the axis and the intersection of the chamfer with the margin.

(d) *Chamfer Relief*—The relief put on the chamfer cutting edge to allow the reamer to cut.

Land: The periphery of that portion of the flute length which is not cut away by the flutes.

(a) *Land Width*—The distance in a diametral plane between the cutting edge and the heel.

(b) *Cutting Edge*—The leading edge of the land.

(c) *Heel*—The following edge of the land.

(d) *Core Diameter*—The diameter of the largest cylinder which would not project into the flutes.

(c) *Relief*—The portion of the land ground away to enable the reamer to cut.

(f) *Relief Angle*—The angle between the relief and a tangent to the outside diameter circle at the beginning of the relief.

(g) *Margin*—The cylindrical part of the land adjacent to the cutting edge.

(h) *Rake Angle*—The angle formed between the cutting face and radial line drawn to the cutting edge.

Flute: That portion of the reamer which is cut away between the lands. Flutes may be either straight or helical. A reamer may have one or more flutes.

(a) *Straight Flutes*—The grooves and lands are parallel to the axis.

335

(b) *Helical Flutes* — (Sometimes called Spiral.) The grooves and lands form a helical path around the axis.

Helix Angle—The angle made by the leading edge of the land with the axis of the reamer.

Shank: That portion between the back end of the flutes and the back end of the reamer exclusive of any recess or guide.

(a) *Straight Shank*—A cylindrical shank.

(b) *Squared Shank*—A shank having a square milled on the back end.

(c) *Taper Shank*—The back end of the shank is ground to fit a taper socket.

(d) *Tang*—A flattened portion on the end of the shank designed to fit the keyslot in the socket to assist in driving the reamer.

Starting Taper: The slight taper on the front end to facilitate the reamer entering the hole.

Pilot: A cylinder on the entering end of a reamer to keep the reamer in proper alinement.

Guide: A cylinder following the flutes of a reamer to keep the reamer in proper alinement.

Recess: (Sometimes called Neck) That portion or portions of the reamer adjacent to the flutes which has the diameter reduced in order to facilitate machining the flutes and grinding the land.

REAMER, CENTER—A reamer for centering or countersinking the end of shafting or other work for use in lathe or grinder work. The included angle is usually 60 degrees.

REAMER, EXPANDING — A reamer with blades so held in the body that they can be adjusted to a larger diameter and again fastened securely. This is usually done to compensate for wear. There are cases where occasional need for slight variations in diameter makes it advisable to adjust the blades for different sized holes.

REAMER, HAND—A reamer to be used by hand. They have a taper on the end to assist in entering the work. Back of this they have the same taper as the machine reamer, from 0.001 to 0.002 inch per inch of diameter for each inch of length.

REAMER, HELICAL—A reamer with helical teeth and flutes. One type, known as the Gammon reamer, is widely used for taper pin work. Many still call them spiral reamers, especially where the helix angle with the axis is slight.

REAMER, MACHINE—Reamers to be used in a machine rather than by hand. They have a chamfer or bevel of 45 degrees at the point. Back of this they have a back taper of from 0.001 to 0.002 inch per inch of diameter for each inch of length.

REAMER, MULTILAND — A reamer having more than the usual number of lands. In addition to the main flutes it has smaller flutes cut in the lands left between them to give the effect of a multibladed reamer. It is frequently combined with a drill point of smaller diameter, as shown.

REAMER, PIPE—A tapered reamer made to chamfer the ends of pipe and pipe fittings. The taper is considerably sharper than the regular pipe taper of $\frac{3}{4}$ inch to the foot. Useful for cutting away the burrs which are formed when pipe is cut with a roller cutter or other cutting-off tool.

REAMER, SPIRAL—See *Reamer, Helical.*

REAMERS, TYPES OF

REAMING ALLOWANCE—The metal to be left by the drill or other tool, to be removed by the reamer.

REAMING SHELL—A coupling for connecting core drill barrels used in oil wells and similar drilling. This was formerly called "swell coupling."

REAUMUR THERMOMETER — A very old thermometer in which freezing was zero and boiling was 80. Practically obsolete. See *Thermometer Graduations.*

RECALESCENCE—One of the critical points in the heat treatment of steels. It is the reverse of calescence. When the steel is heated beyond the critical point, or calescent point, about 1,270 deg. F. for steel, and the heat is shut off, the pyrometer needle will start to drop, then suddenly stop, advance several degrees, and then go on falling. This is the recalescent point. See *Calescence.*

RECEIVING GAGE—See *Gage, Receiving.*

RECESS—A space where material has been removed for some purpose. It may be an enlarged bore at some point in a cylinder, or an opening below the surface, usually to receive another part. In a bore it may also be called a "chamber." It may also be a groove or opening at the end of a cut, as in planer work. The term has no distinct definition.

RECESSING TOOLS—Tools for cutting a recess or groove at the bottom of, or inside the bore of, a hole, machined in a lathe or boring mill. They are hook tools with the cutting edge at right angles to the axis of the bore.

RECIPROCATING — In shop terms, moving back and forth, as the cross head of a steam locomotive or the ram of a shaper, in contrast to circular or rotary motion.

RECOIL—A bouncing back or reverse motion. The reaction when a charge is fired from a gun. Recoil springs or air chambers are used to check this backward movement. There are many kinds of recoil mechanisms.

RED BRASS—One of the most malleable of the brasses. Made of about 85 parts copper and 15 parts zinc.

RE-DRAW — A second drawing operation, either in reducing the diameter of solid metal, as with wire, or to make further changes in the shape of sheet metal products. In both cases it may be necessary to reheat the material to relieve the hardness, or "temper," which has been produced by the drawing operation.

RED HARD STEEL — Steel which remains hard at high temperature, such as turns the tool to a dull red. All high-speed steels belong to this group, the hardness depending on the ingredients in the steel.

RED LEAD—A red granular powder made from oxides of lead. Largely used as a paste for sealing joints in piping and similar places, to prevent leakage. Also, when mixed as paint, used in some places to prevent rust.

RED-SHORT—A term used to describe iron or steel which is brittle when it is red hot. Most materials are ductile at this heat.

RED SHORTNESS—The condition of a metal which is brittle when at a red heat.

REDUCING ATMOSPHERE—A term used in connection with a low temperature flame produced by an excess of air. Also known as a Reducing Flame and a Wet Flame.

REDUCING VALVE—A valve which reduces pressure either by restricting flow of steam, water or air, or by means of pistons of different diameters. Restricting the flow is frequently known as "wire drawing."

REEVES VARIABLE SPEED DRIVE — See *Variable Speed Drives.*

REFLECTOSCOPE — See *Inspection, Supersonic.*

REFRACTORIES — Substances which resist very high heats, such as fire brick and fire clay.

RELIEF—The portion of a cutting tool, back of the cutting edge, which has been removed to prevent dragging in the metal being cut. This is not to provide chip room, only to reduce friction. Chip room is provided by portions cut away back of the relief, and known as clearance. In some cutters there are two clearance angles, first and secondary. The smaller angle of the first or primary clearance provides backing for the tooth and the secondary clearance gives added room for chips to prevent binding. Relief is frequently called "backing off."

RELIEVING LATHE OR ATTACHMENT—A mechanism for securing relief or clearance behind the cutting edge of such tools as formed milling cutters and taps. As the cutter revolves slowly the cutting tool is fed toward the center, reducing the diameter behind the cutting edge. The tool must spring back to its original position before the next cutting edge reaches it, this motion being secured by a strong spring and a suitable cam action. Machines with this mechanism are used by makers of milling cutters, large taps and some other tools. The process is sometimes known as "backing-off."

REMALLOY—A permanent magnet material developed by the Western Electric Co. for use in its telephone apparatus. It is said to replace the more expensive 36-41 cobalt permanent magnet steel.

RESILIENCY — The effort or tendency to spring back after being distorted, as of a leaf spring after it has been stressed from its normal shape. This varies greatly with metals, as, for example, between lead and steel. The former remains bent, while the latter springs back if its elastic limit has not been reached and passed.

RESIN—A solid gum-like substance exuded from trees. It is also made synthetically. It is used in making paints, plasters and pharmaceuticals.

RESINOID—An organic material used as a bond in many kinds of abrasive wheels, such as for snagging castings, or sharpening and gumming saws, at high surface speeds.

RE-STRIKING—An additional blow or blows on a forging to aline, or even up, various portions of the forging.

RESULTANT—This is usually applied to the application of forces to an object, as in a machine. When two equal forces are applied at right angles, the resultant is a force at 45 degrees, which is less than the total of the combined forces because part of each force is expended in opposing the other. The simplest way to check the resultant of two or more forces is to lay out a diagram showing the angles or direction of each force, and have varying lines representing the amount of each. Any book on applied mechanics will show how these diagrams are made and used.

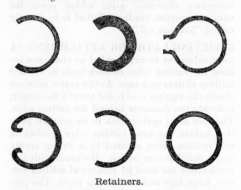

Retainers.

RETAINER—Any device for holding parts of mechanisms in place. Incomplete rings, which spring over a shaft, into a groove, are frequently used to prevent end movement of parts mounted on the shaft. Similar retainers are often used inside a tube or recess to prevent movement of parts in the bore. Some retainers are disks or strips held in place by screws.

RETURN BEND—A curve which forms a letter U. When piping is used to make heating coils along a wall the ends form a letter U and return the steam or hot water to the other end of the heating lines.

RETURN CRANK—An auxiliary crank of less throw than the main crank. It is used in some valve gears of locomotives. The real or effective throw is the distance between the pin of the return crank and the center of the axle. Sometimes called a "half-crank."

REVALON—An alloy of the Revere Copper Co., used for condenser tubes. It contains 76 per cent copper, 22 per cent zinc and 2 per cent aluminum.

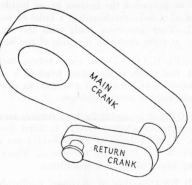

Return crank.

REVERBRATORY FURNACE—See *Furnace, Reverbratory.*

REVERSE CURVE—A curve which reverses its direction and forms a letter S.

REVERSE GEAR—A gear or mechanism which reverses the direction of motion in any kind of machinery, as an automobile, lathe or other machine tool. A gear which can be meshed, or put into contact, in a gearing train to reverse the motion of the driven shaft. The term is also applied to any mechanism which can reverse a motion, whether or not it actually uses gears or other devices, as friction disks.

RHENIUM—A metal that looks like silver but more dense than gold. Extremely resistant to corrosion. Melts at 5738° F., almost as high as tungsten. Little or no technical application as yet but is being considered for lamp filaments and electrical contacts on account of its high melting point. Molybdenum smelter flue dust has been the source of the small amounts so far made in this country.

RHODIUM—A hard metal sometimes found in platinum ores. Used in pen points and for resistance wires. Sp. gr. 12.44. Melts at 3,542 deg. F.

RHOMBOID—A four sided figure with two of the opposite sides of the same length but the other sides unequal. This gives oblique angles at all four corners.

RHOMBUS—A figure having four sides of equal length, but with angles not right angles. It might be called a square which has been deformed by pushing on opposite corners.

RICOCHET—A glancing rebound, as of a bullet which strikes a steel plate at an angle. Stones "skipped" across a body of water frequently act in the same way.

RIDERMIKROKATOR — A Swedish instrument for checking the out-of-roundness of outside diameters of cylindrical parts. There are three points of contact with the work. The instrument is set by a master piece and has points which show the maximum variations, or tolerance, which can be permitted. Being independent of centers in the work, it is well adapted for centerless ground pieces.

RIFFLE—A small file, usually double ended, with the ends curved for finishing curved surfaces in dies and similar work.

RIFLING—The helical grooving of a gun barrel is called rifling. When a bullet is fired, it is forced along these grooves and rotates at a high speed, which insures accuracy of flight. In large guns, the projectile carries a soft copper band which is forced into the rifling grooves and rotates the shell. The rifling is practically a broaching operation; in fact, the newer practice is to use broaches, even on the small bore, hand carried weapons. The older method was to pull a hooked cutting tool through the barrel, making one groove at a time, and frequently needing several passes for a single groove.

RIGHT HAND LATHE TOOL—Long usage has named as a right hand tool one that cuts to the left, viewed from the front of the machine. This is now called a "right-cut" tool, meaning that, as viewed from the front of the tool or back of the lathe, it cuts to the right.

RIGHT-HAND ROTATION—Rotation in the direction of the hands of a timepiece, or clockwise. As applied to right hand screw threads, it means that, when looking at the end of the screw, the nut must travel *away* from the observer when the nut is turned to the right, or clockwise.

RIGHT HAND SCREW THREAD—A screw thread which will move the nut away from the observer when it is turned to the right, or clockwise.

RING BOLT—See *Bolt, Ring*.

RING TURRET LATHE—A turret lathe in which the tools were held horizontally in a vertical ring which surrounded the lathe bed. It was known as the Foster Ring Turret.

RIVET—A pin with a head on one end and the other end riveted, or hammered over, after it is in place. Used to hold two or more sheets together permanently in place of a bolt and nut. There are many types of rivets and rivet heads, a number of which are shown on the next page. In most cases, the rivet body fills the hole when it is put in place before riveting. In some instances of hot riveting the rivet body is smaller than the hole and is enlarged to fill the hole under pressure.

RIVET, BLIND—A rivet which can be put in place from one side only, without the aid of a "dolly" or backer-up. There are several types of blind rivets. One, known as the "cherry" rivet, has a central core which is pulled into a hollow rivet and expands the inner end. The core then breaks off flush with the outside.

RIVET, CHERRY—See *Rivet, Blind*.

RIVET, EXPLOSIVE—A rivet containing an explosive charge at the inner end. When in place a hot iron held on the outer end explodes the charge and expands the inner end. See illustration.

RIVET, HI-SHEAR—A type of rivet developed by North American Aviation for bomber and fighting planes. The rivet is of high tensile steel, heat-treated and cadmium plated. The collar is A17ST aluminum, anodized and waxed. The collar is forced over the end of the rivet and forms itself around the recess as shown, the surplus being cut off by the sharp edge of the button on the rivet. They are made in sizes from $\frac{3}{16}$ to $\frac{3}{4}$ inch. See illusration.

RIVET MACHINE—A machine for making rivets from metal rods.

RIVETER—Usually a portable device operated by air, electricity or hydraulically. Also the operator who manipulates it.

RIVETING MACHINE—A machine for driving, or heading, rivets. It may be operated by mechanical action, by hydraulics, by air or by electricity.

RIVETT-DOCK THREADING TOOL—A tool devised by Herman Dock many years ago for chasing threads in a lathe. It resembles a milling cutter, each tooth being part of the shape of a standard screw thread. Tooth number 1 cuts a small portion of the thread, each succeeding tooth taking out more metal, and the

WAGON BOX	SECTION HEAD	BUTTON OR JACKET HEAD	PAN HEAD	WHEEL HEAD
ROUND HEAD	PIN HEAD	COUNTERSUNK	WASHER HEAD	CONE HEAD
SHOVEL HEAD	BALL HEAD	TRUSS HEAD	OVAL HEAD	LENTIL HEAD
FLATHEAD	OVAL C'S'K	BELT HEAD	FILLISTER	BRAKE BAND

TYPES OF RIVET HEADS.

last tooth finishing the thread. With the tool set at proper depth, the carriage was not fed in at all. Instead the tool was revolved one tooth after each cut. As few threads are now chased in the lathe it is much less used than formerly.

ROCK PIN GAGE—See *Gage, Rock Pin.*

ROCKER ARM—An arm on a shaft which moves through a small arc, or rocks back and forth. Frequently used to move a valve back and forth, either horizontally or vertically, as in a steam engine.

ROCKWELL HARDNESS TEST—A method of testing the hardness of metals or other hard materials by measuring the depth to which a diamond pointed hammer is forced into the material by a given pressure. It differs from the Brinell method largely because it uses a diamond instead of a hardened steel ball. There are several Rockwell scales, designated by letters A to D, and pressures varying from 60 to 150 kilograms, or, roughly, 132, 220 and 330 pounds. A 65 Rockwell C is approximate-

ly equal to 682 Brinell or 94 Scleroscope. See *Hardness,* page 213.

ROD END—The end of a connecting rod which fits over the crank pin or cross head pin.

ROLL PIN—A device for fastening machine parts instead of using a solid pin. It is made by rolling sheet spring metal into a cylinder slightly larger than the holes in the machine parts so that when driven in place it is always a tight fit that will not jar loose.

ROLLED FORGINGS—See *Forging, Rolled.*

ROLLED GEARS—See *Gears, Rolled.*

ROLLED SCREW THREADS—Screw threads formed by rolling the blank between flat or rotating dies, which forces the material into grooves in the dies. The blank is of approximately the *pitch* diameter of the thread, so that the material displaced below the pitch line flows above the pitch line to form the crest, or top of the thread. In some materials this makes a stronger thread than one which is

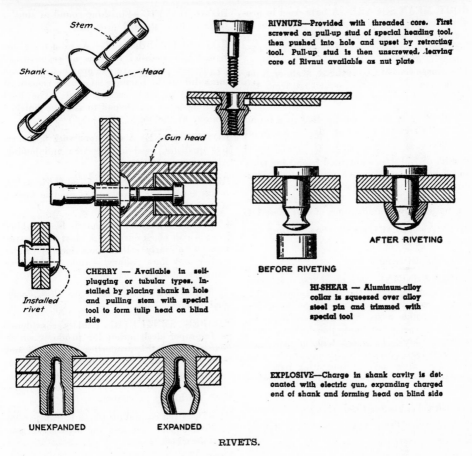

Stem

Shank

Head

RIVNUTS—Provided with threaded core. First screwed on pull-up stud of special heading tool, then pushed into hole and upset by retracting tool. Pull-up stud is then unscrewed, leaving core of Rivnut available as nut plate

Gun head

AFTER RIVETING

BEFORE RIVETING

CHERRY — Available in self-plugging or tubular types. Installed by placing shank in hole and pulling stem with special tool to form tulip head on blind side

Installed rivet

HI-SHEAR — Aluminum-alloy collar is squeezed over alloy steel pin and trimmed with special tool

EXPLOSIVE—Charge in shank cavity is detonated with electric gun, expanding charged end of shank and forming head on blind side

UNEXPANDED   EXPANDED

RIVETS.

cut, as the fibers are not cut but flow into the shape of the thread. In stay rods it permits the use of a rod less than the full diameter of the thread and saves material. The process originated in England over a century ago.

ROLLER BEARING—A bearing in which the load is carried on rollers which may be either straight or tapered. The rollers are sometimes held in cages, but not always. Roller bearings with very small rollers are frequently called needle bearings. See *Bearings*.

ROLLER BURNISHING—A finishing of a metal surface by contact with a polished roller instead of with a surface which remains stationary. In both cases the finish is obtained by compressing the outer surface of the metal.

ROLLER CHAIN SPROCKETS—See under *Sprockets*.

ROLLER RESTS — Supporting rests of any kind in which rollers contact the work to reduce the friction which would be caused by sliding contacts if plain supports were used.

ROLLER TOOLS—See *Screw Machine Tools*.

ROLLS FOR CRUSH FORMING—See *Grinding Wheels, Crush Forming Rolls*.

ROOT DIAMETER — As applied to screw threads, the diameter at the bottom of the threads. In gearing it is the diameter at the bottom of the teeth. In screw threads this is also called the minor diameter. See No. 68 and tables under *Screw Threads; American Standard; Nomenclature, Definitions, and Letter Symbols for*.

ROOT, MEAN SQUARE—A term used in profiling readings, taken from the square root of the mean or average variations. All the readings are added together and squared, then this square is divided by the number of readings. The square root of this is the R. M. S. or Root, Mean Square. It varies somewhat from the arithmetical mean, or average.

ROSE—A term sometimes applied to a round end milling cutter or a bur, also to a type of reamer.

ROSIN—A substance obtained from pine trees and formerly largely used as a flux in soldering. The sap hardens after it comes from the tree and is called rosin. Many of the soldering pastes may contain some of this material.

ROTARY ATTACHMENT—See *Milling Attachment, Rotary.*

ROTARY BUR—See *Bur.*

ROTARY ENGINE—A type of steam or other fluid engine in which the shaft is driven in a circular motion without use of reciprocating pistons or other parts. Steam and gas turbines, and some types of hydraulic mechanism, come under this head. It does not include the type of engine known as the "wobble plate," or cam engine, as these have reciprocating parts but produce rotary motion without connecting rods.

ROTARY FILE—See *Files, Rotary.*

ROTARY MILLING MACHINE—See *Milling Machine, Rotary.*

ROTARY SHEAR—A type of shearing machine for sheet or plate metal in which the cutting blades are round instead of straight. The edges of the blades are beveled to give a better cutting edge. Generally used in cutting light gage sheet metal.

ROTARY VALVE—See *Valve, Rotary.*

ROTO-CAST—A term sometimes applied to centrifugal casting.

ROTO-FINISH—Special applications of tumbling barrels for burring and finishing comparatively small parts. Much careful engineering has been done along this line with excellent results.

ROTO-MILLING—Machining of round surfaces by rotating them in contact with milling cutters instead of single point tools.

ROTO-SHAVING—Finishing round or similar surfaces by a shaving process.

ROTOR-KUT BROACH—A broach so designed that parallel sections of segments of an internal surface are cut progressively from the solid stock, portions of which remain at each side of each cutting tooth. The final finishing teeth are shaped to suit the finished contour of the work.

ROTTENSTONE—A soft stone with fine abrasive qualities, used in polishing and buffing. Also known as "tripoli."

ROUGE—A powder made of red ferric oxide. It has a very fine grain and is used in higher classes of polishing work.

RUBBER—A gummy exudation from rubber trees, which when cured, is a most elastic substance. Formerly called "gum elastic," India rubber and Para rubber. Crude rubber was called caoutchouc.

RUBBER FORMING DIES—See *Dies, Forming, Rubber.*

RUBBER, SYNTHETIC—Usually considered an improper designation for products which have many of the properties of rubber and technically known as "elastoners." They resist oils, gasolines and solvents and are less affected by heat. They are handled by the same machinery as rubber.

RUBY—A red corundum which is transparent. Used as a gem and also for accurate instrument bearings.

RUFF—A term sometimes used for a collar, as on a shaft to prevent end motion.

RULE, HOOK—A rule with a hook square with the end, to position the rule when measuring through or into a hole or recess.

RULE, KEYSEAT—A rule for laying out keyseats on shafting or in hubs. It has V-shaped legs so as to line itself on the shaft or in the bore.

RULE, SHRINK—A rule which is graduated to allow for the shrinkage of different metals in casting. It is used by pattern makers.

RUMBLING BARRELS—See *Tumbler or Tumbling Barrels.*

RUNNER—In foundry work, a ditch which guides molten metal to different parts of the mold, or passages connecting several molds together. It can also mean the waste metal formed in these channels.

RUNNING BLOCK—The movable block of a pair forming a "block and tackle" used in lowering or raising or otherwise moving heavy materials.

RUNNING GEAR — The mechanism which operates any machine apart from the frame or body. In automobiles it includes the frame and is known as the chassis.

RUN-OUT—The amount of eccentricity in any revolving body. Also applied to drills which do not enter the work directly in line with the drill spindle, owing to being deflected when the drill point touches the work. Sometimes known as "drifting" or "wandering."

RUN-OUT, MILLING CUTTER—The amount of eccentricity of a milling cutter. As perfection is seldom if ever attained, definite tolerances are set in many cases. Those shown in the table are for milling cutters.

RUST—An oxide formed on the surface of ferrous metals such as iron and steel, from contact with moist or salt air or chemicals. In extreme cases it goes deep enough to dis-

integrate the metal. It is a chemical action and frequently works below the surface and enlarges the outer dimensions of the piece. It frequently interferes with or prevents the separation of fitted parts, such as nuts and bolts. Oxides also form on other metals but are not usually termed rust.

RUST JOINT—A joint formed by creating corrosion by using cast iron chips, sal-ammoniac or other acid. Sulphur is sometimes used in such a mixture. Special compounds are now available for making rust joints.

RUST INHIBITOR—Anything which delays or prevents the formation of rust. In automobile radiators and similar places it is a chemical which mixes with the water. Some paints for metals contain chemicals which retard the formation of rust on the surface.

RUST REMOVER—A mixture used in removing rust from iron or steel. A common mixture is 3 parts of a grease like vaseline, 2 parts of a light oil and 6 parts of tripoli or other fine abrasive. The first two ingredients can be mixed by heating and the tripoli then added. It is really a mild scouring mixture useful in removing light coatings of rust.

Milling Cutter Run-Out

Cutter Diameter, Inches	Roughing		Finishing	
	Face	Periphery and Chamfer	Face	Periphery and Chamfer
Up to 12	0.001	0.002	0.0005	0.0015
12 to 16	0.0015	0.003	0.00075	0.002
Over 16	0.002	0.004	0.001	0.0025

S

S. A. E. STEELS—Grades of steel approved by the Society of Automotive Engineers. They are so classified that the number of the steel tells the approximate composition. The first number shows the class: 1 is carbon steel; 2 is nickel carbon; 3 is nickel chromium; 4 is molybdenum; 5 is chromium; 6 is chrome vanadium; 7 is tungsten, and 9 is silicon, there being no number 8 as yet. The second figure shows the approximate percentage of the predominating element; and the last two or three numbers show the approximate carbon content in 100ths of 1 per cent. Thus, S. A. E. steel 2350 is a nickel steel with 3 per cent of nickel and 0.50 per cent of carbon. Manganese steels have the letter T before the first number.

S. A. E. TAPERS—See *Tapers, S. A. E.*

S. F. P. M.—A standard abbreviation for surface feet per minute. Used in referring to cutting speed of tools and also to the speed of belts and chains. Sometimes abbreviated to S. F. M.

S I M—Abbreviation for "surface inches per minute." Not a widely used term.

S-WRENCH—An open ended wrench curved like a letter S for convenience in reaching in to confined spaces. Usually has a wrench opening at each end. See *Wrench.*

SADDLE—This usually applies to the part of a machine tool which carries the cutting tool or tools. In a lathe, the saddle moves along the bed on guiding ways, and carries the cross slide and tool post. On a planer it slides along the cross-rail, carrying the swivel, the clapper and the tool clamps. The name is used for parts of machines of various kinds, but usually bears a resemblance to the uses named.

SADDLE JOINT—A sheet metal worker's term for a joint made by bending over the edges of the two sheets which are to be joined, and folding them together. With both edges folded back in reverse hooks they lock together easily.

SAFE EDGE—A smooth edge on a file to insure cutting on the face only.

SAFE SPEEDS FOR GRINDING WHEELS—See *Grinding Wheels, Safe Speed of.*

SAFE WORKING LOAD — The load or stress that can be applied to any mechanism without endangering the machine or the operator. Where stresses alone are concerned, this means below the elastic limit of the material.

SAFETY PLUG—See *Fusible Plug.*

SAFETY VALVE—See *Valve, Safety.*

SALAMANDER—When a furnace is allowed to cool for repairs there is always some iron left in it. This is called a "salamander" and must be removed.

SALAMMONIAC—See *Ammonium Chloride.*

SALT BATHS (MOLTEN), HAZARDS OF—Reports by the National Board of Underwriters indicate that approximately 30 per cent of all heat-treatment is conducted in molten baths, and that the incidence of fires and explosions, accompanied by large property losses, is rising.

Molten salt baths can be divided into three categories:

1. Low-temperature (300-1,000 deg. F.)—the salts being largely nitrates and nitrites, and the bath the most dangerous.

2. Medium-temperature (1,000-1,750 deg. F.) —usually eutectic mixtures of chlorides and carbonates, and cyanides. The last requires special precautions.

3. High-temperature (1,750-2,400 deg. F.)— mixtures of barium chloride, borax, sodium fluoride, silicates, magnesia or lime, and other substances.

Hazards prevalent in the molten salt bath process are:

1. Fire by contact of molten salts with combustibles.

2. Explosion through chemical and physical reactions.

3. Physical danger to operator by gassing or burns.

Causes of Accidents

Steam explosion and spattering—Water may enter the bath in several ways: as carry-over from quench tanks, leaks from pipes or roof, moisture entrained in air for agitating the liquid melt, splashing from rinse tanks, operation of fire-fighting equipment, and tipping of food containers placed on ledges or bath covers for heating.

Air entrapment—Air trapped in tubes or metal work may expand with spattering of molten salt, or rupture the work with explosive violence.

Reaction with combustibles—Free or combined carbonaceous materials (oil, soot, tar, cotton waste, graphite) are easily set on fire by molten baths; molten nitrates react explosively with cyanides, and with aluminum alloys containing 1 or 2 per cent magnesium if heated above 1,000 deg. F.; structural failure of bath container may cause explosive reaction with accumulations of soot, carbon and tar in furnace box.

Reaction with pot material—Nitrates will react with mild steel containers and start brisk combustion at temperatures as low as 1,100 deg. F. For this reason, baths in such containers should be limited to 1,000 deg. F.

Overheating and thermit reaction—Iron oxides in sediment or sludge at bottom of molten nitrate baths may overheat and react with overheated aluminum alloy to cause a vigorous thermit reaction; failure of temperature or heat controls may cause overheating of nitrate bath, particularly overnight or during weekend idling periods; burning through of bath container.

SALT BATH HEATING—A method of heating steel parts while protecting them from contact with air. Barium and other salts are used for the purpose. Lead baths are sometimes used for drawing the temper of steel which has been hardened. Carburizing or case hardening is also done by heating low carbon steels in baths which contain carbon. Carbon penetration up to $\frac{1}{8}$ inch can be secured by long immersion in such baths.

SALTPETER—See *Potassium Nitrate*.

SAMPLE GEAR—See *Gear, Sample*.

SAND BLAST—Sand or other abrasive blown by compressed air to clean the surfaces of metal. This can remove scale and other foreign materials. Sand blasting is also used to produce ground glass surfaces and other matte finishes, and in cleaning buildings. When small steel or iron particles are blown in the same way it is called "shot-blasting."

SAND SLINGER—A machine used in foundries for throwing, or slinging, sand into a mold with enough force to ram the mold as hard as desired.

SANDHOLE—A hole made in castings by sand which broke loose from the mold and flowed into the casting. It not only causes a defect in the casting, but may damage tools which contact the sand.

SAND PAPER—A tough paper coated with various grades of fine, hard sand, and used for various smoothing and finishing operations.

SAPONIFICATION—The reaction of a fat and an alkali to form a soap. In a compounded oil, the amount of fatty material in the lubricant.

SAPPHIRE—A blue variety of corundum. Poor color stones are used for wearing points in instrument construction. They are also used as cutting tools on non-metallic substances. There are synthetic sapphires for various purposes.

SAW, BAND—A continuous metal band with saw teeth on one edge. It is usually guided between rollers and supported by a roller at the back. Originally designed for wood work, it is now used in regular machining operations on metal.

SAW, COLD—A machine and a circular saw for sawing cold metals.

SAW, CROWN—A hollow cylinder with teeth on the edge for cutting round holes out of flat or similar stock. Sometimes called a trepanning saw or hole saw.

Edge hole saw.

SAW, EDGE HOLE—One name for a saw with teeth on the end of a steel cylinder for cutting disks out of a plate. Others call it a trepanning tool. There is usually a pilot or guide in the center which goes into a drilled hole and steadies the saw. Illustration on page 345.

SAW, HACK—A saw blade held in a frame to be used for cutting metals by hand. See *Hack Saw*.

SAW, HACK, POWER—A power driven hack saw having a reciprocating motion and a feeding mechanism, usually a gravity feed.

SAW, HOT—A saw used in cutting hot steel bars. They are usually solid saws from 14 to 50 inches in diameter, about 1.8 inches thick and with teeth spaced from ⅜ to ¾ inch apart. According to Henry Disston, they run somewhat slower than friction disc saws, at about 20,000 surface feet per minute.

SAW, NOTCHED FRICTION—Some friction saws have shallow teeth cut at intervals around the periphery instead of nicking the blade with a chisel as was formerly done. These are V-shaped notches about 3/32 inch deep and spaced to give about 3/32 inch contact with the work, about ¼ to 5/16 inch pitch. The notched spaces are not over ¾ inches long. They generate heat up to 1,800 deg. F., requiring less power the hotter the work. The rim speed may be around 20,000 feet per minute. The notched portions of the blade may be about ⅔ of the circumference.

SAW, SKIP-TOOTH—A band saw with every other tooth omitted to give chip clearance. They can be run at about double the speed of regular band saws. See *Saw Tooth Setting*.

SAW TOOTH ROOF—A roof having angular surfaces, which resembles a saw. The nearly vertical side of each angle has glass and usually faces the north to admit light without sun.

SAW TOOTH SETTING—Saws for cutting metal have three methods of tooth setting. The regular setting has each alternate tooth set in the opposite direction. The *wave* set has three consecutive teeth set to the right, then a straight tooth and the next three teeth set to the left. The *raker* set has first a tooth to the right, then a straight tooth, with the next tooth to the left. The tooth angle is usually about 55 degrees, and the depth of tooth is one-half the pitch, or distance between the teeth.

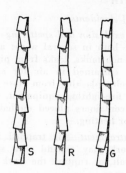

Sawtooth setting. (S) Regular. (R) Rake. (G) Wave.

SAW TOOTH SPACING—Metal cutting saws usually have a 55-degree angle to the teeth, the front being vertical. The spacing depends on the work to be done, as there should be at least two teeth in contact with the work at all times. The spacing is called the pitch, the tooth depth is half the pitch, and the radius at the bottom of the teeth is about 1/5 the pitch.

SAWING, BAND—The use of a continuous or endless metal band having teeth on one edge, and guided between rolls or plates, and with a support behind the back edge. Originally used as a wood working tool, it has become a valuable factor in many metal cutting operations, especially in die work and in forming difficult outlines. Modern band sawing machines have a small electric welder which enables the operator to break the saw for threading or inserting it through holes for internal work. The saw is then welded in a few seconds. In normal use, metal band saws are run at low speed, but on some work the speed exceeds that for wood, the cutting being done by friction, aided by the air drawn into the cut between the teeth, and sometimes by oxygen.

SCAB—A raised spot on a casting caused by some of the surface of the sand mold breaking away during the pouring of the metal in the mold.

SCALE—The hard surface on a casting or forging. In both cases it can usually be removed by pickling if desired, but unless the metal has to be machined, it is usually better to leave the scale. By taking cuts deep enough to keep the point of the tool under the scale, tools are not as badly affected by it.

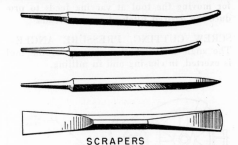

SCRAPERS

SCARF OR SCARF JOINT—A joint made by preparing the edges to be joined by beveling or notching to present a longer mating surface than the thickness of the metal itself. See *Welding, Types of Joints for Arc Welding.*

SCLEROSCOPE—An instrument for measuring hardness by the rebound of a steel ball enclosed in a glass tube, from the surface being tested. Later models use a diamond tipped hammer instead of a ball.

SCORIFY—To separate good metal from slag.

SCOTCH—A term sometimes used to describe blocking to prevent movement. Also used in connection with a prop.

SCOTCH YOKE—See *Cam, Scotch Yoke.*

SCOTTSONIZING—A hardening process which minimizes distortion of steel being so treated. Super-Scottsonizing, a more recent development, gives stainless steel a surface hardness never before attained. The parts are completely finished before hardening, as there is no distortion. Parts so hardened resist corrosion to a remarkable degree. It was developed by C. U. Scott.

SCRAP ALLOWANCE—Allowance for waste of material due to the necessity of allowing for chips and for material to hold parts together while being machined. In turning, it includes material wasted by cutting tools and the end for holding the last piece in the chuck, on bar material. In punch press work it includes the material left between punchings. Much depends here on the shape of the piece and the way in which the work is laid out. Some shapes can be nested together and waste kept at a minimum. This may require staggering the work or reversing the direction of feed, as shown by the two examples. The allowance between punchings varies with the width of the sheet and its thickness. See *Punch Press Scrap.*

SCRAP IRON—A common term which covers both iron and steel that is suitable only for remelting. This may be due to defects or to the size being unsuited for effective use.

SCRAP, PUNCH PRESS WORK—See *Punch Press Scrap.*

SCRAPING—In machine shop terms, to finish a surface with a hand scraper. This implies that the machine work is imperfect and can be improved by removing metal in spots by hand. It is a disputed point among good mechanics, and some of the best known machine tool builders do not scrape bearings. Almost no one scrapes a round bearing now, but this was formerly common practice. The later planers and grinding machines do excellent work, better than most men can scrape. Scraping does provide small oil pockets which may have advantages. Most machine builders "spot" the flat sliding surfaces to please customers even if they are not scraped.

SCREW—A round body having a continuous helical raised ridge advancing along its length. See following definitions of various types of *Screws, Screw Heads,* and *Screw Threads.*

SCREW, BINDING HEAD—A machine screw which is faced square and flat under the head so as to clamp or bind any surface which it contacts. See *Fillister Heads.*

SCREW, BONE—A screw used by surgeons for holding fractured bones in place. They are made of different materials, such as stainless steel, plastics or even of bone itself.

SCREW CHUCK—See *Chuck, Screw.*

SCREW, CLUTCH HEAD—A new type of screw head with a recess so shaped as to afford a grip for a flat piece of steel or a special wrench, as shown.

SCREW, COMPOUND—A screw which has more than one thread on the same bar, usually of different pitches. These are sometimes called differential screws. One thread may be right hand, the other left hand.

SCREW CUTTING, COMPOUND GEARING —The cutting of screw threads where it is necessary to use a second reduction of gear ratios between the spindle and the work.

SCREW CUTTING LATHE—A lathe with gearing, a lead screw and other mechanism

347

for moving the tool at varying feeds to produce the desired pitch of screw threads.

SCREW CUTTING, PRESSURE ANGLE—
The angle at which the pressure of the tool is exerted, in chasing and in milling.

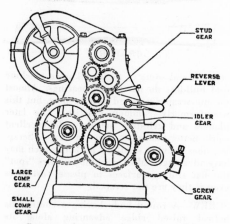

Compound gearing for screw cutting.

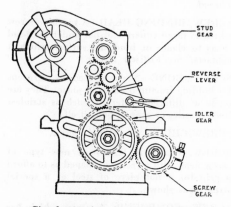

Simple gearing for screw cutting.

SCREW CUTTING, SIMPLE GEARING—The
cutting of screw threads where a simple gear train between the spindle and the work can be used. Where there is a single reduction of the speed ratio between the two.

SCREWDRIVER—Hand tools for tightening screws or removing them from work. Several types are shown on page 352.

SCREW, DIFFERENTIAL—Sometimes called
compound screws. Screws having threads of two or more pitches at different parts of the bar or shaft. Compound screws with two pitches have been used for securing fine movements between parts moving on each thread. Various combinations can be made to secure movement of varying distances. With one screw having 10 threads per inch and another 11 threads per inch a single turn would move one nut approximately 0.010 inch with relation to the other. Screws of this kind are seldom used except in special devices. Tubes or cylinders have been made with internal threads of different pitches for special purposes.

SCREW, ENDLESS—A device for raising water which is credited to Archimedes, the Greek philosopher. It consists of a tube wound in a helix around a cylinder and placed in an inclined position in a tank or body of water. The water fills the tube to the level of the water, and as the cylinder is revolved, the water in the tube runs down the incline of the tube until it reaches the open end at the top. Useful in its day, but it is impractical at present.

SCREW(S), FRENCH AND INTERNATIONAL—These screws have threads with metric dimensions, as shown in the tables. They are of the same form as the old American Standard with a 60-degree angle and flat top and bottom. In translating to inches use 25.4 millimeters per inch. They may be replaced at some later date by the unified thread adopted by Canada, England and the U. S. See *Screw Threads.*

SCREW HEADS—Screw heads are made for different kinds of work and for different industries. The plain slotted head is being replaced by special heads such as the Clutch, Frearson and Phillips, which require special screw drivers for best results. They are stronger heads and less liable to damage than the plain slot. Others are recessed for special wrenches, especially for set screw work. British screw heads are also shown.

SCREW, MACHINE—A screw to be used in a hole tapped in metal. The form of thread is the same as for bolts. Table on page 350 shows diameters from No. 2 to No. 12 or from 0.086 to 0.216 inch. Above ¼ inch they are called bolts. Heads are of different shapes, much as with wood screws.

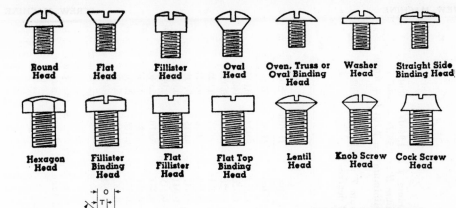

Round Head   **Flat Head**   **Fillister Head**   **Oval Head**   **Oven, Truss or Oval Binding Head**   **Washer Head**   **Straight Side Binding Head**

Hexagon Head   **Fillister Binding Head**   **Flat Fillister Head**   **Flat Top Binding Head**   **Lentil Head**   **Knob Screw Head**   **Cock Screw Head**

Screw head specifications: (A) Diameter of screw head. (D) Diameter of screw body. (H) Thickness of head. (J) Width of slot. (L) Length of screw. (O) Total length of head. (T) Depth of slot.
Dimensions standardized for slotted oval-head wood screws.

BRITISH SCREWHEADS.

Cheese head

Round head

Grub screw

Wood screw

Mushroom head   Gallery screw   Band screw   Raised head

RECESSED HEADS FOR SCREWS AND BOLTS.

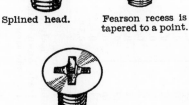

Splined head.   Fearson recess is tapered to a point.

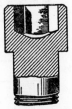

Phillips heads are available with flat planes at the corners or with rounded corners. Ordinary screwdriver can be used although special driver is recommended.

Clutch-head screws and bolts have a special-shaped recess that takes either a special or an ordinary driver. Slight backward twist causes screw or bolt to lock on special driver.

Hexagon-shaped recesses are used where bolts or studs must be as close as possible to walls or structures. Special wrench is necessary.

SCREW HEADS.

349

Machine Screws

Formulas

Head diameter: Maximum $A = 2.040D - 0.003$, Minimum $A = 1.960D - 0.013$.
Height of head: Maximum $H = 0.619D - 0.002$, Minimum $H = 0.552D - 0.007$.
NOTE.—Width of slot: Maximum $J = 0.182D + 0.020$; Minimum $J = 0.164 D + 0.010$.
It is the same in all types of machine screws.
Depth of slot: Maximum $T = 0.288D - 0.002$; Minimum $T = 0.192D - 0.002$.
Countersink angle: maximum, 82 degrees; minimum 80 degrees.

Head Dimensions, Flat Head Machine Screws

Nominal Size	Threads per Inch	D Maximum Diameter	A Head Diameter Max.	A Min.	H Height of Head Max.	H Min.	J Width of Slot Max.	J Min.	T Depth of Slot Max.	T Min.
2	2—56	0.086	0.172	0.156	0.051	0.040	0.036	0.024	0.023	0.015
3	3—48	0.099	0.199	0.181	0.059	0.048	0.038	0.026	0.027	0.017
4	4—40	0.112	0.225	0.207	.007	0.055	0.040	0.028	0.030	0.020
5	5—40	0.125	0.252	0.232	0.075	0.062	0.043	0.031	0.034	0.022
6	6—32	0.138	0.279	0.257	0.083	0.059	0.045	0.033	0.038	0.024
8	8—32	0.164	0.332	0.308	0.100	0.084	0.050	0.037	0.045	0.029
10	10—24—32	0.190	0.385	0.359	0.116	0.098	0.055	0.041	0.053	0.034
12	12—24	0.216	0.438	0.410	0.132	0.112	0.059	0.045	0.060	0.039
¼	¼—20	0.250	0.507	0.477	0.153	0.131	0.066	0.051	0.070	0.046
5⁄16	5⁄16—18	0.3125	0.636	0.600	0.192	0.166	0.077	0.061	0.088	0.058
3⁄8	3⁄8—16	0.375	0.762	0.722	0.230	0.200	0.083	0.072	0.106	0.070
7⁄16	7⁄16—14	0.4375	0.890	0.845	0.269	0.235	0.099	0.083	0.108	0.070
½	½—13	0.500	1.017	0.967	0.307	0.269	0.110	0.094	0.110	0.070

All dimensions in inches.

NOTE:—The unthreaded body diameter of machine screws will have approximately the same tolerances as the pitch diameter of the threads shown in the American National Standard for screw threads, Class 2 Free Fit, where the number of threads per inch are the same.

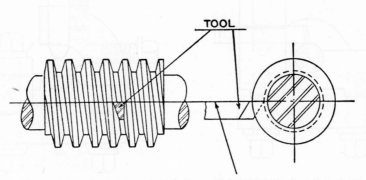

TOOL

P.A. IN THIS "AXIAL" PLANE WHEN THREAD IS CHASED

Worm chased with lathe tool.

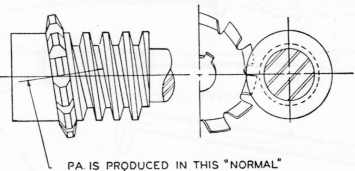

P.A. IS PRODUCED IN THIS "NORMAL" WHEN THREAD IS MILLED

Worm cut with thread milling cutter.

SCREW MACHINE—Originally a small hand operated machine with several tools in a turret for making screws. Really a small turret lathe.

SCREW MACHINE, AUTOMATIC — A machine tool which automatically feeds stock into the machine, controls the cutting tools and other parts, and finishes the parts without an operator. Many semi-automatic machines are often called "automatics."

SCREW MACHINE TOOLS—Tools used in automatic screw machines on a variety of work.

The tools shown are used with Brown & Sharpe automatics. See page 353.

BOX TOOLS—A type of cutting tool used in turning in turret lathes and in automatic screw machines. Several types are shown.

ECHOLS TAP—A form of tap designed to reduce friction in tapping. Alternate teeth are removed from every other land so as to reduce the surfaces in contact with the work.

FORMING TOOLS—Cutting tools which give the work a predetermined shape, or form. They are used in turning, milling and planing.

351

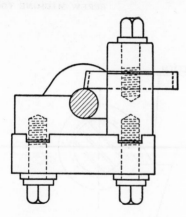

Tangent cutter and solid back rest.

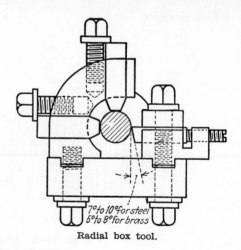

7° to 10° for steel
5° to 8° for brass

Radial box tool.

SCREW MACHINE BOX TOOLS.

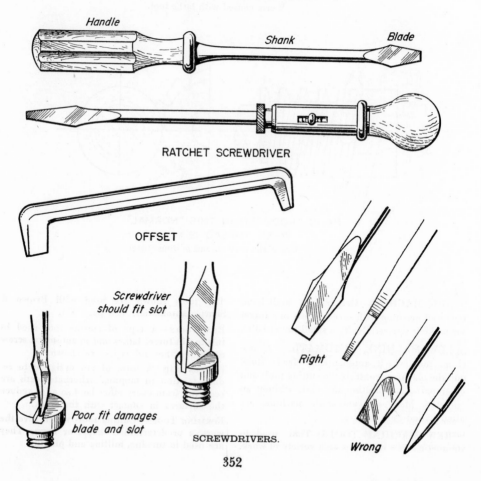

Handle   Shank   Blade

RATCHET SCREWDRIVER

OFFSET

Screwdriver should fit slot

Poor fit damages blade and slot

Right

Wrong

SCREWDRIVERS.

352

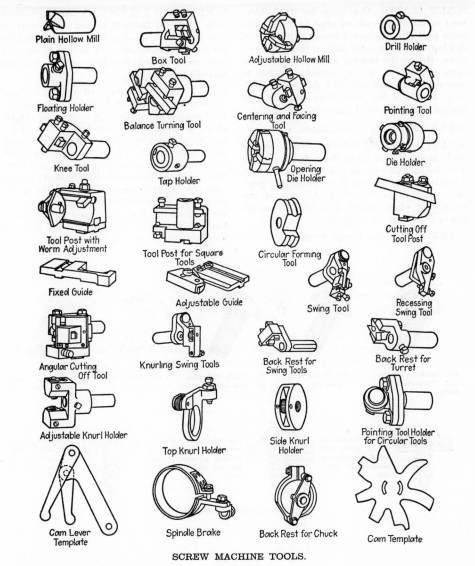

SCREW MACHINE TOOLS.

Plain Hollow Mill

Box Tool

Adjustable Hollow Mill

Drill Holder

Floating Holder

Balance Turning Tool

Centering and Facing Tool

Pointing Tool

Knee Tool

Tap Holder

Opening Die Holder

Die Holder

Tool Post with Worm Adjustment

Tool Post for Square Tools

Circular Forming Tool

Cutting Off Tool Post

Fixed Guide

Adjustable Guide

Swing Tool

Recessing Swing Tool

Angular Cutting Off Tool

Knurling Swing Tools

Back Rest for Swing Tools

Back Rest for Turret

Adjustable Knurl Holder

Top Knurl Holder

Side Knurl Holder

Pointing Tool Holder for Circular Tools

Cam Lever Template

Spindle Brake

Back Rest for Chuck

Cam Template

ROLLER TOOLS—Cutting tools used in turret lathes and screw machines in which the work is supported by rollers against the thrust of the cutting tool.

SCREW, PARKER-KALON — A hardened screw which cuts its own thread in soft steel or other metal. Some have a slot at the end which forms a cutting edge. Largely used in assembling sheet metal parts. The screws have heads which conform to the standards of machine screw heads.

SCREW, PHILLIPS HEAD — A machine or wood screw with slots in the form of a cross, but which do not extend to the edge of the head. Makes a stronger head but requires a special form of wrench or screwdriver. Usually considered desirable for rapid assembly work. See also *Screw Heads*.

SCREW PLATES—One name for die holders used in threading rods or pipe by hand. The name probably originated from the practice of making the dies a solid part of the handle or plate. Before the making of taps and dies became an industry, it was common practice to anneal a worn out file, and drill and tap it to be used as a die, after filing clearance and cutting edges. It was then re-hardened.

SCREW PRESS—See *Press, Screw.*

SCREW, PRESSURE ANGLE—The pressure angle imposed on a screw depends on whether it is chased with a single point tool or cut with a milling cutter. When it is chased, the pressure angle is parallel with the axis of the screw, but when milled it is in the normal plane, as shown on page 351.

SCREW PUMP—See *Pump, Screw.*

SCREW, SELF-TAPPING—A hardened screw with a special form of thread which cuts its own thread when forced into holes drilled the proper size. Also used in fastening sheet or thin metal plates together, cutting its own threads.

SCREW, SET—A screw used to hold or "set" a collar on a shaft or to hold pieces of this kind against movement. Set screws are usually short, threaded their entire length, and have a variety of types of points, although the heads are usually square. Projecting set screw heads were once a common cause of shop accidents. This led to adoption of hollow-head set screws, with square, hexagon or splines on the inside for special wrenches. They are now flush with the outside of the collar and no longer a hazard. The points are designed for different uses, as shown on next page.

For fastening all types and thicknesses of metal

For plastics. Note double slot

For metals and plastics. Note multiple slots

For plastics. Has coarse lead

For metals. Forms rather than cuts, threads

For sheet metal up to 18 gage, plywood, asbestos and composition materials

For sheet metal up to 6 gage, non-ferrous castings, plastics, plywood, asbestos and composition materials

For heavy-gage sheet metal, castings, structural steel, plastics and plywood

For heavy-gage sheet metal, castings, structural steel, plastics and plywood

SELF-TAPPING SCREWS

For heavy-gage sheet metal, castings, forgings, structural steel, plastics and plywood

For fastening such materials as fabric, fiber, leather and cardboard to light-gage sheet metal.

For fastening sheet metal to wood

DRIVE SCREWS.

CUP POINT—Most commonly used. For applications where point must cut into soft steel or other soft metal. Not suitable for hanger-point use

 CONE POINT — Used where part to be held must be spot drilled

 **FLAT POINT**—For anchoring machine parts temporarily to shafting, especially where frequent relocating is necessary with least bruising of shaft. Also used where shaft is hardened and sometimes at back of brass or soft-metal plug

 OVAL POINT—Frequently used where part to be held is spot drilled or with circular or horizontal spline as on shafts

 **HALF-DOG POINT**—Most effective where the screw is in direct contact with a hardened steel tool or other part, unless the part is spot-drilled, in which case an oval or cone point is recommended

 FULL-DOG POINT — For use where desired to have the point go extra deep into the drilled hole in a shaft or other part

 HANGER POINT—For use where part to be held must be spot drilled

 KNURLED POINT—For applications where vibration resistance is particularly important

SET-SCREW POINTS.

SCREW, STICK—One of a number of screws made in multiple on a single rod. Designed by Reece Hutchinson to expedite mass assembly of small products. As shown, the screws are formed complete but not separated. The diameter just above the head of each screw is calculated so that when one screw has been inserted with the proper pressure the screw above its head twists off. This burnishes the head of the screw driven into the work and the

Stick screws.

next screw is ready to be inserted in its threaded hole. They are made in screw numbered sizes from 0 to 5 in mild steel, brass and aluminum.

SCREW STOCK—Soft, free cutting steel for screws and small parts.

SCREW, TRANSLATING—A term given to the class of screw threads which are used in bench vises, lifting jacks, cross and elevating screws for lathes, and similar purposes. They include the 60-degree stub thread, the 29-degree stub Acme thread and the modified-square thread with a 5- or 10-degree side. Details of each are given under separate headings.

SCREW THREAD—A continuous raised helix on a round body, by which it can be inserted, or screwed, into a hole having a similar mating helix, as a nut. The thread can be made by cutting, grinding or rolling.

SCREW THREADS, A. B. C.—The designation of the American-British-Canadian standard of threads used by the Swiss watch industry. This permits use of a round crest of nominal major diameter, or a truncated crest, $\frac{1}{16}$ of the thread depth below nominal major diameter.

SCREW THREADS, ACME — A thread designed by the Acme Machinery Co. many years
ago to replace the square thread, which it has
done almost completely. It has a 29-degree
angle and the main dimensions are shown. It
is much easier to cut than a square thread and
is widely used. The depth of the thread is
one-half the pitch.

SCREW THREADS, ACME, MODIFIED—
Differs from the standard Acme thread by
reducing the depth of the thread from one-
half the pitch to three-eighths of the pitch.

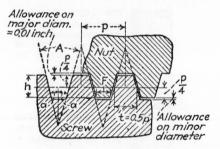

American National Acme screw threads.

Acme Thread General Purpose Sizes

Size Inches	Thrds. per Inch (N)	Basic Dimensions			Thread Data			
		Major Diameter (S)	Pitch Diameter	Minor Diameter (D)	Thickness at Pitch Line (p/2)	Depth of Thread with Clearance (d)	Basic Width of Flat (f)	Helix Angle at Pitch Diam.
¼	16	.2500	.2187	.1875	.0313	.0363	.0232	5° 12′
⁵⁄₁₆	14	.3125	.2768	.2411	.0357	.0407	.0265	4° 42′
⅜	12	.3750	.3333	.2917	.0417	.0467	.0309	4° 33′
⁷⁄₁₆	12	.4375	.3958	.3542	.0417	.0467	.0309	3° 50′
½	10	.5000	.4500	.4000	.0500	.0600	.0371	4° 3′
⅝	8	.6250	.5625	.5000	.0625	.0725	.0463	4° 3′
¾	6	.7500	.6667	.5833	.0833	.0933	.0618	4° 33′
⅞	6	.8750	.7917	.7083	.0833	.0933	.0618	3° 50′
1	5	1.0000	.9000	.8000	.1000	.1100	.0741	4° 3′
1⅛	5	1.1250	1.0250	.9250	.1000	.1100	.0741	3° 33′
1¼	5	1.2500	1.1500	1.0500	.1000	.1100	.0741	3° 10′
1⅜	4	1.3570	1.2500	1.1250	.1250	.1350	.0927	3° 39′
1½	4	1.5000	1.3750	1.2500	.1250	.1350	.0927	3° 19′
1¾	4	1.7500	1.6250	1.5000	.1250	.1350	.0927	2° 48′
2	4	2.0000	1.8750	1.7500	.1250	.1350	.0927	2° 26′
2¼	3	2.2500	2.0833	1.9167	.1667	.1767	.1236	2° 55′
2½	3	2.5000	2.3333	2.1667	.1667	.1767	.1236	2° 43′
2¾	3	2.7500	2.5833	2.4167	.1667	.1767	.1236	2° 21′
3	2	3.0000	2.7500	2.5000	.2500	.2600	.1853	3° 19′
4	2	4.0000	3.7500	3.5000	.2500	.2600	.1853	2° 26′
5	2	5.0000	4.7500	4.5000	.2500	.2600	.1853	1° 55′

These Acme Thread sizes have been adopted both as an A. S. A. standard and a standard for
Federal Services. Complete specifications are given in the A. S. A. B1. 3-1941 and the National
Bureau of Standards Handbook H28. (Basic dimensions for the 10° square thread, 29° stub
thread and 60° stub thread are also included in these pamphlets.)

It is recommended that if a greater lead is required on a given diameter than the thread
listed below it is advisable to use a multiple thread of the required lead rather than a single
thread of that pitch.

American National Acme Screw Threads

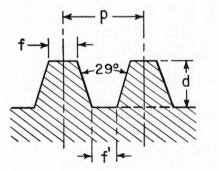

SYMBOLS

D = Depth of thread with clearance

$f = \begin{cases} \text{Tap drill} \\ \text{Minor diameter of nut} \end{cases}$

f' = Width of flat at top of thread

n = Width of flat at bottom of space

n = Number of threads per inch

R = Pitch of thread

S = Minor diameter of screw

T = Major diameter of screw

d = Major diameter of tap

FORMULA
(Approximate)

$$p = \frac{1}{n} \qquad\qquad f = \frac{.3707}{n}$$

$$D = \text{S-p} \qquad\qquad R = \text{S-2d}$$

For 10 or less threads per inch   For more than 10 threads per inch

$$d = \frac{p}{2} \text{ plus } .010 \qquad\qquad d = \frac{p}{2} \text{ plus.005}$$

$$f' = \frac{.3707}{n} \text{ minus } .0052 \qquad\qquad f' = \frac{.3707}{n} \text{ minus } .0026$$

$$T = \text{S plus } .020 \qquad\qquad T = \text{S plus } .010$$

Table of Acme Thread Parts

Pitch (p)	Threads per Inch (n)	Depth of Thread with Clearance (d)	Flat at Top of Thread (f)	Flat at Bottom of Space (f')	Space at Top of Thread	Thickness at Root of Thread
1	1	.5100	.3707	.3655	.6293	.6345
3/4	1⅓	.3850	.2780	.2728	.4720	.4772
1/2	2	.2600	.1854	.1802	.3146	.3198
1/3	3	.1767	.1236	.1184	.2097	.2149
1/4	4	.1350	.0927	.0875	.1573	.1625
1/5	5	.1100	.0741	.0689	.1259	.1311
1/6	6	.0933	.0618	.0566	.1049	.1101
1/7	7	.0814	.0530	.0478	.0899	.0951
1/8	8	.0725	.0463	.0411	.0787	.0839
1/9	9	.0655	.0412	.0360	.0699	.0751
1/10	10	.0600	.0371	.0319	.0629	.0681
1/12	12	.0467	.0309	.0283	.0524	.0550
1/14	14	.0407	.0265	.0239	.0449	.0475
1/16	16	.0363	.0232	.0206	.0393	.0419

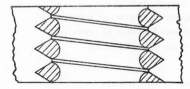

Aero screw threads.

SCREW THREADS, AERO—A type of thread developed primarily for the airplane industry, for replacing threads which have become worn, or stripped in softer metals such as aluminum or magnesium. The hole is retapped with a special oversize tap to receive a coiled insert, as shown in the cross-hatched sections. The Aero screw has a special shaped thread which fits the rounded top of the insert.

SCREW THREADS, AERONAUTICAL, PLUG AND RING GAGES FOR—Inspection of aeronautical screw threads can be expedited by reference to the tables for classes 2 and 3 fits. These are based on the National Bureau of Standards Handbook H28, but are more conveniently arranged for inspection work of sizes from 0-80 to ⅞-14.

SCREW THREADS, AMERICAN NATIONAL—Sizes and pitches included in the American National Coarse Thread Series are as follows:

No. 1—64	⅜″—16	1½″—6
No. 2—56	⁷⁄₁₆″—14	1¾″—5
No. 3—48	½″—13	2″ —4½
No. 4—40	⁹⁄₁₆″—12	2¼″—4½
No. 5—40	⅝″—11	2½″—4
No. 6—32	¾″—10	2¾″—4
No. 8—32	⅞″—9	3″ —4
No. 10—24	1″ —8	3¼″—4
No. 12—24	1⅛″—7	3½″—4
¼″—20	1¼″—7	3¾″—4
⁵⁄₁₆″—18	1⅜″—6	4″ —4

Sizes and pitches included in the American National Fine Thread Series are as follows:

No. 0—80	No. 10—32	⅝″—18
No. 1—72	No. 12—28	¾″—16
No. 2—64	¼″—28	⅞″—14
No. 3—56	⁵⁄₁₆″—24	1″ —14
No. 4—48	⅜″—24	1⅛″—12
No. 5—44	⁷⁄₁₆″—20	1¼″—12
No. 6—40	½″—20	1⅜″—12
No. 8—36	⁹⁄₁₆″—18	1½″—12

Agreement between Britain, Canada, and U. S. on the Unified thread is to use 13 threads per inch on the half-inch size.

SCREW THREADS, AMERICAN STANDARD—See *Screw Threads, Unified and American.*

American Standard Nomenclature, Definitions, and Letter Symbols for Screw Threads.

1. *General*—The purposes of this standard are to establish uniform practices with regard to: (1) Screw-thread nomenclature, and (2) letter symbols for designating dimensions of screw threads for use on drawings, in tables of dimensions which set forth dimensional standards, and in other records, and for expressing mathematical relationships.

2. The standard consists of a glossary of terms, two tables of screw-thread dimensional symbols, five illustrations showing the application of dimensional symbols, and one table of identification symbols.

3. TYPOGRAPHY. In accordance with the usual practice in published text, letter symbols and letter subscripts, whether upper or lower case, should be printed in italic type. An exception is Greek letters; Greek capital letters are always vertical, lower case always resembles italics. In manuscripts this is indicated by underlining each symbol to be italicized. Coefficients, numeral subscripts, and exponents should be printed in vertical Arabic numerals. Standard mathematical notation should be followed.

4. *Definition of Terms*—The terms commonly applied to screw threads may be classified in five general groups, namely: (1) Those relating to types of screw threads; (2) those relating to size of mechanical parts in general; (3) those relating to geometrical elements of both straight and taper screw threads; (4) those relating to dimensions of screw threads;

and (5) those relating only to taper screw threads.

The definitions presented herein apply to theoretically correct thread forms unless otherwise indicated.

5. *Terms Relating to Types of Screw Threads* —Screw threads, and the terms generally applied to designate the types of screw threads, are defined as follows:

6. SCREW THREAD. A screw thread (hereinafter referred to as a thread), is a ridge of uniform section in the form of a helix on the external or internal surface of a cylinder, or in the form of a conical spiral on the external or internal surface of a cone or frustum of a cone. A thread formed on a cylinder is known as a "straight" or "parallel" thread, to distinguish it from a "taper" thread which is formed on a cone or frustum of a cone.

7. EXTERNAL THREAD. An external thread is a thread on the external surface of a cylinder or cone.

8. INTERNAL THREAD. An internal thread is a thread on the internal surface of a hollow cylinder or cone.

9. RIGHT-HAND THREAD. A thread is a right-hand thread if, when viewed axially, it winds in a clockwise and receding direction.

10. LEFT-HAND THREAD. A thread is a left-hand thread if, when viewed axially, it winds in a counterclockwise and receding direction. All left-hand threads are designated "LH."

11. SINGLE THREAD. A single (single-part) thread is one having lead equal to the pitch. (See 53 and 54.)

12. MULTIPLE THREAD. A multiple (multiple-start) thread is one in which the lead is an integral multiple of the pitch. (See 53 and 54.)

13. CLASSES OF THREADS. Classes of threads are distinguished from each other by the amount of tolerance or tolerance and allowance specified.

14. TERMS RELATING TO SIZE OF PARTS— Terms relating to the size of parts, which are generally applicable to mechanical parts, including threads, are defined as follows:

15. DIMENSION. A dimension is a geometrical characteristic such as a diameter, length, angle, circumference, or center distance, of which the size is specified.

16. SIZE. Size is a designation of magnitude.

17. NOMINAL SIZE—The size by which a thread is usually designated without reference to the actual dimensions, as this includes tolerances.

18. BASIC SIZE. The basic size of a dimension is the theoretical size from which the limits of size for that dimension are derived by the application of the allowance and tolerances.

19. DESIGN SIZE. The design size of a dimension is the size in relation to which the limits of tolerance for that dimension are assigned.

20. ACTUAL SIZE. The actual size of a dimension is the measured size of that dimension on an individual part.

21. LIMITS OF SIZE. These limits are the maximum and minimum sizes permissible for a specific dimension.

22. TOLERANCE. The tolerance on a dimension is the total permissible variation in its size. The tolerance is the difference between the limits of size.

23. ALLOWANCE. An allowance is an intentional difference in correlated dimensions of mating parts. It is the minimum clearance (positive allowance) or maximum interference (negative allowance) between such parts.

24. FIT. The fit between two mating parts is the relationship existing between them with respect to the amount of clearance or interference which is present when they are assembled.

25 *Terms Relating to Geometrical Elements of Screw Threads*—Terms relating to geometrical elements of both straight and taper threads are defined as follows:

26. AXIS. The axis of a thread is the axis of its pitch cylinder or cone.

27. PITCH LINE. The pitch line is a generator of the imaginary cylinder or cone specified in the definition of pitch diameter. (See 69.)

28. FORM. The form of thread is its profile in an axial plane for a length of one pitch.

29. BASIC FORM OF THREAD. The basic form of a thread is the theoretical profile of the thread for a length of one pitch in an axial plane, on which the design forms of the threads for both the external and internal threads are based.

30. DESIGN FORMS OF THREAD. The design forms for a thread are the maximum metal forms permitted for the external and internal threads.

31. FUNDAMENTAL TRIANGLE. The fundamental triangle is the triangle whose corners coin-

359

cide with three consecutive intersections of the extended flanks of the basic form.

32. FLANK. The flank (or side) of a thread is either surface connecting the crest with the root, the intersection of which, with an axial plane, is a straight line.

33. LEADING FLANK. The leading flank of a thread is the one which, when the thread is about to be assembled with a mating thread, faces the mating thread.

34. FOLLOWING FLANK. The following flank of a thread is the one which is opposite to the leading flank.

35. PRESSURE FLANK. The pressure flank is that which takes the thrust or load in an assembly. The term is used particularly in relation to buttress and other similar threads.

36. CLEARANCE (OR TRAILING) FLANK. The clearance flank is that which does not take the thrust or load in an assembly.

37. CREST. The crest is that surface of the thread which joins the flanks of the thread and is farthest from the cylinder or cone from which the thread projects.

38. ROOT. The root is that surface of the thread which joins the flanks of adjacent thread forms and is identical with or immediately adjacent to the cylinder or cone from which the thread projects.

39. SHARP CREST (OR CREST APEX). The sharp crest is the apex formed by the intersection of the flanks of a thread when extended, if necessary, beyond the crest.

40. SHARP ROOT (OR ROOT APEX). The sharp root is the apex formed by the intersection of the flanks of adjacent thread forms when extended, if necessary, beyond the root.

41. BASE. The base of a thread is that section of the thread which coincides with the cylinder or cone from which the thread projects.

42. MAJOR CYLINDER OR CONE. (See 67 and 77.)

43. MINOR CYLINDER OR CONE. (See 68 and 79.)

44. PITCH CYLINDER OR CONE. (See 68 and 76.)

45. COMPLETE THREAD. The complete (or full) thread is that part of the thread having full form at both crest and root. When there is a chamfer at the start of the thread, not exceeding two pitches in length, it is included within the length of complete thread.

46. INCOMPLETE THREAD. This is also known as the vanish or washout thread. On straight threads, the incomplete thread is that portion at the end having roots not fully formed by the lead or chamfer on threading tools.

On taper threads, the crest at the end may also be not fully formed due to the intersection of the major cone of an external thread, or the minor cone of an internal thread, with the cylindrical surface of the work.

47. EFFECTIVE THREAD. The effective (or useful) thread includes the complete thread and that portion of the incomplete thread having fully formed roots but having crests not fully formed.

48. TOTAL THREAD. The total thread includes the complete or effective thread and the incomplete thread.

49. VANISH CONE. The vanish cone is an imaginary cone, the surface of which would pass through the roots of the incomplete thread formed by the lead or chamfer of the threading tool.

50. VANISH POINT. The vanish point of an external thread is the intersection of a generator of the vanish cone with a generator of the cylinder of the largest major diameter of the thread.

51. BLUNT START. "Blunt start" designates the removal of the partial thread at the entering end of thread. This is a feature of threaded parts which are repeatedly assembled by hand, such as hose couplings and thread plug gages, to prevent cutting of hands and crossing of threads, and which was formerly known as a "Higbee cut."

52. *Terms Relating to Dimensions of Screw Threads*—Terms relating to dimensions of both straight and taper threads are defined as follows:

53. PITCH. The pitch of a thread is the distance, measured parallel to its axis, between corresponding parts on adjacent thread forms in the same axial plane and on the same side of the axis.

54. LEAD. The lead is the distance a threaded part moves axially, with respect to a fixed mating part, in one complete rotation.

55. THREADS PER INCH. The number of threads per inch is the reciprocal of the pitch in inches. (See 53.)

56. TURNS PER INCH. The number of turns per inch is the reciprocal of the lead in inches. (See 54.)

57. INCLUDED ANGLE. The included angle of a thread (or angle of thread) is the angle between the flanks of the thread measured in an axial plane.

58. FLANK ANGLE. The flank angles are the angles between the individual flanks and the perpendicular to the axis of the thread, measured in an axial plane. A flank angle of a symmetrical thread is commonly termed the "half-angle of thread."

59. LEAD ANGLE. On a straight thread the lead angle is the angle made by the helix of the thread at the pitch line with a plane perpendicular to the axis. On a taper thread, the lead angle at a given axial position is the angle made by the conical spiral of the thread at the pitch line with the plane perpendicular to the axis at that position.

60. THICKNESS. The thickness of thread is the distance between the flanks of the thread measured at a specified position and parallel to the axis.

61. HEIGHT OF FUNDAMENTAL TRIANGLE. The height of the fundamental triangle of a thread, or the height of a sharp V-thread is the distance, measured perpendicular to the axis, between the sharp major and minor cylinders or cones, respectively. (See 78 and 80.)

62. HEIGHT OF THREAD. The height (or depth) of thread is the distance, measured perpendicular to the axis, between the major and minor cylinders or cones, respectively. (See 77 and 79.)

63. ADDENDUM. The addendum of an external thread is the distance, measured perpendicular to the axis, between the minor and pitch cylinders or cones, respectively.

64. DEDENDUM. The dedendum of an external thread is the distance, measured perpendicular to the axis, between the pitch and minor cylinders or cones, respectively. The dedendum of an internal thread is the distance, measured perpendicular to the axis, between the major and pitch cylinders or cones, respectively.

65. CREST TRUNCATION. The crest truncation of a thread is the distance, measured perpendicular to the axis, between the sharp crest (or crest apex) and the clinder or cone which bounds the crest.

66. ROOT TRUNCATION. The root truncation of a thread is the distance, measured perpendicular to the axis, between the sharp root (or root apex) and the cylinder or cone which bounds the root.

67. MAJOR DIAMETER. On a straight thread, the major diameter is the diameter of the imaginary co-axial cylinder which bounds the crest of an external thread or the root of an internal thread.

On a taper thread, the major diameter, at a given position on the thread axis, is the diameter of the major cone at that position. (See 77.)

68. MINOR DIAMETER. On a straight thread, the minor diameter is the diameter of the imaginary co-axial cylinder which bounds the root of an external thread or the crest of an internal thread.

On a taper thread, the minor diameter, at a given position on the thread axis, is the diameter of the minor cone at that position. (See 79.)

69. PITCH DIAMETER (SIMPLE EFFECTIVE DIAMETER). On a straight thread, the pitch diameter is the diameter of the imaginary co-axial cylinder, the surface of which would pass through the thread profiles at such points as to make the width of the groove equal to one-half of the basic pitch. On a perfect thread this occurs at the point where the width of the thread and groove are equal.

On a taper thread, the pitch diameter at a given position on the thread axis is the diameter of the pitch cone at that position. (See 76.)

70. EFFECTIVE SIZE (OR VIRTUAL EFFECTIVE DIAMETER). The effective size of an external or internal thread is the diameter derived by adding to the pitch diameter, in the case of an external thread, or subtracting from the pitch diameter, in the case of an internal thread, the cumulative effects of pitch and angle errors.

71. DEPTH OF THREAD ENGAGEMENT. The depth of thread engagement between two mating threads is the distance, measured perpendicular to the axis, by which their thread forms overlap each other.

72. LENGTH OF THREAD ENGAGEMENT. The length of thread engagement of two mating threads is the distance between the extreme points of contact on the pitch cylinders or cones, measured parallel to the axis.

73. CREST CLEARANCE. The crest clearance in a thread assembly is the distance measured perpendicular to the axis, between the crest of a thread and the root of its mating thread.

(Continued on page 368)

American National Coarse-Thread Series

Standard Machine Screw Threads

In the first table are specified the nominal sizes and basic dimensions of the "American National coarse-thread series." The American National coarse-thread series is recommended for general use in engineering work, in machine construction where conditions are favorable to the use of bolts, screws, and other threaded components, where quick and easy assembly of the parts is desired, and for all work where conditions do not require the use of fine-pitch threads.

Identification		Basic Diameters			Thread Data				
Sizes	Threads per Inch, n	Major Diameter, D	Pitch Diameter, E	Minor Diameter, K	Pitch, p	Depth of Thread, h	Basic Width of Flat, $p/8$	Minimum Width of Flat at Major Diameter of Nut, $p/24$	Helix Angle at Basic Pitch Diameter, s
1	2	3	4	5	6	7	8	9	10
		Inches	Inches	Inches	Inch	Inch	Inch	Inch	Deg. Min.
1	64	0.073	0.0629	0.0527	0.01562	0.01015	0.00195	0.00065	4 31
2	56	0.086	0.0744	0.0628	0.01786	0.01160	0.00223	0.00074	4 22
3	48	0.099	0.0855	0.0719	0.02083	0.01353	0.00260	0.00087	4 26
4	40	0.112	0.0958	0.0795	0.02500	0.01624	0.00312	0.00104	4 45
5	40	0.125	0.1088	0.0925	0.02500	0.01624	0.00312	0.00104	4 11
6	32	0.138	0.1177	0.0974	0.03125	0.02030	0.00391	0.00130	4 50
8	32	0.164	0.1437	0.1234	0.03125	0.02030	0.00391	0.00130	3 58
10	24	0.190	0.1629	0.1359	0.04167	0.02706	0.00521	0.00174	4 39
12	24	0.216	0.1889	0.1619	0.04167	0.02706	0.00521	0.00174	4 1

American National Fine-Thread Series
Standard Machine Screws

	Identification		Basic Diameters			Thread Data				
Sizes	Threads per Inch, n	Major Diameter, D	Pitch Diameter, E	Minor Diameter, K	Pitch, p	Depth of Thread, h	Basic Width of Flat, p/8	Minimum Width of Flat at Major Diameter of Nut, p/24	Helix Angle at Basic Pitch Diameter, s	
1	2	3	4	5	6	7	8	9	10	
		Inches	Inches	Inches	Inch	Inch	Inch	Inch	Deg. Min.	
0	80	0.060	0.0519	0.0438	0.01250	0.00812	0.00156	0.00052	4	23
1	72	0.073	0.0640	0.0550	0.01389	0.00902	0.00174	0.00058	3	57
2	64	0.086	0.0759	0.0657	0.01562	0.01065	0.00195	0.00065	3	45
3	56	0.099	0.0874	0.0758	0.01786	0.01160	0.00223	0.00074	3	43
4	48	0.112	0.0985	0.0849	0.02083	0.01353	0.00260	0.00087	3	51
5	44	0.125	0.1102	0.0955	0.02273	0.01476	0.00284	0.00095	3	45
6	40	0.138	0.1218	0.1055	0.02500	0.01624	0.00312	0.00104	3	44
8	36	0.164	0.1460	0.1279	0.02778	0.01804	0.00347	0.00116	3	28
10	32	0.190	0.1697	0.1494	0.03125	0.02030	0.00391	0.00130	3	21
12	28	0.216	0.1928	0.1696	0.03571	0.02320	0.00446	0.00149	3	22

American Thread Series

Extra-Fine Thread Series—NEF

(Basic Dimensions)

Sizes	Basic Major Diam., D	Thds. per Inch, n	Basic Pitch Diam.,* E	Minor Diameter External Threads K_s	Minor Diameter Internal Threads K_n	Lead Angle at Basic Pitch Dia., λ		Section at Minor Diameter at $D\text{-}2h_b$	Stress Area
	Inches		Inches	Inches	Inches	Deg.	Min.	Sq. In.	Sq. In.
12(.216)	0.2160	32	0.1957	0.1777	0.1822	2	55	0.0242	0.0269
1/4	0.2500	32	0.2297	0.2177	0.2162	2	29	0.0344	0.0377
5/16	0.3125	32	0.2922	0.2742	0.2787	1	57	0.0581	0.0622
3/8	0.3750	32	0.3547	0.3367	0.3412	1	36	0.0878	0.0929
7/16	0.4375	28	0.4143	0.3937	0.3988	1	34	0.1201	0.1270
1/2	0.5000	28	0.4768	0.4562	0.4613	1	22	0.1616	0.1695
9/16	0.5625	24	0.5354	0.5114	0.5174	1	25	0.2030	0.2134
5/8	0.6250	24	0.5979	0.5739	0.5799	1	16	0.2560	0.2676
11/16	0.6875	24	0.6604	0.6364	0.6424	1	9	0.3151	0.3280
3/4	0.7500	20	0.7175	0.6887	0.6959	1	16	0.3685	0.3855
13/16	0.8125	20	0.7800	0.7512	0.7584	1	10	0.4388	0.4573
7/8	0.8750	20	0.8425	0.8137	0.8209	1	5	0.5153	0.5352
15/16	0.9375	20	0.9050	0.8762	0.8834	1	0	0.5979	0.6194
1	1.0000	20	0.9675	0.9387	0.0459	0	57	0.6866	0.7095
1 1/16	1.0625	18	1.0264	0.9943	1.0024	0	59	0.7702	0.7973
1 1/8	1.1250	18	1.0889	1.0568	1.0649	0	56	0.8705	0.8993
1 3/16	1.1875	18	1.1514	1.1193	1.1274	0	53	0.9770	1.0074
1 1/4	1.2500	18	1.2139	1.1818	1.1899	0	50	1.0895	1.1216
1 5/16	1.3125	18	1.2764	1.2443	1.2524	0	48	1.2802	1.2420
1 3/8	1.3750	18	1.3389	1.3068	1.3149	0	45	1.3330	1.3684
1 7/16	1.4375	18	1.4014	1.3693	1.3774	0	43	1.4640	1.5010
1 1/2	1.5000	18	1.4639	1.4318	1.4399	0	42	1.6011	1.6397
1 9/16	1.5625	18	1.5264	1.4943	1.5024	0	40	0.7444	1.7846
1 5/8	1.6250	18	1.5889	1.5568	1.5649	0	38	1.8937	1.9357
1 11/16	1.6875	18	1.6514	1.6193	1.6274	0	37	2.0493	2.0929
1 3/4	1.7500	16	1.7094	1.6733	1.6823	0	40	2.1873	2.2382
2	2.0000	16	1.9594	1.9233	1.9323	0	35	2.8917	2.9051

*British: Effective Diameter.

American Thread Series

8-Pitch Thread Series—8N

(Basic Dimensions)

Sizes	Basic Major Diameter, D	Basic Pitch Diameter,* E	Minor Diameter Ext. Thds. K_s	Minor Diameter Int. Thds. K_n	Lead Angle at Basic Pitch Dia., λ		Section at Minor Diameter at $D\text{-}2h_b$	Stress Area
Inches	Inches	Inches	Inches	Inches	Deg.	Min.	Sq. In.	Sq. In.
1	1.0000	0.9188	0.8466	0.8647	2	29	0.5510	0.6051
1⅛	1.1250	1.0438	0.9716	0.9897	2	11	0.7277	0.7896
1¼	1.2500	1.1688	1.0966	1.1147	1	57	0.9290	0.9985
1⅜	1.3750	1.2938	1.2216	1.2397	1	46	1.1548	1.2319
1½	1.5000	1.4188	1.3466	1.3647	1	36	1.4052	1.4899
1⅝	1.6250	1.5438	1.4716	1.4897	1	29	1.6801	1.7723
1¾	1.7500	1.6688	1.5966	1.6147	1	22	1.9796	2.0792
1⅞	1.8750	1.7938	1.7216	1.7397	1	16	2.3036	2.4107
2	2.0000	1.9188	1.8466	1.8647	1	11	2.6521	2.7665
2⅛	2.1250	2.0438	1.9716	1.9897	1	7	3.0252	3.1469
2¼	2.2500	2.1688	2.0966	2.1147	1	3	3.4228	3.5519
2½	2.5000	2.4188	2.3466	2.3647	0	57	4.2917	4.4352
2¾	2.7500	2.6688	2.5966	2.6147	0	51	5.2588	5.4164
3	3.0000	2.9188	2.8466	2.8647	0	47	6.3240	6.4957
3¼	3.2500	3.1688	3.0966	3.1147	0	43	7.4874	7.6738
3½	3.5000	3.4188	3.3466	3.3647	0	20	8.7490	8.9504
3¾	3.7500	2.6688	3.5966	3.6147	0	37	10.1088	10.3249
4	4.0000	3.9188	3.8466	3.8647	0	35	11.5667	11.7975
4¼	4.2500	4.1688	4.0966	4.1147	0	33	13.1228	13.3683
4½	4.5000	4.4188	4.3466	4.3647	0	31	14.7771	15.0372
4¾	4.7500	4.6688	4.5966	4.6147	0	29	16.5295	16.8042
5	5.0000	4.9188	4.8466	4.8647	0	28	18.3802	18.6694
5¼	5.2500	5.1688	5.0966	5.1147	0	26	20.3290	20.6330
5½	5.5000	5.4188	5.3466	5.3647	0	25	22.3760	22.6945
5¾	5.7500	5.6688	5.5966	5.6147	0	24	24.5211	24.8541
6	6.0000	5.9188	5.8466	5.8647	0	23	26.7645	27.1118

*British: Effective Diameter.

American Thread Series
12-Pitch Thread Series—12N (Basic Dimensions)

Sizes	Basic Major Diameter, D	Basic Pitch Diameter,* E	Minor Diameter Ext. Thds. K_s	Minor Diameter Int. Thds. K_n	Lead Angle at Basic Pitch Dia., λ		Section at Minor Diameter at $D\text{-}2h_b$	Stress Area
Inches	Inches	Inches	Inches	Inches	Deg.	Min.	Sq. In.	Sq. In.
½	0.5000	0.4459	0.3978	0.4098	3	24	0.1205	0.1374
9⁄16	0.5625	0.5084	0.4603	0.4723	2	59	0.1620	0.2319
5⁄8	0.6250	0.5709	0.5228	0.5348	2	40	0.2635	0.2883
11⁄16	0.6875	0.6334	0.5853	0.5973	2	24	0.3234	0.3508
3⁄4	0.7500	0.6959	0.6478	0.6598	2	11	0.3895	0.4195
13⁄16	0.8125	0.7584	0.7103	0.7233	2	0	0.4617	0.4943
7⁄8	0.8750	0.8209	0.7728	0.7848	1	51	0.4617	0.4943
15⁄16	0.9375	0.8834	0.8353	0.8473	1	43	0.5400	0.5753
1	1.0000	0.9459	0.8978	0.9098	1	36	0.6245	0.6624
1 1⁄16	1.0625	1.0084	0.9603	0.9723	1	30	0.7151	0.7556
1 1⁄8	1.1250	1.0709	1.0228	1.0348	1	25	0.8118	0.8550
1 3⁄16	1.1875	1.3334	1.0853	1.0973	1	20	0.9147	0.9604
1 1⁄4	1.2500	1.1959	1.1478	1.1598	1	16	1.0237	1.0721
1 5⁄16	1.3125	1.2584	1.2103	1.2223	1	12	1.1389	1.1898
1 3⁄8	1.3750	1.3209	1.2728	1.2848	1	9	1.2602	1.3138
1 7⁄16	1.4375	1.3834	1.3353	1.3473	1	6	1.3876	1.4438
1 1⁄2	1.5000	1.4459	1.3978	1.4098	1	3	1.5212	1.5800
1 5⁄8	1.6250	1.5709	1.5228	1.5348	0	58	1.8067	1.8701
1 3⁄4	1.7500	1.6959	1.6478	1.6598	0	54	2.1168	2.1853
1 7⁄8	1.8750	1.8209	1.7728	1.7848	0	50	2.4514	2.5250
2	2.0000	1.9459	1.8978	1,9098	0	47	2.8106	2.8892
2 1⁄8	2.1250	2.0709	2.0228	2.0348	0	44	3.1943	3.2779
2 1⁄4	2.2500	2.1959	2.1478	2.1598	0	42	3.6025	3.6914
2 3⁄8	2.3750	2.3209	2.2728	2.2848	0	39	4.0353	4.1291
2 1⁄2	2.5000	2.4459	2.3978	2.4098	0	37	4.4927	4.5916
2 5⁄8	2.6250	2.5709	2.5228	2.5348	0	35	4.9745	5.0784
2 3⁄4	2.7500	2.6959	2.6478	2.6598	0	34	5.4810	5.5900
2 7⁄8	2.8750	2.8209	2.7728	2.7848	0	32	6.0119	6.1259
3	3.0000	2.9459	2.8978	2.9098	0	31	6.6574	6.6865
3 1⁄8	3.1250	3.0709	3.0228	3.0348	0	30	7.1475	2.2714
3 1⁄4	3.2500	3.1959	3.1478	3.1598	0	29	7.7521	7.8812
3 3⁄8	3.3750	3.3209	3.2728	3.2848	0	27	8.3812	8.5152
3 1⁄2	3.5000	3.4459	3.3978	3.4098	0	26	9.0349	0.1740
3 5⁄8	3.6250	3.5709	3.5228	3.5348	0	26	9.7132	9.8570
3 3⁄4	3.7500	3.6959	3.6478	3.6598	0	25	10.4159	10.5649
3 7⁄8	3.8750	3.8209	3.7728	3.7848	0	24	11.1433	11.2970
4	4.0000	3.9459	3.8978	3.9098	0	23	11.8951	12.0540
4 1⁄4	4.2500	4.1959	4.1478	4.1598	0	22	13.4725	13.6411
4 1⁄2	4.5000	4.4459	4.3978	4.4098	0	21	15.1480	15.3265
4 3⁄4	4.7500	4.6959	4.6478	4.6598	0	19	16.9217	17.1099
5	5.0000	4.9459	4.8978	4.9098	0	18	18.7936	18.9916
5 1⁄4	5.2500	5.1959	5.1478	5.1598	0	18	20.7636	20.9717
5 1⁄2	5.5000	5.4459	5.3978	5.4098	0	17	22.8319	23.0496
5 3⁄4	5.7500	5.6959	5.6478	5.6598	0	16	24.9983	25.2257
6	6.0000	5.9459	5.8978	5.9098	0	15	27.2628	27.4998

*British: Effective Diameter.

American Thread Series
16-Pitch Thread Series—16N (Basic Dimensions)

Sizes	Basic Major Diameter, D	Basic Pitch Diameter,* E	Minor Diameter Ext. Thds. K_s	Minor Diameter Int. Thds. K_n	Lead Angle at Basic Pitch Dia., λ		Section at Minor Diameter at D-2h_b	Stress Area
Inches	Inches	Inches	Inches	Inches	Deg.	Min.	Sq. In.	Sq. In.
¾	0.7500	0.7094	0.6733	0.6823	1	36	0.3513	0.3724
¹³⁄₁₆	0.8125	0.7719	0.7358	0.7448	1	29	0.4200	0.4429
⅞	0.8750	0.8344	0.7983	0.8073	1	22	0.4949	0.5197
¹⁵⁄₁₆	0.9375	0.8969	0.8608	0.8698	1	16	0.5759	0.6025
1	1.0000	0.9594	0.9233	0.9323	1	11	0.6630	0.6916
1¹⁄₁₆	1.0625	1.0219	0.9858	0.9948	1	7	0.7563	0.7867
1⅛	1.1250	1.0844	1.0483	1.0573	1	3	0.8557	0.8880
1³⁄₁₆	1.1875	1.1469	1.1108	1.1198	1	0	0.9612	0.9955
1¼	1.2500	1.2094	1.1733	1.1823	0	57	1.0729	1.1090
1⁵⁄₁₆	1.3125	1.2719	1.2358	1.2448	0	54	1.1907	1.2287
1⅜	1.3750	1.3344	1.2983	1.3073	0	51	1.3147	1.3545
1⁷⁄₁₆	1.4375	1.3969	1.3608	1.3698	0	49	1.4448	1.4865
1½	1.5000	1.4594	1.4233	1.4323	0	47	1.5810	1.6246
1⁹⁄₁₆	1.5625	1.5219	1.4858	1.4948	0	45	1.7234	1.7687
1⅝	1.6250	1.5844	1.5483	1.5573	0	43	1.8719	1.9191
1¹¹⁄₁₆	1.6875	1.6469	1.6108	1.6198	0	42	2.0265	2.0757
1¾	1.7500	1.7094	1.6733	1.6823	0	40	2.1873	2.2382
1¹³⁄₁₆	1.8125	1.7719	1.7358	1.7448	0	39	2.3542	2.4070
1⅞	1.8750	1.8344	1.7983	1.8073	0	37	2.5272	2.5819
1¹⁵⁄₁₆	1.9375	1.8969	1.8608	1.8698	0	36	2.7064	2.7629
2	2.0000	1.9594	1.9233	1.9323	0	35	2.8917	2.9501
2¹⁄₁₆	2.0625	2.0219	1.9858	1.9948	0	34	3.0831	3.1434
2⅛	2.1250	2.0844	2.0483	2.0573	0	33	3.2807	3.3427
2³⁄₁₆	2.1875	2.1469	2.1108	2.1198	0	32	3.4844	3.5483
2¼	2.2500	2.2094	2.1733	2.1823	0	31	3.6943	3.7601
2⁵⁄₁₆	2.3125	2.2719	2.2358	2.2448	0	30	3.9103	3.9780
2⅜	2.3750	2.3344	2.2983	2.3073	0	29	4.1324	4.2018
2⁷⁄₁₆	2.4375	2.3969	2.3608	2.3698	0	29	4.3606	4.4319
2½	2.5000	2.4594	2.4233	2.4323	0	28	4.5950	4.6682
2⅝	2.6250	2.5844	2.5483	2.5573	0	26	5.0822	5.1790
2¾	2.7500	2.7094	2.6733	2.6823	0	25	5.5940	5.6745
2⅞	2.8750	2.8344	2.7983	2.8073	0	24	6.1303	6.2143
3	3.0000	2.9594	2.9233	2.9323	0	23	6.6911	6.7789
3⅛	3.1250	3.0844	3.0483	3.0573	0	22	7.2765	7.3678
3¼	3.2500	3.2094	3.1733	3.1823	0	21	7.8864	7.9814
3⅜	3.3750	3.3344	3.2983	3.3073	0	21	8.5209	8.6194
3½	3.5000	3.4594	3.4233	3.4323	0	20	9.1799	9.2821
3⅝	3.6250	3.5844	3.5483	3.5573	0	19	9.8634	9.9691
3¾	3.7500	3.7094	3.6733	3.6823	0	18	10.5715	10.6809
3⅞	3.8750	3.8344	3.7983	3.8073	0	18	11.3042	11.4170
4	4.0000	3.9594	3.9233	3.9323	0	17	12.0614	12.1779
4¼	4.2500	4.2094	4.1733	4.1823	0	16	13.6494	13.7730
4½	4.5000	4.4594	4.4233	4.4323	0	15	15.3355	15.4662
4¾	4.7500	4.7094	4.6733	4.6823	0	15	17.1199	17.2575
5	5.0000	4.9594	4.9233	4.9323	0	14	19.0024	19.1470
5¼	5.2500	5,2094	5.1733	5.1823	0	13	20.9831	21.1350
5½	5.5000	5.4594	5.4233	5.4323	0	13	23.0620	23.2208
5¾	5.7500	5.7094	5.6733	5.6823	0	12	25.2390	25.4047
6	6.0000	5.9594	5.9233	5.9323	0	11	27.5142	27.6868

*British: Effective Diameter.

367

(Continued from page 361)

74. STRESS AREA. The stress area is the assumed area of an externally threaded part which is used for the purpose of computing the tensile strength.

75. *Terms Relating only to Taper Screw Threads*—Terms relating only to taper threads are defined as follows:

76. PITCH CONE. The pitch cone is an imaginary cone, the surface of which would pass through the threaded profiles at such points as to make the width of the groove equal to one-half of the basic pitch. On a perfect thread this occurs at the point where the widths of the thread and groove are equal.

77. MAJOR CONE. The major cone is an imaginary cone having an apex angle equal to that of the pitch cone, the surface of which bounds the crest of an external thread or the root of an internal thread.

78. SHARP MAJOR CONE. The sharp major cone is an imaginary cone having an apex angle equal to that of the pitch cone, the surface of which would pass through the sharp crest of an external thread or the sharp root of an internal thread.

79. MINOR CONE. The minor cone is an imaginary cone having an apex angle equal to that of the pitch cone, the surface of which bounds the root of an external thread or the crest of an internal thread.

80. SHARP MINOR CONE. The sharp minor cone is an imaginary cone having an apex angle equal to that of the pitch cone, the surface of which would pass through the sharp root of an external thread or the sharp crest of an internal thread.

81. STANDOFF. The standoff is the axial distance between specified reference points on external and internal taper threaded members or gages, when assembled with a specified torque or under other specified conditions.

82. *Letter Symbols and Abbreviations*—Symbols associated with screw threads are of two kinds: (1) Letter symbols for designating dimensions of screw threads and threaded products; and (2) abbreviations used as identification symbols for designating various standard thread forms and thread series.

SCREW THREADS, BRITISH ASSOCIATION

—A 47½-degree screw thread with round top and bottom, similar to the Whitworth. Used by the British manufacturers of small screws and instruments. Similar to some of the European watch and instrument screw threads.

SCREW THREADS, BRITISH CYCLE (OR B. S. C.)

—A series of screw threads developed by the cycle industry of Great Britain. It was first formulated by the Cycle Engineers in 1902 to provide a form of thread of suitable strength for cycle work. The first standard was adopted in 1938; the revision in May, 1950.

FORM OF CYCLE THREAD

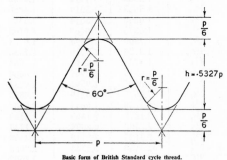

Basic form of British Standard cycle thread.

British Standard Cycle screw threads.

It is a 60-degree thread with a top and bottom radius of ⅙ of the pitch and a height of 0.5327 of the pitch. The form is shown, together with the basic dimensions in sizes from ⅛ to ¾ inch. Special threads run from 1⁷⁄₆₄ to 1⅝ inches. Threads for spokes and nipples are based on the steel wire gage from No. 16 to No. 8, or from 16—0.064 to 8—0.160 inch. The cycle threads were formerly known as the C. E. L. threads and are also designated as B.S.C. threads. See *tables on following pages.*

British Standard Cycle Threads for Bolts and Nuts and Similar Applications
Limits and Tolerances

Bolts   Medium class

1	2	3	4	5	6	7	8	9	10	11
Nominal size	t.p.i.	Major diameter			Effective diameter			Minor diameter		
		max.	tol.	min.	max.	tol.	min.	max.	tol.	min.
in.		in.	in.	in.	in.	in.	in.	in.	in.	in.
⅛	40	0.1250	0.0041	0.1209	0.1117	0.0025	0.1092	0.0984	0.0057	0.0927
⁵⁄₃₂	32	0.1563	0.0045	0.1518	0.1397	0.0028	0.1369	0.1231	0.0063	0.1168
³⁄₁₆	32	0.1875	0.0047	0.1828	0.1709	0.0029	0.1680	0.1543	0.0065	0.1478
⁷⁄₃₂	26	0.2188	0.0051	0.2137	0.1983	0.0032	0.1951	0.1778	0.0071	0.1707
¼	26	0.2500	0.0053	0.2447	0.2295	0.0033	0.2262	0.2090	0.0072	0.2018
⁹⁄₃₂	26	0.2813	0.0054	0.2759	0.2608	0.0034	0.2574	0.2403	0.0074	0.2329
⁵⁄₁₆	26	0.3125	0.0055	0.3070	0.2920	0.0036	0.2884	0.2715	0.0075	0.2640
⅜	26	0.3750	0.0057	0.3693	0.3545	0.0038	0.3507	0.3340	0.0077	0.3263
⁷⁄₁₆	26	0.4375	0.0060	0.4315	0.4170	0.0040	0.4130	0.3965	0.0079	0.3886
½	26	0.5000	0.0061	0.4939	0.4795	0.0042	0.4753	0.4590	0.0081	0.4509
⁹⁄₁₆	26	0.5625	0.0063	0.5562	0.5420	0.0044	0.5376	0.5215	0.0083	0.5132
⅝	26	0.6250	0.0065	0.6185	0.6045	0.0045	0.6000	0.5840	0.0085	0.5755
¹¹⁄₁₆	26	0.6875	0.0067	0.6808	0.6670	0.0047	0.6623	0.6465	0.0086	0.6379
¾	26	0.7500	0.0068	0.7432	0.7295	0.0048	0.7247	0.7090	0.0088	0.7002

British Standard Cycle Threads for Bolts and Nuts and Similar Applications
Limits and Tolerances

Nuts   Free class

1	2	3	4	5	6	7	8	9
Nominal size	t.p.i.	Major diameter	Effective diameter			Minor diameter		
		min.	max.	tol.	min.	max.	tol.	min.
in.		in.	in.	in.	in.	in.	in.	in.
⅛	40	0.1250	0.1155	0.0038	0.1117	0.1074	0.0090	0.0984
⁵⁄₃₂	32	0.1563	0.1439	0.0042	0.1397	0.1334	0.0103	0.1231
³⁄₁₆	32	0.1875	0.1753	0.0044	0.1709	0.1646	0.0103	0.1543
⁷⁄₃₂	26	0.2188	0.2031	0.0048	0.1983	0.1895	0.0117	0.1778
¼	26	0.2500	0.2345	0.0050	0.2295	0.2207	0.0117	0.2090
⁹⁄₃₂	26	0.2813	0.2659	0.0051	0.2608	0.2520	0.0117	0.2403
⁵⁄₁₆	26	0.3125	0.2974	0.0054	0.2920	0.2832	0.0117	0.2715
⅜	26	0.3750	0.3602	0.0057	0.3545	0.3457	0.0117	0.3340
⁷⁄₁₆	26	0.4375	0.4230	0.0060	0.4170	0.4082	0.0117	0.3965
½	26	0.5000	0.4858	0.0063	0.4795	0.4707	0.0117	0.4590
⁹⁄₁₆	26	0.5625	0.5486	0.0066	0.5420	0.5332	0.0117	0.5215
⅝	26	0.6250	0.6113	0.0068	0.6045	0.5957	0.0117	0.5840
¹¹⁄₁₆	26	0.6875	0.6741	0.0071	0.6670	0.6582	0.0117	0.6465
¾	26	0.7500	0.7367	0.0072	0.7295	0.7207	0.0117	0.7090

British Standard Cycle Threads for Bolts and Nuts and Similar Applications

Limits and Tolerances

Nuts　　　　　　　　　　　　　　　　　　　　　　　　　　　　Medium class

1	2	3	4	5	6	7	8	9
Nominal size	t.p.i.	Major diameter	Effective diameter			Minor diameter		
		min.	max.	tol.	min.	max.	tol.	min.
in.		in.	in.	in.	in.	in.	in.	in.
1/8	40	0.1250	0.1142	0.0025	0.1117	0.1074	0.0090	0.0984
5/32	32	0.1563	0.1425	0.0028	0.1397	0.1334	0.0103	0.1231
3/16	32	0.1875	0.1738	0.0029	0.1709	0.1646	0.0103	0.1543
7/32	26	0.2188	0.2015	0.0032	0.1983	0.1895	0.0117	0.1778
1/4	26	0.2500	0.2328	0.0033	0.2295	0.2207	0.0117	0.0290
9/32	26	0.2813	0.2642	0.0034	0.2608	0.2520	0.0117	0.2403
5/16	26	0.3125	0.2956	0.0036	0.2920	0.2832	0.0117	0.2715
3/8	26	0.3750	0.3583	0.0038	0.3545	0.3457	0.0117	0.3340
7/16	26	0.4375	0.4210	0.0040	0.4170	0.4082	0.0117	0.3965
1/2	26	0.5000	0.4837	0.0042	0.4795	0.4707	0.0117	0.4590
9/16	26	0.5625	0.5464	0.0044	0.5420	0.5532	0.0117	0.5215
5/8	26	0.6250	0.6090	0.0045	0.6045	0.5957	0.0117	0.5840
11/16	26	0.6875	0.6717	0.0047	0.6670	0.6582	0.0117	0.6465
3/4	26	0.7500	0.7343	0.0048	0.7295	0.7207	0.0117	0.7090

British Standard Cycle Threads for Bolts and Nuts and Similar Applications

Basic Dimensions

1	2	3	4	5	6	7
Nominal diameter of screw	No. of threads per inch	Pitch	Depth of thread	Basic diameters		
				Major	Effective	Minor
in.				in.	in.	in.
1/8	40	0.02500	0.0133	0.1250	0.1117	0.0984
5/32	32	0.03125	0.0166	0.1563	0.1397	0.1231
3/16	32	0.03125	0.0166	0.1875	0.1709	0.1543
7/32	26	0.03846	0.0205	0.2188	0.1983	0.1778
1/4	26	0.03846	0.0205	0.2500	0.2295	0.2090
9/32	26	0.03846	0.0205	0.2813	0.2608	0.2403
5/16	26	0.03846	0.0205	0.3125	0.2920	0.2715
3/8	26	0.03846	0.0205	0.3750	0.3545	0.3340
7/16	26	0.03846	0.0205	0.4375	0.4170	0.3965
1/2	26	0.03846	0.0205	0.5000	0.4795	0.4590
9/16	26	0.03846	0.0205	0.5625	0.5420	0.5215
5/8	26	0.03846	0.0205	0.6250	0.6045	0.5840
11/16	26	0.03846	0.0205	0.6875	0.6670	0.6465
3/4	26	0.03846	0.0205	0.7500	0.7295	0.7090

British Standard Cycle Threads for Spokes and Nipples

Basic Dimensions

1	2	3	4	5	6	7	8
Nominal diameter of wire*		Number of threads per in. (R.H.)	Pitch	Depth of thread	Basic diameters		
					Major	Effective	Minor
S.W.G.	in.		in.	in.	in.	in.	in.
16	0.064	56	0.01786	0.0095	0.0735	0.0640	0.0545
15	0.072	56	0.01786	0.0095	0.0815	0.0720	0.0625
14	0.080	56	0.01786	0.0095	0.0895	0.0800	0.0705
13	0.092	56	0.01786	0.0095	0.1015	0.0920	0.0825
12	0.104	56	0.01786	0.0095	0.1135	0.1040	0.0945
11	0.116	44	0.02273	0.0121	0.1281	0.1160	0.1039
10	0.128	40	0.02500	0.0133	0.1413	0.1280	0.1147
9	0.144	40	0.02500	0.0133	0.1573	0.1440	0.1307
8	0.160	32	0.03125	0.0166	0.1766	0.1600	0.1434

*The diameter is that of the end portion of the spoke on which the thead is rolled, and is not necessarily the same as that of the body of the spoke; it is equal to the basic (minimum) effective diameter of the spoke thread (Col. 7).

The buttress thread has a 45° angle of thread with one side perpendicular to the axis. The proportion of this thread are shown.

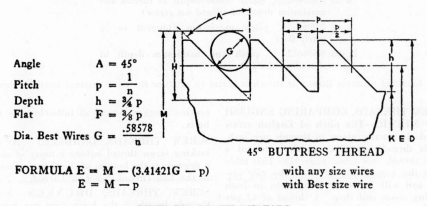

Angle	$A = 45°$
Pitch	$p = \dfrac{1}{n}$
Depth	$h = \frac{3}{4} p$
Flat	$F = \frac{3}{8} p$
Dia. Best Wires	$G = \dfrac{.58578}{n}$

45° BUTTRESS THREAD

$$\text{FORMULA } E = M - (3.41421G - p)$$
$$E = M - p$$

with any size wires

with Best size wire

BUTTRESS SCREW THREADS.

SCREW THREADS, BUTTRESS—A thread having a square face and a 45-degree back angle. It is not as easily machined as the modified buttress thread.

Buttress Threads

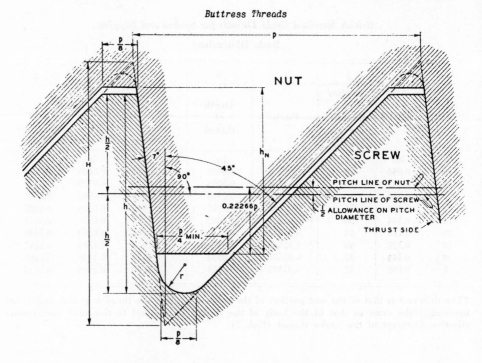

$H = 0.890643 \times pitch$

$h = 0.667892 \times pitch$ (basic depth of thread and maximum depth of thread on screw)

$r = 0.0962 \times pitch$—maximum (tangent to $\frac{1}{8}$ pitch flat)

$h_n = 0.556652 \times pitch$ and maximum depth of thread in the nut

The modified buttress thread as shown is easier to produce than the original buttress thread.

SCREW THREADS, COMPARING ENGLISH AND METRIC—The pitch of English screw threads is usually given in threads per inch. Metric threads are given in the pitch of a single thread. See table, page 373. This table shows the comparison between the two systems and will be found convenient in both drawing room and shop. A thread of 32 per inch has a pitch of 0.0312 inch or 0.794 millimeter. The table will save time whenever comparison becomes necessary for any reason.

SCREW THREADS, CROSSED—When threaded parts are put together without their axes being in the same plane. When one thread

crosses another instead of following the true helix.

SCREW THREADS, DARDELET—A self-locking screw thread having a taper of about 6 degrees at the bottom of the thread. Similar to the Lok-Thread. See *Lok Thread*.

SCREW THREADS, DRUNKEN—Screw threads in which the helix does not have a constant helix angle. When threads were chased by hand it took skill to swing the chaser uniformly enough to secure a constant lead angle. The term is practically obsolete now that screw threads are cut by mechanical means.

Comparison Between English and Metric Screw-Thread Pitches

Common English Pitches			Common Metric Pitches			Designation of Screw System
Threads per Inch	Pitch		Pitch		Threads per Inch	
	Inches	mm	mm	Inches		
4	0.2500	6.350	8.0	0.3150	3.2	
4½	.2222	5.644	7.5	.2953	3.4	
5	.2000	5.080	7.0	.2756	3.6	
6	.1667	4.233	6.5	.2559	3.9	
7	.1434	3.629	6.0	.2362	4.2	
7½	.1333	3.387	5.5	.2165	4.6	
8	.1250	3.175	5.0	.1968	5.1	International System (Grosse Mecanique) Screws of 6 mm Dia. and above
9	.1111	2.822	4.5	.1772	5.6	
10	.1000	2.540	4.0	.1575	6.4	
11	.0909	2.309	3.5	.1378	7.3	
11½	.0870	2.209	3.0	.1181	8.5	
12	.0833	2.117	2.5	.0984	10.2	
13	.0769	1,954	2.0	.0787	12.7	
14	.0714	1.814	1.75	.0689	14.5	
16	.0625	1.588	1.50	.0591	16.9	
18	.0556	1.411	1.25	.0492	20.3	French System (Petite Mecanique) Screws below 6 mm Dia. (Small machine screws)
20	.0500	1.270	1.00	.0394	25.4	
24	.0417	1.058	.90	.0354	28.2	
27	.0370	.941	.75	.0295	33.9	
28	.0357	.907	.60	.0236	42.3	
32	.0312	.794	.45	.0177	56.4	Small machine screws and watch-makers screws. Sizes common to both
36	.0278	.706	.42	.0165	60.5	
40	.0250	.635	.39	.0154	65.1	
44	.0227	.577	.36	.0142	70.6	
48	.0208	.529	.33	.0130	77	
56	.0179	.454	.30	.0118	85	
64	.0156	.397	.27	.0106	94	
72	.0139	.353	.24	.0094	106	
80	.0125	.318	.21	.0083	121	
			.19	.0075	134	
			.17	.0067	149	Watch-makers screws
			.15	.0059	169	
			.13	.0051	195	
			.11	.0043	231	

SCREW THREAD CHASERS—See *Chasers, Screw Thread.*

SCREW THREADS, CONSTANTS FOR PITCH AND ROOT DIAMETERS—To find the pitch diameter or root diameter of any screw thread between 3 and 72 threads per inch, subtract the constant for the number of threads per inch from the outside diameter. The pitch diameter of a 2-inch screw with 24 threads per inch would be 2 inches minus 0.0271 inch for an American National thread, or 2 inches minus 0.0267 for a 55-degree Whitworth thread. It must be remembered that future Whitworth threads will be 60 degrees.

Constants for Finding Pitch Diameter and Root Diameter of Screw Threads

Threads Per Inch	Constants for Finding Pitch Diameter			Constants for Finding Root Diameter		
	U.S.S. Thread	Whit. Thread	Theoretical V	U.S.S. Thread	Whit. Thread	Theoretical V
72	.0090	.0089	.0120	.01804	.01786	.02406
64	.0101	.0100	.0315	.02030	.02001	.02706
60	.0108	.0107	.0144	.02165	.02134	.02887
56	.0116	.0114	.0155	.02320	.02286	.03093
50	.0130	.0128	.0173	.02598	.02562	.03464
48	.0135	.0133	.0180	.02706	.02668	.03608
44	.0148	.0146	.0197	.02952	.02910	.03936
40	.0162	.0160	.0217	.03248	.03202	.04330
36	.0180	.0178	.0241	.03608	.03558	.04811
32	.0203	.0200	.0271	.04059	.04002	.05413
30	.0217	.0213	.0289	.04330	.04268	.05773
28	.0232	.0229	.0309	.04639	.04574	.06186
27	.0241	.0237	.0321	.04812	.04742	.06416
26	.0250	.0246	.0333	.04996	.04926	.06662
24	.0271	.0267	.0361	.05413	.05336	.07217
22	.0295	.0291	.0394	.05905	.05821	.07873
20	.0325	.0320	.0433	0.6495	.06403	.08660
18	.0361	.0355	.0481	.07217	.07114	.09623
16	.0406	.0400	.0541	.08119	.08004	.10825
14	.0464	.0457	.0619	.09279	.09147	.12372
13	.0499	.0493	.0666	.09993	.09851	.13323
12	.0541	.0533	.0722	.10852	.10672	.14434
11½	.0565	.0557	.0753	.11296	.11132	.15062
11	.0590	.0582	.0787	.11809	.11642	.15746
10	.0649	.0640	.0866	.12990	.12806	.17321
9	.0721	.0711	.0962	.14434	.14230	.19245
8	.0812	.0800	.1082	.16238	.16008	.21651
7	.0928	.0914	.1237	.18558	.18295	.24744
6	.1082	.1066	.1443	.21651	.21344	.28868
5½	.1180	.1164	.1575	.23619	.23284	.31492
5	.1299	.1280	.1732	.25891	.25613	.34641
4½	.1433	.1422	.1924	.28868	.28458	.38490
4	.1624	.1601	.2165	.32476	.32017	.43301
3½	.1855	.1830	.2474	.37115	.36590	.49487
3¼	.1998	.1970	.2665	.39970	.39404	.53294
3	.2165	.2134	.2887	.43301	.42689	.57733

To find the pitch diameter or root diameter of any screw thread, subtract the constant for the number of threads per inch from the outside diameter.

American National Rolled Threads for Lamp-Base Screw Shells
(Dimensions in Inches)

Size	Threads per Inch	Pitch	Depth of Thread	Radius	Major Diameter		Minor Diameter	
					6	7	8	9
1	2	3	4	5	Max.	Min.	Max.	Min.
Miniature...	14	0.07143	0.020	0.0210	0.375	0.370	0.335	0.330
Candelabra..	10	0.10000	0.025	0.0312	0.465	0.460	0.415	0.410
Intermediate.	9	0.11111	0.027	0.0353	0.651	0.645	0.597	0.591
Medium.....	7	0.14286	0.033	0.0470	1.037	1.031	0.971	0.965
Mogul......	4	0.25000	0.050	0.0906	1.555	1.545	1.455	1.455

American National Rolled Threads for Socket Screw Shells
(Dimensions in Inches)

Size	Threads per Inch	Pitch	Depth of Thread	Radius	Major Diameter		Minor Diameter	
					6	7	8	9
1	2	3	4	5	Max.	Min.	Max.	Min.
Miniature....	14	0.07143	0.020	0.0210	0.3835	0.3775	0.3435	0.3375
Candelabra..	10	0.10000	0.025	0.0312	0.476	0.470	0.426	0.420
Intermediate.	9	0.11111	0.027	0.0353	0.664	0.657	0.610	0.603
Medium.....	7	0.14286	0.033	0.0470	1.053	1.045	0.987	0.979
Mogul......	4	0.25000	0.050	0.906	1.577	1.565	1.477	1.465

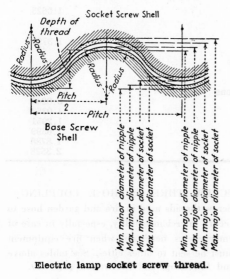

Electric lamp socket screw thread.

SCREW THREADS, ELECTRIC LAMP SOCKETS—These threads have been standardized for interchangeability and safety. There are five sizes, from miniature to mogul, as shown, for base screw shells and socket screw shells. The form of thread is also shown.

SCREW THREADS, EIGHT PITCH—A series of screw threads with 8 threads per inch regardless of diameter. The screws run from 1 to 6 inches in diameter. They are used for bolts in high-pressure pipe flanges, cylinder head studs and similar places.

Length of Thread for Hose Couplings and Nipples

Service and Nominal Size	Threads per Inch	Length of Nipple L	Depth of Coupling H	Thread Length for Coupling T	Length of Pilot I	Inside Diameter of Nipple C	Approx. Number of Threads in Length "T"
Garden							
1/2, 5/8, 3/4	11 1/2	9/16	17/32	3/8	1/8	25/32	4 1/4
Chemical							
3/4, 1	8	5/8	19/32	15/32	5/32	1 1/32	3 3/4
Fire							
1 1/2	9	5/8	19/32	15/32	5/32	1 17/32	4 1/4
Other Connections							
1/2	14	1/2	15/32	5/16	1/8	17/32	4 1/4
3/4	14	9/16	17/32	3/8	1/8	25/32	5 1/4
1—	11 1/2	9/16	17/32	3/8	5/32	1 1/32	4 1/4
1 1/4	11 1/2	5/8	19/32	15/32	5/32	1 9/32	5 1/2
1 1/2	11 1/2	5/8	19/32	15/32	5/32	1 17/32	5 1/2
2—	11 1/2	3/4	23/32	19/32	3/16	2 1/32	6 3/4

All dimensions given in inches.

Thread and chamfer angles: "X" equals 60 deg; "Y" equals 35 deg.

Basic Thread Dimensions

Service and Nominal Size	Number of Threads per Inch	Outside Diameter of Nipple Thread (Max)
Garden and Similar Hose		
1/2, 5/8, 3/4	11 1/2	1.0625
Chemical Engine and Booster Hose		
3/4, 1	8	1.3750
Fire Protection Hose		
1 1/2	9	1.9900
Steam, Water, Air, Oil, and All Other Hose Connections		
1/2	14	0.8248
3/4	14	1.0353
1	11 1/2	1.2951
1 1/4	11 1/2	1.6399
1 1/2	11 1/2	1.8788
2	11 1/2	2.3528

All dimensions given in inches.

SCREW THREADS, GAS CYLINDER—Screw threads used in connection with gas cylinder valve outlets of various types. They have been standardized to prevent cross connections between equipment of different types where such connections might be hazardous. See table page 386.

SCREW THREADS, HOSE COUPLING—Screw threads used in fire and garden hose to secure interchangeability, especially in case of emergencies necessary when fire equipment must be sent to other cities. See tables above and following, and illustration page 379.

HOSE COUPLING SCREW THREADS

NIPPLE.

Service and Nominal Size	Threads per Inch	Pitch	Depth of Thread	Major Diameter			Pitch Diameter			Minor Diam
				Max	Tol	Min	Max	Tol	Min	Max
Garden* 1/2, 5/8, 3/4	11½	0.08696	0.05648	1.0625	0.0170	1.0455	1.0060	0.0085	0.9975	0.9495
Chemical 3/4, 1	8	0.12500	0.08119	1.3750	0.0222	1.3528	1.2938	0.0111	1.2827	1.2126
Fire 1½	9	0.11111	0.07217	1.9900	0.0222	1.9678	1.9178	0.0111	1.9067	1.8457
Other Connections[1]										
1/2	14	0.07143	0.04639	0.8248	0.0140	0.8108	0.7784	0.0070	0.7714	0.7320
3/4	14	0.07143	0.04639	1.0353	0.0140	1.0213	0.9889	0.0070	0.9819	0.9425
*1—	11½	0.08696	0.05648	1.2951	0.0170	1.2781	1.2386	0.0085	1.2301	1.1821
*1¼—	11½	0.08696	0.05648	1.6399	0.0170	1.6229	1.5834	0.0085	1.5749	1.5269
*1½—	11½	0.08696	0.05648	1.8788	0.0170	1.8618	1.8223	0.0085	1.8138	1.7658
*2—	11½	0.08696	0.05648	2.3528	0.0170	2.3358	2.2963	0.0085	2.2878	2.2398

All dimensions given in inches.

[1] These dimensions permit hose connections to American Standard Straight Pipe Thread.

[2] Dimensions for the minimum major diameter of the coupling correspond to the basic flat ($1/8 \times p$), and the profile at the major diameter produced by a worn tool must not fall below the basic outline. The maximum major diameter of the coupling shall be that corresponding to a flat at the major diameter of the coupling equal to $1/24 \times p$, and may be determined by adding $12/9 \times h$ (or $0.7939 p$) to the maximum pitch diameter of the coupling.

[3] Dimensions given for the maximum minor diameter of the nipple are figured to the intersection of the worn tool arc with a center line through crest and root. The minimum minor diameter of the nipple shall be that corresponding to a flat at the minor diameter of the nipple equal to $1/24 \times p$, and may be determined by subtracting $12/9 \times h$ (or $0.7939 p$) from the minimum pitch diameter of the nipple.

* The limiting dimensions for these sizes are identical with the dimensions given in the 1921, 1924, 1928, and 1933 Reports of the National Screw Thread Commission.

377

HOSE COUPLING SCREW THREADS

Detail Thread Dimensions

Basic thread form is American National Standard, having an included angle of 60 deg. and truncated top and bottom.

COUPLING.

Service and Nominal Size	Threads per Inch	Pitch	Depth of Thread	Major Diam Min²	Pitch Diameter			Minor Diameter		
					Max	Tol	Min	Max³	Tol	Min
Garden* 1/2, 5/8, 3/4	11½	0.08696	0.05648	1.0725	1.0245	0.0085	1.0160	0.9765	0.0170	0.9595
Chemical 3/4, 1	8	0.12500	0.08119	1.3870	1.3169	0.0111	1.3058	1.2468	0.0222	1.2246
Fire 1½	9	0.11111	0.07217	2.0020	1.9409	0.0111	1.9298	1.8799	0.0222	1.8577
Other Connections¹										
1/2	14	0.07143	0.04639	0.8323	0.7929	0.0070	0.7859	0.7535	0.0140	0.7395
3/4	14	0.07143	0.04639	1.0428	1.0034	0.0070	0.9964	0.9640	0.0140	0.9500
*1	11½	0.08696	0.05648	1.3051	1.2571	0.0085	1.2486	1.2091	0.0170	1.1921
*1¼	11½	0.08696	0.05648	1.6499	1.6019	0.0085	1.5934	1.5539	0.0170	1.5369
*1½	11½	0.08696	0.05648	1.8888	1.8408	0.0085	1.8323	1.7928	0.0170	1.7758
*2	11½	0.08696	0.05648	2.3628	2.3148	0.0085	2.3063	2.2668	0.0170	2.2498

THREAD FORMS COMMONLY USED ...

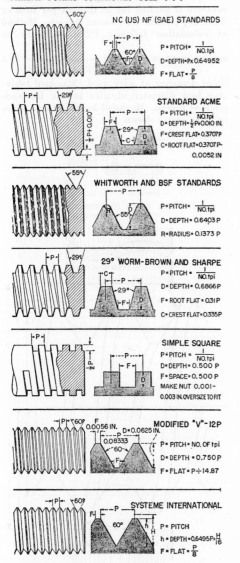

NC (US) NF (SAE) STANDARDS

P = PITCH = $\frac{1}{NO.tpi}$
D = DEPTH = P × 0.64952
F = FLAT = $\frac{P}{8}$

STANDARD ACME

P = PITCH = $\frac{1}{NO.tpi}$
D = DEPTH = $\frac{1}{2}$P + 0.010 IN.
F = CREST FLAT = 0.3707 P
C = ROOT FLAT = 0.3707 P − 0.0052 IN

WHITWORTH AND BSF STANDARDS

P = PITCH = $\frac{1}{NO.tpi}$
D = DEPTH = 0.6403 P
R = RADIUS = 0.1373 P

29° WORM-BROWN AND SHARPE

P = PITCH = $\frac{1}{NO.tpi}$
D = DEPTH = 0.6866 P
F = ROOT FLAT = 0.31 P
C = CREST FLAT = 0.335 P

SIMPLE SQUARE

P = PITCH = $\frac{1}{NO.tpi}$
D = DEPTH = 0.500 P
F = SPACE = 0.500 P
MAKE NUT 0.001 − 0.003 IN. OVERSIZE TO FIT

MODIFIED "V"-12P

P = PITCH = NO. OF tpi
D = DEPTH = 0.750 P
F = FLAT = P ÷ 14.87

SYSTEME INTERNATIONAL

P = PITCH
h = DEPTH = 0.6495 P + $\frac{H}{16}$
F = FLAT = $\frac{P}{8}$

Screw-thread forms commonly used.

SCREW THREADS, HOWARD WATCH—A 45-degree V-thread which was largely used by watchmakers before the adoption of the new standards.

SCREW THREADS, HUGHES—A form of thread designed by the Hughes Tool Co. for use in oil tool pipe joints. They are of Acme

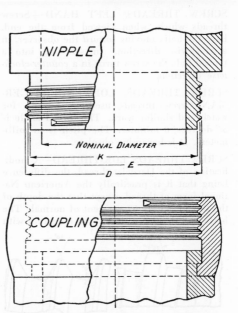

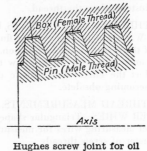

Hose coupling screw threads. American National hose coupling and American National fire-hose coupling threads.

form, 4 threads per inch and a taper of 3⅜ inch per foot, which makes 8 degrees each side of the center line, or an inclined taper of 16 degrees. There is a clearance of 0.010 inch at the top and bottom of the threads.

Hughes screw joint for oil well tools.

SCREW THREADS, JUMP—A shop term for threads on different diameters, such as used in the breech blocks of artillery. Named because the tool has to jump back as the larger diameter reaches it. The different diameters are in the same plane and permit the block to be inserted in the breech of the gun and tightened by a small part of a turn.

SCREW THREADS, LEFT HAND — Screw threads which, when viewed from the end, have the helix moving *toward* the observer, in a clockwise direction. In screwing into a tapped hole the screw turns in a *counter-clockwise* direction.

SCREW THREADS, LOEWENHERZ - GERMAN—Screw threads used in Europe for watch and similar work. The thread angle is 53 degrees, 8 minutes. The pitch is in millimeters. It is becoming obsolete.

SCREW THREADS, LOK-THREAD—A modification of the Dardelet thread, the difference being that it is practically the American National form of thread except that the depth of the thread is only 60 per cent of normal. The bottom of the thread is tapered 6 degrees with

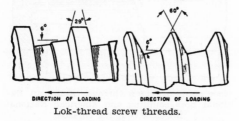

Lok-thread screw threads.

the axis, the larger diameter being toward the point of the stud or bolt. As the nut is tightened, the top of the nut thread is forced up on the 6 degree surface of the stud. This deforms the thread in the nut and binds it on the bolt, putting the tension on the body of the bolt instead of on the thread.

SCREW THREAD MEASUREMENTS, FLUSH WIRES—Wires which come even or flush with the top of the threads when in position. When used in connection with Acme screw threads, they neglect the effect of the angle of lead, and are becoming obsolete.

SCREW THREAD MEASUREMENTS, ROOT DIAMETER WIRES—Triangular shaped high-speed steel measuring wires for measuring the root diameter of screw threads.

SCREW THREADS, MEASURING WITH WIRES—A method of measuring the pitch diameter of a screw by placing wires of the right diameter in the thread angles and measuring across their outer diameter. Two systems are used, one using two wires and one using three wires. The three-wire system is more popular. The "best" wire to use is one which contacts the threads at the pitch line. Larger wires can be used but are not advised.

The pressure used is important. One-pound pressure is advised for 20 threads per inch or finer, 2½ pounds for coarser threads. Method of calculation follows:

$$\text{Pitch diameter} = \text{measurement over wires} + \frac{0.866025}{\text{Thds. per inch}} - 3$$

times diameter of wire used. Standard tables give best diameter of wire to use for each pitch of thread. Means of holding three wires in position are shown.

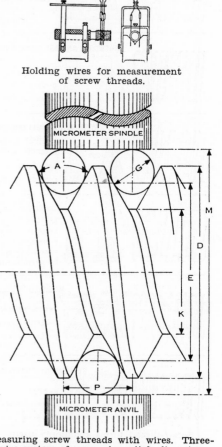

Holding wires for measurement of screw threads.

Measuring screw threads with wires. Three-wire system of measuring pitch diameter.
M = measurement over wires   G = diameter of wire
K = root diameter   P = pitch
D = major diameter of thread   E = pitch diameter
    A = angle of thread

SCREW THREADS, METRIC—Metric threads are designated by the distance in millimeters from one thread to the next instead of giving

the number per centimeter or decimeter. See *Screw Threads, Comparing English and Metric.*

No. Thds. per Inch.	$G = \frac{.57735}{N}$ Dia. Best Wire	$H = \frac{.86602}{N}$ Depth V Thd.	$h = \frac{.64951}{N}$ Depth US. Thd.	$N = \frac{\text{No. Thds.}}{\text{Per Inch}}$ Min. Wire	Max. Wire
80	.00722″	.01083″	.00812″	80	50
72	.00802	.01203	.00902	72	44
64	.00902	.01353	.01014	64	40
56	.01031	.01546	.01160	56	36
50	.01155	.01732	.01299	50	32
48	.01203	.01804	.01353	50	28
44	.01312	.01968	.01476	50	26
40	.01443	.02165	.01624	44	24
36	.01604	.02406	.01804	40	22
32	.01804	.02706	.02030	36	20
30	.01924	.02887	.02161	32	19
28	.02062	.03093	.02319	30	18
27	.02138	.03207	.02406	30	18
26	.02221	.03331	.02498	28	16
24	.02406	.03608	.02706	26	16
22	.02624	.03936	.02952	24	14
20	.02887	.04330	.03248	22	13
18	.03207	.04811	.03608	20	11½
16	.03608	.05413	.04060	18	10
14	.04124	.06186	.04640	14	9
13	.04441	.06662	.04996	14	9
12	.04811	.07217	:05413	13	8
11½	.05020	.07531	.05648	12	8
11	.05249	.07873	.05904	11½	7
10	.05774	.08660	.06495	11	6
9	.06415	.09622	.07218	10	6
8	.07217	.10825	.08119	9	5½
7½	.07698	.11547	.08660	8	4½
7	.08248	.12372	.09279	8	4½
6	.09623	.14434	.10825	6	4
5½	.10497	.15746	.11805	6	4
5	.11547	.17320	.12990	5½	4
4½	.12830	.19245	.14434	5	4
4	.14434	.21651	.16238	4½	

Note: — Sometimes taps have an outside diameter **over basic,** and the minimum wires given may not project above the tops of the thread.

Modified square screw thread (10-degree).

SCREW THREADS, MODIFIED BUTTRESS
—Modified buttress threads have a 7-degree

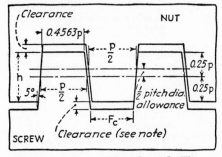

Measuring Screw Threads with Wires

angle on the face of the threads, making a total of 52 degrees from the back face. Details are shown and dimensions given. See *Screw Threads, Buttress.*

SCREW THREADS, MODIFIED SQUARE— Owing to the difficulty of cutting screw threads with the sides exactly 90 degrees from the axis, they are seldom used. Where it is felt that the 29-degree Acme thread is too great an angle, the angle of 10 degrees is used and called a "10-degree square thread." Some use a 15-degree angle.

SCREW THREADS, MONGREL—Any threads which are not standard in either pitch or angle. The same as bastard threads.

SCREW THREADS, MULTIPLE OR MULTI-START—Screws with two or more leads on a single screw. Used to secure rapid leads without full depth of threads. A double thread is a "two-lead" screw, a triple thread a "three-lead" screw, etc. They give rapid advance to moving parts with a thread of little depth. Especially useful on hollow screws or threaded parts.

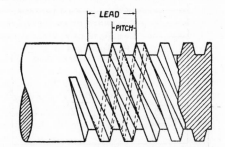

Multiple of multiple-start screw threads.

SCREW THREADS, N. H. S.—The Swiss standard of screw threads for watches. N. H. S. are the initials of Normes re L'industries Horologere Suissex.

SCREW THREADS, OIL WELL—A modified Acme thread designed by Hughes Tool Co. for use on oil well tools. See *Screw Threads, Hughes.*

SCREW THREADS, NEW YORK WATCH CO.—55-degree V-threads used many years ago.

SCREW THREADS, PARALLEL — British term for straight screw threads or those of uniform diameter.

SCREW THREADS, PIPE—American (Briggs) standard pipe threads are tapered 1 inch in 16, or ¾ inch per foot. They are 60-degree threads of National form with flat or rounded top and bottom. Thread angle is measured from the axis and not from the tapered outside. Standard sizes are given on page 384. Points at which threads are measured are shown. Pipes are also made with straight threads but are not generally used for carrying internal pressure. These sizes are also shown. The pitch of pipe threads varies from the British mainly because they use a finer pitch thread on account of using pipe with thinner walls. These

are also given under *Screw Threads, Pipe, British.*

SCREW THREADS, PIPE, BRITISH—British pipe threads as made in this country conform to the British Engineering Standards Committee. The taper is ¾ inch per foot, as with the American. The thread is a modified Whitworth of 55-degree angle, the depth being $0.4925 \times$ the pitch. The number of threads per inch is more than with American, 11 per inch being used on all pipe above ⅞ inch in diameter. This may be changed to 60 degree angle as in A. B. C. threads.

Screw Threads

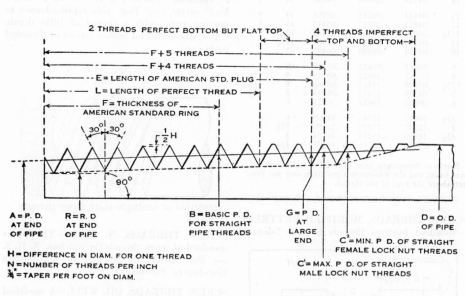

Pipe screw threads. American (Briggs) Pipe Standard (with lock nut thread and basic pipe sizes).

American Standard Pipe Threads

NPTF SIZE	PITCH, p	PD AT END OF EXT THREAD, E_0	PD AT END OF INT THREAD, E_1	HAND ENGAGEMENT, L_1		LENGTH OF FULL THREAD, L_2		VANISH THREADS V PLUS FULL THREAD TOLER PLUS SHOULDER CLEAR. ($V + 1p + \frac{1}{2}p$)		SHOULDER LENGTH $L_1 + (3p$ APPROX)	EXTERNAL THREAD FOR DRAW ($L_4 - L_1$)		LENGTH OF INTERNAL FULL THREAD ($L_1 + L_3$)		OUTSIDE DIAMETER OF FITTING, D_1	OUTSIDE DIAMETER OF PIPE, D
	in.	in.	in.	in.	thd	in.	thd	in.	thd	in.	in.	thd	in.	thd	in.	in.
1	2	3	4	5	6	7	8	9	10	11	12	13	14	15	16	17
1⁄16-27	0.03704	0.27118	0.28118	0.160	4.32	0.2611	7.05	0.1139	3.075	0.3750	0.1011	2.73	0.2711	7.32	0.315	0.3125
1⁄8-27	0.03704	0.36351	0.37360	0.1615	4.36	0.2638	7.12	0.1112	3.072	0.3750	0.1023	2.76	0.2726	7.36	0.407	0.405
1⁄4-18	0.05556	0.47739	0.49163	0.2278	4.10	0.4018	7.23	0.1607	2.892	0.5625	0.1740	3.13	0.3945	7.10	0.546	0.540
3⁄8-18	0.05556	0.61201	0.62701	0.240	4.32	0.4078	7.34	0.1547	2.791	0.5625	0.1678	3.02	0.4067	7.32	0.681	0.675
1⁄2-14	0.07143	0.75843	0.77843	0.320	4.48	0.5337	7.47	0.2163	3.028	0.7500	0.2137	2.99	0.5343	7.48	0.850	0.840
3⁄4-14	0.07143	0.96768	0.98887	0.339	4.75	0.5457	7.64	0.2043	2.860	0.7500	0.2067	2.89	0.5533	7.75	1.060	1.050
1-11½	0.08696	1.21363	1.23863	0.400	4.60	0.6828	7.85	0.2547	2.929	0.9375	0.2828	3.25	0.6609	7.60	1.327	1.315
1¼-11½	0.08696	1.55713	1.58338	0.420	4.83	0.7068	8.13	0.2620	3.013	0.9688	0.2868	3.30	0.6809	7.83	1.672	1.660
1½-11½	0.08696	1.79609	1.82234	0.420	4.83	0.7235	8.32	0.2765	3.180	1.0000	0.3035	3.49	0.6809	7.83	1.912	1.900
2-11½	0.08696	2.28902	2.29627	0.436	5.01	0.7565	8.70	0.2747	3.159	1.0312	0.3205	3.69	0.6969	8.01	2.387	2.375
2½-8	0.12500	2.71953	2.76216	0.682	5.46	1.1374	9.10	0.3781	3.025	1.5156	0.4555	3.64	1.0570	8.46	2.893	2.875
3-8	0.12500	3.34063	3.38850	0.766	6.13	1.2000	9.60	0.3781	3.025	1.5781	0.4340	3.47	1.1410	9.13	3.518	3.500

British Standard Pipe Threads and Pipe Gage Threads
American Practice

Pipe Size Nominal Inside Diameter Inches	Approx. Outside Diameter of Pipe Inches	Threads Per Inch (N)	Pitch Inches (P)	Depth of Full Form Pipe Thread Inches (H)	Truncation from Single Thread Depth on Gage Threads Inches (T)	Pitch Diameter at Gaging Point Inches	Distance from Small End to Gaging Point Inches (F)	Major Diameter of Pipe Thread at Gaging Point Inches	Major Diameter of Plug Gage at Gaging Point P&W Modified Form Inches	Minor Diameter of Ring Gage at Gaging Notch P&W Modified Form Inches	Length of Plug and Ring Inches	Minimum Length of Thread on Pipe Inches
1/8	13/32	28	.03571	.0229	.0026	.3601	.1563	.383	.3777	.3425	.3114	3/8
1/4	17/32	19	.05263	.0337	.0039	.4843	.1875	.518	.5102	.4584	.3625	7/16
3/8	11/16	19	.05263	.0337	.0039	.6223	.2500	.656	.6482	.5964	.4083	1/2
1/2	27/32	14	.07143	.0457	.0053	.7793	.2500	.825	.8144	.7441	.5208	5/8
5/8	15/16	14	.07143	.0457	.0053	.8563	.2500	.902	.8914	.8211	.5208	5/8
3/4	1 1/16	14	.07143	.0457	.0053	.9953	.3750	1.041	1.0304	.9601	.6125	3/4
7/8	1 7/32	14	.07143	.0457	.0053	1.1433	.3750	1.189	1.1784	1.1081	.6125	3/4
1	1 11/32	11	.09091	.0582	.0067	1.2508	.3750	1.309	1.2956	1.2060	.7250	7/8
1 1/4	1 11/16	11	.09091	.0582	.0067	1.5918	.5000	1.650	1.6366	1.5470	.8167	1
1 1/2	1 29/32	11	.09091	.0582	.0067	1.8238	.5000	1.882	1.8686	1.7790	.8167	1
1 3/4	2 5/32	11	.09091	.0582	.0067	2.0578	.6250	2.116	2.1026	2.0130	.9084	1 1/8
2	2 3/8	11	.09091	.0582	.0067	2.2888	.6250	2.347	2.3336	2.2440	.9084	1 1/8
2 1/4	2 5/8	11	.09091	.0582	.0067	2.5288	.6875	2.587	2.5736	2.4840	.9915	1 1/4
2 1/2	2 7/8	11	.09091	.0582	.0067	2.9018	.6875	2.960	2.9466	2.8570	.9915	1 1/4
2 3/4	3 1/4	11	.09091	.0582	.0067	3.1518	.8125	3.210	3.1966	3.1070	1.1021	1 3/8
3	3 1/2	11	.09091	.0582	.0067	3.4018	.8125	3.460	3.4466	3.3570	1.1021	1 3/8
3 1/4	3 3/4	11	.09091	.0582	.0067	3.6418	.8750	3.700	3.6866	3.5970	1.2042	1 1/2
3 1/2	4	11	.09091	.0582	.0067	3.8918	.8750	3.950	3.9366	3.8470	1.2042	1 1/2
3 3/4	4 1/4	11	.09091	.0582	.0067	4.1418	.8750	4.200	4.1866	4.0970	1.2042	1 1/2
4	4 1/2	11	.09091	.0582	.0067	4.3918	1.0000	4.450	4.4366	4.3470	1.2958	1 5/8
4 1/2	5	11	.09091	.0582	.0067	4.8918	1.0000	4.950	4.9366	4.8470	1.2958	1 5/8
5	5 1/2	11	.09091	.0582	.0067	5.3918	1.1250	5.450	5.4366	5.3470	1.3875	1 3/4
5 1/2	6	11	.09091	.0582	.0067	5.8918	1.2500	5.950	5.9366	5.8470	1.4792	1 7/8
6	6 1/2	11	.09091	.0582	.0067	6.3918	1.3750	6.450	6.4366	6.3470	1.5708	2

American National Pipe Threads and Pipe Gage Threads with Locknut Threads and Basic Straight Pipe Sizes

Pipe Size Inches	Outside Diameter Pipe Inches (D)	Threads Per Inch (N)	Pitch Inches (P)	Depth of Thread .8 P Inches	Pitch Diameter at Gaging Notch Basic Straight Inches (B)	Pitch Diameter at End of Pipe Inches (A)	Thickness of American Standard Ring Gage (also Distance from small end to gaging notch) Inches (F)	Length of American Standard Plug (Effective Length of Thread on Pipe) Inches (E)	Length of Perfect Thread Inches (G)	Total Length of Thread Inches (H*)	Maximum Pitch Diameter Straight Male Locknut Thread Inches (C1)	Minimum Pitch Diameter Straight Female Locknut Thread Inches (C2)
1/8	.405	27	.03704	.0296	.3748	.3635	.180	.2638	.2638	.3749	.3840	.3863
1/4	.540	18	.05556	.0444	.4899	.4774	.200	.4018	.2907	.5685	.5038	.5073
3/8	.675	18	.05556	.0444	.6270	.6120	.240	.4078	.2967	.5745	.6409	.6444
1/2	.840	14	.07143	.0571	.7784	.7584	.320	.5337	.3908	.7480	.7963	.8008
3/4	1.050	14	.07143	.0571	.9889	.9677	.339	.5457	.4028	.7600	1.0067	1.0112
1	1.315	11½	.08696	.0696	1.2386	1.2136	.400	.6828	.5089	.9437	1.2604	1.2658
1 1/4	1.660	11½	.08696	.0696	1.5834	1.5571	.420	.7068	.5329	.9677	1.6051	1.6106
1 1/2	1.900	11½	.08696	.0696	1.7223	1.7961	.420	.7235	.5496	.9844	1.8441	1.8495
2	2.375	11½	.08696	.0696	2.2963	2.2690	.436	.7565	.5826	1.0174	2.3180	2.3234
2 1/4	2.875	8	.12500	.1000	2.7622	2.7195	.682	1.1375	.8875	1.5125	2.7934	2.8012
3	3.500	8	.12500	.1000	3.3885	3.3406	.766	1.2000	.9500	1.5750	3.4198	3.4276
3 1/2	4.000	8	.12500	.1000	3.8888	3.8375	.821	1.2500	1.0000	1.6250	3.9201	3.9279
4	4.500	8	.12500	.1000	4.3871	4.3344	.844	1.3000	1.0500	1.6750	4.4184	28012
4 1/2	5.000	8	.12500	.1000	4.8850	4.8313	.875	1.3500	1.1000	1.7250	4.9172	4.4262
5	5.563	8	.12500	.1000	5.4493	5.3907	.937	1.4063	1.1563	1.7813	5.4806	4.9250
6	6.625	8	.12500	.1000	6.5060	6.4461	.958	1.5125	1.2625	1.8875	6.5372	5.4884
8	8.625	8	.12500	.1000	8.5000	8.4336	1.063	1.7125	1.4625	2.0875	8.5313	6.5450
10	10.750	8	.12500	.1000	10.6209	10.5453	1.210	1.9250	1.6750	2.3000	10.6522	10.6600
12	12.750	8	.12500	.1000	12.6178	12.5328	1.360	2.1250	1.8750	2.5000	12.6491	12.6569

*3 or 4 imperfect threads may be used. When using 4 imperfect threads add one pitch (P) to column H.

Use of Taper Pipe Threads on Neck Connections of Compressed Gas Cylinders and Valves

Gas	Size	Symbol[1] (designation of thread)	Length[2]	Remarks
1	2	3	4	5
	Inch		Inches	
Acetylene	¾	¾"–14NPT	⅞	
Air Water pumped	1	1"–14NPT	1	
Air oil pumped	¾	¾"–14NPT	⅞	
	¾	¾"–14NPT	⅞	
Ammonia, anhydrous	¾	¾"–14NPT	⅞	
Carbon dioxide	¾	¾"–14NPT	⅞	
Chlorine No. 1	¾	¾"–14NPT	1⅛	Regular pipe thread.
Chlorine No. 2[3]	¾	¾"–14NPT–Spec.	1⅛	Oversize 0.0179 in. (4 turns).
Chlorine No. 3[3]	¾	¾"–14NPT–Spec.	1⅛	Oversize 0.0380 in. (8½ turns).
Chlorine No. 4[3]	¾	¾"–14NPT–Spec.	1⅛	Oversize 0.0625 in. (14 turns).
Helium	¾	¾"–14NPT	⅞	
Hydrogen	¾	¾"–14NPT	⅞	
Nitrogen, water pumped	¾	¾"–14NPT	⅞	
Nitrogen, oil pumped	¾	¾"–14NPT	⅞	
Nitrous oxide	½	½"–14NPT	¾	
Oxygen	½	½"–14NPT	¾	
	¾	¾"–14NPT	⅞	
	1	1"–14NPT	1	
Oxygen (medical)	½	½"–14NPT	¾	

[1]The symbol ¾" NPT stands for American pipe threads, the ¾ in. sizes having 14 threads per inch.

[2]The valve neck shall be threaded the entire length indicated in this column. The threads shall be full form, smooth, clean, and concentric to the axis of the valve.

[3]All four sizes are of the American National pipe thread form. Numbers 2, 3, and 4, are valves made to fit enlarged threads in cylinders.

SCREW THREADS, PLATING—When screw threads are plated it affects their diameter, depending on the kind and amount of plate used. Chromium plate alone is usually about 0.0001 inch thick. When plates of copper, nickel and then chromium are used, the thickness of plate may be 0.00075 inch. Cadmium plate, for rust prevention, is about 0.0002 inch thick.

SCREW THREADS, RIGHT HAND—Screw threads which, when looked at from the end, have the helix moving away from the observer in a clockwise direction. In screwing into a tapped hole the screw turns *clockwise.*

SCREW THREADS, ROLLED—Screw threads formed by rolling the blank between flat or round dies, usually the former. Some use a blank the pitch diameter of the thread and force the metal up into the die. Others use a blank the size of the bolt or screw and

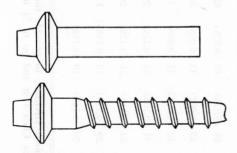

In rolling the screw spike, the finished spike is appreciably longer than the blank from which it is rolled.

All proportions are approximate:

Blank diameter	⅞ in.
Root diameter	⅝ in.
Pitch thread	½ in.
Collar	1⅝ in.
Finished length	6½ in.
Blank length	5⅜ in.

Square projection on umbrella head for driving.

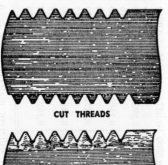

CUT THREADS

ROLLED THREADS

Comparison of grain of metal in cut and rolled threads.

ROLLED SCREW THREADS.

lengthen the blank as the thread is formed. The former is generally used. The illustration, page 387, shows the method.

SCREW THREADS, SQUARE—Few threads are now made with 90-degree or square sides, on account of the difficulty of clearing the tool. They are usually modified with a 10- or 15-degree angle on the side. See *Screw Threads, Modified Square.*

SCREW THREADS, STUB—Screw threads with less than standard depth, just as stub tooth gears have shorter teeth than standard. Two types of stub screw threads are shown. Useful where fast threads, or coarse pitches, are desired on thin walled tubes or sleeves.

SCREW THREADS, STUD—See *Stud.*

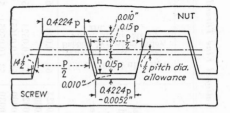

29-degree stub thread.

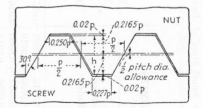

60-degree stub thread.

STUB SCREW THREADS.

SCREW THREAD SYMBOLS—In designating standard screw threads the following letters are used: A—external threads; B—internal threads; U N C—coarse threads; U N F—fine threads; U N E F—extra fine threads; 8 N—threads of 8-pitch per inch regardless of diameter; 12 N—threads of 12-pitch per inch regardless of diameter; 16 N—threads of 16-pitch per inch regardless of diameter; U N S—special pitch, diameter and length of engagement. The U denotes the new Unified thread.

SCREW THREADS, TAP DRILL—See tables. (See also *Drill, Tap.*)

Tap Drills for Small Sizes of American National Fine Thread—Class 3 FIT*

Size of Screw and Threads	Dia. Body or Major. Dia. Screw	LIMITS			Internal Thread Minor Diameter	TAP DRILL SIZES			
		Basic Pitch Dia.	Tapped Hole	Screw		75% to 80% Full Thr'd — Wrought Brass, Nickel, Babbitt, Wr. Alum. Alloy, Fiber, White Metal, Hd. Rubber	70% to 75% Full Thr'd — Mild Steel, Cast Alum., Cast Iron, Cast Brass	65% to 75% Full Thr'd — Bronze, Tool Steel, Drop Forging, Stainless Steel, Cast Steel, Nickel Copper	Clearance Drill
00-96	0.047 +0.0000 −0.0032	0.0402	+0.0010 −0.0000	+0.0000 −0.0010	0.0357 +0.0024 −0.0000	64 (0.036)	63 (0.037)	63 (0.037)	55 (0.052)
0-80	0.060 +0.0000 −0.0034	0.0519	+0.0013 −0.0000	+0.0000 −0.0013	0.0465 +0.0027 −0.0000	55 (0.052) 56 (0.0465)	55 (0.052)	55 (0.052)	51 (0.067)
1-72	0.073 +0.0000 −0.0036	0.0640	+0.0013 −0.0000	+0.0000 −0.0013	0.058 +0.0030 −0.0000	53 (0.0595)	53 (0.0595)	52 (0.0635)	47 (0.0785)
2-64	0.086 +0.0000 −0.0038	0.0759	+0.0014 −0.0000	+0.0000 −0.0014	0.0691 +0.0033 −0.0000	50 (0.070)	49 (0.073)	48 (0.076)	42 (0.0935)
3-56	0.099 +0.0000 −0.0040	0.0874	+0.0015 −0.0000	+0.0000 −0.0015	0.0797 +0.0037 −0.0000	46 (0.081)	45 (0.082)	44 (0.086)	36 (0.065)
4-48	0.112 +0.0000 −0.0044	0.0985	+0.0016 −0.0000	+0.0000 −0.0016	0.0894 +0.0043 −0.0000	43 (0.089)	42 (0.0935)	41 (0.096)	31 (0.120)
5-44	0.125 +0.0000 −0.0046	0.1102	+0.0016 −0.0000	+0.0000 −0.0016	0.1004 +0.0045 −0.0000	38 (0.1015)	37 (0.104)	35 (0.110)	29 (0.136)
6-40	0.138 +0.0000 −0.0048	0.1218	+0.0017 −0.0000	+0.0000 −0.0017	0.1109 +0.0049 −0.0000	33 (0.113)	32 (0.116)	31 (0.120)	26 (0.147)
8-36	0.164 +0.0000 −0.0050	0.1460	+0.0018 −0.0000	+0.0000 −0.0018	0.1339 +0.0052 −0.0000	29 (0.136)	29 (0.136)	28 (0.1405)	17 (0.173)
10-32	0.190 +0.0000 −0.0054	0.1697	+0.0019 −0.0000	+0.0000 −0.0019	0.1562 +0.0056 −0.0000	21 (0.159)	20 (0.161)	19 (0.166)	7 (0.201)

*These tap drills for different materials have been adopted by Kollsman Instrument Division, to provide the accuracy required in aviation instruments. The tolerances on pitch diameter apply only to Class 3 fit and up to ½ inch length of thread engagement.

Basic Thread Dimensions and Tap Drill Sizes
French and International Standard

Formula: $p =$ pitch; $d =$ depth $= p$ x. 64952; $f =$ flat $= \dfrac{p}{8}$

Nominal Diameter m/m	Pitch m/m			Pitch Diameter m/m	Root Diameter m/m	Commercial Tap Drill to Produce Approx. 75% Full Thread
	French Std.	International Std. (DIN)	Optional			
1.5	.35	....	....	1.273	1.05	1.1
2	....	.40	....	1.740	1.48	1.6
2	.45	....	....	1.708	1.42	1.5
2	....	....	.50	1.675	1.35	1.5
2.3	....	.40	....	2.040	1.78	1.9
2.5	.45	....	....	2.208	1.92	2.0
2.6	....	.45	....	2.308	2.02	2.1
3	....	.50	....	2.675	2.35	2.5
3	.60	....	....	2.610	2.22	2.4
3	....	....	.75	2.513	2.03	2.25
3.5	.60	.60	....	3.110	2.72	2.9
4	....	.70	....	3.545	3.09	3.3
4	.75	....	....	3.513	3.03	3.25
4.5	.75	.75	....	4.013	3.53	3.75
5	....	....	.75	4.513	4.03	4.25
5	....	.80	....	4.480	3.96	4.2
5	.90	....	....	4.415	3.83	4.1
5	....	....	1.00	4.350	3.70	4.0
5.5	....	....	.75	5.013	4.53	4.75
5.5	.90	.90	....	4.915	4.33	4.6
6	1.00	1.00	....	5.350	4.70	5.0
6	....	....	1.25	5.188	4.38	4.8
7	1.00	1.00	....	6.350	5.70	6.0
7	....	....	1.25	6.188	5.38	5.8
8	1.00	....	....	7.350	6.70	7.0
8	....	1.25	....	7.188	6.38	6.8
9	1.00	....	....	8.350	7.70	8.0
9	....	1.25	....	8.188	7.38	7.8
10	....	....	1.25	9.188	8.38	8.8
10	1.50	1.50	....	9.026	8.05	8.6
11	....	1.50	....	10.026	9.05	9.6

(Concluded on following page)

Basic Thread Dimensions and Tap Drill Sizes—Continued

French and International Standard

Nominal Diameter m/m	Pitch m/m			Pitch Diameter m/m	Root Diameter m/m	Commercial Tap Drill to Produce Approx. 75% Full Thread
	French Std.	International Std. (DIN)	Optional			
12	....	....	1.25	11.188	10.38	11.0
12	1.50	....	....	11.026	10.05	10.5
12	....	1.75	....	10.863	9.73	10.5
13	....	....	1.50	12.026	11.05	11.5
13	....	....	1.75	11.863	10.73	11.5
13	....	....	2.00	11.701	10.40	11.0
14	....	....	1.25*	13.188	12.38	13.0
14	....	....	1.75	12.863	11.73	12.5
14	2.00	2.00	....	12.701	11.40	12.0
15	....	....	1.75	13.863	12.73	13.5
15	....	....	2.00	13.701	12.40	13.0
16	2.00	2.00	....	14.701	13.40	14.0
17	....	....	2.00	15.701	14.40	15.0
18	....	....	1.50*	17.026	16.05	16.5
18	....	....	2.00	16.701	15.40	16.0
18	2.50	2.50	....	16.376	14.75	15.5
19	....	....	2.50	17.376	15.75	16.5
20	....	....	2.00	18.701	17.40	18.0
20	2.50	2.50	....	18.376	16.75	17.5
22	2.50	2.50	....	20.376	18.75	19.5
24	3.00	3.00	....	22.051	20.10	21.0
26	3.00	....	....	24.051	22.10	23.0
27	....	3.00	....	25.051	23.10	24.0
28	3.00	....	....	26.051	24.10	25.0
30	3.50	3.50	....	27.727	25.45	26.5
32	3.50	....	....	29.727	27.45	28.5
33	....	3.50	....	30.727	28.45	29.5
34	3.50	....	....	31.727	29.45	30.5
36	4.00	4.00	....	33.402	30.80	32.0
38	4.00	....	....	35.402	32.80	34.0
39	....	4.00	....	36.402	33.80	35.0
40	4.00	....	....	37.402	34.80	36.0
42	4.50	4.50	....	39.077	36.15	37.0
44	4.50	....	....	41.077	38.15	39.0
45	....	4.50	....	42.077	39.15	40.0
46	4.50	....	....	43.077	40.15	41.0
48	5.00	5.00	....	44.752	41.50	43.0
50	5.00	....	....	46.752	43.50	45.0

*Spark Plug Sizes.

SCREW THREADS, THURY'S WATCH —
Watch screw threads having a 47½-degree
angle, developed in Switzerland and used by
the E. Howard Co. for balance screws. Also
used in England for clocks and small instruments.

SCREW THREADS, TRUNCATED—Threads
having less depth than standard threads.

SCREW THREADS, UNIFIED — The new
standard adopted by Canada, England and the
United States to secure greater interchangeability of threaded parts. There has been sim-
plification in the number of classes of fits and
it is hoped that the one class of limits can be
used in nearly all cases.

The most significant modification in the
Unified and American Screw Thread Standard
is the addition of Classes 2A and 2B.

Class 2A is an external thread classification
which provides an allowance or clearance between its maximum metal condition and the
maximum metal condition of any class of
internal thread in which it assembles. This
clearance minimizes galling and seizing in
high-cycle wrenching and high temperature
applications. It also accommodates plating
when required. Class 2A is recognized as
standard practice for production of screws,
bolts and other threaded fasteners. Class 2B
is a realistic approach to tolerances required
in production of standard nuts.

Changing to Classes 2A and 2B does not
affect strength or interchangeability. Components are mechanically and functionally interchangeable in any combinations of the old
and new classes.

The only change in the thread form is the
rounded root, which makes a stronger bolt.
The top or crest may be rounded if desired.
The illustration and tables give essential details. There are six series of threads: Coarse,
fine, extra-fine, and the one-pitch series having
8, 12 and 16 threads per inch, regardless of
diameter. The coarse series has 9 screw sizes,
from 0.073, with 64 threads per inch, to 0.216
with 24 threads. The fine series has 10 screw
sizes, from 0.60, with 80 threads per inch, to
0.216 with 28 threads. The extra-fine has but
one screw size, 0.216, with 32 threads per inch.
Bolts in the coarse series run from ¼-inch, 20
threads, to 4-inch, with 4 threads. The fine
series has ¼-inch with 28 threads, to 1½-inch,
with 12 threads. Extra-fine has various pitches
from ¼-inch, 32 threads, to 2-inch, with 16
threads. Tables must be consulted to see their
full scope. The fine thread series was formerly
called the S. A. E. thread, and before that the
A. L. A. M. thread, the latter meaning Association of Licensed Automobile Manufacturers,
which was dissolved with the Selden patent
and followed by the Society of Automotive
Engineers.

The importance of threaded fastenings
makes it advisable to become thoroughly
familiar with the new standards. Tables of
basic dimensions are given. Details as to allowances and tolerances require many pages
of tables and can be secured from the American Standards Association.

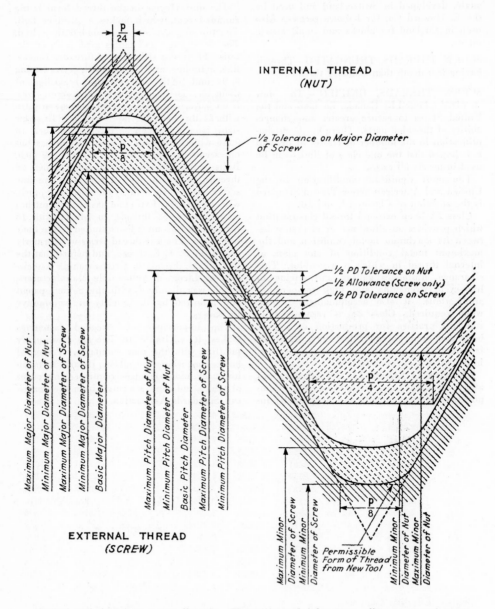

$\frac{p}{24}$

INTERNAL THREAD
(NUT)

½ Tolerance on *Major Diameter*
of Screw

$\frac{p}{8}$

½ PD Tolerance on *Nut*
½ Allowance *(Screw only)*
½ PD Tolerance on *Screw*

$\frac{p}{4}$

Maximum Major Diameter of Nut
Minimum Major Diameter of Nut
Maximum Major Diameter of Screw
Minimum Major Diameter of Screw
Basic Major Diameter

Maximum Pitch Diameter of Nut
Minimum Pitch Diameter of Nut
Basic Pitch Diameter
Maximum Pitch Diameter of Screw
Minimum Pitch Diameter of Screw

EXTERNAL THREAD
(SCREW)

$\frac{p}{8}$

Maximum Minor Diameter of Screw
Minimum Minor Diameter of Screw

*Permissible
Form of Thread
from New Tool*

Minimum Minor Diameter of Nut
Maximum Minor Diameter of Nut

Unified and American screw threads. Disposition of tolerances, allowances and crest
clearances for Unified and American Classes 1A, 2A, 1B, and 2B.

Unified and American Thread Series

Coarse-Thread Series—UNC and NC

(Basic Dimensions)

Sizes	Basic Major Diam., D	Thds. per Inch, n	Basic Pitch Diam.,* E	Minor Diameter External Threads K_s	Minor Diameter Internal Threads K_n	Lead Angle at Basic Pitch Dia., λ		Section at Minor Diameter at $D\text{-}2h_b$	Stress Area
	Inches		Inches	Inches	Inches	Deg.	Min.	Sq. In.	Sq. In.
1(.073)	0.0730	64	0.0629	0.0538	0.0561	4	31	0.0022	0.0026
2(.086)	0.0860	56	0.0744	0.0641	0.0667	4	22	0.0031	0.0036
3(.099)	0.0990	48	0.0855	0.0734	0.0764	4	26	0.0041	0.0048
4(.112)	0.1120	40	0.0958	0.8313	0.0849	4	45	0.0050	0.0060
5(.125)	0.1250	40	0.1088	0.0943	0.0979	4	11	0.0067	0.0079
6(.138)	0.1380	32	0.1177	0.0997	0.1042	4	50	0.0075	0.0090
8(.164)	0.1640	32	0.1437	0.1257	0.1302	4	58	0.0120	0.0139
10(.190)	0.1900	24	0.1629	0.1389	0.1449	4	39	0.0145	0.0174
12(.216)	0.2160	24	0.1889	0.1649	0.1709	4	1	0.0206	0.0240
¼	**0.2500**	**20**	**0.2175**	**0.1887**	**0.1959**	**4**	**11**	**0.0269**	**0.0317**
⁵⁄₁₆	**0.3125**	**18**	**0.2764**	**0.2443**	**0.2524**	**3**	**40**	**0.0454**	**0.0522**
⅜	**0.3750**	**16**	**0.3344**	**0.2983**	**0.3073**	**3**	**24**	**0.0678**	**0.0773**
⁷⁄₁₆	**0.4375**	**14**	**0.3911**	**0.3499**	**0.3602**	**3**	**20**	**0.0933**	**0.1060**
½	**0.5000**	**13**	**0.4500**	**0.4056**	**0.4167**	**2**	**7**	**0.1257**	**0.1416**
½	**0.5000**	**12**	**.04459**	**0.3978**	**0.4098**	**3**	**24**	**0.1205**	**0.1374**
⁹⁄₁₆	**0.5625**	**12**	**0.5084**	**0.4603**	**0.4723**	**2**	**59**	**0.1620**	**0.1816**
⅝	**0.6250**	**11**	**0.5660**	**0.5135**	**0.5266**	**2**	**56**	**0.2018**	**0.2256**
¾	**0.7500**	**10**	**0.6850**	**0.6273**	**0.6417**	**2**	**40**	**0.3020**	**0.3340**
⅞	**0.8750**	**9**	**0.8028**	**0.7387**	**0.7547**	**2**	**31**	**0.4193**	**0.4612**
1	**1.0000**	**8**	**0.9188**	**0.8466**	**0.8647**	**2**	**29**	**0.5510**	**0.6051**
1⅛	**1.1250**	**7**	**1.0322**	**0.9497**	**0.9704**	**2**	**31**	**0.6391**	**0.7627**
1¼	**1.2500**	**7**	**1.1572**	**1.0747**	**1.0954**	**2**	**15**	**0.8898**	**0.9684**
1⅜	**1.3750**	**6**	**1.2667**	**1.1705**	**1.1946**	**2**	**24**	**1.0541**	**1.1538**
1½	**1.5000**	**6**	**1.3917**	**1.2955**	**1.3196**	**2**	**11**	**1.2938**	**1.4041**
1¾	**1.7500**	**5**	**1.6201**	**1.5046**	**1.5335**	**2**	**15**	**1.7441**	**1.8983**
2	**2.0000**	**4½**	**1.8557**	**1.7274**	**1.7594**	**2**	**11**	**2.3001**	**2.4971**
2¼	**2.5000**	**4½**	**2.1057**	**1.9774**	**2.0094**	**1**	**55**	**3.0212**	**3.2464**
2½	**2.5000**	**4**	**2.3376**	**2.1933**	**2.2294**	**1**	**57**	**3.7161**	**3.9976**
2¾	**2.7500**	**4**	**2.5876**	**2.4433**	**2.4794**	**1**	**46**	**4.6194**	**4.9326**
3	**3.0000**	**4**	**2.8376**	**2.6933**	**2.7294**	**1**	**36**	**5.6209**	**5.9659**
3¼	**3.2500**	**4**	**3.0876**	**29.433**	**2.9794**	**1**	**29**	**6.7205**	**7.0992**
3½	**3.5000**	**4**	**3.3376**	**3.1933**	**3.2294**	**1**	**22**	**7.9183**	**8.3268**
3¾	**3.7500**	**4**	**3.5876**	**3.4433**	**3.4794**	**1**	**16**	**9.2143**	**9.6546**
4	**4.0000**	**4**	**3.8276**	**3.6933**	**3.7294**	**1**	**11**	**10.6084**	**11.0805**

*British: Effective Diameter.

Bold type indicates Unified threads—UMC.

Unified and American Thread Series

Fine Thread Series—UNF and NF

(Basic Dimensions)

Sizes	Basic Major Diam., D	Thds. per Inch, n	Basic Pitch Diam.,* E	Minor Diameter External Threads K_s	Minor Diameter Internal Threads K_n	Lead Angle at Basic Pitch Dia., λ		Section at Minor Diameter at $D\text{-}2h_b$	Stress Area
	Inches		Inches	Inches	Inches	Deg.	Min.	Sq. In.	Sq. In.
0 (.060)	0.0600	80	0.0519	0.0447	0.0465	4	23	0.0015	0.0018
1 (.073)	0.0730	72	0.0640	0.0560	0.0580	3	57	0.0024	0.0027
2 (.086)	0.0860	64	0.0759	0.0688	0.0691	3	45	0.0034	0.0039
3 (.099)	0.0990	56	0.0874	0.0711	0.0797	3	43	0.0045	0.0052
4 (.112)	0.1120	48	0.0985	0.0864	0.0894	3	51	0.0057	0.0065
5 (.125)	0.1250	44	0.1102	0.0971	0.1004	3	45	0.0072	0.0082
6 (.138)	0.1380	40	0.1218	0.1073	0.1109	3	44	0.0087	0.0101
8 (.164)	0.1640	36	0.1460	0.1299	0.1339	3	28	0.0128	0.0146
10 (.190)	0.1900	32	0.1697	0.1517	0.1562	3	21	0.0175	0.0199
12 (.216)	0.2160	28	0.1928	0.1722	0.1773	3	22	0.0226	0.0257
¼	0.2500	28	0.2268	0.2062	0.2113	2	52	0.0326	0.0362
⁵⁄₁₆	0.3125	24	0.2854	0.2614	0.2674	2	40	0.0524	0.0579
⅜	0.3750	24	0.3479	0.3239	0.3299	2	11	0.0809	0.0876
⁷⁄₁₆	0.4375	20	0.4050	0.3762	0.3834	2	15	0.1090	0.1185
½	0.5000	20	0.4675	0.4387	0.4459	1	57	0.1486	0.1597
⁹⁄₁₆	0.5625	18	0.5264	0.4943	0.5024	1	55	0.1888	0.2026
⅝	0.6250	18	0.5889	0.5568	0.5649	1	43	0.2400	0.2555
¾	0.7500	16	0.7094	0.6733	0.6823	1	36	0.3513	0.3724
⅞	0.8750	14	0.8286	0.7874	0.7977	1	34	0.4805	0.5088
1	1.0000	12	0.9459	0.8978	0.9098	1	36	0.6245	0.6624
1⅛	1.1250	12	1.0709	1.0228	1.0348	1	25	0.8118	0.8549
1¼	1.2500	12	1.1959	1.1478	1.1598	1	16	1.0237	1,0721
1⅜	1.3750	12	1.3209	1.2728	1.2848	1	9	1.2602	1.3137
1½	1.5000	12	1.4459	1.3978	1.4098	1	3	1.5212	1.5799

*British: Effective Diameter.

Bold type indicates Unified threads—UMC.

SCREW THREADS, V—Screw threads with a sharp crest and sharp at the bottom. In general use before adoption of the Whitworth rounded top and bottom and the flat top and bottom of the Sellers, which is the basis for the present American National Standard. As threading tools became dull they failed to produce a sharp thread. Flat or rounded bottoms of threads made a stronger bolt.

SCREW THREADS, WATCH AND INSTRU-
MENT—Although watch screw threads are
being standardized, it is well to know that
threads of both 45 and 60 degrees were used
by the E. Howard Watch Co. and a 55-degree
thread by the New York Standard Watch Co.
The Thury Swiss thread is also a watchmaker's
thread. Horological or watch screw threads
have been standardized by the watch industry
in connection with the American Standards
Association. Some have a 50-degree angle and
some 60 degrees, as seen from the tables. The
tables, page 396 and 397 are by the Hamilton
Watch Co.

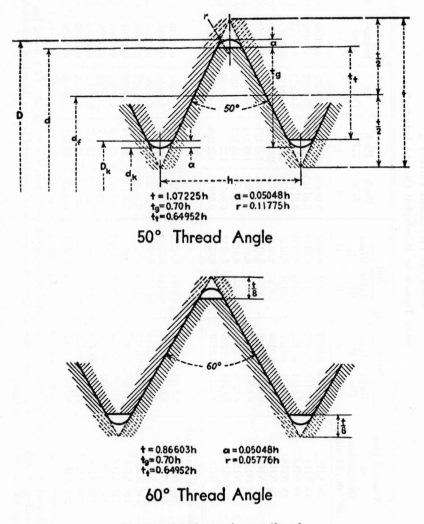

t = 1.07225h   a = 0.05048h
tg = 0.70h   r = 0.11775h
tt = 0.64952h

50° Thread Angle

t = 0.86603h   a = 0.05048h
tg = 0.70h   r = 0.05776h
tt = 0.64952h

60° Thread Angle

Watch and instrument screw threads.

Watch and Instruments Threads—I
Screw Threads for Horological (Watch) Industry*

Nominal Size or Designation	Screw		Nut		Pitch Dia.	Pitch T.P.I.	Depth of Threads	Depth of Engagement	Clearance	Root Radius
	Major Dia. d	Minor Dia. d_k	Major Dia. D	Minor Dia. D_k	d_f	l/h	t_s	t'	a	r
50° thread angle										
30 NHS	0.0118	0.0077	0.0121	0.0080	0.00990	338 2/3	0.00205	0.00190	0.00015	0.00035
35 NHS	0.0138	0.0097	0.0141	0.0100	0.01185	338 2/3	0.00205	0.00190	0.00015	0.00035
40 NHS	0.0157	0.0102	0.0161	0.0106	0.01320	254	0.00275	0.00255	0.00020	0.00046
45 NHS	0.0177	0.0122	0.0181	0.0126	0.01515	254	0.00275	0.00255	0.00020	0.00046
50 NHS	0.0197	0.0128	0.0202	0.0133	0.01650	203 1/5	0.00345	0.00320	0.00025	0.00058
55 NHS	0.0217	0.0148	0.0222	0.0153	0.01845	203 1/5	0.00345	0.00320	0.00025	0.00058
60 NHS	0.0236	0.0153	0.0242	0.0159	0.01980	169 1/3	0.00415	0.00385	0.00030	0.00070
70 NHS	0.0276	0.0180	0.0283	0.0187	0.02310	145 1/7	0.00480	0.00445	0.00035	0.00081
80 NHS	0.0315	0.0205	0.0323	0.0213	0.02640	127	0.00550	0.00510	0.00040	0.00093
90 NHS	0.0354	0.0230	0.0363	0.0239	0.02970	112 8/9	0.00620	0.00575	0.00045	0.00104
60° deg. thread angle										
110 NHS	0.0394	0.0256	0.0404	0.0266	0.03300	101 3/5	0.00690	0.00640	0.00050	0.00057
110 NHS	0.0433	0.0295	0.0443	0.0305	0.03690	101 3/5	0.00690	0.00640	0.00050	0.00057
120 NHS	0.0472	0.0334	0.0482	0.0344	0.04085	101 3/5	0.00690	0.00640	0.00050	0.00057
130 NHS	0.0512	0.0347	0.0524	0.0359	0.04350	84 2/3	0.00825	0.00765	0.00060	0.00068
140 NHS	0.0551	0.0386	0.0563	0.0398	0.04745	84 2/3	0.00825	0.00765	0.00060	0.00068
150 NHS	0.0591	0.0426	0.0603	0.0438	0.05145	84 2/3	0.00825	0.00765	0.00060	0.00068
160 NHS	0.0630	0.0437	0.0644	0.0451	0.05405	72 4/7	0.00965	0.00895	0.00070	0.00080
170 NHS	0.0669	0.0476	0.0683	0.0490	0.05800	72 4/7	0.00965	0.00895	0.00070	0.00080
180 NHS	0.0709	0.0516	0.0723	0.0530	0.06190	72 4/7	0.00965	0.00895	0.00070	0.00080
200 NHS	0.0787	0.0567	0.0803	0.0583	0.06850	63 1/2	0.01100	0.01020	0.00080	0.00091

*This screw thread series, based on the Swiss NHS thread series but transposed into inch units, has been adopted by Hamilton Watch Co. for all new watch designs. It is now being considered by the American Standards Association as a standard for the watch industry.

Watch and Instrument Threads—II

Diameter Tolerances for Watch Screw Thread Series*

Nominal Size or Designation	Major Diameter Screw		Pitch Diameter Screw		Major Diameter Nut		3-Wire Measurement		
	Max.	Min.	Max.	Min.	Min.	Max.	Wire Size	Max.	Min.
30 NHS	0.0118	0.0112	0.00090	0.00945	0.0080	0.0088	0.00180	0.01278	0.01233
35 NHS	0.0138	0.0132	0.01185	0.01140	0.0100	0.0108	0.00180	0.01478	0.01433
40 NHS	0.0157	0.0149	0.01320	0.01260	0.0106	0.0116	0.00240	0.01700	0.01640
45 NHS	0.0177	0.0169	0.01515	0.01455	0.0126	0.0136	0.00240	0.01900	0.01840
50 NHS	0.0197	0.0188	0.01650	0.01580	0.0133	0.0145	0.00300	0.02133	0.02063
55 NHS	0.0217	0.0208	0.01845	0.01775	0.0153	0.0165	0.00300	0.02333	0.02263
60 NHS	0.0236	0.0225	0.01980	0.01895	0.0159	0.0173	0.00360	0.02555	0.02470
70 NHS	0.0276	0.0263	0.02310	0.02215	0.0187	0.0203	0.00420	0.02988	0.02893
80 NHS	0.0315	0.0301	0.02640	0.02535	0.0213	0.0231	0.00480	0.03410	0.03305
90 NHS	0.0354	0.0338	0.02970	0.02850	0.0239	0.0259	0.00540	0.03833	0.03713

*These tolerances, established by Hamilton Watch Co., include sizes 30 NHS to 90 NHS (50-deg. Series). The wire sizes and maximum and minimum measurements given in the table hold the required tolerance on the pitch diameter.

SCREW THREAD WIRES — See *Screw Thread, Measuring with Wires.*

SCREW, WELDING—A screw with a head designed to be welded to sheet metal or to other parts. Several forms are used to suit different conditions.

SCREW, WOOD—A screw with threads designed to hold firmly in wood. The threads are thin with large spaces between, and the screws usually have a sharp or gimlet point. Diameters, threads, slots and head diameters are approximately the same for all types of

WOOD SCREWS.

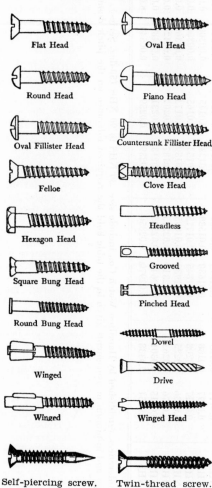

Flat Head

Oval Head

Round Head

Piano Head

Oval Fillister Head

Countersunk Fillister Head

Felloe

Clove Head

Headless

Hexagon Head

Grooved

Square Bung Head

Pinched Head

Round Bung Head

Dowel

Winged

Drive

Winged

Winged Head

Self-piercing screw.

Twin-thread screw.

head except for the round-head screws. The length is measured from the largest diameter of the bearing surface of the head to the point. A ten per cent variation in number of threads per inch is allowed. See *Machine Screw Heads*, page 349.

SCREWING MACHINES—A British term for screw machines.

SCRIBER—A pointed steel tool with hardened ends for marking, or scribing, lines on metal in laying out work.

Scribers.

SCROLL CHUCK—A three- or four-jawed chuck in which the jaws are operated by a *scroll*, which is a plate with a spiral groove that engages teeth in the jaws, moving them in unison. It is one type of universal chuck. See *Chuck, Scroll*.

SEA-COAL FACING—A dust made from pulverized soft coal and used as a facing, or cover, of sand molds to prevent the sand in opposite parts of the flasks from clinging together.

SEAMING PRESS—A press for sheet metal work which bends the edges and locks them together in a seam.

SEAMLESS TUBING—Tubing made from a solid bar either by an extrusion process or by working it over a central bar while in a plastic condition.

SEAMLESS TUBING TOLERANCES—Tolerances on cold drawn tube vary with the diameter, and with the finish. On small tubes, the outside diameter tolerance is plus and the inner tolerance minus. Outside diameter tolerances vary from plus 0.005 to 0.015 inch up to 5-inch tubes. Inside tolerances are from 0.005 to 0.010 inch.

SEAR—The end of a pawl or detent which engages a ratchet wheel. The term is also used in rifle work for a small part which acts in the same way in the firing mechanism.

SEAT—Any surface in any mechanism which meets or supports another part and prevents passage between them. A valve seat in the body of the valve receives the valve on the end of the stem. While this is usually applied to a moving and a stationary part, it is sometimes used where the parts remain together.

SECANT—See *Angle Constants*.

SECOND CUT—A grade of file tooth of medium coarseness. Two coarse grades are *rough* and *bastard,* the latter being between rough and second cut. See *Files.*

SECOND TAP—A tap with a few end threads tapered to follow the first or taper tap. Often called a *plug* tap.

SECONDARY HARDENING—A term given to the hardness developed by tempering high alloy steels.

SECTION OR SECTION VIEW—A view of a part showing it as cut in parts so as to show the shapes of the inner portions. In such a view the solid parts of the piece are marked by lines running at an angle, usually 45 degrees, called cross-hatching. See *Drawings.*

SECTION LINES—Lines on a drawing to show how parts look below the surface or when cut in two. Such parts are said to be shown in section. The lines are usually at a 45-degree angle from the base lines. Standard methods of section lining have been adopted to show different kinds of materials by using different types of lines. See *Drawings.*

SECTOR—The part of a circle lying between two radius lines, as well as the arc which is included. In a milling machine dividing head, the two arms which limit the movement of the indexing pin are called the "sector." A device used on an index plate of a dividing head to indicate the number of holes to be included at each advance of the index crank, in dividing circles. The sector can be set to include as small or as large an arc as desired. A sector is also that part of a circle included between the two arms.

SEGMENT—The part of a circle bounded by two radial lines and the included arc of the circumference. In shop terms it is practically the same as a quadrant.

SEGMENT GEAR—See *Gear, Segment.*

SEGMENT OF A SPHERE—The part of a sphere cut off by a line or plane, or between two parallel lines or planes.

SELECTIVE ASSEMBLY—The assembling of parts which have been *selected,* or graded, according to size. Pistons and piston pins are usually selected, or divided, into groups varying by 0.0005 inch. Cylinder bores and piston pin holes are measured and marked in similar variations. In assembling, parts are selected which will give the desired fit with each other.

As these parts wear in service it is necessary to select replacements in the same way.

SELENIUM—A by-product of tank slimes of electrolytic copper refining. Most valuable because of its change in electrical conductivity when exposed to light. Used in "electric eyes" in counting, scanning or sorting machines, safety devices and light meters, as well as electric rectifiers. Similar to tellurium in many ways. Both are used in vulcanizing rubber, either alone or with sulphur.

SELF-LOCKING SCREW THREADS—See *Screw Threads, Dardelet* and *Lok-Thread.*

SELF-TAPPING SCREWS—See *Screw, Self-Tapping.*

SELLERS DRIVE—This refers to the worm drive on the Sellers planer, which was distinctive for many years. See *Planer, Sellers Type.*

SELLERS TAPER—See *Taper, Sellers.*

SELLERS THREAD—Original name for what is now the American National Standard form of thread, from William Sellers, who first proposed it.

SEMI-AUTOMATIC MACHINE—Any machine in which the machine operations are performed automatically. Most chucking machines come under this head, such as the Bullard Mult-Au-Matic and the Fay lathe. They are loaded by hand, and so are not fully automatic.

SEMS—A screw, when combined with a loose washer, into one unit, is called a sems. The thread is rolled after the washer is put in place. The washer is held between the end of the thread and the head.

SENSITIVE DRILLING MACHINE—A term usually applied to any drilling machine with a hand instead of a power feed, from the fact that the hand feed is more sensitive than a power feed. Usually applied to machines for drilling rather small holes. See *Drilling Machine, Precision.*

SERRATED SHAFT—Shaft serrations are really shallow splines with much steeper sides than the regular spline uses. They serve the same purpose on small diameter shafts as the splines do on large shafts. They are also used to permit angular adjustment between the shaft and piece with the serrated hole, as in some automotive installations. Where straight

Shaft Ends and Fittings for Serrated Shafts
S. A. E. Recommended Practice

Straight Shafts

Nominal diam.	Pitch diam. Max.	Pitch diam. Min.	N	b, deg.	Hole Large diam., min.	Hole Small diam. Max.	Hole Small diam. Min.	Shaft Outside diam. Max.	Shaft Outside diam. Min.	Shaft Inside diam., max.
⅛	0.122	0.120	36	80	0.125	0.118	0.117	0.124	0.123	0.116
3/16	0.182	0.180	36	80	0.187	0.176	0.175	0.186	0.185	0.174
¼	0.243	0.241	36	80	0.250	0.235	0.234	0.249	0.248	0.233
3/16	0.303	0.301	36	80	0.312	0.293	0.292	0.311	0.310	0.291
⅜	0.363	0.361	36	80	0.375	0.352	0.351	0.374	0.373	0.350
½	0.485	0.483	36	80	0.500	0.469	0.468	0.499	0.498	0.467
⅝	0.605	0.603	36	80	0.625	0.584	0.583	0.624	0.623	0.582
¾	0.733	0.731	48	82½	0.750	0.716	0.714	0.749	0.747	0.713
⅞	0.855	0.853	48	82½	0.875	0.835	0.833	0.874	0.872	0.832
1	0.977	0.975	48	82½	1.000	0.954	0.952	0.999	0.997	0.951
1⅛	1.098	1.096	48	82½	1.125	1.071	1.069	1.124	1.122	1.068
1¼	1.220	1.218	48	82½	1.250	1.190	1.188	1.249	1.247	1.187
1⅜	1.342	1.340	48	82½	1.375	1.309	1.307	1.374	1.372	1.306
1½	1.464	1.462	48	82½	1.500	1.428	1.426	1.499	1.497	1.425
1¾	1.708	1.706	48	82½	1.750	1.666	1.664	1.749	1.747	1.663
2	1.952	1.949	48	82½	2.000	1.904	1.902	1.999	1.997	1.901
2¼	2.196	2.193	48	82½	2.250	2.142	2.140	2.249	2.247	2.139
2½	2.440	2.437	48	82½	2.500	2.380	2.378	2.499	2.497	2.377
2¾	2.684	2.681	48	82½	2.750	2.618	2.616	2.749	2.747	2.615
3	2.928	2.925	48	82½	3.000	2.856	2.854	2.999	2.997	2.853

sides are used, the angle varies from 80 to 90 degrees.

SERRATED SHAFT ENDS—Shafts with shallow 90-degree grooves.

SERRATIONS, INVOLUTE—Serrations, or small grooves parallel with the axis of a shaft or hole, with the sides forming an involute curve. These have been standardized as having a 45-degree pressure angle, as of January, 1949.

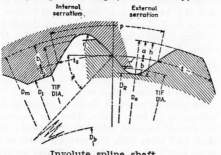

Involute spline shaft.

They are based on an involute form as generated by a straight side hob of the form shown. These serrations not only prevent the shaft from turning in the hole but also provide means of changing the relative position of the two parts by moving the shaft one or more notches and re-entering the hole. The pitch designation is the same as for involute splines and Fellows stub tooth gears. The first number gives number of teeth per inch of diameter, the second the equivalent depth of tooth. In this case the depth is always one-half that of a normal gear tooth of the same diametral pitch. For tapered fits, ¾ inch per foot is recommended and measurements are taken at the large diameter. There is no bearing at top or bottom. Tooth forms for hobs, Fellows cutters and broaches for internal serrations are shown. They are measured with wires the same as gear teeth. See *Splines Involute*.

SET (IN A SAW)—The way in which the teeth are bent to the side. It is also any permanent deformation in metal or other material beyond the elastic limit. See *Saws*.

SET HAMMER—See *Hammer, Set*.

SET SCREW—See *Screw, Set*.

SETTING-UP TIME—Time required to prepare a machine for a new job. This may or may not include time necessary to remove tools and fixtures used on the previous job. Most shops consider it better to charge both the setting up and removal of tools and fixtures to the job on which they are used. This should not be confused with "down time," which refers to the time a machine is out of commission for repairs or adjustments to the machine itself.

SHAFT, COUNTER—The shaft, and necessary accompanying hangers and pulleys, for driving an individual machine. The whole setup is usually mounted on the ceiling over the machine to be driven, and has loose pulleys and shifting belts of different frictions to drive the machine in either direction. See *Countershaft*.

SHAFT ENDS, SPLINE—See *Spline Shaft Ends*.

SHAFT, FLEXIBLE—A shaft made of a helical spring or of jointed parts to transmit power in varying directions. It is confined in a case or tube.

SHAFT COUPLING—See *Couplings*.

SHAFT, LINE—In shops with belt driven machinery the line shaft is the main shaft in each department. Belts from this shaft drive countershafts over each machine.

SHAFT, MULEY—A shaft, usually vertical, which supports pulleys guiding a belt between pulleys which are not in line. Frequently used where it is necessary to drive shafting at right angles to the source of power.

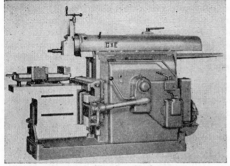

Gould & Eberhardt shaper.

Pratt Whitney vertical shaper.

SHAPER—A machine tool for finishing a flat surface in which the work is held in a vise and the tool, which is held in a horizontal ram, travels over the work. A type of planer in which the feed is obtained by moving the work sideways under the tool. The ram is driven by various crank devices which give a rapid movement on the return stroke. Hydraulic driven shapers are also in successful use. Generally used for short-stroke planer work. A similar machine tool in which the ram is vertical is called a slotter. See *Slotter*.

SHAPER, VERTICAL—A shaper in which the ram is vertical, as in a slotter. Operating mechanism varies with different makes. Generally used in tool room work.

SHAVER, GEAR TOOTH—A machine which "shaves" or corrects imperfections in gear teeth after they have been cut on regular machines. It removes very little metal and is used before the gear is hardened. With unhardened gears it may be a finishing operation.

SHAVING—In machine work, the removal of very small particles or shavings of metal. Its greatest application is in the finishing of gears. This is done by several methods, such as parallel, diagonal or other cutting edges.

SHEAR PIN—A pin of such size that it will be sheared off, and thus stop or disconnect moving parts, before the machine parts which it connects are damaged. Largely used in the propeller shafts of small motor boats and similar places.

SHEARS—Tools for cutting metals between two blades.

SHEARS, LATHE OR OTHER MACHINE TOOL—The ways or surfaces on which the tool carriage or other parts move in alinement with the spindle. The same term is applied to the vees used on machine tools.

SHEAR OR SHEAR LEGS—Two or three heavy struts of wood or metal used by riggers in lifting and handling heavy weights.

SHEAR RIVETS—See *Rivet, Hi-Shear.*

SHEAR STEEL—A term formerly given to a steel developed by Benjamin Huntsman in England in 1740. He introduced carbon into wrought iron and hammered and welded strips into a single piece. It was largely used in cutlery.

SHEAR STRENGTH—See *Strength of Materials.*

SHEAVE—A pulley with a grooved, or V-shaped, rim to hold round or V-belts and give friction surface for them to drive or be driven. Some use the term for the pulleys in a pulley block that carry the rope or cable used.

SHEDDER—A plate or ring usually operated by springs or by rubber to eject work from a die. It acts as a "stripper" or "ejector."

SHEET METAL GAGES—See *Gages, Wire and Sheet.*

SHELLAC—An Indian insect product used in finishes for patterns and other wood work. It is dissolved and "thinned" by alcohol when necessary.

SHELL MILLING CUTTER—See *Milling Cutters, Shell.*

SHELL REAMER—See *Reamer, Shell.*

SHERADIZING—This produces a coating of zinc on steels to prevent corrosion. Various compositions of zinc are used, with temperatures about 750 deg. F. Material is packed in drums which are rotated for several hours in the furnace. For some work a somewhat lower temperature is suggested. While this is not usually considered as effective as cadmium plating, it is used successfully in many places.

SHIELDED ARC WELDING—See *Welding, Shielded Arc.*

SHIFTER FORKS—Arms to guide belts from tight to loose pulley on countershafts. Also, any arms or fingers which shift mechanism of any kind.

SHIM—A thin piece of wood or metal used to space two parts of machinery in correct position. Used largely between the two parts of a bearing on a round shaft. As the bearing wears, thin pieces are removed, which allow the two parts to be brought closer together and to secure a better fit on the shaft. Shims are also used between surfaces which do not move, to secure correct alinement of parts.

SHINGLING—A steel working term denoting the improvement of iron by eliminating impurities by a series of squeezing and hammering operations. Little used at present.

SHIVER—A very localized name for a small pulley or wheel. Sometimes applied to a wedge.

SHOE—An intermediate piece between a stationary and a moving part, such as a crosshead shoe in steam locomotive practice or on stationary engines. Also used in various types of machinery. This shoe takes the wear and can be replaced much more easily than either the guide or the crosshead. It is sometimes called a "slipper" or "gib" in some sections.

SHOP FURNITURE—Work benches, racks, tables, lockers, vise stands and similar equipment used in the shop.

SHOP TRANSPORT—Methods used in moving material from one point to another. This may be by tote boxes, by hand, by power trucks or by cranes of any kind.

SHOP TRIANGLES—See *Triangles, Shop.*

SHOP TRIGONOMETRY—Calculations used in the shop in connection with sine bars, laying out holes at correct locations. It includes angle constant, angles of polygons, and angles of different kinds and their relation to each other, as they are used in securing accurate work in the shop. See *Angle Constants, Sine, Tangent,* and *Sine Bar.*

SHORE—A brace used to hold walls or parts of machinery in an upright position. Usually a temporary matter while erection is going on. Similar to the term "shears" used in erecting or handling weights in dock work.

SHORT LEAD MILLING ATTACHMENT—See *Milling Machines, Short Lead Attachment.*

SHOT BLASTING — Blowing steel pellets against the surface of castings, forgings or finished work by air pressure. Usually done to remove burnt sand and scale, the same as sand blasting. For use on finished work, see *Shot Peening.*

SHOT PEENING—Blowing steel pellets or balls against finished surfaces by air pressure. This produces a series of small, shallow indentations which break up the continuity of the surface and hardens it to some extent. It is believed to lessen probability of fracture from small surface defects. It sometimes raises points on the surface which must be ground down to the proper dimension.

SHOULDER—A projection made by large diameters on shafting or by raised portions on flat surfaces.

SHRINK FIT—A fit made by expanding the outer member by heat to increase its diameter so the inner member can be put in place. On cooling, the outer member contracts and holds the two pieces together. The same effect is now secured on small work by cooling the inner member with dry ice or its equivalent, instead of heating the outer member. This permits use of this method in cases where heat would distort the outer member, as in cylinder blocks, where valve seats are now held by this method. This is sometimes called "expansion" fit because the inserted member expands to secure a fit. See *Expansion Fit.*

SHRINK FIT, COMPOUND — A term describing the fitting of parts by both expansion and contraction. While the receiving member is heated to expand it, the member to be inserted is frozen to reduce its size. When the parts are assembled the outer piece contracts and the inner member expands.

SHRINKAGE—Contraction due to changes in temperature in metals, or to a drying out of moisture in wood and other substances. Castings shrink away from their mold in cooling. Patternmakers have "shrink rules" which show how much to allow for this shrinkage with different metals.

SHRINKAGE ALLOWANCE FOR LOCOMOTIVE TIRES—The Association of American Railroads recommends a shrinkage of 1/80 inch for tires on 38-inch and 1/60 inch for 90-inch centers, varying uniformly between those limits. Shrinkage for tires on wheel centers

Shrinkage Allowance for Locomotive Tires

Diameter Exact Center (In.)	Tire Bore (In.)	Desired Tire Shrinkage (In.)	Tolerance Tire Shrinkage Min.	Tolerance Tire Shrinkage Max.
20	19.979	.021	.019	.025
22	21.977	.023	.021	.027
24	23.975	.025	.023	.029
26	25.973	.027	.025	.031
28	27.971	.029	.027	.032
30	29.969	.031	.029	.035
32	31.967	.033	.031	.037
34	33.965	.035	.033	.039
36	35.962	.038	.036	.042
38	37.960	.040	.038	.044
40	39.958	.042	.040	.046
42	41.955	.045	.043	.049
44	43.952	.048	.046	.053
46	45.950	.050	.048	.056
48	47.947	.053	.051	.060
50	49.944	.056	.054	.063
52	51.941	.059	.057	.066
54	53.938	.062	.060	.070
56	55.935	.065	.063	.073
58	57.932	.068	.066	.076
60	59.929	.071	.069	.079
62	61.925	.075	.073	.083
64	63.922	.078	.076	.086
66	65.919	.081	.079	.089
68	67.916	.084	.082	.092
70	69.912	.088	.086	.096
72	71.909	.091	.089	.099
74	73.905	.095	.093	.103
76	75.902	.098	.096	.106
78	77.898	.102	.100	.110

between 20 and 78 inches in diameter are shown in the table.

SHRINKAGE OF METALS—Makers of deep freeze chilling equipment give the approximate shrinkage of metals, from room temperature of 70 deg. F. to minus 100 deg. F., for parts 2 inches in diameter, as follows:

Tool steel	.0022″
Phosphor bronze	.0032″
Aluminum bronze	.0032″
Brass	.0036″
Aluminum	.0043″
Magnesium	.0045″

Other diameters shrink proportionately

A general rule is that tool steel will shrink

0.001 inch, per inch of diameter, when chilled to minus 120 deg. F.; other metals in proportion as shown in the table. For safe fits in diameters below 2 inches, the receiving member should also be heated.

SHROUDED GEAR— See *Gear, Shrouded.*

SHUTTLE PUNCH AND DIE—A punch and die made of steel plate in which the punch is not fixed but is placed in a guide directly over the die and forced through the sheet to be punched. It is for short runs only. Sometimes called the continental die.

SIDE OR STRADDLE CUTTERS—See *Milling, Straddle.*

SIDE RAKE—Angular clearance behind or below the cutting edge. See *Single-Point Tools.*

SILENT CHAIN BELTS—See *Belt, Link.*

SILENT CHAIN SPROCKETS—See under *Sprockets.*

SILICATE GRINDING WHEELS—Abrasive wheels made with a silicate bond. Largely used for grinding edge tools where heat must be kept at a minimum.

SILICON—A non-metallic element used in various metals for deoxidizing them when melted. Sp. gr. 2.35. Melts at 2,615 deg. F.

SILICON BRONZE—A copper alloy with small quantities of silicon. One standard alloy is 98.55 per cent copper, 1.40 per cent tin and 0.05 per cent silicon. It is made under various trade names.

SILICON CARBIDE ABRASIVES—See *Abrasives, Silicon Carbide.*

SILICON COPPER—Copper with silicon to harden it. It is very brittle when 10 per cent of silicon is used.

SILICON IRON—Iron with silicon as an alloy to make it more rust resistant.

SILICON MANGANESE—Silicon is used as an aid in adding manganese to steel.

SILICON STEEL—Steel to which silicon is added to increase its magnetic permeability, wear, and acid resisting qualities.

SILICONES—A group of synthetic, semi-organic compounds combining many desirable features of organic and inorganic substances. They contain silicon oxygen. Silicone products include oils and greases, rubber, resins and water repellants.

SILICONE RUBBER—A synthetic rubber which has several good qualities for use in mechanical fields. These include high heat resistance, flexibility at low temperatures and little permanent set. These make it very good for gaskets in either high or low temperature applications.

SILVER—A white metal used largely for coins, tableware and jewelry. The sp. gr. is 10.7. Melts at 1,762 deg. F. Sterling silver is 925 parts silver per 1,000; sometimes called "925 fine." Coin silver in the U. S. and most countries is 900 parts silver to 100 parts copper. In some Latin American countries it is 835 parts silver to 165 parts copper.

SILVER NITRATE—A poisonous liquid made by dissolving silver in nitric acid. It is used in silvering mirrors and in silver plating.

SILVER SOLDER—High melting solder for strong joints. Copper-zinc brazing alloys with some silver are used in torch soldering. Silver content varies from 10 to 80 per cent.

SIMPLIFIED SIZES—This refers primarily to tables of drills, wires and similar parts in which some of the less used sizes are eliminated. Some of the old standard sizes were so nearly alike that it was unnecessary to use them all. Using the simplified lists avoids the necessity of making or carrying as many sizes in stock as formerly. They have not been approved by drill makers and may be abandoned.

SINE—With two radial lines of equal length, the sine is the length of a line at 90 degrees from one line to the outer end of the other line. See *Trigonometrical Functions.*

SINE OF AN ANGLE—See *Angle Constants.*

SINE BAR—A device for accurately measuring angles by the length of a perpendicular
(Continued on page 414.)

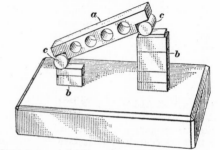

Sine bar. (a) Sine bar. (b) Gage blocks. (c) Gaging rolls.

Sines for the DoAll Five-inch Sine Bar

Min.	6°	7°	8°	9°	10°	11°
0'	0.522642	0.609347	0.695865	0.782172	0.868241	0.954045
1'	0.524089	0.610790	0.697306	0.783609	0.869673	0.955473
2'	0.525535	0.612234	0.698746	0.785045	0.871105	0.956900
3'	0.526981	0.613677	0.700186	0.786482	0.872538	0.958328
4'	0.528428	0.615121	0.701626	0.787918	0.873970	0.959755
5'	0.529874	0.616564	0.703066	0.789354	0.875402	0.961182
6'	0.531320	0.618007	9.704506	0.790790	0.876834	0.962610
7'	0.532766	0.619451	0.705946	0.792226	0.878265	0.964037
8'	0.534213	0.620894	0.707386	0.793662	0.879697	0.965464
9'	0.535659	0.622337	0.708826	0.795098	0.881129	0.966891
10'	0.537105	0.623780	0.710265	0.796534	0.882561	0.968318
11'	0.538551	0.625223	0.711705	0.797970	0.883992	0.969745
12'	0.539997	0.626666	0.713145	0.799406	0.885424	0.971172
13'	0.541443	0.628109	0.714584	0.800842	0.886855	0.972598
14'	0.542888	0.629552	0.716024	0.802277	0.888286	0.974025
15'	0.544334	0.630995	0.717463	0.803713	0.889718	0.975452
16'	0.545780	0.632438	0.718902	0.805148	0.891149	0.976878
17'	0.547226	0.633880	0.720342	0.806583	0.892580	0.978304
18'	0.548761	0.635323	0.721781	0.808019	0.894011	0.979731
19'	0.550117	0.636766	0.723220	0.809454	0.895442	0.981157
20'	0.551563	0.638208	0.724659	0.810890	0.896873	0.982583
21'	0.553008	0.639651	0.726098	0.812325	0.898304	0.984009
22'	0.554454	0.641093	0.727537	0.813760	0.899734	0.985435
23'	0.555889	0.642536	0.728976	0.815195	0.901165	0.986861
24'	0.557345	0.643978	0.730415	0.816630	0.902596	0.988287
25'	0.558790	0.645420	0.731854	0.818064	0.904026	0.989712
26'	0.560235	0.646862	0.733293	0.819499	0.905457	0.991138
27'	0.563126	0.648305	0.734731	0.820934	0.906887	0.992563
28'	0.561681	0.649747	0.736170	0.822369	0.908317	0.993989
29'	0.564571	0.651189	0.737608	0.823803	0.909747	0.995414
30'	0.566016	0.652631	0.739047	0.825238	0.911178	0.996840
31'	0.567461	0.654073	0.740485	0.826672	0.912608	0.998265
32'	0.568906	0.655515	0.741924	0.828107	0.914038	0.999690
33'	0.570351	0.656957	0.743362	0.829541	0.915467	1.001115
34'	0.571796	0.658398	0.744800	0.830975	0.916897	1.002540
35'	0.573241	0.659840	0.746239	0.832410	0.918327	1.003965
36'	0.574686	0.661282	0.747677	0.838844	0.919757	1.005390
37'	0.576130	0.662724	0.749115	0.835278	0.921186	1.006814
38'	0.577575	0.664165	0.750553	0.836712	0.922616	1.008239
39'	0.579020	0.665607	0.751991	0.838146	0.924045	1.009663
40'	0.580464	0.667048	0.753428	0.839579	0.925475	1.011088
41'	0.581909	0.668489	0.754866	0.841013	0.926904	1.012512
42'	0.583354	0.669931	0.756304	0.842447	0.928333	1.013936
43'	0.584798	0.671372	0.757742	0.843880	0.929762	1.015361
44'	0.586243	0.672813	0.759179	0.845314	0.931191	1.016785
45'	0.587687	0.674255	0.760617	0.846747	0.932620	1.018209
46'	0.589131	0.675696	0.762054	0.848181	0.934049	1.019633
47'	0.590576	0.677137	0.763492	0.849614	0.935478	0.021056
48'	0.592020	0.678578	0.764929	0.851047	0.936906	1.022480
49'	0.593464	0.680019	0.766366	0.852481	0.938335	1.023904
50'	0.594908	0.681460	0.767804	0.853914	0.939764	1.025327
51'	0.596352	0.682900	0.769241	0.855347	0.941192	1.026751
52'	0.597796	0.684341	0.770678	0.856780	0.942621	1.028174
53'	0.599240	0.685782	0.772115	0.858213	0.944049	1.029598
54'	0.600684	0.688663	0.773552	0.859645	0.945477	1.031021
55'	0.603128	0.688663	0.774989	0.861078	0.946905	1.032444
56'	0.603572	0.690104	0.776426	0.862511	0.948333	1.033867
57'	0.605016	0.691544	0.777862	0.863943	0.949761	1.035290
58'	0.606459	0.692985	0.779299	0.865375	0.951189	1.036713
59'	0.607903	0.694425	0.780736	0.866808	0.952617	1.038136
60'	0.609347	0.695865	0.782172	0.868241	0.954045	1.039558

Sines for the DoAll Five-inch Sine Bar

Min.	12°	13°	14°	15°	16°	17°
0′	1.039558	1.124755	1.209609	1.294095	1.378187	1.461858
1′	1.040981	1.126172	1.211021	1.295500	1.379585	1.463249
2′	1.042404	1.127589	1.212432	1.296905	1.380983	1.464640
3′	1.043826	1.129006	1.213843	1.298309	1.382380	1.466031
4′	1.045248	1.130423	1.215264	1.299714	1.383778	1.467421
5′	1.046671	1.131840	1.216664	1.301118	1.385176	1.468811
6′	1.048093	1.133256	1.218075	1.302522	1.386573	1.470202
7′	1.049515	1.134673	1.219486	1.303927	1.387971	1.471592
8′	1.050937	1.136089	1.220896	1.305331	1.389368	1.472982
9′	1.052359	1.137506	1.222306	1.306735	1.390765	1.474371
10′	1.053781	1.138922	1.223717	1.308138	1.392162	1.475761
11′	1.055202	1.140338	1.225127	1.309542	1.393559	1.477151
12′	1.056624	1.141754	1.226537	1.310946	1.394955	1.478540
13′	1.058045	1.143170	1.227947	1.312349	1.396352	1.479930
14′	1.059467	1.144586	1.229357	1.313753	1.397749	1.481319
15′	1.060888	1.146002	1.230766	1.315156	1.399145	1.482708
16′	1.062310	1.147418	1.232176	1.316559	1.400541	1.484097
17′	1.063731	1.148833	1.233586	1.317962	1.401937	1.485486
18′	1.065152	1.150249	1.234995	1.319365	1.403333	1.486874
19′	1.066573	1.151664	1.236404	1.320768	1.404729	1.488263
20′	1.067994	1.153079	1.237814	1.322171	1.406125	1.489651
21′	1.069415	1.154494	1.239223	1.323573	1.407521	1.491040
22′	1.070835	1.155910	1.240632	1.324976	1.408916	1.492428
23′	1.072256	1.157325	1.242041	1.326378	1.410312	1.493816
24′	1.073677	1.158739	1.243449	1.327781	1.411707	1.495204
25′	1.075097	1.160154	1.244858	1.329183	1.413102	1.496592
26′	1.076517	1.161569	1.246267	1.330585	1.414498	1.497979
27′	1.077938	1.162984	1.247675	1.331987	1.415892	1.499367
28′	1.079358	1.164398	1.249084	1.333388	1.417287	1.500754
29′	1.080778	1.165812	1.250492	1.334790	1.418682	1.502142
30′	1.082198	1.167227	1.251900	1.336192	1.420077	1.503529
31′	1.083618	1.168641	1.253308	1.337593	1.421471	1.504916
32′	1.085038	1.170055	1.254716	1.338995	1.422866	1.506303
33′	1.086457	1.171469	1.256124	1.340396	1.424260	1.507690
34′	1.087877	1.172883	1.257532	1.341797	1.425654	1.509076
35′	1.089297	1.174297	1.258939	1.343198	1.427048	1.510463
36′	1.090716	1.175710	1.260347	1.344599	1.428442	1.511849
37′	1.092135	1.177124	1.261754	1.346000	1.429836	1.513236
38′	1.093555	1.178538	1.263161	1.347401	1.431229	1.514622
39′	1.094974	1.179951	1.264569	1.348801	1.432623	1.516008
40′	1.096393	1.181364	1.265976	1.350202	1.434016	1.517394
41′	1.097812	1.182778	1.267383	1.351602	1.435409	1.518780
42′	1.099231	1.184191	1.267790	1.353002	1.436803	1.520165
43′	1.100650	1.185604	1.270196	1.354402	1.438196	1.521551
44′	1.102068	1.187017	1.271603	1.355802	1.439588	1.522936
45′	1.103487	1.188429	1.273010	1.357202	1.440981	1.524321
46′	1.104906	1.189842	1.274416	1.358602	1.442374	1.525707
47′	1.106324	1.191255	1.275822	1.360002	1.443766	1.527092
48′	1.107742	1.192667	1.277229	1.361401	1.445159	1.528476
49′	1.109161	1.194080	1.278635	1.362801	1.446551	1.529861
50′	1.110579	1.195492	1.280041	1.364200	1.447943	1.531246
51′	1.111997	1.196904	1.281447	1.365599	1.449335	1.532630
52′	1.113415	1.198316	1.282853	1.366998	1.405727	1.534015
53′	1.114833	1.199728	1.284258	1.368397	1.452119	1.535399
54′	1.116251	1.201140	1.285664	1.369796	1.453511	1.536783
55′	1.117668	1.202552	1.287069	1.371195	1.454902	1.538167
56′	1.119086	1.203964	1.288475	1.372593	1.456294	1.539551
57′	1.120503	1.205375	1.289880	1.373992	1.457685	1.540935
58′	1.121921	1.206787	1.291285	1.375390	1.459076	1.542318
59′	1.123338	1.208198	1.292690	1.376789	1.460467	1.543702
60′	1.124755	1.209609	1.294095	1.378187	1.461858	1.545085

Sines for the DoAll Five-inch Sine Bar

Min.	18°	19°	20°	21°	22°	23°
0'	1.545085	1.627841	1.710101	1,791740	1.873033	1.953656
1'	1.546468	1.629216	1.711467	1.793197	1.874381	1.954994
2'	1.547851	1.630591	1.712834	1.794555	1.875730	1.956333
3'	1.549234	1.631966	1.714200	1.795913	1.877078	1.957671
4'	1.550617	1.633340	1.715566	1.797270	1.878426	1.959010
5'	1.552000	1.634715	1.716932	1.798627	1.879774	1.960348
6'	1.553382	1.636089	1.718298	1.799984	1.881121	1.961686
7'	1.554764	1.637464	1.719664	1.801341	1.882469	1.963023
8'	1.556147	1.638838	1.721030	1.802698	1.883816	1.964361
9'	1.557529	1.640212	1.722395	1.804054	1.885163	1.965698
10'	1.558911	1.641586	1.723761	1.805410	1.886510	1.967035
11'	1.560293	1.642960	1.725126	1.806767	1.887857	1.968373
12'	1.561675	1.644333	1.726491	1.808123	1.889204	1.966709
13'	1.563056	1.645707	1.727856	1.809479	1.890550	1.971046
14'	1.564438	1.647880	1.729221	1.810834	1.891897	1.972383
15'	1.565819	1.648453	1.730585	1.812190	1.893243	1.973719
16'	1.567200	1.649826	1.731950	1.813546	1.894589	1.975055
17'	1.568581	1.651199	1.733314	1.814901	1.895935	1.976394
18'	1.569962	1.652572	1.734678	1.816256	1.897281	1.977727
19'	1.571343	1.653945	1.736042	1.817611	1.898626	1.979063
20'	1.572724	1.655317	1.737406	1.818966	1.899972	1.980399
21'	1.574104	1.656689	1.738770	1.820321	1.901317	1.981734
22'	1.575485	1.658062	1.740133	1.821675	1.902662	1.983069
23'	1.576865	1.659434	1.741497	1.823030	1.904007	1.984404
24'	1.578245	1.660806	1.742860	1.824384	1.905352	1.985739
25'	1.579625	1.662177	1.744223	1.825738	1.906696	1.987074
26'	1.581005	1.663549	1.745586	1.827092	1.908041	1.988409
27'	1.582385	1.664921	1.746949	1.828446	1.909385	1.989743
28'	1.583764	1.666292	1.748312	1.829799	1.910729	1.991077
29'	1.585144	1.667663	1.749674	1.831153	1.912073	1.992411
30'	1.586523	1.669034	1.751037	1.832506	1.913417	1.993745
31'	1.587902	1.670405	1.752399	1.833859	1.914761	1.995079
32'	1.589282	1.671776	1.753761	1.835212	1.916104	1.996413
33'	1.590660	1.673147	1.755123	1.836565	1.917448	1.997746
34'	1.592039	1.674517	1.756485	1.837918	1.918791	1.999079
35'	1.593418	1.675888	1.757847	1.839270	1.920134	2.000412
36'	1.594796	1.677258	1.759208	1.840623	1.921477	2.001745
37'	1.596175	1.678628	1.760570	1.841975	1.922819	2.003078
38'	1.597553	1.679998	1.761931	1.843327	1.924162	2.004410
39'	1.598931	1.681368	1.763292	1.844679	1.925504	2.005743
40'	1.600309	1.682737	1.764653	1.846031	1.926846	2.007075
41'	1.601687	1.684107	1.766014	1.847382	1.928188	2.008407
42'	1.603065	1.685476	1.767374	1.848734	1.929530	2.009739
43'	1.604442	1.686845	1.768735	1.850085	1.930872	2.011071
44'	1.605820	1.688215	1.770095	1.851436	1.932213	2.012402
45'	1.607197	1.689584	1.771455	1.852787	1.933555	2.013733
46'	1.608574	1.690952	1.772815	1.854138	1.934896	2.015065
47'	1.609951	1.692321	1.774175	1.855489	1.936237	1.016396
48'	1.611328	1.693690	1.775535	1.856839	1.937578	2.017726
49'	1.612705	1.695058	1.776894	1.858189	1.938919	2.019057
50'	1.614082	1.696426	1.778254	1.859539	1.940259	2.020388
51'	1.615458	1.697794	1.779613	1.860890	1.941600	2.021718
52'	1.616835	1.699168	1.780972	1.862240	1.942940	2.023048
53'	1.618211	1.700530	1.782331	1.863589	1.944280	2.024378
54'	1.619587	1.701898	1.783690	1,864939	1.945620	2.025708
55'	1.620963	1.703265	1.785049	1.866288	1.946959	2.027038
56'	1.622339	1.704633	1.786407	1.867657	1.948299	2.028367
57'	1.623714	1.706000	1.787765	1.868987	1.949638	2.029696
58'	1.625090	1.707367	1.789124	1.870336	1.950978	2.031025
59'	1.626465	1.708734	1.790482	1.871684	1.952317	2.032354
60'	1.627841	1.710101	1.791840	1.873033	1.953656	2.033683

Sines for the DoAll Five-inch Sine Bar

Min.	24°	25°	26°	27°	28°	29°
0'	2.033683	2.113091	2.191856	2.269952	2.347358	2.424048
1'	2.035012	2.114409	2.193163	2.271248	2.348642	2.425320
2'	2.036340	2.115727	2.194470	2.272544	2.349926	2.426592
3'	2.037668	2.117045	2.195777	2.273839	2.351209	2.427863
4'	2.038997	2.118362	2.197083	2.275135	2.352493	2.429135
5'	2.040324	2.119680	2.198390	2.276430	2.353776	2.430406
6'	2.041652	2.120997	2.199696	2.277724	2.355059	2.431677
7'	2.042980	2.122314	2.201002	2.279019	2.356342	2.432948
8'	2.044307	2.123631	2.202308	2.280314	2.357625	2.434218
9'	2.045634	2.124948	2.203613	2.281608	2.358907	2.435488
10'	2.046961	2.126264	2.204919	2.282902	2.360190	2.436759
11'	2.048288	2.127580	2.206224	2.284196	2.361472	2.438029
12'	2.049615	2.128896	2.207529	2.285490	2.362754	2.439298
13'	2.050942	2.130212	2.208834	2.286783	2.364035	2.440568
14'	2.052268	2.131528	2.210139	2.288076	2.365317	2.441837
15'	2.053594	2.132844	2.211443	2.289370	2.366598	2.443106
16'	2.054920	2.134159	2.212748	2.290662	2.367879	2.444375
17'	2.056246	2.135474	2.214052	2.291955	2.369160	2.445644
18'	2.057572	2.136789	2.215356	2.293248	2.370441	2.446912
19'	2.058897	2.138104	2.216660	2.294540	2.371721	2.448180
20'	2.060223	2.139419	2.217963	2.295832	2.373002	2.449449
21'	2.061548	2.140733	2.219267	2.297124	2.374282	2.450716
22'	2.062873	2.142048	2.220570	2.298416	2.375562	2.451984
23'	2.064197	2.143362	2.221873	2.299707	2.376841	2.453251
24'	2.065522	2.144676	2.223176	2.300999	2.378121	2.454519
25'	2.066847	2.145989	2.224478	2.302290	2.379400	2.455786
26'	2.068171	2.147303	2.225781	2.303581	2.380679	2.457053
27'	2.069495	2.148616	2.227083	2.304872	2.381958	2.458319
28'	2.070819	2.149930	2.228385	2.306162	2.383237	2.459586
29'	2.072143	2.151243	2.229687	2.307453	2.384515	2.460852
30'	2.073466	2.152555	2.230989	2.308743	2.385794	2.462118
31'	2.074790	2.153868	2.232291	2.310033	2.387072	2.463384
32'	2.076113	2.155181	2.233592	2.311232	2.388350	2.464649
33'	2.077436	2.156493	2.234893	2.312612	2.389627	2.465914
34'	2.078759	2.157805	2.236194	2.313902	2.390905	2.467180
35'	2.080081	2.159117	2.237495	2.315191	2.392182	2.468445
36'	2.081404	2.160429	2.238795	2.316480	2.393459	2.469709
37'	2.082726	2.161740	2.240096	2.317769	2.394736	2.470974
38'	2.084048	2.163052	2.241396	2.319058	2.396013	2.472238
39'	2.085370	2.164363	2.242696	2.320346	2.397289	2.473502
40'	2.086692	2.165674	2.243996	2.321634	2.398565	2.474766
41'	2.088014	2.166985	2.245295	2.322922	2.399842	2.476030
42'	2.089335	2.168295	2.246595	2.324210	2.401117	2.477293
43'	2.090657	2.169606	2.247894	2.325498	2.402393	2.478557
44'	2.091978	2.170916	2.249193	2.326785	2.403669	2.479820
45'	2.093299	2.172226	2.250492	2.328073	2.404944	2.481082
46'	2.094619	2.173536	2.251791	2.329360	2.466219	2.482345
47'	2.095940	2.174846	2.253089	2.330646	2.407494	2.483608
48'	2.097260	2.176155	2.254388	2.331933	2.408768	2.484870
49'	2.098581	2.177465	2.255686	2.333220	2.410043	2.486132
50'	2.099901	2.178774	2.256984	2.334506	2.411317	2.487394
51'	2.101220	2.180083	2.258281	2.335792	2.412591	2.488655
52'	2.102540	2.181392	2.259579	2.337078	2.413865	2.489917
53'	2.103860	2.182700	2.260876	2.338364	2.415138	2.491178
54'	2.105179	2.184009	2.262173	2.339649	2.416412	2.492439
55'	2.106498	2.185317	2.263470	2.340934	2.417685	2.493699
56'	2.107817	2.186625	2.264767	2.342219	2.418958	2.494960
57'	2.109136	2.187933	2.266064	2.343504	2.420231	2.496220
58'	2.110455	2.189241	2.267360	2.344789	2.421503	2.497480
59'	2.111773	2.190548	2.268656	2.346073	2.422776	2.498740
60'	2.113091	2.191856	2.269952	2.347358	2.424048	2.500000

Sines for the DoAll Five-inch Sine Bar

Min.	30°	31°	32°	34°	33°	35°
0'	2.500000	2.575190	2.649596	2.723195	2.796964	2.867882
1'	2.501259	2.576437	2.650830	2.724415	2.797170	2.869073
2'	2.502519	2.577683	2.652063	2.725634	2.798376	2.870264
3'	2.503778	2.578929	2.653296	2.726853	2.799581	2.871455
4'	2.505037	2.580175	2.654528	2.728072	2.800786	2.872646
5'	2.506295	2.581421	2.655761	2.729291	2.801990	2.873836
6'	2.507554	2.582667	2.656993	2.730510	2.803195	2.875026
7'	2.508812	2.583912	2.658225	2.731728	2.804399	2.876216
8'	2.510070	2.585157	2.659457	2.732946	2.805603	2.877406
9'	2.511328	2.586402	2.660688	2.734164	2.806807	2.878595
10'	2.512585	2.587646	2.661919	2.735382	2.808010	2.879784
11'	2.513843	2.588891	2.663150	2.736599	2.809214	2.880973
12'	2.515100	2.590135	2.664381	2.737816	2.810417	2.882162
13'	2.516357	2.591379	2.665612	2.739033	2.811620	2.883350
14'	2.517613	2.592623	2.666842	2.740250	2.812822	2.884538
15'	2.518870	2.593866	2.668073	2.741466	2.814025	2.885726
16'	2.520126	2.595110	2.669302	2.742682	2.815227	2.886916
17'	2.521382	2.596353	2.760532	2.743898	2.816429	2.888101
18'	2.522638	2.597595	2.671762	2.745114	2.817630	2.889288
19'	2.523894	2.598838	2.672991	2.747545	2.818832	2.890475
20'	2.525149	2.600080	2.674220	2.746330	2.820033	2.891662
21'	2.526404	2.601323	2.675449	2.748760	2.821234	2.892848
22'	2.527659	2.602565	2.676677	2.749975	2.822434	2.894034
23'	2.528914	2.603807	2.677906	2.751189	2.823635	2.895220
24'	2.530169	2.605048	2.679134	2.752404	2.824835	2.896406
25'	2.531423	2.606289	2.608362	2.753618	2.826035	2.897591
26'	2.532677	2.607531	2.681589	2.754832	2.827235	2.898776
27'	2.533931	2.608771	2.682817	2.756045	2.828434	2.899961
28'	2.535185	2.610012	2.684044	2.757259	2.829633	2.901146
29'	2.536438	2.611253	2.865271	2.758472	2.830832	2.902330
30'	2.537692	2.612493	2.686498	2.759685	2.832031	2.903515
31'	2.538945	2.613733	2.687725	2.760898	2.833230	2.904699
32'	2.540198	2.614973	2.688951	2.762110	2.834428	2.905882
33'	2.541450	2.616212	2.690177	2.763322	2.835626	2.907066
34'	2.542703	2.617451	2.691403	2.764534	2.836824	2.908249
35'	2.543955	2.618691	2.692628	2.765746	2.838021	2.909432
36'	2.545207	2.619929	2.693854	2.766958	2.839219	2.910615
37'	2.546459	2.621168	2.695079	2.768169	2.840416	2.911797
38'	2.547710	2.622407	2.696304	2.769380	2.841613	2.912979
39'	2.548962	2.623645	2.697529	2.770591	2.842809	2.914161
40'	2.550213	2.624883	2.698753	2.771802	2.844006	2.915343
41'	2.551464	2.626121	2.699977	2.773012	2.845202	2.916525
42'	2.552715	2.627358	2.701202	2.774222	2.846398	2.917706
43'	2.553965	2.628596	2.702425	2.775432	2.847593	2.918887
44'	2.555215	2.629833	2.703649	2.776642	2.848789	2.920068
45'	2.556465	2.631070	2.704872	2.777851	2.849984	2.921248
46'	2.557715	2.632306	2.706095	2.779060	2.851179	2.922429
47'	2.558965	2.633543	2.707318	2.780269	2.852373	2.923609
48'	2.560214	2.634779	2.708541	2.781478	2.853568	2.924788
49'	2.561463	2.636015	2.709763	2.782687	2.854762	2.925968
50'	2.562712	2.637251	2.710986	2.783895	2.855956	2.927147
51'	2.563961	2.638486	2.712208	2.785103	2.857150	2.928326
52'	2.565210	2.639722	2.713429	2.786311	2.858343	2.929505
53'	2.566458	2.640957	2.714651	2.787518	2.859536	2.930683
54'	2.567706	2.642192	2.715872	2.788725	2.860729	2.931862
55'	2.568954	2.643426	2.717093	2.789933	2.861922	2.933040
56'	2.570202	2.644661	2.718314	2.791139	2.863115	2.934218
57'	2.571449	2.645895	2.719535	2.972346	2.864307	2.935395
58'	2.572696	2.647129	2.720755	2.793552	2.865499	2.936572
59'	2.573943	2.648363	2.721975	2.794759	2.866691	2.937749
60'	2.575190	2.649596	2.723195	2.795964	2.867882	2.938913

Sines for the DoAll Five-inch Sine Bar

Min.	36°	37°	38°	39°	40°	41°
0'	2.938913	3.009075	3.078307	3.146602	3.213938	3.280295
1'	2.940103	3.010236	3.079453	3.147732	3.215052	3.281393
2'	2.941279	3.011398	3.080599	3.148862	3.216166	3.282490
3'	2.942455	3.012559	3.081744	3.149992	3.217279	3.283587
4'	2.943631	3.013719	3.082890	3.151121	3.218392	3.284684
5'	2.944806	3.014880	3.084035	3.152250	3.219505	3.285780
6'	2.945982	3.016040	3.085179	3.133379	3.220618	3.286876
7'	2.947157	3.017200	3.086324	3.154508	3.221730	3.287972
8'	2.948332	3.018359	3.087468	3.155636	3.222843	3.289608
9'	2.949506	3.019519	3.088612	3.156764	3.223954	3.290163
10'	2.950680	3.020678	3.089755	3.157892	3.225066	3.291258
11'	2.951854	3.021837	3.090899	3.159019	3.226177	3.292353
12'	2.953028	3.022995	3.092042	3.160146	3.227288	3.293447
13'	2.954202	3.024154	3.093185	3.161273	3.228399	3.294541
14'	2.955375	3.025312	3.094327	3.162400	3.229510	3.295635
15'	2.956548	3.026470	3.095470	3.162527	3.230620	3.296729
16'	2.957721	3.027627	3.096612	3.164653	3.231730	3.297822
17'	2.958894	3.028785	3.097754	3.165779	3.232839	3.298915
18'	2.960066	3.029942	3.098895	3.166904	3.233949	3.300008
19'	2.961238	3.031099	3.100036	3.168030	3.235058	3.301101
20'	2.962410	3.032255	3.101177	3.169155	3.236167	3.302193
21'	2.963581	3.033412	3.102318	3.170280	3.237275	3.303285
22'	2.964753	3.034568	3.103459	3.171404	3.238384	3.304377
23'	2.965924	3.035724	3.104599	3.172528	3.239492	3.305468
24'	2.967094	3.036879	3.105739	3.173652	3.240599	3.306559
25'	2.968265	3.038034	3.106879	3.174776	3.241707	3.307650
26'	2.969435	3.039189	3.108018	3.175900	3.242814	3.308741
27'	2.970605	3.040344	3.109157	3.177023	3.243921	3.309831
28'	2.971775	3.041499	3.110296	3.178146	3.245028	3.310921
29'	2.972945	3.042653	3.111435	3.179269	3.246134	3.312011
30'	2.974114	3.043807	3.112573	3.180391	3.247240	3.313100
31'	2.975283	3.044961	3.113711	3.181513	3.248346	3.314189
32'	2.976452	3.046114	3.114849	3.182635	3.249452	3.315278
33'	2.977620	3.047268	3.115987	3.183757	3.250557	3.316367
34'	2.978788	3.048421	3.117124	3.184878	3.251662	3.317455
35'	2.979957	3.049573	3.118261	3.185999	3.252767	3.318543
36'	2.981124	3.050726	3.119398	3.187120	3.253871	3.319631
37'	2.982292	3.051878	3.120534	3.188240	3.254975	3.320718
38'	2.983459	3.053030	3.121671	3.189361	3.256079	3.321806
39'	2.984626	3.054182	3.122807	3.190481	3.257183	3.322893
40'	2.985793	3.055333	3.123942	3.191600	3.258286	3.323979
41'	2.986959	3.056484	3.125078	3.192720	3.259389	3.325066
42'	2.988126	3.057635	3.126213	3.193839	3.260492	3.326152
43'	2.989292	3.058786	3.127348	3.194958	3.261594	3.327237
44'	2.990457	3.059936	3.128483	3.196077	3.262697	3.328323
45'	2.991623	3.061086	3.129617	3.197195	3.263799	3.329408
46'	2.992788	3.062236	3.130751	3.198313	3.264900	3.330493
47'	2.993953	3.063386	3.131885	3.199431	3.266002	3.331578
48'	2.995118	3.064535	3.133019	3.200548	3.267103	3.332662
49'	2.996282	3.065685	3.134152	3.201666	3.268204	3.333746
50'	2.997447	3.066833	3.135285	3.202783	3.269304	3.334830
51'	2.998611	3.076982	3.136418	3.203899	3.270405	3.335914
52'	2.999774	3.069130	3.137551	3.205016	3.271505	3.336997
53'	3.000938	3.070278	3.138683	3.206132	3.272605	3.338080
54'	3.002101	3.071426	3.139815	3.207248	3.273704	3.339163
55'	3.003264	3.072574	3.140947	3.208364	3.274803	3.340245
56'	3.004427	3.073721	3.142078	3.209479	3.275902	3.341327
57'	3.005589	3.074868	3.143210	3.210594	3.277001	3.342409
58'	3.006751	3.076015	3.144341	3.211709	3.278099	3.343491
59'	3.007913	3.077161	3.145471	3.212824	3.279197	3.344572
60'	3.009075	3.078307	3.146602	3.213938	3.280295	3.345653

Sines for the DoAll Five-inch Sine Bar

Min.	42°	43°	44°	45°	46°	47°
0′	3.345653	3.409992	3.473392	3.535534	3.596699	3.656768
1′	3.346734	3.411055	3.474338	3.536562	3.597709	3.657760
2′	3.347814	3.412119	3.475384	3.537590	3.598719	3.658752
3′	3.348894	3.413182	3.476429	4.538618	3.599729	3.659743
4′	3.349974	3.414244	3.477474	3.539645	3.600738	3.660734
5′	3.351054	3.415307	3.478519	3.540672	3.601747	3.661724
6′	3.352133	3.416369	3.479564	3.541699	3.602755	3.662714
7′	3.353212	3.417431	3.480608	3.542726	3.603764	3.663704
8′	3.354291	3.418492	3.481652	3.543752	3.604772	3.664694
9′	3.355369	3.419553	3.482696	3.544778	3.605780	3.665683
10′	3.356447	3.420614	3.483739	3.545803	3.606787	3.666672
11′	3.357525	3.421675	3.484783	3.546829	3.608801	3.667661
12′	3.358603	3.422735	3.485825	3.547854	3.606794	3.669649
13′	3.359680	3.423796	3.486868	3.548878	3.609808	3.669637
14′	3.360757	3.424855	3.487910	3.549903	3.610814	3.670625
15′	3.361834	3.425915	3.488952	3.550927	3.611820	3.671612
16′	3.362910	3.426974	3.489994	3.551951	3.612825	3.672600
17′	3.363987	3.428033	3.491035	3.552974	3.613831	3.673586
18′	3.365062	3.429092	3.492076	3.553997	3.614836	3.674573
19′	3.366138	3.430150	3.493117	3.555020	3.615840	3.675559
20′	3.367213	3.431208	3.494158	3.556043	3.616845	3.676545
21′	3.368288	3.432266	3.495198	3.557065	3.617849	3.677531
22′	3.369363	3.433323	3.496238	3.558087	3.618853	3.678516
23′	3.370438	3.434381	3.497277	3.559109	3.619856	3.679501
24′	3.371512	3.435437	3.498317	3.560130	3.620859	3.680485
25′	3.372586	3.436494	3.499356	3.561151	3.621862	3.681470
26′	3.373659	3.437550	3.500394	3.562172	3.622865	3.682454
27′	3.374733	3.438606	3.501433	3.563193	3.623867	3.683437
28′	3.375806	3.439662	3.502471	3.564213	3.624869	3.684421
29′	3.376878	3.440718	3.503509	3.565233	3.625870	3.685040
30′	3.377951	3.441773	3.504546	3.566252	3.626872	3.686387
31′	3.379023	3.442828	3.505583	3.567271	3.627873	3.687369
32′	3.380095	3.443882	3.506620	3.568290	3.628874	3.688351
33′	3.381167	3.444937	3.507657	3.569309	3.629874	3.689333
34′	3.382238	3.445991	3.508693	3.570327	3.630874	3.690315
35′	3.383309	3.447044	3.509729	3.571346	3.631874	3.691296
36′	3.384380	3.448098	3.510765	3.572363	3.632873	3.692277
37′	3.385450	3.449151	3.511801	3.573381	3.633872	3.693257
38′	3.386520	3.450204	3.512836	3.574398	3.634871	3.694237
39′	3.387590	3.451256	3.513871	3.575415	3.635870	3.695217
40′	3.388660	3.452308	3.514905	3.576431	3.636868	3.696197
41′	3.389729	3.453360	3.515939	3.577448	3.637866	3.697176
42′	3.390798	3.454412	3.516973	3.578464	3.638864	3.698155
43′	3.391867	3.455463	3.518057	3.579479	3.639861	3.699134
44′	3.392935	3.456514	3.519040	3.580495	3.640858	3.700112
45′	3.394004	3.457565	3.520074	3.581510	3.641855	3.701091
46′	3.395072	3.458616	3.521106	3.582524	3.642851	3.702068
47′	3.396139	3.459666	3.522139	3.583539	3.643847	3.703046
48′	3.397206	3.460716	3.523171	2.584553	3.644843	3.704023
49′	3.398273	3.461765	3.524203	3.585567	3.645839	3.705000
50′	3.399340	3.462815	3.525234	3.586580	3.646834	3.705976
51′	3.400407	3.463864	3.526266	3.587594	3.647829	3.706952
52′	3.401473	3.464912	3.527297	3.588606	3.648823	3.707928
53′	3.402539	3.465961	3.528327	3.589619	3.649817	3.708904
54′	3.403604	3.467009	3.529358	3.590631	3.650811	3.709879
55′	3.404670	3.468057	3.530388	3.591643	3.651805	3.710854
56′	3.405735	3.469104	3.531418	3.592655	3.652798	3.711829
57′	3.406799	3.470152	3.532447	3.593667	3.653791	3.712803
58′	3.407864	3.471199	3.533476	3.594678	3.654785	3.713777
59′	3.408928	3.472245	3.534505	3.595688	3.655776	3.714751
60′	3.409992	3.473292	3.535534	2.596699	3.656768	3.715724

Sines for the DoAll Five-inch Sine Bar

Min.	48°	49°	50°	51°	52°	53°
0'	3.715724	3.773548	3.830222	3.885730	3.940054	3.993177
1'	3.716697	3.774502	3.831157	3.886645	3.940949	3.994053
2'	3.717670	3.775456	3.832091	3.887560	3.941844	3.994927
3'	3.718642	3.776409	3.833025	3.888474	3.942739	3.995802
4'	3.719614	3.777362	3.833959	3.889388	3.943633	3.996676
5'	3.720586	3.778315	3.834893	3.890302	3.944527	3.997550
6'	3.721558	3.779267	3.835826	3.891216	3.945420	3.998423
7'	3.722529	3.780219	3.836758	3.892129	3.946314	3.999296
8'	3.723500	3.781171	3.837691	3.893042	3.947207	4.000169
9'	3.724470	3.782123	3.838623	3.893954	3.948099	4.001042
10'	3.725440	3.783074	3.839555	3.894866	3.948991	4.001914
11'	3.726410	3.784025	3.840486	3.895778	3.949883	4.002785
12'	3.727380	3.784975	3.841418	3.896690	3.950775	4.003657
13'	3.728349	3.785925	3.842348	3.897601	3.951666	4.004528
14'	3.729318	3.786875	3.843279	3.898512	3.952557	4.005399
15'	3.730287	3.787825	3.844209	3.899422	3.953448	4.006269
16'	3.731255	3.788774	3.845139	3.900333	3.954338	4.007139
17'	3.732223	3.789723	3.846068	3.901242	3.955228	4.008009
18'	3.733191	3.790672	3.846998	3.902152	3.956118	4.008878
19'	3.734158	3.791620	3.847927	3.903061	3.957007	4.009747
20'	3.735125	3.792568	3.848855	3.903970	3.957896	4.010616
21'	3.736092	3.793515	3.849783	3.904879	3.958784	4.011484
22'	3.737058	3.794463	3.850711	3.905787	3.959673	4.012352
23'	3.738025	3.795410	3.851639	3.906695	3.960561	4.013220
24'	3.738990	3.796356	3.852566	3.907602	3.961448	4.014087
25'	3.739956	3.797303	3.853493	3.908510	3.962335	4.014954
26'	3.740921	3.798249	3.854420	3.909416	3.963222	4.015821
27'	3.741886	3.799195	3.855346	3.910323	3.964109	4.016687
28'	3.742850	3.800140	3.856272	3.911229	3.964995	4.017553
29'	3.743815	3.801085	3.857198	3.912135	3.965881	4.018419
30'	3.744779	3.802030	3.858123	3.913041	3.966767	4.019284
31'	3.745742	3.802974	3.859048	3.913946	3.976652	4.020149
32'	3.746705	3.803918	3.859972	3.914851	3.968537	4.021014
33'	3.747668	3.804862	3.860897	3.915755	3.969421	4.021878
34'	3.748631	3.805806	3.861821	3.916660	3.970306	4.022742
35'	3.749593	3.806749	3.862744	3.917564	3.971189	4.023606
36'	3.750555	3.807691	3.863668	3.918467	3.972073	4.024469
37'	3.751517	3.808634	3.864591	3.919370	3.972956	4.025332
38'	3.752478	3.809576	3.865513	3.920273	3.973839	4.026194
39'	3.753439	3.810519	3.866436	3.921176	3.974722	4.027057
40'	3.754400	3.811459	3.867358	3.922078	3.975604	4.027919
41'	3.755361	3.812401	3.868280	3.922980	3.976486	4.028780
42'	3.756321	3.813342	3.869201	3.923882	3.977367	4.029641
43'	3.757280	3.814282	3.870122	3.924783	3.978249	4.030502
44'	3.758240	3.815222	3.871043	3.925684	3.979129	4.031363
45'	3.759199	3.816162	3.871963	3.926585	3.980010	4.032223
46'	3.760158	3.817102	3.872883	3.927485	3.980890	4.033083
47'	3.761116	3.818041	3.873803	3.928385	3.981770	4.033942
48'	3.762074	3.818980	3.874722	3.929284	3.982650	4.034801
49'	3.763032	3.819919	3.875641	3.930184	3.983529	4.035660
50'	3.763990	3.820857	3.876560	3.391083	3.984408	4.036519
51'	3.764947	3.821795	3.777479	3.931981	9.985286	4.037377
52'	3.765904	3.822733	3.878397	3.932879	3.986164	4.038235
53'	3.766861	3.823670	3.879315	3.933777	3.987042	4.039092
54'	3.767817	3.824607	3.880232	3.934675	3.987920	4.039949
55'	3.768773	3.825544	3.881149	3.935572	3.988797	4.040806
56'	3.769728	3.826480	3.882066	3.936469	3.989674	4.041663
57'	3.770684	3.827416	3.882982	3.937366	3.990550	4.042519
58'	3.771639	3.828352	3.883898	3.938262	3.991426	4.043374
59'	3.772593	3.829287	3.884814	3.939158	3.992302	4.044230
60'	3.773548	3.830222	3.885730	3.940054	3.993177	4.045085

Sines for the DoAll Five-inch Sine Bar

Min.	54°	55°	56°	57°	59°	58°
0′	4.045085	4.095760	4.145188	4.193353	4.240240	4.285836
1′	4.045940	4.096594	4.146001	4.194145	4.241011	4.286585
2′	4.046974	4.097428	4.146814	4.194936	4.241781	4.287334
3′	4.047648	4.098261	4.147626	4.195728	4.242551	4.288082
4′	4.048502	4.099094	4.148438	4.196519	4.243320	4.288830
5′	4.049355	4.099927	4.149250	4.197309	4.244090	4.289577
6′	4.050208	4.100759	4.150061	4.198099	4.244858	4.290324
7′	4.051061	4.101591	4.150872	4.198889	4.245627	4.291071
8′	4.051913	4.102423	4.151683	4.199679	4.246395	4.291818
9′	4.052765	4.103254	4.152493	4.200468	4.247162	4.292564
10′	4.053617	4.014085	4.153303	4.201256	4.247930	4.293309
11′	4.054468	4.104916	4.154113	4.202045	4.248697	4.294054
12′	4.055319	4.105746	4.154922	4.202833	4.249463	4.294799
13′	4.056170	4.106576	4.155731	4.203621	4.250230	4.295544
14′	4.057020	4.107405	4.156540	4.204408	4.250996	4.296288
15′	4.057870	4.108235	4.157348	4.205195	4.251761	4.297032
16′	4.058719	4.109063	4.158156	4.205982	4.252526	4.297775
17′	4.059569	4.109892	4.158963	4.206768	4.253291	4.298519
18′	4.060418	4.110720	4.159771	4.207554	4.254055	4.299261
19′	4.061266	4.111548	4.160577	4.208340	4.254820	4.300004
20′	4.062114	4.112375	4.161384	4.209125	4.255583	4.300746
21′	4.062962	4.113203	4.162190	4.209905	4.256347	4.301487
22′	4.063810	4.114029	4.162996	4.201694	4.257110	4.302229
23′	4.064657	4.114856	4.163801	4.211478	4.257872	4.302970
24′	4.065504	4.115682	4.164606	4.212262	4.258635	4.303710
25′	4.066350	4.116507	4.165411	4.213045	4.259397	4.304450
26′	4.067196	4.117333	4.166215	4.213828	4.260158	4.305190
27′	4.068042	4.118158	4.167019	4.214611	4.260919	4.305930
28′	4.068888	4.118983	4.167823	4.215393	4.261680	4.306669
29′	4.069733	4.119807	4.168626	4.216176	4.262441	4.307407
30′	4.070578	4.120631	4.169429	4.216957	4.263201	4.308146
31′	4.071422	4.121464	4.170232	4.217738	4.263961	4.308884
32′	4.072266	4.122278	4.171034	4.218519	4.264720	4.309621
33′	4.073110	4.123101	4.171836	4.219300	4.265479	4.310359
34′	4.073953	4.123923	4.172637	4.220080	4.266238	4.311096
35′	4.074796	4.124746	4.173438	4.220860	4.266996	4.311832
36′	4.075639	4.125567	4.174239	4.221640	4.267754	4.312568
37′	4.076481	4.126389	4.175040	4.222419	4.268512	4.313304
38′	4.077323	4.127210	4.175840	4.223197	4.269269	4.314040
39′	4.078165	4.128031	4.176640	4.223976	4.270026	4.314775
40′	4.079006	4.128851	4.117439	4.224754	4.270782	4.315509
41′	4.079847	4.129672	4.178238	4.225532	4.271538	4.316244
42′	4.080688	4.130491	4.179037	4.226309	4.272294	4.316978
43′	4.081528	4.131311	4.179835	4.227806	4.273050	4.317711
44′	4.082368	4.132130	4.180633	4.227863	4.273805	4.318445
45′	4.083208	4.132949	4.181431	4.228639	4.274559	4.319177
46′	4.084047	4.133767	4.182228	4.229415	4.275314	4.319910
47′	4.084886	4.134585	4.183025	4.230191	4.276068	4.320642
48′	4.085724	4.135403	4.183821	4.230966	4.276821	4.321374
49′	4.086563	4.136220	4.184618	4.231741	4.277574	4.322105
50′	4.087400	4.137037	4.185414	4.232515	4.278327	4.332836
51′	4.088238	4.137854	4.186209	4.233289	4.279080	4.323567
52′	4.089075	4.138670	4.187004	4.234063	4.279832	4.324297
53′	4.089912	4.139486	4.187799	4.234836	4.280584	4.325027
54′	4.090749	4.140302	4.188594	4.235610	4.281335	4.325757
55′	4.091585	4.141117	4.189388	4.236382	4.282086	4.326486
56′	4.092420	4.141932	4.190181	4.237155	4.282837	4.327215
57′	4.093256	4.142746	4.190975	4.237927	4.283588	4.327944
58′	4.094091	4.143560	4.191768	4.238698	4.284338	4.328672
59′	4.094926	4.144374	4.192560	4.239469	4.285087	4.329400
60′	4.095760	4.145188	4.193353	4.240240	4.285836	4.330127

Tolerances for Sine Bars, Blocks and Plates

Commercial Class

1	2	3	4	5
	Bar	Buttons or Cylinders		
Size	Working surface to be flat, square with sides and parallel (if double), within	Cylinders to be alike round and straight, within	Cylinders to be parallel with each other and with working surface of bar, within	Cylinders to be at nominal center distance, ±
in.	in.	in.	in.	in.
5	0.00010	0.00005	0.00010	0.0002
10	0.00015	0.00005	0.00015	0.0003
20	0.00020	0.00006	0.00020	0.0004
(Laboratory Class)				
5	0.000050	0.00003	0.000050	0.00010
10	0.000075	0.00003	0.000075	0.00015
20	0.000100	0.00004	0.000100	0.00020

line dropped from one end of a circular arc to, or upon, the radius, or distance from the other end, directly beneath the end of the arc. Sine bars can be of any length but are made either 5 or 10 inches from center to center of the disks or pins, for convenience in making calculations.

The disks or pins at the ends of the sine bar must be of the same diameter and spaced with the centers either 5 or 10 inches apart, as accurately as can be measured. In use, the measurements are taken from the outside of the disks, as it is more convenient than using the centers. Measured with a 10-inch sine bar the reading is *ten times* the actual sine of the angle at which the bar is set, as sine tables are given at a radius of 1 inch.

SINE BAR MILLING TABLE — A milling table with a sine bar base to make it easy to secure any desired angle between the work and the table.

SINE BLOCK FIXTURE OR PLATE — A block or plate providing reference surfaces, with two cylinders or buttons attached to the block or plate to provide for measurement of angles in the same way as the sine bar. Provision is usually made for attachment of accessories or work pieces to any surface of the block.

SINE PLATE — A plate having measuring studs of the same diameter which are accurately spaced on 5- or 10-inch centers.

SINGLE-DUAL MACHINE — A term applied to a machine having a single work spindle but two working tables so one can be loaded while the tools are at work on the other.

SINGLE POINT BORING — Boring with a single-pointed tool. The most accurate method of securing holes as nearly round as possible. On metal work it is now common practice to use carbide tools, although diamonds are used on some of the softer metals, and frequently on plastics and hard rubber. It is sometimes called "diamond boring" even when diamonds are not used.

SINGLE POINT THREADING — Cutting screw threads with a single-point tool, in distinction to cutting them with a die, or grinding them.

SINGLE-POINT TOOLS — Tools having a single cutting point. Usually applied to tools used in a lathe, boring mill, planer or shaper. Also the tools held in bars for boring accurate holes. The size of a tool refers to the shank which is held in the tool post and is given in the following order: Width of shank, W; height of shank, H, and total tool length, L,

414

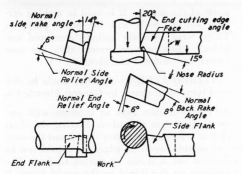

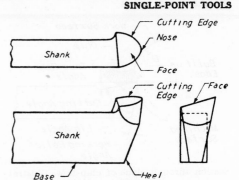

Right-cut, straight-shank, single-point, raised-face, forged-type tool.

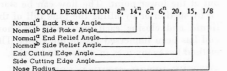

TOOL DESIGNATION 8, 14, 6, 6, 20, 15, 1/8

Normal[a] Back Rake Angle
Normal[b] Side Rake Angle
Normal[a] End Relief Angle
Normal[b] Side Relief Angle
End Cutting Edge Angle
Side Cutting Edge Angle
Nose Radius

A typical solid tool of high-speed steel, ground for turning steel of about 250 to 300 Brinell. Rake and relief angles are shown as normal to cutting edges.

such as $\frac{3}{4} \times 1\frac{1}{2} \times 8$ inches. The various elements are shown.

To simplify the designation of these elements they are standardized as shown in the "key," with an example below it. This saves time as well as misunderstandings. The other illustrations show standard practice in the use of terms for various parts.

Single-point tools include various shapes of

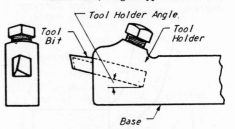

Tool bit and holder.

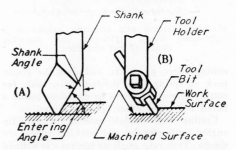

Bent tools. (A) Forged left-bent shank right-hand tool. (B) Right-cut tool bit in right-bent holder.

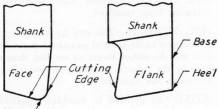

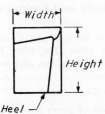

Right-cut, straight-shank, single-point ground tool.

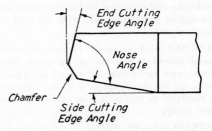

Tool angles, forming the cutting edges on a ground tool.

(Illustrations continued on page 416.)

415

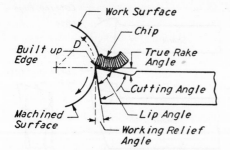

Section through plane of chip-flow, illustrating working angles.

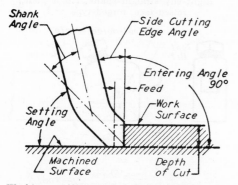

Working, setting and entering angles of a right-bent shank right-cut tool, showing depth of cut and feed.

cutting edges, or points, including the gooseneck or spring tool, skiving tools, tools for cutting recesses, grooves or chamfers inside a bored hole, and other special shapes.

Cutting edge angles, entering angles, lip angles, setting angles and working angles are shown. True rake angle or top rake is defined as: The slope of the tool face toward the tool base from the active cutting edge in the direction of chip flow. It is a combination of the back-rake and side-rake angles and varies with the setting of the tool and with the feed and depth of cut.

SINKHEAD—A reservoir for excess molten metal placed at the top of an ingot, which feeds extra metal into the top of an ingot to make up for shrinkage as it cools This head is insulated to retain its heat so the metal can flow easily.

SINKING—See *Die Sinking.*

SINTERING—A process of fusing powders into a solid mass at less than the melting

point of the metals. It is used in making carbide cutting tools and for other purposes. These were formerly called "cemented carbides," which was incorrect; they are now known as "sintered carbides."

SINTERED ALNICO—An alloy made in sintered form for magnets, by General Electric Co.

SIPHON—A tube bent in U shape with one end longer than the other. Placing the short end in a vessel containing liquid and the long end outside, over the edge, the liquid can be drained out if it can be started to flow. The pressure on the liquid in the vessel forces it out at the lower point. The flow can be started by suction or by filling the pipe full of the liquid and closing each end until the short end has been immersed inside the vessel. The method has many uses in various industries.

SIXTEEN PITCH THREAD SERIES—A series of screw threads of 16 pitch, regardless of diameter, from ¾ inch to 4 inches. Used for adjusting collars and retaining nuts for bearings. See *Screw Threads* for details.

SIZE, ACTUAL—The dimension of a part as actually measured. It is presumably within the high and low limits prescribed for the part. Measurements are assumed to be made at 68 deg. F.

SIZE, BASIC—The theoretical size, or dimension, for a perfect part.

SIZE LIMITS — Extreme sizes permitted in variation from standard.

SIZE, NOMINAL—The size by which a part is referred to in general practice. A one-inch bolt may be either larger or smaller than one inch by the amount of tolerance which is permitted in the standards.

SIZING—As applied to machine operations, the final operation which finishes the piece to size. Finishing or sizing by cold pressing is known as coining.

SKELP—A trade name for the iron plates used in making welded iron pipe. The plate is rolled so that the edges meet, or lap, and are then welded into a tube.

SKEW GEARING—See *Gear, Bevel.*

SKIDS—Open frame work of heavy timber to support machinery or various other materials for moving or for shipping. A skid frequently forms the base for a packing case when a

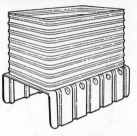

Steel box skid.

machine is to be shipped by rail or sea. The term also applies to steel or wooden bases or platforms on which material is loaded and stored.

SKIP-TOOTH SAW—See *Saw, Skip Tooth.*

SKIP WELDING—See *Welding, Skip.*

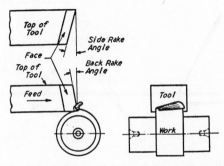

Rectangularly shaped skiving tool.

SKIVING—The forming of work by feeding a cutting or forming tool under or over the work tangent to it instead of feeding it radially against the work.

SKY-HOOK—In some sections, any hook fastened to the ceiling or roof to hold a block and tackle for hoisting machinery into position. In steam engineering and railroad circles some use it to describe a boiler tube cleaner.

SLAB—A rolled, semi-finished ingot of metal, usually flat in shape. The width is at least 10 times the cross-sectional area, which is not less than 16 square inches. Rolling mill term.

SLAG—The waste material that forms on melted metal, largely cinders and impurities. Sometimes called "dross."

SLANT HEIGHT—The length of the inclined side of a cone or triangle.

SLEDGE—A heavy hammer. See *Hammer, Sledge.*

SLEEVE—A tube or hollow cylinder supporting or covering a spindle of a machine. It frequently acts as a bearing through which the spindle can move endwise as well as rotate, or while it is rotating. Called a "quill" in some localities.

SLEEVE NUTS—See *Nuts, Sleeve.*

SLEEVE VALVE—See *Valve, Sleeve.*

SLICK—A small tool used in foundries in smoothing or repairing sand molds which have become broken in any way. They are of different shapes, sometimes being like a spoon on one end. The term is also used to refer to any smooth or slippery surface.

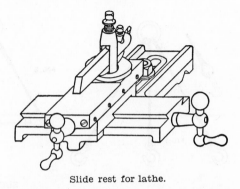

Slide rest for lathe.

SLIDE REST—A tool carrying rest for use on lathes not provided with a carriage fed along the bed by power; primarily for use on bench or hand lathes. It provides means for feeding the tool along the bed and across the lathe, for facing or cutting off. Some are provided with a swiveling or compound base to enable angular surfaces to be turned. The one shown is for a South Bend bench lathe.

SLIDE RULE—A calculating device with one or more graduated scales which slide in the main rule. Also made in circular form.

SLIDE VALVE—See *Valve, Slide.*

SLIDING GEAR—A gear which slides on a keyed or splined shaft to engage or disengage other gears.

SLING—A loop of rope or chain used in hoisting heavy material. The usual method is to have two short chains, each with hooks, as

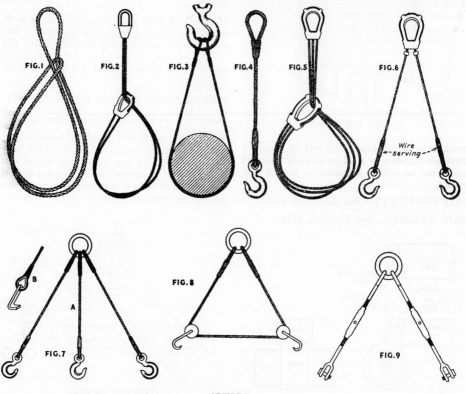

FIG.1 FIG.2 FIG.3 FIG.4 FIG.5 FIG.6

Wire serving

FIG.8

B

A

FIG.7

FIG.9

SLINGS.

(Fig. 1) The endless sling, usually formed into a noose, known as a choker or anchor hitch, is slipped around the object to be lifted, free bight being placed on crane hook. (Fig. 2) Bights are sometimes threaded through drop-forged thimbles. Single-rope slings are made of spliced eyes (Fig. 3), or an eye and hook (Fig. 4). Equalizing thimbles (Fig. 5) permit making slings with several ropes in parallel or single sling with hooks (Fig. 6). (Fig. 7) For heavy loads 3- and 4-leg slings are fitted with hooks or eyes according to the object to be handled. Special plate hooks (Fig. 7B and 8) are used instead of picking up the load on the bill or point of a hook.

6 x 19 PLOW STEEL ROPE					IRON COIL CHAIN					3-PART BRAIDED SLING (ATLAS)				
Rope dia. in.	Single leg Verti-cal	2-leg slings			Bas-ket hitch	Stock dia. in.	Single leg Verti-cal	2-leg slings			Bas-ket hitch	Dia. of rope used in.	Single leg Verti-cal	2-leg slings			Bas-ket hitch
		60°	45°	30°				60°	45°	30°				60°	45°	30°	
⅜	1.20	2.08	1.70	1.20	1.70	⅜	0.90	1.56	1.28	0.90	1.28	⅛	0.77	1.34	1.10	0.77	1.10
½	2.05	3.55	2.90	2.05	2.90	½	1.50	2.60	2.14	1.50	2.14	3/16	1.71	2.96	2.42	1.71	2.42
⅝	3.15	5.46	4.45	3.15	4.45	⅝	2.31	4.02	3.28	2.31	3.28	¼	3.25	5.63	4.60	3.25	4.60
¾	4.50	7.79	6.36	4.50	6.36	¾	3.38	5.88	4.80	3.38	4.80	5/16	5.04	8.73	7.13	5.04	7.13
⅞	5.67	9.82	8.02	5.67	8.02	⅞	4.67	8.12	6.64	4.67	6.64	⅜	7.06	12.23	9.98	7.06	9.98
1	7.39	12.80	10.45	7.39	10.45	1	6.20	10.80	8.80	6.20	8.80	7/16	9.41	16.30	13.31	9.41	13.31
1⅛	8.18	14.17	11.57	8.18	11.57	1⅛	7.80	13.58	11.08	7.80	11.08	½	12.10	20.96	17.11	12.10	17.11
1¼	10.09	17.48	14.27	10.09	14.27	1¼	9.60	16.70	13.62	9.60	13.62	9/16	15.12	26.19	21.38	15.12	21.38

Note: (1) Angles are between sling legs and horizontal. (2) For 3- and 4-leg slings, multiply 2-leg loads by 1½ and 2 respectively.

shown. The position of these chains affects their lifting capacity, as shown by the table. At an angle of 120 degrees they only have half the capacity as when both are straight.

Slings are used in many ways and in many forms, 10 being shown herewith.

Precautions in connection with their use are:

NEVER:

1. Overload a sling.
2. Apply the load suddenly.
3. Insert a hook in chain link.
4. Carry the load on a hook point.
5. Use a sling that looks unsafe.
6. Hammer a sling into place.
7. Fasten a sling over sharp corners.
8. Cross, kink or twist a sling.
9. Let the load rest on a sling.
10. Drag a sling from under a load.
11. Trust a sling that has been stretched.
12. Carry an unbalanced load.

Safe loading depends much on the way the sling is arranged on the load. The table gives a good general idea of the safe loadings.

SLIP GEAR—See *Gear, Slip.*

SLIP WASHER—See *Washer, Slip.*

SLIT—Usually means a narrow groove to receive a thin piece of metal or other material. Also used to describe cutting sheet metal into strips for use in a punch press or elsewhere.

SLITTING SAW—See *Milling Cutters.*

SLOT—A groove, usually with straight sides, as for holding a key. A keyway is one form of a slot. They are usually lengthwise of a shaft or other member, but in flat surfaces they may go in any direction. They are used to locate another part in a definite location, or to permit it to be moved only in a definite direction. They may be straight or curved to meet specified conditions. They may be cut with end milling cutters, by broaching or with peripheral cutters, as well as by planing, shaping or slotting. See *Keyway* or *Key Seat.*

SLOT FILE—See *File, Slot.*

SLOTTED CHUCK—A sleeve with a slot across the end for driving flat work in the lathe. Used in making flat reamers or taps.

SLOTTED WASHER—Same as slip washer. See *Washer, Slip.*

SLOTTER—Primarily a machine tool having a vertical ram-carried tool which cuts slots or other surfaces by vertical movement. Its greatest use at present is in railway shops. Small sizes of these machines are now called *vertical shapers* and are used largely in tool room and similar work. They have a quick-return movement which saves time on the up, or return, stroke. See *Shaper, Vertical.*

SLOTTING — Cutting a slot or outline by means of a reciprocating tool in a slotting machine, which may be called a vertical shaper. Slotting is also done with a milling cutter, or by broaching.

SLOTTING ATTACHMENT — See *Milling Machine, Slotting Attachment.*

SLOW TAPER—See *Taper, Slow.*

SLUDGE—Sediment which collects in crankcases and other oil reservoirs and in steam boilers. The former is, of course, largely hard grease, while the latter may be mud or other impurities in the water.

SLUE OR SLEW—To turn away from the direction desired. Sometimes used as a direction to move a machine to the right or left, usually while it is being erected.

SLUG—Any small piece, such as a punching from sheet or plate. Usually a waste piece, although sometimes usable for other work. Blanks used in coining or extruding are sometimes called slugs.

SLURRY—A mixture used for covering surfaces to be soldered, or babbitted before the solder or babbit is applied. Magnesia, water glass and water are used in connection with babbitting. The same term may be used for other mixtures used for other purposes.

SLUSH OR SLUSHING—The covering used to prevent rusting of finished parts of metals which are affected by the atmosphere; it is usually some sort of light grease or heavy oil. White lead and oil were formerly used, but the coating is hard to remove. There are also rust-resisting compounds which resemble a varnish.

SMALL TOOLS—A term which usually means drills, taps, dies, reamers, milling cutters and the like. It is also sometimes applied to pliers, tongs and wrenches. Small tools which wear out regularly and fairly rapidly, such as drills, are usually called "perishable tools," or "expendable tools," after Navy practice. The term "small tools" should not be applied to small machine tools, such as bench lathes or shapers, or to tools used by machinists, such as calipers.

SMELT—Fusing or melting as when ore is reduced to obtain the metals it contains.

SNAGGING—This usually refers to the rough grinding of castings or forgings to remove the fins or flash, or rough parts commonly called "snags." On light work the piece to be snagged is held against a coarse grinding wheel mounted on a floor stand grinder. For heavy work the grinding wheel is mounted on a swing-grinder, which is a frame allowing the wheel to be moved over the surface of the casting or forging. In other cases a portable grinder is used, powered either by air or by an electric motor. See *Grinder, Swing* and *Grinder Portable.*

SNAIL—This term is applied both to cams and to special milling cutters. As a cam, it gives a long, probably continuous motion, due to a helix on its periphery. Some newer types of gear cutters also resemble a snail and have been called "snailback" cutters.

SNAIL-BACK FLY TOOL FOR CUTTING WORM GEARS—See *Gear, Worm, Snail-Back Cutter.*

SNAP FLASK—See *Flask, Snap.*

SNAP GAGE—See *Gage, Snap.*

SNATCH BLOCK—A pulley block with a side opening for receiving the rope instead of having it threaded through between the pulley and the frame of the block. This term also is sometimes used to designate the block attached to the movable object being handled.

SNIFTING VALVES—See *Valve, Snifting.*

SNIPS—Heavy hand shears for cutting sheet metal.

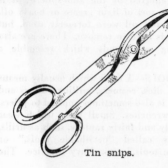

Tin snips.

SNUG FIT—See under *Fits, Classification of.*

SOAK OR SOAKING—As applied to steel or to heat treatment of any kind, the keeping of metal in the furnace for a period after it has reached the desired temperature largely to insure even heating of the metal all the way through.

SOCKET—An opening, usually in the end of some part which has to be turned, such as a set screw or bolt. Also in fixed pieces to hold separate parts or accessories.

SOCKET, GRIP—A device for driving drills and similar tools with either a straight or taper shank.

SOCKET SCREWS OR BOLTS—See *Bolt, Socket.*

SOCKET WRENCH—See *Wrench.*

SODIUM—A soft, silvery metal. Melts at about 212° F. Boils at about 1650° F. Used in some bearing alloys of lead to increase hardness.

SODIUM CYANIDE—A salt used in carburizing or surface hardening of low carbon steel, in the same way as cyanide of potassium.

SOFT GRINDING WHEEL — See *Grinding Wheels.*

SOFT GRITS—See *Grinding, Soft Grits.*

SOFT PATCH—See *Patch, Soft.*

SOFT SOLDER—See *Solder, Soft.*

SOFT STEEL—Steel of low carbon content, and which has not been case hardened or carbonized on the surface. One that can be easily machined.

SOLDER — A fusible alloy used in joining metals by application of comparatively low heats. Various mixtures of tin and lead are generally used. A very common mixture, known as "half-and-half" contains half tin and half lead. Hard solder requires more heat for melting than soft solder and is used for specially strong joints. The mixture includes such metals as zinc, copper and silver. Hard soldering is sometimes called brazing. Soft solder fuses at a low temperature, using low melting metals, such as bismuth, in place of lead.

SOLDER, COLD—A recent development by Reynolds Metals Corp. Made of powdered aluminum mixed with a solvent into a dough-like consistency resembling plastic wood. When applied cold to perfectly clean metal surfaces it adheres strongly as the solvent evaporates.

SOLDER, SOFT—A solder which melts at a low temperature. The Cerro-Metals are sometimes used as soft solders, for uniting parts which should not be subjected to high temperatures. The solders generally used in shop work are known as soft solders, sometimes to distinguish them from brazing, which is also called hard soldering.

SOLDERING — The forming of a metallic joint with an alloy which fuses at a lower temperature than the metals it unites.

SOLDERING IRON—These are usually made of a copper point on a steel shank, and with a wooden handle. The copper is heated to store heat enough to melt the solder being used. Formerly heated in a forge or by a gasoline torch, most soldering irons are now heated by an electric resistance in the copper point. The point is applied to the solder laid on the joint to be fused.

SOLUBLE OILS—Oils which are soluble in water. They provide more lubricant than plain water and guard against rusting of the parts being machined.

SOLVENTS—Liquids which dissolve different materials.

SOW—The channel or ditch dug in the sand of a blast furnace for carrying the molten iron to the molds which form the iron into numerous "pigs." The molding floor is sometimes known as the "sow-and-pigs."

SOW BLOCK—A block of hardened steel on an anvil to retard wear on the anvil face. Also called anvil cap.

SPALL—Small particles which flake or chip from metal or stone surfaces.

SPANNER WRENCH — There are varying ideas as to what constitutes a spanner wrench both in this country and abroad. See *Wrench*.

SPARK TEST OF STEELS—A method of indicating kind of steel by shape and color of sparks, credited to the late John F. Keller of Purdue University. His original chart included a number of kinds of steel. A late reference shows but three grades, low-carbon and cast steel; high-carbon steel, and alloy

steel. Newly machined surfaces of all three are quite similar, presenting a very smooth surface and a bright gray color. The illustration on page 422 shows the kind of sparks that are given off by a grinding wheel; the data beside them will help identify the kind of steel being ground.

SPECIFIC GRAVITY—The weight of any material as compared with an equal *volume* of water, when considering solids and liquids. For gases, air at certain temperatures and density is taken as the unit. For example, the specific gravity of gold is 19 because one cubic inch of gold weighs 19 times as much as one cubic inch of water.

SPECIFIC GRAVITY OF OIL—For volume purchasing, the weight of a gallon of oil is found by multiplying the specific gravity by 50 and dividing by 6.

SPECIFIC HEAT—The number of British Thermal Units to raise the temperature of one pound of any substance 1 degree Fahrenheit, or the number of calories necessary to raise the temperature of 1 gram (metric) 1 degree Centigrade.

Specific Heat of Common Materials

Aluminum	.212	Rubber, hard	.339
Brass	.092	Silver	.056
Bronze	.104	Steel	.118
Cast Iron	.113	Tantalum	.033
Copper	.092	Tin	.054
Glass	.180	Tungsten	.034
Marble	.206	Zinc	.093
Nickel	.109		

Source of information for Specific Heat "The Engineers' Manual" by Ralph G. Hudson, S.B., M.I.T.

SPECTROMETER, X-RAY — A development which gives faster analysis of X-ray examinations. No film is used, a Geiger counter being substituted for it. Electronic coupling circuits driven by a scanning motor sweep through the spectrum produced by irradiation of the specimen by an X-ray source and cause a tracing to be made on a chart in the recorder. It has the advantage of requiring only minutes as against hours by older methods.

SPECULUM—A hard white alloy of 50 parts copper, 21 parts zinc and 29 parts tin. It takes a high polish. An alloy of the same name used for mirrors and reflecting telescopes is 2 parts

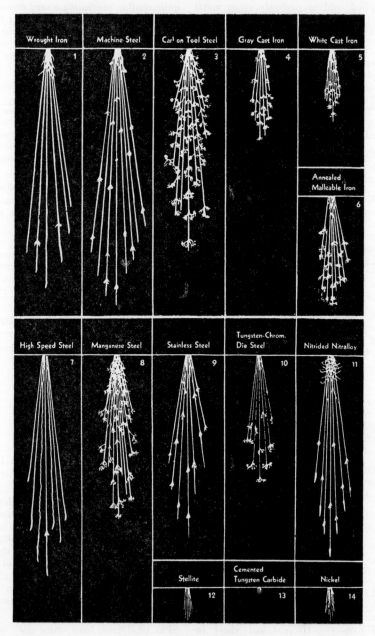

SPARK TEST OF STEELS.

copper and 1 part tin with a little arsenic to harden it.

SPEED INDICATOR—A small device, usually actuated by a worm and gear, for counting the number of revolutions of a shaft for a given period of time. It is usually pressed against the end of the shaft, in the center hole, but some have been made with a friction pad which did not require a center. Speed of a revolving body also can be determined by a stroboscope. See *Stroboscope*.

SPEED LATHE—See *Lathe, Speed*.

SPEED OF WORK OR TOOL SURFACES—The speed in feet per minute of work or tools at varying revolutions per minute. See table.

SPEED PULLEY—A term sometimes applied to a cone pulley, having different diameters to secure varying speeds.

Work or Tool R.p.m. for Cutting Speeds from 40 to 500 S.f.p.m.

Tool or Work Dia. (Inches)	SURFACE FEET PER MINUTE														
	40	50	60	70	80	90	100	125	150	175	200	250	300	400	500
1/16	2445	3056	3667	..	..	..	..	..	..	..	..	..	..	..	..
1/8	1222	1529	1833	2139	2445	2750	3056	..	..	..	..	..	..	..	..
3/16	815	1019	1222	1426	1630	1833	2037	2544	3056	3565	..	..	..	..	..
1/4	611	764	917	1070	1222	1375	1528	1908	2292	2674	3056	..	..	..	..
5/16	489	611	733	856	978	1100	1222	1526	1833	2139	2444	3056	..	..	..
3/8	407	509	611	713	815	917	1019	1272	1528	1783	2036	2547	3056	..	..
7/16	349	437	524	611	698	786	873	1090	1310	1528	1748	2183	2619	3492	..
1/2	306	382	458	535	611	688	764	954	1146	1337	1528	1910	2292	3056	..
5/8	244	306	367	428	489	550	611	763	917	1070	1224	1528	1834	2445	3056
3/4	204	255	306	357	407	458	509	636	764	891	1016	1273	1528	2037	2547
1	153	191	229	267	306	344	382	477	573	668	764	955	1146	1528	1910
1 1/4	122	153	183	214	244	275	306	382	458	535	612	764	917	1222	1528
1 1/2	102	127	153	178	204	229	255	318	382	445	510	637	764	1019	1273
1 3/4	87	109	131	153	175	196	218	273	327	382	436	546	655	873	1091
2	76	96	115	134	153	172	191	239	287	334	382	477	573	764	955
2 1/4	68	85	102	119	136	153	170	212	255	297	340	424	509	679	849
2 1/2	61	76	92	107	122	138	153	191	229	268	306	382	458	612	764
2 3/4	56	70	83	97	111	125	139	174	208	243	278	347	417	556	694
3	51	64	76	89	102	115	127	159	191	223	255	318	382	510	637
3 1/4	47	59	71	82	94	106	118	147	176	206	234	294	353	470	588
3 1/2	44	55	66	76	87	98	109	136	164	191	218	273	328	437	546
3 3/4	41	51	61	71	82	92	102	127	153	178	204	255	306	407	509
4	38	58	57	67	76	86	96	119	143	167	191	239	287	382	478
4 1/2	34	42	51	59	68	76	85	106	127	149	170	212	255	340	425
5	31	38	46	54	61	69	76	96	115	134	153	191	229	306	382
5 1/2	28	35	42	49	56	63	70	87	104	122	139	174	209	278	348
6	25	32	38	45	51	57	64	80	96	112	127	159	191	255	319
6 1/2	23	29	35	41	47	53	59	74	88	103	118	147	176	235	294
7	22	27	33	38	44	49	55	68	82	96	109	136	164	218	273
7 1/2	20	26	31	36	41	46	51	64	76	89	102	127	153	204	255
8	19	24	29	33	38	43	48	60	72	84	95	119	143	191	239
8 1/2	18	23	27	32	36	40	45	56	67	78	90	112	135	180	225
9	17	21	26	30	34	38	42	53	64	74	85	106	127	170	212
9 1/2	16	20	24	28	32	36	40	50	60	70	80	100	121	161	201
10	15	19	23	27	31	34	38	48	57	67	76	95	115	153	191

SPEKALUMINATE — An aluminum finish for metals and plastics which has a luster resembling that of cadmium. It does not peel or flake and resists rust and tarnish. It is stable in heat up to 1,000 deg. F.

SPELTER—Zinc in the form of slabs or ingots. Also an alloy of copper and zinc used in brazing.

SPHERODIZING—A type of annealing with a prolonged heating of the steel at a temperature near the critcal point. This is followed by very slow cooling to produce a globular condition of the carbide. This produces a structure that has been found desirable to meet severe cold forming operations.

SPIDER—A central frame or hub with radiating arms which carry a rim or other body. It is not used in connection with pulleys, but rather as the supporting and driving member of other mechanisms.

SPIEGELEISEN OR SPEIGEL IRON — A white cast iron with considerable carbon and usually some manganese.

SPIGOT—A British term for any projecting surface which locates a mating part. In this country it would be called a boss or a hub. Sometimes called a gudgeon. Sometimes a faucet.

SPINDLE—In machine tools and other mechanisms it is the shaft which carries either the cutting tools or the work which is being machined. In a lathe, the spindle in the headstock is called the "live" spindle and the one in the tailstock the "dead" spindle, or "tail" spindle. In some mechanisms almost any shaft can be called a spindle. While most spindles revolve, some only move longitudinally and are frequently made square instead of round.

SPINDLE NOSES, LATHE — Lathe spindle noses were formerly threaded and face plates and chucks screwed in place. As they were not standardized, adapters were necessary when face plates or chucks were used on other lathes. The new standards have no screw threads, both chucks and face plates being bolted in place after being centered by a 3-inch to the foot tapered surface (14-deg., 15-min. included angle). One type uses a 3½-inch taper (16-deg., 35-min., 40-sec. included angle). Several types of standard spindle noses are available for lathes of different types and sizes.

Face plates and chucks are held by socket head cap screws and in some cases by cam locks for quick handling. Dowels and driving buttons and keys are also provided. The number of sizes and styles and their application makes it necessary to refer to the American Standards Association B 5.9 standard which was sponsored by the Society of Automobile Engineers, the National Machine Tool Builders Association, the Metal Cutting Institute and the American Society of Mechanical Engineers.

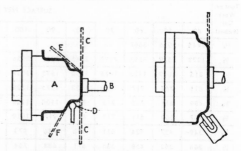

Spinning. Action of tools that spin flat metal over forms. (A) Form used. (B) Center which folds flat sheet (C) against the form. (D) Spinning tool which forces the sheet against the form. (E and F) Positions of sheet while being formed.

SPINNING — The forming of sheet metal which is revolved in a lathe, with a wooden or metal form of the shape desired. The metal is forced against the form as it revolves,

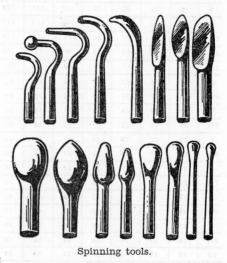

Spinning tools.

by a smooth ended tool, shaped for the kind of work to be done. It is principally used where a comparatively few pieces are needed, and where the expense of punches and forming dies is not justified. In a few cases, however, spinning has been developed to the point where it is done automatically at a lower cost than with dies.

SPINNING TOOLS—Tools used in forming sheet metal over forms while it is revolved in a lathe. They force the sheet metal against the form, as shown in spinning.

SPIRAL—A line which is constantly changing its radius from a central point, such as a clock spring or the scroll of a universal chuck. The terms helical and spiral are too frequently confused. Helical gears are frequently called spiral gears. The same is true of reamers and other tools. A screw thread is a helix, not a spiral.

SPIRAL BEVEL GEARS—Although these are really helical gears with a varying diameter, the term is so fixed that it seems inadvisable to attempt to change it. They are replacing straight and skew bevel gears in most places. See *Gears, Spiral Bevel.*

SPIRAL, FAST—A term incorrectly applied to milling cutter teeth having a sharp helix angle, in the same way we speak of a "fast" screw thread. There are no spiral milling cutters, in the correct application of the term.

SPIRAL (HELICAL) FLUTED TAP—A tap with helical flutes designed for use in aluminum, magnesium, die cast metals, soft cast iron, brass, copper, or other stringy materials. The helical flutes help to clear the tap of chips.

SPIRAL (HELICAL) POINTED TAP—The name is a misnomer. It is really a tap having a negative entrance angle which forces the chips ahead of the tap. It should not be used in blind holes unless there is ample chip clearance in a large recess. Designed particularly for use in sheet metal or thin plates. See *Taps, Spiral Pointed.*

SPIRIT LEVEL — Commonly known as a level. It is primarily a small straight alcohol filled glass tube mounted in a frame so that when the bubble is in the center of the tube it indicates that the work is level.

SPLASH LUBRICATION — See *Lubrication, Splash.*

SPLICE—The joining of two pieces, as with belting. This can either refer to joining the ends of a belt or to adding or inserting a piece to make the belt of the proper length. Sometimes used as denoting the lengthening of any material. See *Belting.*

SPLINE—Usually means raised portions of a shaft which fit into corresponding grooves in a pulley or some sliding member. They can either permit end movement or can be used as a permanent fastening. They are of various forms, having square sides, sides curved like an involute gear tooth, or simply angular sides. The latter are usually known as "serrated shafts." In some places the term also applies to the groove or slot in which the spline fits, as a "splined shaft," meaning a shaft with a slot or keyway of any length. Feed shafts of lathes are frequently made in this way, with the key or "feather" sliding along the feed shaft as the carriage moves.

SPLINE CUTTER—See *Milling Cutters.*

SPLINE FITS, KEY FITS—In splined connections where the splines fit on the *sides* instead of top or bottom.

SPLINE FITS, MINOR DIAMETER — In splined connections where the outer member fits on the *top* of the splines of the shaft.

SPLINE FITS, MAJOR DIAMETER — In splined connections, where the outer member bears on the shaft *between* the splines, or at its minor diameter.

SPLINE, FULL FILLET—A spline with a full fillet at the base of the teeth to increase strength of teeth. See page 427.

SPLINE, INVOLUTE—A spline or fixed key having sides forming an involute curve, similar to gear teeth. When made loose enough to slide they tend to center themselves. See page 430.

SPLINE WAYS—A term usually applied to the splined recesses cut in the shaft to receive the corresponding members, or splines, in the hub or female piece. This refers to straight ended splines, not involute. Proportions for 4, 6, 10 and 16 splines are shown in the table, for use under different conditions.

SPLINE SHAFT ENDS—See table.

SPLINED SHAFT—A shaft with solid raised keys, formed by milling and hobbing. They usually vary in number from 4 to 16 in auto-

Spline Formulas for W, h, and d, (In Inches)

No. of Splines	W for All Fits	A Permanent Fit		B To Slide, Not under Load		C To Slide under Load	
		h	d	h	d	h	d
4	0.241D*	0.075D	0.850D	0.125D	0.750D		
6	0.250D	0.050D	0.900D	0.075D	0.850D	0.100D	0.800D
10	0.156D	0.045D	0.910D	0.070D	0.860D	0.095D	0.810D
16	0.098D	0.045D	0.910D	0.070D	0.850D	0.095D	0.810D

Radii on corners of splines not to exceed 0.015 inch.

Splines shall not be more than 0.006 inch per foot out of parallel with respect to the axis of the shaft.

No allowance is made for radii on corners or for clearance. Dimensions are intended to apply to only the soft-broached hole. Allowance must be made for machining.

*Four splines, for fits A and B only.

---

motive work. The sides may be straight or of an involute curve, these being now considered more satisfactory.

Formula for Finding Root Width of Splineways

The following formula will be found useful for calculating the root width of splineways on splined shafts:

$$\sin\left(\frac{\dfrac{360°}{N} - 2A}{2}\right) \times B = W$$

in which N = number of splines.

B = diameter of shaft at the root of the splineway.

Angle A must first be computed as follows:

$$\sin A = \frac{T}{2} \div \frac{B}{2}, \text{ or } \sin A = \frac{T}{B}$$

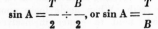

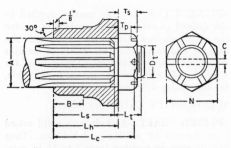

Permanent-fit spline shaft ends.

in which T = width of spline.

B = diameter of shaft at root of splineway.

W = width of splined recess.

D = largest inside diameter

d = smallest inside diameter

h = height of tooth or $\frac{1}{2}(D - d)$.

SPLINES, BASIC TOOTH PROPORTIONS

—In both internal and external splines the basic dimensions are pitch diameter, circular pitch, circular tooth thickness, addendum, dedendum, major and minor diameters. The internal spline is held to basic dimensions and external spline varied to secure the desired fit. The basic formulas are:

$$\text{Circular pitch} = \frac{3.1416}{\text{diametral pitch*}}$$

$$\text{Pitch diameter} = \frac{\text{number of teeth}}{\text{diametral pitch*}}$$

$$\text{Addendum dedendum} = \frac{0.500}{\text{diametral pitch*}}$$

$$\text{Major diameter} = \frac{\text{number of teeth} + 1}{\text{diametral pitch*}}$$

$$\text{Circular tooth thicknss} = \frac{1.5708}{\text{diametral pitch*}}$$

$$\text{Minor diameter} = \frac{\text{number of teeth} - 1}{\text{diametral pitch*}}$$

*The diametral pitch referred to is that which determines the diameter as 8 in an 8/10 pitch.

SPLINES, INVOLUTE—Splines with involute sides are favored because of the self-centering action. American Standards Association standard has 30-degree pressure angle and uses fractional diametral pitches. This means that the tooth *form* is the same as a gear of the same pitch as the *numerator* of the fraction. The depth is *half* that of the *denominator* of a similar gear.

Full Fillet Spline Tooth Proportions

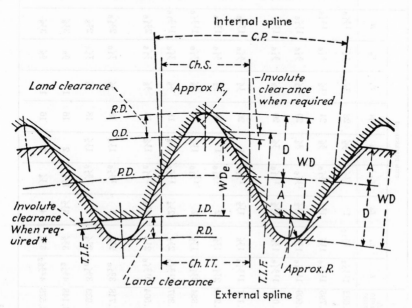

Diametral pitch	P	$=$	As specified by numerator of fraction
Number of teeth	N	$=$	As specified
Circular pitch	CP	$=$	$3.1416/P$
Addendum	A	$=$	$0.500/P$
Dedendum	D	$=$	Addendum + land clearance
Land clearance		$=$	Determined by layout
Working depth	WD_c	$=$	$2 \times$ addendum
Whole depth	WD	$=$	Addendum + dedendum
Basic arc space and tooth thickness		$=$	$1.5708/P$
Chordal tooth (external) thickness	$ChTT$	$=$	$D \times sin\dfrac{90°}{N}$ + tolerance
Chordal space (internal)	ChS	$=$	$D \times sin\dfrac{90°}{N}$ = basic
Pitch diameter (basic)	PD	$=$	N/P

Permanent-Fit Spline Shaft Ends for Universal Joints and Similar Applications

NOM SHAFT DIAM	10-SPLINE SHAFT[a]			10-SPLINE HOLE[a]			HUB DIMENSIONS									C	A^b	B
	D_s +0.000 −0.001	W_s +0.000 −0.0015	d_s +0.000 −0.010	D_h	W_h +0.000 −0.0015	d_h +0.010 −0.000	L_c	L_s	L_h	L_t	D_t	tpi	T_s	T_p	N			
3/4	0.749	0.1170	0.632	0.751 / 0.749	0.1170	0.682	1 11/32	15/16	1	17/32	1/2	28	7/16	1/4	13/16	1/8	1 1/8	5/8
7/8	0.874	0.1370	0.745	0.876 / 0.874	0.1370	0.795	1 11/16	1 1/8	1 1/4	11/16	5/8	24	1/2	5/16	15/16	5/32	1 1/4	3/4
1	0.999	0.1560	0.859	1.001 / 0.999	0.1560	0.909	1 15/16	1 3/8	1 1/2	1 1/16	3/4	20	1/2	5/16	1 1/16	5/32	1 3/8	7/8
1 1/8	1.124	0.1760	0.973	1.126 / 1.124	0.1760	1.023	1 15/16	1 3/8	1 1/2	11/16	7/8	20	1/2	5/16	1 1/4	5/32	1 1/2	7/8
1 1/4	1.249	0.1950	1.087	1.251 / 1.249	0.1950	1.137	1 15/16	1 3/8	1 1/2	11/16	1	20	1/2	5/16	1 7/16	5/32	1 3/4	7/8
1 3/8	1.374	0.2150	1.200	1.376 / 1.374	0.2150	1.250	2 7/16	1 7/8	2	11/16	1	20	1/2	5/16	1 7/16	5/32	2	1
1 1/2	1.499	0.2340	1.304	1.501 / 1.499	0.2340	1.364	2 7/16	1 7/8	2	13/16	1 1/4	18	5/8	7/16	1 13/16	5/32	2 1/4	1
1 5/8	1.624	0.2540	1.347	1.627 / 1.624	0.2540	1.397	2 13/16	2 1/8	2 1/4	13/16	1 1/4	18	5/8	7/16	1 13/16	5/32	2 3/8	1 1/4
1 3/4	1.749	0.2730	1.454	1.752 / 1.749	0.2730	1.504	2 13/16	2 1/8	2 1/4	13/16	1 1/4	18	5/8	7/16	2 3/16	5/32	2 1/2	1 1/4
2	1.999	0.3120	1.668	2.002 / 1.999	0.3120	1.718	3 9/16	2 7/8	3	13/16	1 1/4	18	5/8	7/16	2 3/16	5/32	2 3/4	1 1/2
2 1/4	2.249	0.3510	1.883	2.252 / 2.249	0.3510	1.933	3 9/16	2 7/8	3	13/16	1 1/2	18	5/8	7/16	2 3/8	5/32	3	1 1/2
2 1/2	2.499	0.3900	2.098	2.502 / 2.499	0.3900	2.148	4 9/32	3 3/8	3 1/2	1 1/4	2	16	1	5/8	3 1/8	7/32	3 1/2	1 3/4
3	2.999	0.4680	2.528	3.002 / 2.999	0.4680	2.578	4 25/32	3 7/8	4	1 1/4	2	16	1	5/8	3 1/8	7/32	4	2

(a) SAE Standard Involute Spline optional.

(b) Tolerance for ground finish, nominal + 0.003, — 0.002; and when specified, the maximum eccentricity with respect to the hole shall be 0.002 (indicator reading 0.004). Tolerance for lathe fiinish, nominal + 1/32, — 0.

PARALLEL-SIDE SPLINES FOR SOFT-BROACHED HOLES IN FITTINGS

Sixteen-Spline Fittings

NOMINAL DIAMETER	FOR ALL FITS				16A, PERMANENT FIT			16B, TO SLIDE WHEN NOT UNDER LOAD			16C, TO SLIDE WHEN UNDER LOAD		
	D		W		d		T	d		T	d		T
	Min	Max	Min	Max	Min	Max		Min	Max		Min	Max	
2	1.997	2.000	0.193	0.196	1.817	1.820	1375	1.717	1.720	2083	1.617	1.620	2751
2½	2.497	2.500	0.242	0.245	2.273	2.275	2149	2.147	2.150	3255	2.022	2.025	4299
3	2.997	3.000	0.291	0.294	2.727	2.730	3094	2.577	2.580	4687	2.427	2.430	6190
3½	3.497	3.500	0.340	0.343	3.182	3.185	4212	3.007	3.010	6378	2.832	2.835	8428
4	3.997	4.000	0.389	0.392	3.637	3.640	5501	3.437	3.440	8333	3.237	3.240	11005
4½	4.497	4.500	0.438	0.441	4.092	4.095	6962	3.867	3.870	10546	3.642	3.645	13928
5	4.997	5.000	0.487	0.490	4.547	4.550	8595	4.297	4.300	13020	4.047	4.050	17195
5½	5.497	5.500	0.536	0.539	5.002	5.005	10395	4.727	4.730	15754	4.452	4.455	20806
6	5.997	6.000	0.585	0.588	5.457	5.460	12377	5.157	5.160	18749	4.857	4.860	24760

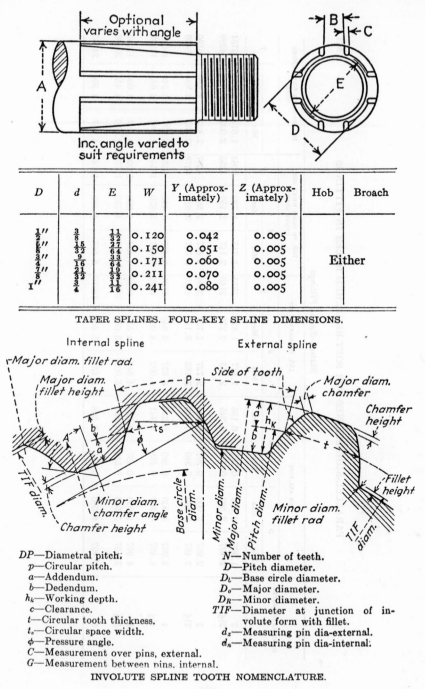

TAPER SPLINES. FOUR-KEY SPLINE DIMENSIONS.

D	d	E	W	Y (Approximately)	Z (Approximately)	Hob	Broach
$\frac{1}{2}''$	$\frac{3}{8}$	$\frac{11}{32}$	0.120	0.042	0.005		
$\frac{5}{8}''$	$\frac{15}{32}$	$\frac{27}{64}$	0.150	0.051	0.005		
$\frac{3}{4}''$	$\frac{9}{16}$	$\frac{33}{64}$	0.171	0.060	0.005	Either	
$\frac{7}{8}''$	$\frac{21}{32}$	$\frac{19}{32}$	0.211	0.070	0.005		
$1''$	$\frac{3}{4}$	$\frac{11}{16}$	0.241	0.080	0.005		

DP—Diametral pitch.
p—Circular pitch.
a—Addendum.
b—Dedendum.
h_k—Working depth.
c—Clearance.
t—Circular tooth thickness.
t_s—Circular space width.
ϕ—Pressure angle.
C—Measurement over pins, external.
G—Measurement between pins, internal.

N—Number of teeth.
D—Pitch diameter.
D_t—Base circle diameter.
D_o—Major diameter.
D_R—Minor diameter.
TIF—Diameter at junction of involute form with fillet.
d_x—Measuring pin dia-external.
d_n—Measuring pin dia-internal.

INVOLUTE SPLINE TOOTH NOMENCLATURE.

430

SPLINES, TAPER — A development of the Barber-Colman Co., in which the splined shaft is straight on the outside but the splines are cut usually by hobbing, on a taper to permit the parts to be drawn together to form a snug fit and prevent end movement. The female member is bored to a corresponding taper and broached with a straight broach, making a very simple operation. The taper makes it self-centering.

SPLIT NUT—See *Nut, Half.*

SPLIT PIN—Any pin having the end split to be opened to prevent removal from the hole in which the pin is inserted. This British name sometimes applied to a cotter pin.

SPLIT PULLEY—A pulley made in halves to be clamped on a shaft. This avoided the necessity of sliding pulleys along a shaft, or of removing some pulleys to get new ones in their proper places.

SPONTANEOUS COMBUSTION—Ignition or burning due to chemical action rather than to application of heat or fire. Oily rags frequently cause fires by spontaneous combustion.

SPOON—A small foundryman's trowel shaped like a spoon.

SPOT OR SPOTTING—Shop usage gives two meanings. One is to polish a surface by a small rotating abrasive which makes a series of spots that somewhat resemble scraping but are only for ornament. The other is to make layout marks from which machining operations are performed, as in drilling.

SPOT FACE—To face, or finish, the surface around a hole which has been drilled or bored. It is customary to have a raised section around the hole, which keeps the facing above the surface of the metal, but this is not always done. The same term is sometimes used for the finishing of any spot, or raised portion of a casting. Also see *Back Face.*

SPOT WELD—See *Welding, Spot.*

SPRAG — Usually a piece of wood to be thrown between the spokes of a car wheel to prevent further movement. Seldom used except around coal mines and similar places.

SPRAY GUN, AIR POWERED — A metal spraying gun in which the mechanism which feeds the wire to be sprayed is driven by compressed air instead of an electric motor.

SPRAY GUNS—Devices for heating metal wire or powder and blowing it forcibly against the surface to which it is to adhere. The wire gun is most in use, the wire being fed through the flame automatically by a small electric motor. In one type of gun the wire is fed by a small air driven motor, but this is not common. The wire is fed through an oxy-acetylene flame which melts the wire just before it is blown against the metal to be covered. The powder gun introduces gas and air through separate hoses to the mixing chamber and to the nozzle. Compressed air draws the powder into the flame in the center of the nozzle and blows it on the surface to be plated. Guns built in a similar way are also used for spraying paint.

SPRAYED METAL, PREPARATIONS FOR— As the bond between the sprayed surface and the metal sprayed on it is purely mechanical, the surface must be prepared by roughening it in some way. Rough turning, or the cutting of fine threads which may have the tops rolled to provide cavities between them, are common methods. Where worn shafts are to be built up, the worn portions are turned true before roughening.

SPRAYED METAL, SHRINKAGE OF— Sprayed metals shrink as they cool, the amount varying with the metal to be sprayed. This seldom causes trouble in thin coatings, but may be serious in some cases. There the coating is not continuous, as on flat surfaces or in bores with keyways, the shrinkage may tend to cause a loosening of the bond between the base and the sprayed metal. Where a thick coating must be applied, it is best to do so in thin layers, giving time for cooling between the layers.

SPRAYED METAL, WHAT HOLDS IT?— While there are different theories as to why sprayed metals sticks to a cold surface, the following quotation from the American Machinist of May 19, 1948, seems to be accepted:

"Present thought is that particles are bonded by a combination of mechanical interlock and oxide cementation. During projection, the globules of molten metal are covered with a thin film of oxide. Upon striking, the globules flatten, increasing their surface area and rupturing the oxide film. This exposes pure metal which firmly adheres to the thin oxide already formed on the particle that has just struck. Thus, although present knowledge on the subject is not complete, it is felt that oxide cemen-

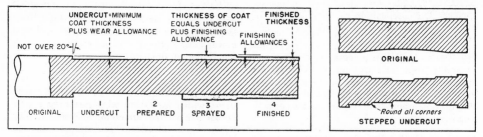

Shaft reclamation requires four steps. These are illustrated in sequence from left to right. Worn section is machined or ground undersize (1). Entire undercut is cleaned and roughened (2), then sprayed oversize (3) Coating is machined or ground to finished size (4) Stepped undercut saves expense on heavily worn shafts

Preparations for sprayed metal.

tation plus physical interlock play the major roles in the attachment of particles to one another."

SPRING-BACK ALLOWANCE — An allowance that must be made when bending metals of a springy nature, as stainless steel, spring brass and others. This means that a piece must be bent more than desired for the finished angle to allow for it to spring back to the desired angle. For stainless steel and a 90-degree angle, the die is made with an angle of 84½ degrees, as shown. Also see *Dies, Spring-Back Allowance.*

SPRINGS — *Compression* — A helical spring which tends to shorten in action.

Helical—A spring coiled on a mandrel, lengthwise of its axis, like a screw thread. It may be of uniform diameter or in the form of a cone.

Leaf—A spring made of flat stock with one or more layers.

Spiral—A spring with all the coils in one plane, as a clock spring. Usually of flat stock.

Extension—A helical spring which lengthens in action.

Torsion—A helical spring which acts by coiling or uncoiling.

Valve—A helical spring for seating valves and similar work. It is wound on a conical mandrel so that one coil rests inside the other. When completely closed it becomes a spiral spring. Sometimes called a "conical" spring.

SPRINGS, COIL—Springs of different types are shown and their functions named.

SPRING DIES—See *Dies, Prong or Spring.*

SPRINGS, HELICAL OR COIL — Springs made by coiling spring wire around rods or mandrels of the desired size. They are divided into three classes—compression, extension and torsion. In compression springs the coils are spaced to permit closing when in use. Extension springs are wound with coils touching. Torsion springs are to act when twisted around their axis. Examples of all three type are shown.

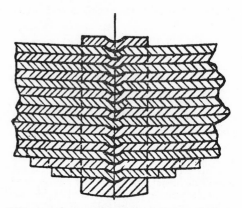

Nibbed springs. Spring band nibbed and depressed: Spring band shall have a depression suitable for the nib on the lower spring leaf, and the top of the band shall have a suitable nib pressed in it to fit into the depression in the top spring leaf. The nib in the top of spring band may be pressed cold.

SPRINGS, NIBBED—Leaf springs on locomotives have a depression, or slight bend, which prevents end movement when they are banded together, as shown. These depressions are known as "nibs."

432

SPRING STEEL—Any steel used in making springs. The composition varies widely and includes music wire. It requires proper heat treatment for best results.

SPRINGS, STRIPPER—Springs used in punch press die work for stripping or removing the surplus metal, or the work itself, from the die or punch. These have advantages over solid strippers sometimes used for this purpose.

SPRING TOOL—A single-point tool for lathe, planer or shaper, so bent as to permit the cutting edge to spring away from a hard spot in the work. It is seldom used at present. Sometimes called a "goose-neck."

SPRING, VOLUTE—A spring of the spiral type with the center coils pulled away from the outer coils to form a cone. Each coil is of a different diameter and in a different plane from that of the adjoining coil.

SPROCKET OR SPROCKET WHEEL—A wheel with teeth on the periphery to fit chains of different types used in transmitting power. In open link chain, the chain is driven by projecting teeth which go between the links. In silent chain, the chain has projections which fit into recesses or grooves in the wheel or pulley.

COIL SPRINGS.

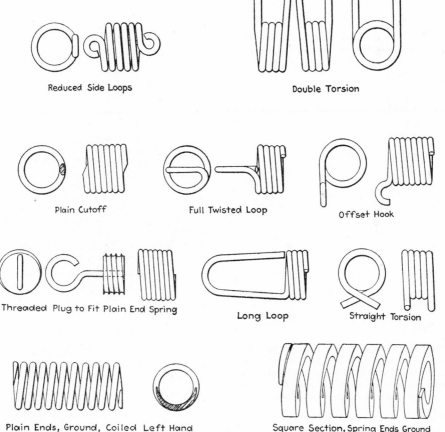

Reduced Side Loops

Double Torsion

Plain Cutoff

Full Twisted Loop

Offset Hook

Threaded Plug to Fit Plain End Spring

Long Loop

Straight Torsion

Plain Ends, Ground, Coiled Left Hand

Square Section, Spring Ends Ground

SPROCKETS—*Block Chain*—Sprockets made for using block chains. See *Block Chains*.

Link Chain—Sprockets made with teeth which fit the open link type of chain. This is used in exposed places and for rough work.

Roller Chain—Sprockets with teeth which fit roller chains. Sometimes used interchangeably with block chains.

Silent Chain—Sprockets made with special V-shaped indentations which fit the teeth of silent chain. Designed by Hans Renolds and widely used before the coming of the V-belt, which has largely replaced the chain in such places as machine tools and similar machine, except where positive transmission is necessary.

SPROCKET WHEEL—A type of gear on which chains are used for driving.

SPRUE—Excess metal on a casting where the metal is poured into the mold. The same term is used for the depression in a duplicate forging die which connects the two forgings. Both are sometimes known as "gate."

SPRUE CUTTER—A small shearing machine, frequently operated by foot power, for cutting sprues from castings.

SPUR GEAR—See *Gear, Spur*.

SQUARE, CENTER—A tool for finding the center of a round bar by placing it across the end and scribing lines in two different positions. The intersection shows the center. Not as much used as formerly. See *Center Square*.

SQUARE CENTER—A lathe center with a square or pyramid point, for driving work having a square hole in the end. Not good for heavy work.

SQUARE, COMBINATION—A tool that combines a square, level, center square and protractor.

SQUARE CORNERS—Square corners which have a 90-degree angle, can be made without instruments of any kind except something which will measure length fairly accurately, such as a yardstick or foot rule. Any triangle whose sides are in the ratio of 3, 4 and 5 has a 90-degree angle at the square corner. These figures can be in inches, miles or fractions of an inch; the result is always 90 degrees.

SQUARE DRILL—A special tool, which is not properly a drill, for cutting square holes in metal. The cutting tool is forced to follow the desired path by a guide against the shank. It can also cut holes of other shapes by using suitable guides.

SQUARE OF A NUMBER—Multiplying a a number by itself gives the *square* or second power. This makes 4 the square or second power of 2; 9 the square of 3, etc.

SQUARE ROOT OF A NUMBER—Finding the number which, multiplied by itself, will give the number in the problem. This is the reverse of "squaring a number" or raising it to its second power. This is used in solving many mechanical problems. As an example, 5 is the square root of 25.

SQUARE THREAD—See *Screw Threads, Square*.

SQUARE, TRY—A small square with the head and blade at 90 degrees for trying or testing the squareness of work.

SQUEEZER—In steel making, the machine which presses or squeezes balls of metal formed by puddling, to squeeze out impurities.

SQUIRTING METAL—A method of forcing some of the softer metals to form hollow shapes by flowing around a punch as it is forced against the metal blank, as shown. Here the punch causes the metal to flow up around the punch, although it is only confined, or guided, for a short distance by the surrounding die. Metal can also be forced down through a suitable opening if the end of the punch is smaller than the hole in the die through which it is forced. Soft metals act much like wax under similar pressure. It is a form of metal extrusion.

STACKER—A motor driven shop truck with mechanism for lifting material to be piled in stacks. The illustration shows a "fork truck" stacking pallets loaded with work.

STAGGER—Arranging pins or rivets on each side of a central line so the pin on one side is opposite the space on the other side. This is used in many forms of riveting, as it makes a stronger joint than where the holes are opposite each other.

STAGGERED TOOTH CUTTERS—Cutters in which cutting edges of alternate teeth are offset to secure a freer cutting action. See *Milling Cutter*.

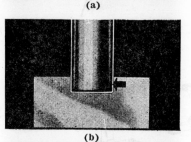

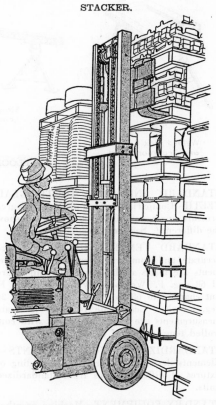

(a)

(b)

(c)

Squirting metal. (a) A slug of aluminum is struck one sharp blow in a die by a punch. (b) Because the die is larger than the punch, the metal flows out of the die and shoots up the punch. (c) The space between the die and punch determines wall thickness. The external design features are incorporated in the die, and the internal features in the punch.

STAINLESS IRON—Similar to stainless steel, except that from 9 to 20 per cent of chromium is added to the iron to resist corrosion.

STAINLESS STEELS—Steels to which enough chromium has been added to resist corrosion. This varies from 12 to 18 per cent in most cases.

STAKE—In some localities, a small anvil which fits into a hole in the top, or face, of a regular anvil. The hole is at the end opposthe point or horn.

STAKING—Usually a compression of metal around a pin or shaft, to help hold it in place firmly. It is similar to riveting, except that there is no head formed on either piece. In some constructions there is a small groove around the shaft at the surface of the main metal and staking forces metal into the groove.

STALK—A foundry term for a bar or rod used inside sand cores to support them. It may or may not have projections, according to the shape of the core.

STALL—To slow down or stop a machine wth an overload. This may be entirely due to a cut which is too heavy or to undue friction, or both. Stalling a tool in a cut is very apt to ruin the tool.

STACKER.

Ford truck tiering pallet loads of a wide variety of shapes and sizes.

STAMPINGS—In the United States, these are sheet metal parts made by cutting and forming. In England, the term refers to forgings by drop hammer or forging machine. There the term "pressings" is used in place of stampings.

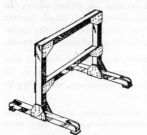

Picture Frame
4-Point Support

Picture Frame
3-Point Support

Box Beam
Gussets and
Trunnion Stand

Single Beam
Long Fixture

Single Beam
Short Fixture

Welded Box Beam
and Trunnion Stand

FLOOR STANDS.

STANDARD AND STUB TOOTH GEAR TEETH—Comparisons of standard 14½-degree pressure angle and 20-degree stub teeth show the difference. See *Gear Teeth, Stub.*

STANDARD TEMPERATURE—To insure accurate and comparable readings, measurements are made at the standard temperature of 68 deg. F. We formerly used 70 deg. F. but changed to 68 so as to compare with 20 deg. C. when Centigrade is used. Accurate measurements are made in a room with controlled temperature of 68 deg. F.

STANDARDIZED FIXTURE ELEMENTS—Elements designed to permit the building of fixtures of different types from standardized units.

STAND-BY EQUIPMENT—Machine or other equipment in excess of that actually needed for normal production, to prevent curtailing production when one or more machines have to be stopped for repairs. Many managers consider it necessary to have from 10 to 20 per cent surplus equipment to insure continuous production. A machine which is not producing is said to be "down."

STANDS, FLOOR—Fixtures to support work above the floor for various operations. Those shown were used in building large airplanes, but similar designs are useful in many places.

STAR FEED—An intermittent feed used on boring bars and similar tools. A spoked or star wheel at the end of the feed screw strikes a pin as the bar revolves and turns the feed screw a portion of a revolution.

STAR WHEEL—Usually a hand wheel with five points, to give a good grip to the hand. Wheels with four, six or more points are also called star wheels.

STARTS—In screw cutting practice, the number of threads on a screw. A single thread is a single "start." The term is seldom used for less than three starts, which means there are three distinct screw threads, with the lead three times the pitch, as measured from thread to thread. The object is to get a "fast" thread of shallow depth. A screw with four threads per inch and with four "starts" will have threads only as deep as a 16-pitch thread, but will move a nut ¼ inch each turn of the screw. See *Screw Threads, Multiple or Multi-Start*.

STATIC LOAD—A steady load without motion of any kind, such as a truck stopped on a bridge or a weight hanging by a wire or beam.

STATUARY BRONZE—Alloys of 85 to 90 per cent copper, with tin, zinc and lead in varying proportions.

STAVE—One of the bars or pins which form the teeth in a lantern gear. See *Gear, Lantern*.

STAY—A support to strengthen a structure or mechanism of any kind. In the case of masts or similar structures, wires are used, sometimes called guy wires.

STAYBOLTS—Bolts used in steam boilers to tie the fire box sheet to the boiler shell. They are frequently quite long and are threaded at both ends, each screwing into one of the boiler sheets. It is important that the threads on each end of the staybolt be of the same pitch and with a uniform helix. Both sheets are tapped with the same long tap to secure uniform thread helix. These bolts hold the sheets at the proper distance apart and prevent bulging from the pressure between them. They must also be tight in both sheets to prevent leakage of steam. They are riveted over at each end. Many staybolts are hollow, at least for several inches at each end, so that a broken bolt is detected by the escape of steam at the end. The breaks usually occur near either boiler sheet.

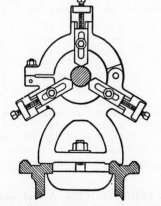

Steady rest. Center rest mounted on lathe bed.

STEADY RESTS—Stationary supports for long work between centers of a lathe, or for the outer end of work held in a chuck or on a face plate. Frequently used when boring the end of a piece held in a chuck. See *Roller Rests* and *Follow Rests*.

STEEL—Iron with some dissolved carbon, but no free graphite as in cast iron. Various amounts of carbon give different qualities to steel. When heated and cooled suddenly it becomes hard, the hardness depending on the amount of carbon. Unless the carbon exceeds 0.15 per cent there is almost no hardening. Low carbon steels vary from 0.15 to 0.30 per cent of carbon, medium steels from 0.30 to 0.60 per cent and high carbon steels from 0.60 to 0.90 per cent. Carbon was formerly designated by "points" which equalled decimals of 1 per cent. Thus, a "60-point steel" had 0.60 per cent carbon.

STEEL, 6-6-2²—High speed steel with 6 parts tungsten, 6 parts molybdenum and 4 parts chromium. The last number, 2, is squared, or multiplied by itself, which makes 4 in this case. There seems to be little reason for designating the chromium content in this manner.

STEEL, 18-4-1—A high speed steel with 18 parts tungsten, 4 parts chromium and 1 part vanadium.

STEEL, 18-4-2—The same steel, but with twice as much vanadium. It is somewhat tougher than the 18-4-1 steel. In some high speed steels the tungsten varies from 14 to 20 parts.

STEEL BARS, HOT-ROLLED CARBON—The American Iron & Steel Institute and the National Bureau of Standards have developed a simplified list of sizes for round steel bars for various uses, as follows:

SIMPLIFIED SIZES

Table 1—Rounds for All Purposes

Nominal Sizes, inclusive (inches)	Fractional increments (inches)
¼ to ²⁹⁄₃₂	Advancing by ¹⁄₆₄ths.
²⁹⁄₃₂ to 2¹⁄₁₆	Advancing by ¹⁄₃₂nds.
2¹⁄₁₆ to 4⅛	Advancing by ¹⁄₁₆ths.
4⅛ to 6¼	Advancing by ⅛ths.
6¼ to 8¼	Advancing by ¼ths.

*Table 2—Rounds for Bolts and Rivets**

Decimal Sizes (inches)		
0.365	0.865	1.235
0.445	0.912	1.297
0.490	0.990	1.360
0.615	1.047	1.422
0.680	1.110	1.485
0.740	1.172	

*Diameters listed in tables 2 and 3 are sizes intermediate to those listed fractionally in table 1. However, many diameters listed in table 1 are also regularly ordered by their decimal equivalents, for bolt and rivet stock for general purposes.

*Table 3—Rounds for Heated-Treated Studs**

Decimal Sizes (inches)		
0.507	0.883	1.261
0.632	1.009	1.387
0.758	1.135	1.514

*See footnote above.

Table 4—Squares

Nominal Sizes, inclusive (inches)	Fractional increments (inches)
¼ to 1³⁄₁₆	Advancing by ¹⁄₃₂nds.
1³⁄₁₆ to 4¼	Advancing by ¹⁄₁₆ths.
4¼ to 5½	Advancing by ¼ths.

Table 5—Hexagons

Nominal Sizes, inclusive (inches)	Fractional increments (inches)
¼ to 2¹⁄₁₆	Advancing by ¹⁄₃₂nds.
2¹⁄₁₆ to 4¹⁄₁₆	Advancing by ¹⁄₁₆ths.

STEEL, CARPENTER CONE TEST—This test uses a steel cone specimen 5 inches long, ¼ inch in diameter at one end and 1¼ inches at the other. The cone is quenched in brine from any desired temperature, then split lengthwise with a thin abrasive wheel. The flat surface is then etched with 1 part hydrochloric acid and 1 part water. The dark outer surface shows the depth of the hardness layer.

STEEL, CHROME VANADIUM—A steel containing about 0.87 per cent chromium and 0.18 per cent vanadium. It is a very tough steel with an elastic limit of about 191,000 pounds per square inch.

STEEL, CHROMIUM—A hard and tough alloy with from 1 to 2 per cent chromium. Largely used in automobiles and for armor plate and projectiles.

STEEL, COBALT—A tungsten high speed steel with cobalt added to give higher "red-hardness." It also tends to make the steel somewhat more brittle. The percentage of cobalt is under 13.

STEEL, COLD ROLLED—Either Bessemer or open-hearth steel with a carbon content of from 0.12 to 0.20 per cent. It has a bright, smooth surface and is quite accurate as to size. It can be case-hardened, but will not harden or temper by heating and quenching.

STEEL, ELECTRICAL—A flat rolled steel made especially for use in electrical apparatus, processed to develop definite magnetic and physical properties for such uses. It contains up to 6 per cent silicon, and is produced in gages and sizes suitable for electrical work. Standards of the American Iron & Steel Institute are shown herewith, together with thickness tolerances.

Manufacturers' Standard Electrical Sheet Gage

Electrical Sheet Gage No.	Thickness, In.	Electrical Sheet Gage No.	Thickness, In.
32	0.0100	20	0.0375
30	0.0125	19	0.0435
29	0.0140	18	0.0500
28	0.0155	17	0.0560
27	0.0170	16	0.0625
26	0.0185	15	0.0700
25	0.0220	14	0.0780
24	0.0250	13	0.0940
23	0.0280	12	0.1090
22	0.0310	11	0.1250
21	0.0340		

STEEL, FERRO-SILICON—A steel containing 97.6 per cent iron, 2 per cent silicon and 0.4 per cent carbon. This makes a hard alloy.

Permissible Variations in Thickness of Flat Rolled Electrical Sheets

Electrical Sheet Gage Number (Inclusive)	Equivalent Thickness In. (Inclusive)	Permissible Variation Over or Under, In.
32 to 27	0.0100 to 0.0170	0.002
26 to 22	0.0185 to 0.0310	0.003
21 to 20	0.0340 to 0.0375	0.004
19 to 18	0.0435 to 0.0500	0.005
17 to 15	0.0560 to 0.0700	0.006
14	0.0780	0.007
13	0.0940	0.008

NOTE: Thickness is measured at any point on a sheet not less than ⅜ inch in from an edge.

STEEL, HARDNESS AND STRENGTH — There is an approximate relationship between the hardness and strength of fully quenched and tempered steels. Some use this as a guide to hardness as it affects the machineability of steels in the same way as others use Brinell or Rockwell hardness numbers. The table is more accurate for steels with 0.30 per cent carbon or higher.

Hardness and Machineability of Steels, 0.30 Per Cent Carbon or Over

Hardness Rockwell "C"	Brinell	Tensile Strength	Yield Point
14	197	93,000/103,000	69,000/ 78,000
16	207	98,000/108,000	73,000/ 84,000
18	217	103,000/114,000	76,000/ 90,000
20	223	106,000/117,000	79,000/ 93,000
22	235	112,000/124,000	85,000/ 99,000
24	248	118,000/131,000	92,000/107,000
26	262	124,000/138,000	99,000/114,000
28	277	131,000/146,000	107,000/122,000
30	293	138,000/154,000	116,000/131,000
32	311	146,000/164,000	125,000/141,000
34	321	151,000/170,000	131,000/146,000
36	341	160,000/180,000	141,000/157,000
38	363	171,000/193,000	153,000/170,000
40	379	178,000/201,000	163,000/179,000
42	401	188,000/222,000	176,000/185,000

STEEL, HIGH SPEED—Steels which retain hardness when heated, as in cutting metals at high speed. Some typical compositions of high speed steels are given below:

Chemical Composition of High Speed Steel— Per Cent*

Tungsten W	Molybdenum Mo	Chromium Cr	Vanadium V	Cobalt Co	Boron Addition
Alloy Constituents and Symbols					
Tungsten High Speed Steels					
18		4	1		
18		4	2		
18		4	3¼		
18		4	1	4	
18		4	2	8	
22		5	1.5	12	
14		4	2		
14		4	2	5	
Molybdenum High Speed Steels					
1.5	8	4	1		
5	4	4	1.5		
	8	4	2		
	8	4	1	2.5	Yes
1.5	8	4	1	4	
	8	4	1.5	8	
	9	4	4		Yes
6	6	4	1.5		

*The percentage of alloying elements may vary slightly, according to the practice of the individual supplier.

STEEL, MOLYBDENUM OR "MOLY" — A high speed steel using molybdenum either with or without tungsten and vanadium. It has a tendency to decarbonize in hardening unless protected by a borax or copper oxide base compound.

STEEL, NATIONAL EMERGENCY — Shortage of certain alloys during World War II led to substitution of other alloys in the endeavor to secure similar results. N. E. steels were steels which used no chromium, vanadium, tungsten or manganese and only a little molybdenum. When properly hardened they had very good wearing qualities.

STEEL, NONMAGNETIC—Chrome-Nickel stainless steels of what is known as Type 300 are non-magnetic when annealed. Type 310 is non-magnetic under all conditions.

STEEL, POINTS OF—A former method of designating the percentage of carbon. One per cent was 100 points. A 125-point steel had 1.25 per cent of carbon. Carbon content is now given in percentages.

STEEL PRODUCTS, RAIL—These are standard hot rolled bars, bands and shapes rerolled from standard T-section railroad rails. They are about 50 per cent stronger than medium-carbon steel and can be punched and sheared or moderately formed. This steel is used for fence posts, structural tubing, agricultural implements, scaffolding and similar purposes.

STEEL, S. A. E. NUMBERING SYSTEM—The Society of Automotive Engineers have adopted a system of designating various steels used in the industry by numbers which give the contents of the steel in round numbers. Carbon steels use number 1, nickel steels number 2, nickel-chrome steels number 3, molybdenum steels number 4, chromium steels number 5, vanadium steels number 6, tungsten steels number 7, and silicon manganese steels number 9, as shown in the table. Details of the system are given in the S. A. E. Handbook.

S.A.E. Standard Steel Numbering System
(Society of Automotive Engineers)

Type of Steel	Numerals and Digits
Carbon Steels	1xxx
Plain Carbon	10xx
Free Cutting (Screw Stock)	11xx
Free Cutting, Manganese	X13xx
High Manganese	T13xx
Nickel Steels	2xxx
0.50% Nickel	20xx
1.50% Nickel	21xx
3.50% Nickel	23xx
5.00% Nickel	25xx
Nickel Chromium Steels	3xxx
1.25% Nickel, 0.60% Chromium	31xx
1.75% Nickel, 1.00% Chromium	32xx
3.50% Nickel, 1.50% Chromium	33xx
3.00% Nickel, 0.80% Chromium	34xx
Corrosion and Heat Resisting Steels	30xxx
Molybdenum Steels	4xxx
Chromium	41xx
Chromium Nickel	43xx
Nickel	46xx
	and 48xx
Chromium Steels	5xxx
Low Chromium	51xx
Medium Chromium	52xxx
Corrosion and Heat Resisting	51xxx
Chromium Vanadium Steels	6xxx
Tungsten Steels	7xxx
	and 7xxxx
Silicon Manganese Steels	9xxx

STEEL, SOFT—A term formerly applied only to low carbon steel. It can also mean high carbon steel which has been annealed until it can be easily worked.

STEEL, STANDARD SIZES AND SHAPES—While steel shapes can be ordered and secured to close limits, the following are considered as standard by the industry:
To 1 inch in size, inclusive, by 64ths.
From 1 to 2 inches, inclusive, by 32nds.
Over 2 inches, by 16ths.
This includes round, square and hexagonal shapes.

STEEL, TURBO-HEARTH—A new method of producing steel rapidly, announced by both the Carnegie-Illinois Steel Co. and the Jones & Laughlin Corp. It produces steel of open hearth quality by forcing jets of air across the surface of liquid pig iron. It attempts to combine the good points of the open hearth and acid Bessemer processes.

STEP-BACK WELDING—See *Welding, Step-Back Method.*

STEP OR STEPPED BEARING—See *Bearing, Step.*

STEP-DOWN TEST—This uses a sample of steel or other metal which is machined to different diameters or thicknesses so as to inspect the quality of the metal at different points.

STEP DRILLING—See *Drilling, Step.*

STEP PUNCHING—See *Punching, Step.*

STEPPED CONTOUR—A form or shape consisting of one or more steps instead of the usual curved forms.

STEPPED-JAW LATHE CHUCKS—Chucks with jaws having a series of steps. When some of the jaws are reversed they can hold odd shaped work easily. See *Chuck, Step.*

STEPPED PULLEY—See *Pulley, Stepped.*

STICK SCREWS—See *Screw, Stick.*

STILLSON WRENCH—See *Wrench, Stillson.*

STOCKING CUTTER—For preliminary milling operation to remove excess metal prior to finishing operation.

STOCKS, RATCHET—Similar to drill, ratchet. Used for holding threading dies for pipe and other work.

STOP—Any projection which is used to stop any moving part or piece of material coming in contact with it. Stops on a planer table control the table movement in both directions. In press work, stops of many kinds are used to locate the sheet in its proper position.

STOP-OFF—A foundry term for changing the shape of a mold by stopping off, or blocking, gates or passages to certain parts of the mold.

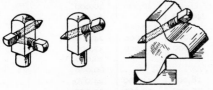

Planer stops.

STOPS, PLANER—Devices for locating and in some cases for holding work on a planer bed. They are made in various forms to suit different classes of work.

STOP, TRIGGER—A stop used in press work to stop the sheet and then be depressed like a trigger, by the die. It comes back into place as soon as the next piece is fed into the press.

STOP WATCH—See *Watch, Stop.*

STOVE BOLT—Discarded term for a machine screw supplied with a nut.

STRADDLE MILL—See *Milling, Straddle.*

STRAIGHT EDGE—A bar of metal, usually cast iron, having one edge machined and scraped flat and true. They are made like a truss to prevent distortion. Small ones are sometimes made of steel. Used to check the accuracy of flat surfaces. For extreme accuracy light waves are used, especially on small objects. Draftsmen also sometimes refer to their rules as straightedges.

STRAIN HARDENING — The hardening of some materials by subjecting them to strains or stresses. Similar to "work-hardening" by the stresses imposed while the metal is being worked on. Spinning is a good example of work-hardening which strains the metal.

STRAP—Any piece which holds other parts together. In steam engine work, a U-shaped piece which holds the halves of bearing brasses in place on the crankpin. Locomotive practice has largely abandoned the adjustable bearings on the connecting rods, and so the strap is no longer used for this purpose. Then, too, the growing use of diesel locomotives has greatly minimized the use of many such locomotive features.

STRAPPING—A method of finishing metal parts by holding them against a belt or strap covered with abrasive. It usually runs over two pulleys and permits grinding curved and unusual shaped surfaces.

STRAPPING MACHINES—An abrasive machine having two flanged pulleys which carry a canvas or similar belt having an abrasive on the outer surface. The flexibility of the fabric belt permits the finishing of rounded and other irregular surfaces by a skilled operator. The belt is first coated with glue and passed through loose abrasive of the proper grade. When the glue dries, the belt is ready for use. They usually run from 2,000 to 2,500 ft. per minute, although carefully cemented belts may be run at much higher speeds.

STRENGTH, ABSOLUTE — The breaking strength, which is always much more than the safe working strength.

STRENGTH OF MATERIALS—The strength of materials must be considered from several angles—compression, shear, tension and torsion. Compression strength resists squeezing; shear strength resists cutting or breaking at right angles to the length; tension resists pulling apart lengthwise, and torsion resists twisting. Different metals behave in different ways. Cast iron may resist compression up to 90,000 pounds per square inch but pull apart at 22,000 pounds. Tables are available to show the various qualities of the different materials.

STRESS RELIEF—Relieving stresses in metal by heating to a temperature slightly below the critical range, followed by slow cooling.

STRICKLE—A foundry term for a tool used in smoothing surfaces of cores or molds.

STRING JIG—See *Jig, String.*

STRING PLANING — Planing a number of pieces at once, where they are clamped lengthwise of the table, in a string.

Strength of Materials

Material	Shear	Compression	Tension
Aluminum, cast...............	12,000	12,000	15,000
Soft sheet............	15,000	....	15,000
Half hard sheet.......	19,000	60,000	19,000
Hard sheet...........	25,000	....	28,000
Asbestos millboard...............	3,800		
Brass, cast.................	36,000	30,000	30,000
Drawing, soft sheet.......	30,000	....	47,000
Half hard sheet........	35,000	....	60,000
Hard sheet.........	40,000	....	85,000
Bronze, gun metal............	....	20,000	40,000
Phosphor, soft sheet......	40,000	....	45,000
Manganese...............	....	120,000	70,000
Copper, cast............	25,000	40,000	24,000
Rolled...............	28,000	60,000	37,000
Wire, annealed........	....	....	36,000
Wire, unannealed.......	....	....	60,000
Dow-metal, cast...........	18,000	44,000	24,000
Duralumin, soft sheet...........	30,000	50,000	35,000
Treated.............	35,000	60,000	55,000
Treated and cold rolled	40,000	75,000	75,000
Fibre, hard.................	24,000		
German silver, half hard.........	32,000		
Iron, cast..................	25,000	90,000	22,000
Iron cast (2 per cent nickel)	50,000	150,000	50,000
Iron (25 per cent steel).........	30,000	90,000	30,000
Iron, wrought.............	40,000	46,000	50,000
Iron wire, annealed........	....	....	45,000
Iron wire, unannealed......	....	....	80,000
Lead..................	4,000	....	3,000
Leather, chrome.............	7,000	....	10,000
Oak.............	7,000	....	4,000
Rawhide.............	13,000		
Monel metal, cast.............	60,000	....	75,000
Rolled...........	65,000	90,000	95,000
Nicro copper.............	30,000	....	37,000
Paper, hollow die.............	3,000		
Flat punch.............	8,500		
Bristol board, flat punch...	4,800		
Strawboard, flat punch	3,500		
Silver............	30,000	....	38,000
Steel, casting..............	60,000	65,000	70,000
Boiler plate.............	60,000	70,000	70,000
Cold drawn rod...........	58,000	....	65,000

STRIPPER—A piece, usually a thin plate, mounted over a punch press die, to pull the work off the punch on the return stroke. See also *Punching*.

STRIPPER BOLT—See *Bolts, Stripper*.

STRIPPER SPRINGS—See *Springs, Stripper*.

STRIPPING PLATE — In foundry work, a plate having an outline similar to the pattern. It is placed over the pattern and rests on the sand mold to prevent parts of the mold from being lifted out when the pattern is removed.

STROBOSCOPE — A device or instrument which seems to stop the motion of a moving part so that its action can be observed. The simplest form is a slotted disk which revolves at the speed of the moving part to be studied. One device has a flash light which is synchronized with the speed of the revolving part. It is useful in studying the vibration or other action of a mechanism in actual use. It can also be used as a speed counter.

STROKE—The distance a part moves in one-half its cycle. An engine has a stroke as long as the piston travel from one end of the cylinder to the other. The same is true of the ram of a shaper or slotter. It is twice the length of the crank throw when this causes the movement. In a cam it is the extreme movement produced. See *Crank Throw.*

STRUT—A brace to keep other parts at their proper distance from each other.

STUB END—A short piece. It is used in connection with bar steel, meaning the end which is too short to be used in the regular work. In gearing, "stub" means the use of gear teeth of less than standard, or usual, length.

STUB GEAR TEETH—See *Gears, Stub Tooth.*

STUB SCREW THREADS—Screw threads of less than standard depth. Useful where fast threads, or coarse pitches, are desired on thin walled tubes or sleeves. See *Screw Threads, Stub.*

STUDS—Bolts threaded on both ends, one end screwing into a hole tapped in some machine part, and not to be removed when the nut is unscrewed. The fixed end may be slightly oversize to insure holding when nut is unscrewed. Some have used a slightly different pitch to secure holding. Studs screwed in alu-

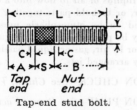

Tap-end stud bolt.

minum or soft metals usually have a coarser thread on the fixed end. Also short rods or projections to locate or hold a separate part of a mechanism. Sometimes called stud bolt. See table page 444.

STUD, CLAMPING—A stud used in connection with strap clamps of various kinds. Size depends on the pressure to be applied. The table suggests safe sizes for pressures up to 3,550 pounds per square inch.

Stud Size Selection

Clamping Pressure Required, Lb.	Stud Size NC Thread
Under 100	$\frac{1}{4}$—20
100—185	$\frac{5}{16}$—18
185—275	$\frac{3}{8}$—16
275—375	$\frac{7}{16}$—14
375—500	$\frac{1}{2}$—13
500—650	$\frac{9}{16}$—12
650—800	$\frac{5}{8}$—11
800—1200	$\frac{3}{4}$—10
1200—1675	$\frac{7}{8}$— 9
1675—2250	1— 8
2250—3550	$1\frac{1}{4}$— 7

STUD, COLLAR—A stud with a collar which acts as an end bearing for gears, cams or levers. It often has a cross hole at the end for a cotter pin to hold the gear or lever in place.

STUD FITS—This refers to the end of the stud which is screwed into fixed position, as in a cylinder block. See tables under *Studs.*

STUD, FLAT ENDED—A piece threaded in the central portion and with the ends flattened, for special uses, especially in the automotive industry. They are not used in the same way as regular studs.

STUD SETTER—A device which grips the threaded outer ends of the stud so that it can be screwed into the tapped hole which is to receive it. After the stud is screwed into its proper depth, or "set," the jaws of the stud setter open and pull off the stud. Sometimes called a "stud-driver." Illustration page 444.

STUD, SHOULDER—A stud with a shoulder to limit the depth it can be screwed into a hole. Used for mounting gears or levers which bear against the part into which the stud is screwed.

STUFFING BOX—A chamber or recess for holding packing of some kind, around a rod or valve stem, to prevent leakage around the rod or stem. Largely used in valves of various kinds and in pumps, steam engines and other mechanisms. The packing may be either some

Stud Specifications

Sizes	Threads per inch	Interference on pitch diameter		Pitch diameter tolerances	
		Minimum	Maximum	Stud	Tapped hole
1	2	3	4	5	6
		Inch	Inch	Inch	Inch
5/16	18	0.0005	0.0046	0.0015	0.0026
3/8	16	.0005	.0051	.0016	.0030
7/16	14	.0007	.0057	.0018	.0032
1/2	13	.0009	.0062	.0019	.0034
9/16	12	.0011	.0066	.0020	.0035
5/8	11	.0012	.0069	.0021	.0036
3/4	10	.0013	.0073	.0023	.0037
7/8	9	.0013	.0074	.0024	.0037
1	8	.0013	.0075	.0025	.0037
1 1/8	7	.0014	.0076	.0025	.0037
1 1/4	7	.0014	.0076	.0025	.0037
1 3/8	6	.0014	.0076	.0025	.0037
1 1/2	6	.0016	.0081	.0025	.0040

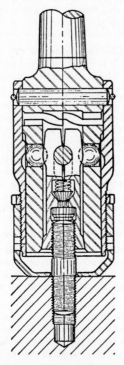

Stud setter. Drive completed—jaws open automatically, releasing the tool.

fibrous material, or metal, usually of the softer metals. The packing is held in place by a nut or gland, which either screws in place or is held by bolts or studs.

SUB-ASSEMBLY — A collection of units or component parts which form a distinct part of a completed mechanism.

SUB-PRESS DIES—Former name of punch and die sets. See *Punch and Die Sets.*

SUB-SOW BLOCK—One name for a die holder used in drop or steam hammer work. It raises the die above the anvil.

SUCTION—The creation of a partial vacuum, causing liquids or air to flow into a cylinder or chamber, or to hold parts together when they are acted on by atmospheric pressure. Suction may be produced by centrifugal or piston pumps, or by air, gas or liquid passing through properly arranged jets.

SUCTION CHUCK—See *Chuck, Vacuum.*

SUCTION PUMP—See *Pump, Vacuum.*

SULPHUR—A pale yellow element abundantly found as a natural substance in the earth. Sometimes called brimstone. It is both a lubricant and coolant. It is mixed in some cutting oils. Sp. gr. 2.05. Melts at 232 deg. F.

SULPHURIC ACID—A combination of sulphur, hydrogen and oxygen, sometimes used in etching names or designs on steel.

SUMP—A chamber or receptacle in the base of a pump or a machine, which collects oil or water, and from which such oil or water is pumped out. In the case of oil or of coolant used in machining, it is pumped back to a reservoir where it is strained and cleaned and then recirculated.

SUN AND PLANET GEARING—A gear mechanism in which one gear travels around a central gear, as the earth travels around the sun in the planetary system. This is done in planetary gear transmissions and was used in many early automobiles. A notable example was the Model T Ford. Similar gear reductions are used in some other types of machinery. See *Gearing* and *Gears, Planetary*.

SUNK KEY—A key which is embedded in the shaft as though it were part of the shaft itself. The keyway is the length of the key. Some call this a feather key, but the usual idea of a feather key is one that slides in a splined shaft.

SUPER-BRONZE—A term sometimes applied to brasses with aluminum or manganese alloys. It is made under various trade names.

SUPERCREST TAPS—See *Taps, Supercrest*.

SUPERFINISH—The finish produced by moving fine abrasive stones over a piece of work, in a number of different directions. Devised by D. A. Wallace of the Chrysler Corp. in 1938 for use on automobile parts. Used in different ways by different concerns.

SUPERMIKE—A device for measuring screw threads, made by the Pratt & Whitney Co. See *Measurement, Screw Thread, Supermike*.

SUPERSONIC INSPECTION—See *Inspection, Supersonic*.

SUPERSONIC THRURAY—A device for comparing new parts with a standard part of the same kind, as to soundness of spot welds, laminations in sheet products, quality of bond in bi-metals, quality of bond in clad and plated materials, and homogeneity of sintered materials. The work piece is placed between two "searching units" which are immersed in oil or water. One searching unit transmits the supersonic vibration and the other acts as a reservoir. It works rapidly. It is made by the Sperry Gyroscope Corp.

SUPPLEMENTARY ANGLES—When the sum of two angles equals 180 degrees they are called supplementary angles.

SURFACE ANALYZER—A device for measuring, or indicating the condition of, a work surface. It indicates flaws, or scratches as small as a millionth of an inch—called a micro-inch. Similar machines are called profilometers by some makers.

SURFACE FEET PER MINUTE—The speed, in lineal feet, at which the surface of work being cut, or of rotating tools, travels when in use. As both the work and cutting tools are usually shown in inches, it is necessary to divide by 12 to get the result in feet. As the surface of a round piece is 3.1416 times the diameter, it is sometimes easier to divide 3.1416 by 12, which gives 0.262, and get the surface speed by multiplying the diameter in inches by 0.262 and by the revolutions per minute, or R. P. M. A 10-inch grinding wheel running at 1,000 R. P. M. then has a surface speed of $0.262 \times 10 \times 1,000$ or 2,620 feet per minute.

SURFACE FINISH, A. S. A. STANDARDS—When surfaces are measured in root-mean-square inches, the A. S. A. standards are shown in the table below. A micro-inch is one-millionth part of an inch.

SURFACE GAGE—See *Gage, Surface*.

Surface Finish A. S. A. Standards

Roughness Symbol	Root-Mean-Square Inches	Height of Irregularities Micro-Inches
63M	.063	63,000
16M	.016	16,000
4M	.004	4,000
1M	.001	1,000
250	.00025	250
63	.000063	63
32	.000032	32
16	.000016	16
8	.000008	8
4	.000004	4
2	.000002	2
1	.000001	1
½	.0000005	½
¼	.00000025	¼

SURFACE PLATES—Cast iron plates scraped flat for inspection and testing purposes. Supposed to be made in sets of three, so that each has a perfect bearing on each others. They are now being made of granite, marble and glass, and are frequently finished by grinding.

SWAGE BLOCK—A blacksmith's accessory, consisting of a heavy cast iron block with holes of various sizes and shapes. It also has grooves or depressions on the sides for helping to form different objects while they are hot.

SWAGING—Changing the shape of a piece of metal by continued impacts. This may be by heavy or light hammers which rotate around the work, or by other methods. It is usually applied to reducing the diameter of round rods or bars, or of tubing. It is done hot or cold, depending on the size of the work. Used on all classes of work from automobile axles to fine jewelry.

SWAGING HAMMER—A swaging block held on a hammer handle for guidance. It is struck by a sledge when held in the desired position.

SWAGING MACHINE—A machine which forms cold metal by pressure, usually in progressive stages instead of instantaneously. Rotating hammers are usually employed for this work.

SWARF—A shop name for the material which collects in coolant tanks of grinding machines. It consists of small particles of abrasive and of the materials being ground. It is frequently passed through a magnetic separator to remove small particles of iron or steel that might scratch the work if pumped back over it. Some call it sludge.

SWASH PLATE—A name given to any plate or disk which revolves at an angle from its axis and gives a cam action to other parts of the mechanism. Both steam and internal combustion engines have been made with swash plates instead of cranks, but have never been very useful. Pumps are also made in the same manner. The swash plate gives (or receives) reciprocating motion to pistons or parts parallel with the shaft of the plate itself. An early swash plate steam engine is shown. This was built by Colt's Armory in the 1860's. A modification now being employed is known as the *cam* engine.

SWEATING—Another term for soft soldering. It is usually done by heating the two surfaces with solder, pressing them together and applying heat. See *Soldering*.

SWEDGING—Same as swaging.

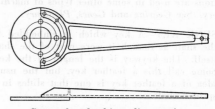

Sweep for checking alignment.

SWEEP—An arm used in checking alinement of spindles of boring and similar machines with the column runways and tables. The sweep is attached to the spindle sleeve, not to the spindle itself, and has a dial indicator at the outer end. It should be as light as possible with suitable stiffness. The design is suggested by Giddings & Lewis.

Also, a foundry term for a method of making sand molds of round objects, such as pulleys, by sweeping a board of the proper contour around a central post and so forming the sand into the shape desired. This obviated making large patterns, and was successfully used in many foundries.

SWELL COUPLING—See *Reaming Shell*.

SWING—Applied to lathes and other machine tools in this country, it means the largest diameter that can be turned or otherwise machined. In Great Britain, however, the term swing means the distance from the lathe center to the shears or ways.

SWING GRINDER—See *Grinder, Swing*.

SWISS PATTERN FILES—See *Files, Swiss Pattern* under *File Names*.

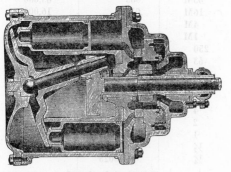

Swash plate engine.

446

SWISS (THURY'S) SCREW THREAD—See *Screw Threads, Thury's Watch.*

SWIVEL—To turn or allow a turning motion, usually in the same plane. The term is also used for turning in other planes, as a front axle swiveling under a cart. It is also applied to the part which permits turning or swiveling.

SWIVEL-HEAD LATHE—See *Lathe, Swivel Head.*

SYKES GEAR CUTTING METHOD — See *Gear Cutting, Sykes Method.*

SYMBOLS OF SCREW THREAD STANDARDS—See *Screw Thread Symbols.*

SYNCHRONIZE—To make two or more parts move at proper relation to each other. This is especially important in automatic machinery, where certain movements must be made and completed before others start. The term is also used to mean working in unison, as setting watches so as to show exactly the same time.

T-BOLT—Bolts with heads made to fit T-slots. Standard sizes are shown in the table. They are used in holding fixtures and work on tables of machine tools for machining. A bolt with a cross handle is also called a T-bolt.

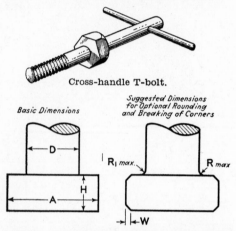

Cross-handle T-bolt.

T-bolts: (A) Diameter of head. (D) Diameter of bolt. (H) Thickness of head. (R) Radius in corner. (W) Width of bevel.

T-BOLT, NUT AND WASHER—T-bolt dimensions are given in the table. Illustrations show the way in which T-bolts, nut and washers are used in clamping work to a machine table.

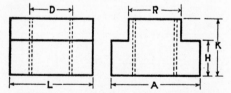

T-nut details. (A) Diameter of nut. (D) Diameter of bolt thread. (H) Minor thickness of nut. (K) Full thickness of nut. (R) Width of nut where is fits slot in plane table.

T-IRON—A form of structural material rolled in the shape of a letter T. Usually of steel instead of iron.

T-LATHE—See *Lathe, "T."*

T-NUTS—Special nuts made to fit T-slots in machine tables for use with bolts holding work on the tables. They have been standardized to fit T-slots, which are now also standardized.

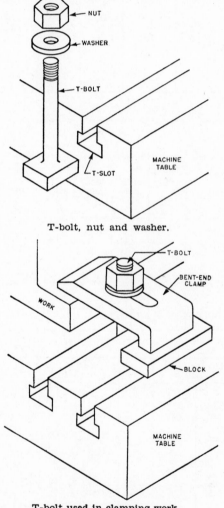

T-bolt, nut and washer.

T-bolt used in clamping work.
Use of bent-end clamp in a setup.

448

T-Bolt—Main Dimensions

Diameter of T-bolt [1,2] (D)	Threads per Inch [1]	Bolt Head Dimensions and Tolerances							Rounding or Breaking of Corners	
		Width across Flats (A)			Width across Corners	Height (H)			R	W
		Maximum (Basic)	Tolerance (Minus)	Minimum		Maximum (Basic)	Tolerance (Minus)	Minimum	Maximum	Maximum
1/4	20	15/32	0.031	7/16	0.663	5/32	0.016	9/64	1/64	1/32
5/16	18	9/16	0.031	17/32	0.796	3/16	0.016	11/64	1/64	1/32
3/8	16	11/16	0.031	21/32	0.972	1/4	0.016	15/64	1/64	1/32
1/2	13	7/8	0.031	27/32	1.238	5/16	0.016	19/64	1/64	1/16
5/8	11	1 1/8	0 031	1 3/32	1.591	13/32	0 016	25/64	1/32	1/16
3/4	10	1 5/16	0.031	1 9/32	1.856	17/32	0 031	1/2	1/32	1/16
1	8	1 11/16	0.031	1 21/32	2.387	11/16	0.031	21/32	1/32	1/16
1 1/4	7	2 1/16	0 031	2 1/32	2.917	15/16	0.031	29/32	1/32	1/16
1 1/2	6	2 1/2	0.031	2 15/32	3.536	1 3/16	0.031	1 5/32	1/32	1/16

T-Bolt Specifications

Diameter of T-bolt [2,3]	Width of Throat [1,2,3] (d)	Depth of Throat (T)		Head Space Dimensions and Tolerances						Rounding or Breaking of Corners		
		Maximum	Minimum	Width (a)			Depth (h)			r	w	u
				Maximum (Basic)	Tolerance (Minus)	Minimum	Maximum (Basic)	Tolerance (Minus)	Minimum	Maximum	Maximum	Maximum
1/4	9/32	3/8	1/8	9/16	0.063	1/2	15/64	0.031	13/64	1/64	1/64	1/32
5/16	11/32	7/16	5/32	21/32	0.063	19/32	17/64	0.031	15/64	1/64	1/32	1/32
3/8	7/16	9/16	7/32	25/32	0.063	23/32	21/64	0.031	19/64	1/64	1/32	1/32
1/2	9/16	11/16	5/16	31/32	0.063	29/32	25/64	0.031	23/64	1/64	1/32	1/32
5/8	11/16	7/8	7/16	1 1/4	0.063	1 3/16	31/64	0.031	29/64	1/32	1/32	3/64
3/4	13/16	1 1/16	9/16	1 15/32	0.094	1 3/8	5/8	0.031	19/32	1/32	1/32	3/64
1	1 1/16	1 1/4	3/4	1 27/32	0.094	1 3/4	53/64	0.047	25/32	1/32	1/16	3/64
1 1/4	1 5/16	1 9/16	1	2 7/32	0 094	2 1/8	1 3/32	0.063	1 1/32	1/32	1/16	3/64
1 1/2	1 9/16	1 15/16	1 1/4	2 21/32	0 094	2 9/16	1 11/32	0 063	1 9/32	1/32	1/16	3/64

T-Nut Specifications

Tap for Stud [3] (D) Diameter	Threads per Inch	Width of Throat T-slot	Width of Tongue (R)			Width of Nut [2] (A)			Height of Nut [2] (H)			Total Thickness, including Tongue (K)	Length of Nut [1] (L)
			Maximum (Basic)	Tolerance (Minus)	Minimum	Maximum (Basic)	Tolerance (Minus)	Minimum	Maximum (Basic)	Tolerance (Minus)	Minimum		
1/4	20	11/32	0.330	0.010	0.320	9/16	0.031	17/32	3/16	0.016	11/64	9/32	9/16
5/16	18	7/16	0.418	0.010	0.408	11/16	0.031	21/32	1/4	0.016	15/64	3/8	11/16
3/8	16	9/16	0.543	0.010	0.533	7/8	0.031	27/32	5/16	0.016	19/64	17/32	7/8
1/2	13	11/16	0.668	0.010	0.658	1 1/8	0.031	1 3/32	13/32	0.016	25/64	25/32	1 5/16
5/8	11	13/16	0.783	0.010	0.773	1 5/16	0.031	1 9/32	17/32	0.031	1/2	25/32	1 5/16
3/4	10	1 1/16	1.033	0.015	1.018	1 11/16	0.031	1 21/32	11/16	0.031	21/32	1	1 11/16
1	8	1 5/16	1.273	0 015	1.258	2 1/16	0.031	2 1/32	15/16	0.031	29/32	1 5/16	2 1/16
1 1/4	7	1 9/16	1.523	0.015	1 508	2 1/2	0.031	2 15/32	1 3/16	0.031	1 5/32	1 5/8	2 1/2

T-Slot Specifications

Diameter of T-bolt [1]	Tongue Dimensions			Depth of Seat [4]	Total Thickness	Screw Dimensions				
	Width [1],[3]	Length [2]	Projection [4]			Diameter of Screw	Number of Screw	Threads per Inch	Diameter of Head	Thickness of Head
	(R)	(L)	(P)	(S)	(K)	(D)			(A)	(G)
1/4	9/32	3/8	3/32	1/8	7/32	0.125	5	40	0.196	0.081
5/16	11/32	15/32	1/8	5/32	9/32	0.164	8	32	0.260	0.107
3/8	7/16	9/16	1/8	3/16	5/16	0.190	10	24	0.303	0.124
1/2	9/16	3/4	1/8	7/32	11/32	1/4	.....	20	0.375	0.130
5/8	11/16	15/16	1/8	1/4	3/8	1/4	.....	20	0.375	0.130
3/4	13/16	1 1/8	5/32	9/32	7/16	5/16	.....	18	0.438	0.150
1	1 1/16	1 1/2	7/32	11/32	9/16	3/8	.....	16	0.500	0.170
1 1/4	1 5/16	1 7/8	1/4	3/8	5/8	3/8	.....	16	0.500	0.170
1 1/2	1 9/16	2 1/4	5/16	7/16	3/4	1/2	.....	13	0.625	0.210

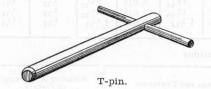

T-pin.

T-PIN—A pin having a cross handle for convenience in putting it in place or removing it.

T-SLOT—T-shaped slots, usually milled, to provide room for the heads of bolts used in holding work on machine tables. Sizes and shapes of T-slots have been standardized to secure interchangeability between machines made by different builders. Some of the standards are shown in the illustrations.

T-SLOT CUTTERS—See *Milling Cutters, T-Slot.*

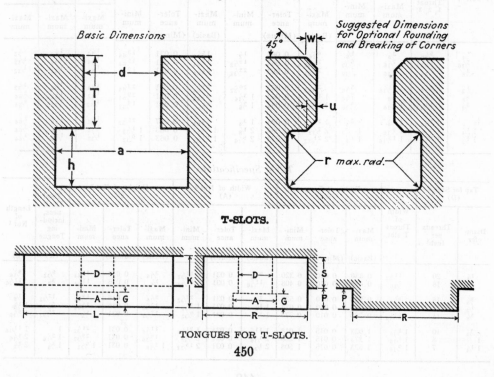

Basic Dimensions

Suggested Dimensions for Optional Rounding and Breaking of Corners

T-SLOTS.

TONGUES FOR T-SLOTS.

450

T-SLOTS, TONGUE FOR—These are really special nuts made to fit T-slot seats and threaded to receive bolts used for clamping work on a machine. They have been standardized to conform with T-slots, as shown. Both tongues and tongue seats are made reversible to be used with two sizes of T-bolts, and for two widths of tongue seats.

T-SQUARE—A straight edge with a head at one end 90 degrees from the blade. Used on the drawing board for drawing parallel lines and as a base for triangles. Sometimes made with a blade that can be adjusted to other angles.

TACHOMETER—An instrument which shows at a glance the number of revolutions at which an engine or shaft is turning, differing from a speed indicator in this respect. Airplane instrument boards have a tachometer for each engine to show the pilot at all times just what each engine is doing.

TACKLE—The term is used in many industries to indicate apparatus used. In a machine shop it generally refers to the collection of ropes, pulley blocks, hooks and other paraphernalia used in moving machinery.

TAIN—A little used term for tinfoil or thin tin plate.

TAKE-UP — The adjustment of two moving parts to restore the original clearance between them. An idler pulley which maintains proper tension in a driving belt is also called a take-up in some places.

TALC—A soft oily mineral used in various forms. Used as a skin preparation and in making what is called French chalk. Also known as soapstone.

TAMP—To ram or pound down, as in foundries, for compacting sand in molds to resist the pressure of molten metal as it is poured in.

TANG—The projecting part of a file or similar tool, which goes into a wooden handle. Also the flattened end of a tapered drill shank which goes in the slot in the spindle or in an adapter, for helping to drive the drill. See under *Drills, Twist, Names of Parts*.

TANGENT—A straight line touching a circle, as a ruler or straight edge laid on the rim of a pulley. See *Trigonometry*.

TANGENT CHASER — See *Chasers, Screw Threads*.

TANGENT CUTTING TOOL—Any tool used in forming and in thread cutting die heads, which lies tangent to the surface of the work. Skiving tools come under this head. Also see *Chasers, Screw Threads*.

TANGENTIAL FEED—See *Feed, Tangential*. Used in hobbing worm gears. See also *Gear, Hobbing*.

TANITE—A trade name for a composition of abrasive with a special cement for use in grinding wheels and other shapes.

TANTALUM—A metal somewhat like platinum, used in lamp filaments and to resist acids. Sp. gr. 16.6. Melts at 5,162 deg. F.

TANTALUM CARBIDE—Heavy, hard crystals used in making tools of sintered carbide. Melts at about 7,000 deg. F.

TAP—See also: *Tapped* (p. 460), *Tapping* (p. 460 ff.), *Taps* (pp. 462-463).

TAP AND THREAD TERMS — Standard names for various parts of standard taps.

TAP, BENT SHANK—Tap used for continuous threading of nuts in nut-tapping machines.

TAP DRILLS—Drills used for holes that are to be tapped. A full depth of thread is *very* seldom necessary, as a 75 per cent depth of thread in a nut is approximately as strong as the bolt. In deep holes or in small sizes 50 per cent of full thread in the nut is sufficient. A simple rule is to use the threads per inch as the denominator with 1 as a numerator, and subtract this from the nominal size of the bolt. For an 8-pitch thread, this means use of a drill $\frac{1}{8}$ inch smaller than the basic size of the tap. For 20 threads per inch, deduct $\frac{1}{20}$ from the bolt diameter. This gives about 77 per cent depth of thread. See *Drills, Tapping*.

TAP DRILLS FOR INSTRUMENT SCREW THREADS—See *Screw Threads, Watch and Instrument*.

TAP DRILL SIZES—See *Drills, Tapping*.

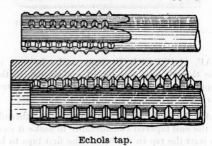

Echols tap.

TAP, ECHOLS—A tap from which every other tooth is removed on alternating lands. This leaves only half the number of teeth on each land and on the whole tap. It reduces the cutting friction. Now called "interrupted."

TAP, HOOK—Taps for nut tapping machines in which the shank is curved 180 degrees. As nuts are tapped they slide up on the shank and are forced off the back end into a receptacle. The taps are not reversed, which makes this a continuous operation.

Two hook taps—one empty, one full of taps.

TAP, MASTER—An accurate tap intended for finishing the threads in a screw cutting die. Master taps are also used in places where it is necessary to have the tapped hole finished accurately.

TAP, SPIRAL POINTED—A tap with the first cutting edges ground at a fairly sharp angle. Some grind the first edges in a helix. A few taps are made with helical flutes, which are erroneously called spiral.

Spiral pointed tap (helical pointed or "gun" tap).

TAP, SUPERCREST—Taps with the top of the threads over-size to cut a clearance in the tapped hole to avoid the possibility of interference. Designed by Ralph E. Flanders.

TAP, TAPER—Usually a tap with the threads at the end tapered considerably to make it easy to start the tap in the hole. The first taps to be

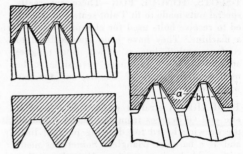

Supercrest tap: Supercrest tap avoids interference at top of thread.

used, in a set of three. Pipe taps are also tapered but are usually called "pipe taps." See *Taps*.

Taper tap.

TAPER, BROWN & SHARPE—A system of tapers approximately one-half inch per foot originated by the Brown & Sharpe Mfg. Co. for their milling machines. The table on page 454 shows the dimensions. See also *Tapers, Standard*.

TAPER, FAST—A taper with a large included angle, such as the $3\frac{1}{2}$-inch-per-foot now used in milling and other machine tool spindles. Sometimes called a *self-releasing* taper because it is released more easily than *slow tapers*.

TAPER, JARNO—A system of tapers originated by Oscar J. Beale of Brown & Sharpe many years ago. Knowing the number of the taper, one could find all the dimensions by the simple formulas shown. It was adopted by several machine tool builders but was never as widely used as it deserved. It has given way to the standard taper adopted by the American Standards Association.

$$\text{Taper per Foot} = 0.6 \text{ Inch.}$$
$$\text{Taper per Inch} = 0.05 \text{ Inch.}$$
$$\text{Diam. Large End} = \frac{\text{No. of Taper}}{8}$$
$$\text{Diam. Small End} = \frac{\text{No. of Taper}}{10}$$
$$\text{Length of Taper} = \frac{\text{No. of Taper}}{2}$$

In the Jarno system, the taper of which is 0.6 inch per foot or 1 in 20, the number of the

TAP AND SCREW THREAD TERMS.

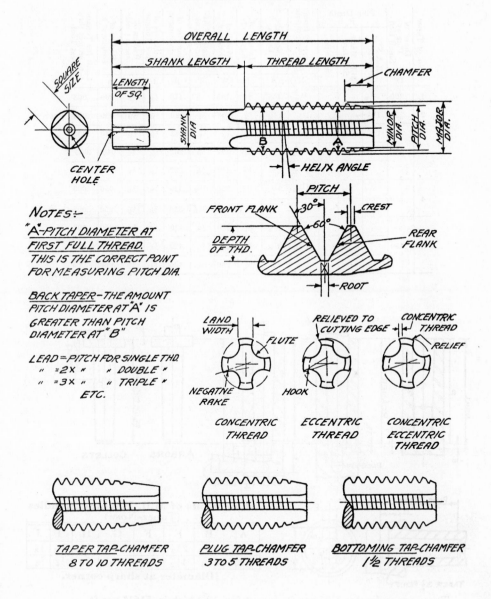

NOTES:-

"A"-PITCH DIAMETER AT FIRST FULL THREAD. THIS IS THE CORRECT POINT FOR MEASURING PITCH DIA.

BACK TAPER—THE AMOUNT PITCH DIAMETER AT "A" IS GREATER THAN PITCH DIAMETER AT "B"

LEAD = PITCH FOR SINGLE THD.
" = 2X " " DOUBLE "
" = 3X " " TRIPLE "
ETC.

CONCENTRIC THREAD   ECCENTRIC THREAD   CONCENTRIC ECCENTRIC THREAD

TAPER TAP-CHAMFER
8 TO 10 THREADS

PLUG TAP-CHAMFER
3 TO 5 THREADS

BOTTOMING TAP-CHAMFER
1½ THREADS

453

Brown & Sharpe Tapers

No. of Taper	Diam. of Plug at Small End	Plug Depth P			Keyway from End of Spindle	Shank Depth	Length of Keyway†	Width of Keyway	Length of Arbor Tongue	Diameter of Arbor Tongue	Thickness of Arbor Tongue	Radius of Tongue Circle	Radius of Tongue at a	Limit for Tongue —to project thru Test Tool
	D	B & S* Standard	Mill. Mach. Standard	Miscell.	K	S	L	W	T	d	t	c	a	
1	.200	15/16			15/16	1 3/16	3/8	.135	3/16	.170	1/8	3/16	.030	.003
2	.250	1 3/16			1 11/64	1 1/2	1/2	.166	1/4	.220	5/32	3/16	.030	.003
		1 1/2			1 15/32	1 7/8	5/8	.197	5/16	.282	3/16	3/16	.040	.003
3	.312			1 3/4	1 23/32	2 1/8	5/8	.197	5/16	.282	3/16	3/16	.040	.003
				2	1 31/32	2 3/8	5/8	.197	5/16	.282	3/16	3/16	.040	.003
			1 1/4		1 13/64	1 21/32	11/16	.228	11/32	.320	7/32	5/16	.050	.003
4	.350	1 11/16			1 41/64	2 3/32	11/16	.228	11/32	.320	7/32	5/16	.050	.003
			1 3/4		1 11/16	2 3/16	3/4	.260	3/8	.420	1/4	5/16	.060	.003
5	.450			2	1 15/16	2 7/16	3/4	.260	3/8	.420	1/4	5/16	.060	.003
		2 1/8			2 1/16	2 9/16	3/4	.260	3/8	.420	1/4	5/16	.060	.003

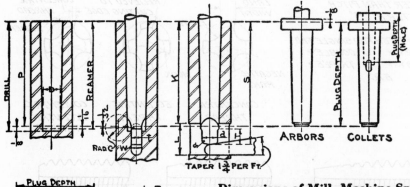

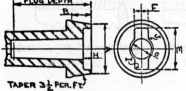

Dimensions of Mill. Machine Spindles
(Taper-Nose)

A‡	B	E	F	G	H	I	J
3.045	2	2 1/2	1	1 3/8	5/8	3/16	1/8
5.255	2 1/8	4 1/2	1 1/2	2 13/32	7/8	1/4	1/4

‡Diameter at sharp corner.

Taper approximates 1-2″ per ft. except No. 10 which is .5161″ per ft.

454

taper is the key by which all the dimensions are immediately determined. That is, the number of the taper is the number of tenths of an inch in diameter at the small end, the number of eighths of an inch at the large end, and the number of halves of an inch in length or depth. For example: the No. 6 taper is six-eighths (3-4) inch diameter at large end, six-tenths (6-10) inch diameter at the small end and six-halves (3) inches in length. Similarly, the No. 16 taper is sixteen-eighths, or 2 inches diameter at the large end; sixteen-tenths or 1.6 inches at the small end and sixteen-halves or 8 inches in length.

TAPER, MILLING MACHINE—Milling machine makers have adopted four standard sizes for the tapers in the spindle noses of their machines. These are shown herewith. The taper is 3½ inches per foot in all sizes.

TAPER, MORSE—The taper originated by the Morse Twist Drill Co. and most largely used for drill shanks and similar tools. It was supposed to be ⅝ inch per foot, but lack of precise measuring methods at the time accounts for slight errors in the taper as shown in the table. See *Taper, Standard.*

TAPER PER FOOT—Total taper measured between the two surfaces. The table gives both the included angle and the angle with the center line or axis.

TAPER, SELLERS—A taper originated many years ago by William Sellers, designer of the screw thread now used. It was first known as the Sellers, then the Franklin Institute, and now the American national. The Sellers taper was ¾ inch per foot, the same as now used in "slow tapers" (or self-holding tapers) in sizes above 2 inches. The Sellers taper also included a key the whole length of the shank but had no tang.

TAPER(S), STANDARD—Three tapers are now used in "self-holding" tools such as drills. These are also known as "slow" tapers, on account of the small angle. The standard now includes 3 of the old Brown & Sharpe and 8 of the old Morse taper, and 11 larger size tapers of the ¾ inch per foot series. The Brown & Sharpe taper was supposed to be ½ inch per foot and the Morse ⅝ inch per foot. Owing to lack of fine measuring facilities when these were established, the tapers varied somewhat. The present standards are given in the table.

TAPER, SLOW—A taper with a small included angle, as the Brown & Sharpe and Morse tapers. Named to distinguish it from the 3½ inch per foot taper now used in milling and other machine tool spindles.

TAPER SPLINES—See *Splines, Taper.*

TAPER THREADING—Cutting or chasing a thread with the tailstock set off center, with the tool set at right angles to the axis of the work, or using a taper attachment.

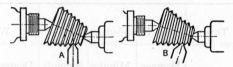

Taper threading. Setting tools in taper-thread work. (A) Incorrect tool setting produces deformed thread. (B) Correct tool setting produces thread with normal angles.

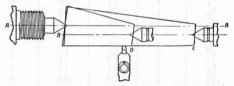

With the tailstock set over the same amount, pieces of different lengths are machined with different tapers.

Taper turning: (A) Lathe spindle, also tail spindle. (B) Lathe center. (C) Small diameter of long piece. (D) Small diameter of short piece.

TAPER TURNING—Tapers are turned in a lathe by setting the tail stock out of center line, as shown. There are also taper attachments where an adjustable bar at the back of the lathe controls the movement of the tool carriage.

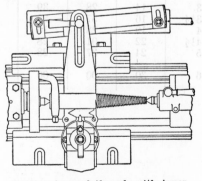

Cutting tapered threads with taper attachment. See also page 460.

Taper Per Foot

Taper per Foot	Included Angle			With Center Line			Height of Gage Block for 5″ Sine Bar	
	Degrees	Minutes	Seconds	Degrees	Minutes	Seconds	For Included Angle	Taper from Center Line
1/8	0	35	48	0	17	53	0.052080	0.026015
3/16	0	53	43	0	26	51	0.078125	0.039060
1/4	1	11	38	0	35	48	0.104165	0.052080
5/16	1	29	32	0	44	46	0.130210	0.065105
3/8	1	47	27	0	53	43	0.156250	0.078125
7/16	2	05	22	1	02	40	0.182290	0.091145
1/2	2	23	17	1	11	37	0.208335	0.104165
9/16	2	41	12	1	20	35	0.234375	0.117190
5/8	2	59	08	1	29	32	0.260420	0.130210
11/16	3	17	04	1	38	29	0.286460	0.143230
3/4	3	35	00	1	47	27	0.312500	0.156250
13/16	3	52	56	1	56	24	0.338540	0.169270
7/8	4	10	54	2	05	21	0.364585	0.182280
15/16	4	28	51	2	14	19	0.390625	0.195315
1	4	46	48	2	23	17	0.416650	0.208335
1¼	6	00	29	2	59	08	0.523330	0.260420
1½	7	10	51	3	35	00	0.625000	0.312500
1¾	8	23	08	4	10	54	0.729165	0.364585
2	9	35	39	4	46	48	0.833330	0.416660
2½	12	03	14	5	58	45	1.041665	0.520830
3	14	28	39	7	10	51	1.250000	0.625000
3½	16	57	28	8	23	08	1.458330	0.729165
4	19	28	16	9	35	39	1.666666	0.833333
4½	22	01	28	10	48	25	1.875000	0.937500
5	24	37	28	12	01	29	2.083330	1.041665
6	30	00	00	14	28	39	2.500000	1.250000

Morse Tapers

Number of Taper	Plug		Shank		H	P	Tongue					Keyway		K	Amount of Taper per Inch of Length	Amount of Taper per Foot of Length	Number of Key
	D	A	B	S			t	T	d	R	a	W	L				
	Diameter Small End	Diameter at End of Socket	Whole Length	Depth	Depth of Hole	Standard Plug Depth	Thickness	Length	Diameter	Radius	Radius	Width	Length	End of Socket to Keyway			
0	0.252	0.3561	2 11/32	2 11/32	2 1/32	2	0.1562	1/4	0.235	5/32	0.04	0.160	9/16	1 15/16	0.05205	0.62460	0
1	0.369	0.475	2 9/16	2 7/16	2 3/16	2 1/8	0.2031	3/8	0.343	3/16	0.05	0.213	3/4	2 1/16	0.04988	0.59858	1
2	0.572	0.700	3 1/8	2 15/16	2 5/8	2 9/16	0.250	7/16	17/32	1/4	0.06	0.260	7/8	2 1/2	0.04995	0.59941	2
3	0.778	0.938	3 7/8	3 11/16	3 1/4	3 3/16	0.3125	9/16	23/32	9/32	0.08	0.322	1 3/16	3 1/16	0.05020	0.60235	3
4	1.020	1.231	4 7/8	4 5/8	4 1/8	4 1/16	0.4687	5/8	31/32	5/16	0.10	0.478	1 1/4	3 7/8	0.05194	0.62326	4
5	1.475	1.748	6 1/8	5 7/8	5 1/4	5 3/16	0.6250	3/4	1 13/32	3/8	0.12	0.635	1 1/2	4 15/16	0.05263	0.63151	5
6	2.116	2.494	8 9/16	8 1/4	7 3/8	7 1/4	0.750	1 1/8	2	1/2	0.15	0.760	1 3/4	7	0.05214	0.62565	6
7	2.750	3.270	11 5/8	11 1/4	10 5/8	10	1.1250	1 3/8	2 5/8	3/4	1.18	1.135	2 5/8	9 1/4	0.05200	0.6240	7

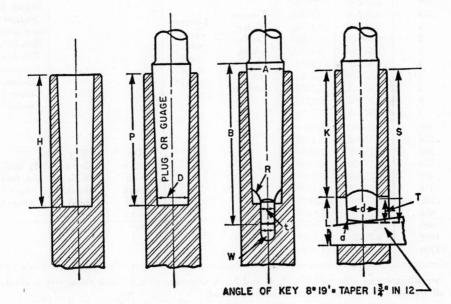

ANGLE OF KEY 8° 19' = TAPER 1 3/4° IN 12

Milling Machine Tapers

No. of Taper	D Inches	d Inches	L Inches	E Inches	S Inches	K Inches
30	1¼	.692	2⅞	½	2.7493	.6255
		.685			2.7488	.6252
40	1¾	1.005	3⅞	⅝	3.4993	.6255
		.997			3.4988	.6252
50	2¾	1.568	5½	¾	5.0618	1.0006
		1.559			5.0613	1.0002
60	4¼	2.381	8⅝	1½	8.7180	1.000
		2.371			8.7175	.999

Standard Taper Series—Basic Dimension

(In Inches)

No. of Taper	Taper per Foot	Diameter at Gage Line¹ A	Means of Driving and Holding				Origin of Series
239	0.50200	0.23922					
299	0.50200	0.29968					Brown &
375	0.50200	0.37525	Tongue				Sharpe
1	0.59858	0.47500	drive	Tongue			taper series
2	0.59941	0.70000	with	drive			Nos. 239,
3	0.60235	0.93800	shank	with			299, 375
4	0.62326	1.2310	held	shank			
4½	0.62400	1.5000	in by	held			Morse
5	0.63151	1.7480	friction	in by			taper
6	0.62565	2.4940					series
7	0.62400	3.2700					
200	0.75000	1.9999					
250	0.75000	2.4999					
300	0.75000	2.9999			Key	Key	¾ inch
350	0.75000	3.4999			drive	drive	per foot
400	0.75000	3.9999			with	with	taper
450	0.75000	4.4999			shank	shank	series
500	0.75000	4.9999			held	held	
600	0.75000	5.9999			in by	in by	
800	0.75000	7.9999			key	drawbolt	
1000	0.75000	9.9999					
1200	0.75000	11.9999					

¹See illustrations with tables 2, 3, 4, and 5. A tolerance of 0.005 inch either way is alloded on all fractions dimensions unless otherwise noted.

Tapers Per Foot in Inches and Corresponding Angles.

Taper Per Foot	Included Angle			Angle with Center Line			Taper Per Foot	Included Angle			Angle with Center Line		
	Deg.	Min.	Sec.	Deg.	Min.	Sec.		Deg.	Min.	Sec.	Deg.	Min.	Sec.
1/64	0	4	28	0	2	14	1	4	46	18	2	23	9
1/32	0	8	58	0	4	29	1⅛	5	22	40	2	41	50
1/16	0	17	53	0	8	57	1¼	5	57	48	2	58	54
3/32	0	26	52	0	13	26	1⅜	6	33	26	3	16	43
⅛	0	35	48	0	17	54	1½	7	9	10	3	34	35
5/32	0	44	44	0	22	22	1⅝	7	44	48	3	52	24
3/16	0	53	44	0	26	52	1¾	8	20	26	4	10	13
7/32	1	2	36	0	31	18	1⅞	8	56	2	4	28	1
¼	1	11	36	0	35	48	2	9	31	36	4	45	48
9/32	1	20	30	0	40	15	2¼	10	42	42	5	21	21
5/16	1	29	30	0	44	45	2½	11	53	36	5	56	48
11/32	1	38	26	0	49	13	2¾	13	4	24	6	32	12
⅜	1	47	24	0	53	42	3	14	15	0	7	7	30
13/32	1	56	24	0	58	12	3¼	15	25	24	7	42	42
7/16	2	5	18	1	2	39	3½	16	35	40	8	17	50
15/32	2	14	16	1	7	8	—3¾	17	45	40	8	52	50
½	2	23	10	1	11	35	4	18	55	24	9	27	42
17/32	2	32	4	1	16	2	—4¼	20	5	2	10	2	31
9/16	2	41	4	1	20	32	4½	21	14	20	10	37	10
19/32	2	50	2	1	25	1	—4¾	22	23	22	11	11	41
⅝	2	59	0	1	29	30	5	23	32	12	11	46	6
21/32	3	7	56	1	33	58	—5¼	24	40	42	12	20	21
11/16	3	16	54	1	38	27	5½	25	48	48	12	54	24
23/32	3	25	50	1	42	55	—5¾	26	56	46	13	28	23
¾	3	34	44	1	47	21	6	28	4	20	14	2	10
25/32	3	43	44	1	51	52	6¼	29	11	34	14	35	47
13/16	3	52	38	1	56	19	6½	30	18	26	15	9	13
27/32	4	1	32	2	0	46	6¾	31	25	2	15	42	31
⅞	4	10	32	2	5	16	7	32	31	12	16	15	36
29/32	4	19	26	2	9	43	7¼	33	37	44	16	48	32
15/16	4	28	24	2	14	12	7½	34	42	30	17	21	15
31/32	4	37	20	2	18	40	8	35	47	32	17	53	46
							8¾	36	52	12	18	26	6

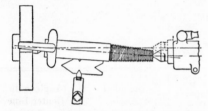

Cutting tapered threads with tailstock center set over.

TAPER (S), S. A. E.—A taper used in the automotive industry for fitting shaft ends into connections of various kinds. The taper is 1.5 inches per foot with a plus or minus tolerance of 0.005 inch. The connections usually have a straight key in addition to the taper, which is merely for centering the parts.

TAPPING MACHINES—Machines for driving taps into drilled holes and reversing the spindles so as to run the tap out again. They may have a single spindle or as many as desired. Some mass production shops tap 100 or more holes at one operation. Special machines are made for tapping nuts.

TAPPING SCREW—Screws which make their own thread as they are forced into place. Some have a tapered or gimlet point, while others are straight with flutes or grooves which make them into a sort of tap. See *Screw, Self-Tapping.*

TAPPING SPEEDS—Tapping speeds vary with the material being machined and the kind of taps used. The tapping lubricant also affects the speed to be used. The Besley Co. suggests the following speeds for carbon and for high speed taps, but does not recommend carbon

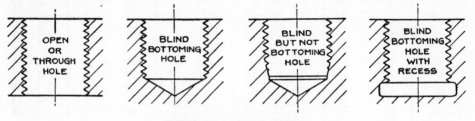

TYPES OF TAPPED HOLES.

TAPPED HOLES, TYPES OF—Tapping of holes through a plate and of holes which do not go through requires varying treatment. The illustration shows four types of tapped holes. The first has been tapped clear through the plate. The second has been finish tapped with a bottoming tap. The third has been tapped with a plug, or second tap, and shows the taper on the end of the tap. The fourth is tapped with a bottoming tap which could go into the recess and give a full thread all the way down.

TAPPET—Usually a projection which contacts and moves a valve, as in a gas engine. Tappets are also used in many types of machinery to move other parts at specified intervals.

TAPPING—Removing molten metal from a furnace by opening the hole at the bottom from which the metal flows into molds or ladles.

The same term applies to the cutting of screw threads by the use of a *tap*, usually in a drilled hole.

taps for the metals marked with an asterisk. See following page.

Size Limitations of ½-13 NC Nut and Screw For Class 1-2-3 and 4 Fits

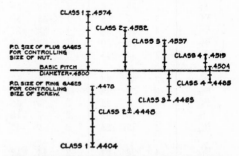

The horizontal line represents the basic pitch diameter. The vertical lines the variable pitch diameter sizes of the screw and the nut. Divisions represent thousandths of an inch. Note in Class 1 the maximum size of the screw is below basic pitch diameter. In Class 4 it is above the basic pitch diameter. The minimum size of nut for all classes is the basic pitch diameter.

Tapping Speeds

Suggested speeds, lubricants and approximate angle of cutting edge when tapping various materials

| Material | Feet per Minute | | Lubricant | Approximate Angle of Cutting Edge |
	Carbon Taps	High Speed Taps		
Allegheny metal	*	15-30	Sulphur base oil	10°-15° Hook
Aluminum	45-50	90-110	Kerosene and lard oil or light mineral oil	10°-15° Hook
Bakelite	30-35	60-80	Dry	4°- 6° Hook
Brass	45-50	90-110	Compound or light base oil	Radial to 5° Rake
Bronze	20-30	40-70	Compound or light base oil	6°-10° Rake
Bronze-manganese	*	30-50	Light base oil	8°-10° Rake
Copper	45-50	40-110	Light base oil	15°-20° Hook
Die castings, aluminum	30-35	60-80	Kerosene and lard oil	10°-15° Hook
Die castings, zinc	30-35	60-80	Compound	10°-15° Hook
Duralumin	45-50	90-110	Compound or kerosene and lard oil	10°-15° Hook
Fiber	40-45	80-100	Dry	4°- 6° Hook
Iron—cast	35-45	70-100	Dry or compound	Radial to 5° Rake
Iron—malleable	*	35-70	Compound or sulphur base oil	Radial to 5° Rake
Monel metal	*	20-30	Sulphur base oil or kerosene and lard oil	10°-15° Hook
Nickel silver	35-40	75-40	Sulphur base oil or kerosene and lard oil	15°-20° Hook
Rubber hard	40-45	80-100	Dry	10°-15° Hook
Steel—cast	*	20-35	Sulphur base oil	10°-15° Rake
Steel—chromium	*	20-35	Sulphur base oil	10°-15° Hook
Steel—machinery	20-30	40-70	Compound, sulphur base oil or kerosene and paraffin	8°-12° Rake
Steel—manganese	*	10-20	Compound, sulphur base oil or kerosene and paraffin	10°-15° Rake
Steel—molybdenum	*	20-35	Sulphur base oil	10°-15° Rake
Steel—nickel	*	25-40	Sulphur base oil	10°-15° Hook
Cold punched nuts	25-35	60-80	Compound or sulphur base oil	8°-12° Rake
SAE 1020 screw stock	30-45	65-90	Sulphur base oil	8°-12° Rake
Steel—stainless	*	15-30	Sulphur base oil	10°-15° Hook
Steel—tool	15-20	25-40	Sulphur base oil or kerosene and lard oil	8°-12° Rake
Steel tungsten	*	20-35	Sulphur base oil	10°-15° Hook
Steel—vanadium	*	25-40	Sulphur base oil	10°-15° Rake

*Use of carbon steel taps not recommended for tapping these metals.

Speeds for Carbon Steel Tapper Taps

Tap diam.	Ft. per min.	R. p. m.	Tap diam.	Ft. per min.	R. p. m.
¼	45	690	1¼	20	61
⅜	40	408	1½	18	46
½	35	260	1¾	18	39
⅝	32	196	2	16	30
¾	30	154	2¼	14	24
⅞	26	112	2½	12	18
1	24	90			

TAPPING TOLERANCES

TAPPING TOLERANCES—Permissible variations from standard as shown by an example of a ½-inch National Coarse 13-pitch screw and nut for classes 1, 2, 3 and 4 fits by Greenfield Tap & Die Co. See page 460.

TAPS AND SCREW THREADS—

DEFINITIONS — The following definitions, which enter into specifications and methods of designation, refer both to taps and to screw threads. They represent the accepted meanings of terms used in ordering, and using, taps and screws.

Angle of thread: The included angle between the thread sides, measured in a plane including the tap axis.

Backed Off: A term used to describe a tap which is relieved eccentrically in the angle of the thread. Usually the backing-off does not begin exactly at the cutting edge.

Back taper: A slight relief on a tap which makes the pitch diameter near the shank end of the thread somewhat smaller than that near the point of the tap.

Base of thread: The distance through the bottom of the thread between two adjacent roots.

Basic size: A theoretical or nominal size of pitch diameter, major diameter, or root diameter.

Chamfer (sometimes referred to as "start" or "pointing"): The method of pointing or tapering the end of the thread, to distribute the work over several threads.

Crest clearance: The space between the top of the thread and the root of its mating thread.

Flat on shank: A cut-away portion of the shank of a tap which serves as a seat for a set-screw.

Gun tap: Same as helical point.

Helical point: A method of sharpening the point of a tap to give a shear cut on the first few threads.

Helix angle: The angle made by the helix of the thread at its pitch diameter with a plane perpendicular to the axis of the thread.

Hook: Rake or undercut on the faces of the teeth of a tap. This is varied for different materials and conditions of tapping.

Interrupted thread: Applied to taps with an odd number of flutes. Every other thread is removed, thus removing part of the cutting friction of the tap in a hole.

Land: The portion of a tap which is not cut away by the flute; in other words, the portion upon which the threads are made.

Large Shank: A term applied to a tap which has a shank diameter approximately equal to the major diameter of the thread. Used on smaller taps for added strength.

Lead: The distance a screw or tap advances along its axis in making one complete turn.

Major diameter (otherwise known as outside diameter): The largest diameter of the outside of the thread.

Minor diameter (otherwise known as root diameter): The smallest diameter of the thread, measured diametrically across two opposite roots.

Necking: The cut-away portion of a tap between the threaded portion and the shank.

Pitch: The distance from a point on the screw thread to a corresponding point on the next thread, measured parallel to the axis.

Pitch diameter: On a straight thread, the diameter of an imaginary cylinder passing through the threads in such a way as to make equal the width of the threads and the width of the corresponding spaces cut by the surface of the cylinder.

Small shank: Applied to a tap which has its shank size equal to or less than the root diameter of the thread. This is common to hand taps of $\frac{7}{16}$ in. and larger.

Spiral point: See *Helical point*.

Square: Flatted portion of the end of a tap used for driving the tap positively.

Straight thread: A thread where the pitch diameter continues the same from one end to the other, except for the back-taper relief.

Taper thread: A thread which has a pitch diameter increasing according to some constant ratio.

TAP(S), STANDARD SYSTEM OF MARKING—Tap manufacturers now mark them as follows:

NC—American National Coarse Thread Series.

NF—American National Fine Thread Series.

N—American National 8, 12 and 16 pitch Series.

NS—American National Special Thread Series.

NH—American National Hose Coupling Threads.

NPT—American National Taper Pipe Threads.

NPS—American National Straight Pipe Threads.

GREASE — a standardized undersize straight pipe thread for grease cup fitting.

STEAM—a straight pipe thread used on coupling taps.

CONDUIT — an oversize straight pipe thread used on coupling taps.

V—a 60-degree V thread usually with both crest and root flatted several thousandths from the theoretical to the user's specifications.

ACME—a standardized 29-degree thread.

SB—manufacturer's stove bolt standard thread. Such marking as USS, USF, SAE, and ASME are now obsolete.
See *Screw Threads, Unified.*

TAPS, TERMS USED FOR GROUND TAPS— Taps which do not have the threads finished by grinding are known as "cut" taps. Taps marked C G have the threads ground but not to the closest tolerances. Taps marked P G are precision ground for extra fine work. Taps marked P G 01 have a basic pitch diameter 0.0005 inch below standard. Taps marked P G 1 are basic plus 0.0005 inch. Taps marked P G 2 are basic diameter plus 0.0005 to basic plus 0.001 inch. Taps marked P G 3 are basic plus 0.001 to basic plus 0.0015 inch.

TEE—A type of pipe coupling with two openings in line and another at right angles. It resembles the letter T, which gives it its name.

TEEMING — A foundry term for pouring molten metal from the ladle into the mold.

TELESCOPING GAGE—A gage where one part slides inside another to allow insertion inside an opening. Indicators show the size when it is lengthened in the work and before removal.

TELLURIUM—A substance secured from a powder in the reduction of tellurium oxide. Sp. gr. 6.2 Melts at about 840 deg. F. Similar to selenium in many ways. See *Selenium.*

TEMPER—This usually refers to the hardness of a metal such as steel or brass. Hardening steel by heating and quenching is called tempering. It is also called heat-treating, although this now refers to manipulations which do not increase or control the metal's hardness but affects its stability and other qualities. The temper or hardness of steel is indicated by the color which comes on a polished place and is known as "temper color."

TEMPERATURES, CONVERSIONS F R O M CENTIGRADE TO FAHRENHEIT—Temperature conversions from one system to the other can be made by the simple formulas shown at end of table on page 464.

TEMPLATE OR TEMPLET — This usually means a sheet metal pattern of a shape to be cut in other material. In some cases the outline is simply drawn on the metal to be machined and it is cut away to the line drawn. In profiling and similar machine work, the template guides a tracer which controls the position of the cutting tool, and the outline is followed automatically. In some machines, the guiding is controlled by electrical contacts, while in others both air and hydraulic controls have been used.

TENON—A part shaped to fit into a recess known as a mortise. See *Mortise.*

TENSILE STRENGTH—The degree to which a piece resists efforts to pull it apart. There is a point at which the metal begins to yield, or stretch, known as the "yield point." After this it elongates until it finally breaks. The yield point is the important point in most cases, although the elongation tells whether it is liable to part suddenly on reaching the yield point. See also *Strength of Materials.*

TENSILE STRENGTH TEST—Measuring the breaking strength of a test specimen. In this case a bolt is held in the heads shown and the heads pulled apart until the bolt

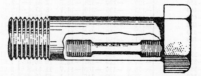

For bolts 1½ in. diameter and over, test specimens will be taken from the section of the bolt indicated in the drawing.

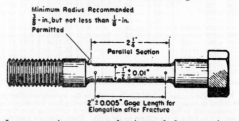

Large specimens may be turned down as indicated in order to utilize available testing machines.

breaks, the force necessary being accurately measured. Regular test specimens are cut from designated parts of the metal to be tested and gripped by special jaws while being pulled apart. The test machines register the point at which the test piece begins to stretch, the length of elongation before failure, and the point at which it breaks.

TERNE PLATE—Plates of Bessemer or open hearth steel with a coating of a 20 per cent tin, 80 per cent lead alloy. Made by the dip process for roofing. To "terne" means to coat a plate with an alloy of tin and lead.

TEST SPECIMENS—Small portions of material taken from metal parts to be tested for strength in various directions. Many specifications state the portions of the metal from which the test specimen is to be taken. For bolts over 1½ inches in diameter, for example, the test specimen must be taken from the portion of the bolt shown. Illus. p. 463.)

TESTING MACHINE—While the term applies to all kinds of tests, in shop language it means a machine for checking the tensile, compressive and torsional, or twisting, strength of

metals. They are made in a number of ways and in both small and very large sizes. In most cases small specimens of the material are prepared and tested. Some of the large machines test full sized beams, but small samples are generally used. See *Tensile Strength Test.*

TEXTOLITE—A General Electric product used for making quiet gears. It consists of layers of canvas or similar fabric impregnated with plastic material. It was one of the early substitutes for rawhide for this purpose.

THALLIUM—A metal similar to lead; it resists acids, except sulphuric. Sp. gr. 11.85. Melts at 570 deg. F.

THERMAL UNIT—A method of comparing and calculating quantities of heat. A common unit is the heat required to raise one pound of water one degree Fahrenheit.

THERMIT AND THERMIT WELDING—A mixture of aluminum and pure iron oxide in powder form. When lighted it produces heat at about 4,600 deg. F. It has been used for welding steel rail ends and repairing broken steel castings. Is now largely replaced by flame or electric welding.

Temperatures—Conversions from Centigrade to Fahrenheit or vice-versa.

−459.4–0				1–50				51–100				101–750			
C.	F.	C.	F.	C.	F.	C.	F.	C.	F.	C.	F.	C.	F.	C.	F.
−273	−459.4	−134	−210	−346	−17.2	1	33.8−	3.33	26	78.8	10.6	51	123.8	24.4	76	168.8	43	110	230	177	350	662	260	500	932

−459.4–0		1–50		51–100		101–750	
C. F.	C. F.	C. F.	C. F.	C. F.	C. F.	C. F.	C. F.
−273 −459.4	−134 −210 −346	−17.2 1 33.8−	3.33 26 78.8	10.6 51 123.8	24.4 76 168.8	43 110 230	177 350 662	260 500 932
−268 −450	−129 −200 −328	−16.7 2 35.6−	2.78 27 80.6	11.1 52 125.6	25.0 77 170.6	49 120 248	182 360 680	266 510 950
−262 −440	−123 −190 −310	−16.1 3 37.4−	2.22 28 82.4	11.7 53 127.4	25.6 78 172.4	54 130 266	188 370 698	271 520 968
−257 −430	−118 −180 −292	−15.6 4 39.2−	1.67 29 84.2	12.2 54 129.2	26.1 79 174.2	60 140 284	193 380 716	277 530 986
−251 −420	−112 −170 −274	−15.0 5 41.0−	1.11 30 86.0	12.8 55 131.0	26.7 80 176.0	66 150 302	199 390 734	282 540 1004
−246 −410	−107 −160 −256	−14.4 6 42.8−	0.56 31 87.8	13.3 56 132.8	27.2 81 177.8	71 160 320	204 400 752	288 550 1022
−240 −400	−101 −150 −238	−13.9 7 44.6	0 32 89.6	13.9 57 134.6	27.8 82 179.6	77 170 338	210 410 770	293 560 1040
−234 −390	−95.6 −140 −220	−13.3 8 46.4	0.56 33 91.4	14.4 58 136.4	28.3 83 181.4	82 180 356	216 420 788	299 570 1058
−229 −380	−90.0 −130 −202	−12.8 9 48.2	1.11 34 93.2	15.0 59 138.2	28.9 84 183.2	88 190 374	221 430 806	304 580 1076
−223 −370	−84.4 −120 −184	−12.2 10 50.0	1.67 35 95.0	15.6 60 140.0	29.4 85 185.0	93 200 392	227 440 824	310 590 1094
−218 −360	−78.9 −110 −166	−11.7 11 51.8	2.22 36 96.8	16.1 61 141.8	30.0 86 186.8	99 210 410	232 450 842	316 600 1112
−212 −350	−73.3 −100 −148	−11.1 12 53.6	2.78 37 98.6	16.7 62 143.6	30.6 87 188.6	100 212 413	238 460 860	321 610 1130
−207 −340	−67.8 −90 −130	−10.6 13 55.4	3.33 38 100.4	17.2 63 145.4	31.1 88 190.4	104 220 428	243 470 878	327 620 1148
−201 −330	−62.2 −80 −112	−10.0 14 57.2	3.89 39 102.2	17.8 64 147.2	31.7 89 192.2	110 230 446	249 480 896	332 630 1166
−196 −320	−56.7 −70 −94	−9.44 15 59.0	4.44 40 104.0	18.3 65 149.0	32.2 90 194.0	116 240 464	254 490 914	338 640 1184
−190 −310	−51.1 −60 −76	−8.89 16 61.8	5.00 41 105.8	18.9 66 150.8	32.8 91 195.8	121 250 482		343 650 1202
−184 −300	−45.6 −50 −58	−8.33 17 63.6	5.56 42 107.6	19.4 67 152.6	33.3 92 197.6	127 260 500		349 660 1220
−179 −290	−40.0 −40 −40	−7.78 18 65.4	6.11 43 109.4	20.0 68 154.4	33.9 93 199.4	132 270 518		354 670 1238
−173 −280	−34.4 −30 −22	−7.22 19 67.2	6.67 44 111.2	20.6 69 156.2	34.4 94 201.2	138 280 536		360 680 1256
−169 −273 −459.4	−28.9 −20 −4	−6.67 20 68.0	7.22 45 113.0	21.1 70 158.0	35.0 95 203.0	143 290 554		366 690 1274
−168 −270 −454	−23.3 −10 14	−6.11 21 69.8	7.78 46 114.8	21.7 71 159.8	35.6 96 204.8	149 300 572		371 700 1292
−162 −260 −436	−17.8 0 32	−5.56 22 71.6	8.33 47 116.6	22.2 72 161.6	36.1 97 206.6	154 310 590		377 710 1310
−157 −250 −418		−5.00 23 73.4	8.89 48 118.4	22.8 73 163.4	36.7 98 208.4	160 320 608		382 720 1328
−151 −240 −400		−4.44 24 75.2	9.44 49 120.2	23.3 74 165.2	37.2 99 210.2	166 330 626		388 730 1346
−146 −230 −382		−3.89 25 77.0	10.0 50 122.0	23.9 75 167.0	37.8 100 212.0	171 340 644		393 740 1364
−140 −220 −304								399 750 1382

NOTE.—The numbers in bold-face type refer to the temperature either in degrees Centigrade or Fahrenheit which it is desired to convert into the other scale. If converting from Fahrenheit degrees to Centigrade degrees the equivalent temperature will be found in the left column, while if converting from degrees Centigrade to degrees Fahrenheit, the answer will be found in the column on the right. These tables are a revision of those by Albert Sauveur, Professor of Metallurgy and Metallography, Harvard University, Cambridge, Mass. Copyright, 1920.

INTERPOLATION FACTORS			
C.	F.	C.	F.
0.56	1	1.8	3.33	6	10.8
1.11	2	3.6	3.89	7	12.6
1.67	3	5.4	4.44	8	14.4
2.22	4	7.2	5.00	9	16.2
2.78	5	9.0	5.56	10	18.0

THERMO-COUPLE—A temperature measuring device made by joining two metals which expand at different rates when heated. These are connected to an indicating device which is graduated to show the temperature which causes the deflection of the indicating needle or hand. The device is used in measuring the heat of furnaces or of metals being heated. In the latter case, the thermo-couple is placed in a cavity in the metal, while the indicating mechanism is outside the furnace.

THERMO-METALS—Any two metals with different rates of expansion, when joined so that temperature changes bend or deform the metals and control thermostatic devices.

THERMOMETER GRADUATIONS—The two most used thermometer graduations are Centigrade (sometimes called Metric) and Fahrenheit. The Reaumur thermometer is practically obsolete. Both Centigrade and Reaumur use zero for freezing, while Fahrenheit uses 32. Reaumur used 80 degrees as the boiling point, Centigrade uses 100 and Fahrenheit uses 212 degrees. To change Centigrade to Fahrenheit—multiply by 9, divide by 5 and add 32; Centigrade to Reaumur—multiply by 4, divide by 5; Fahreheit to Centigrade—subtract 32, multiply by 5, divide by 9; Fahrenheit to Reaumur—substract 32, multiply by 4, divide by 9; Reaumur to Centigrade—divide by 4, multiply by 5; Reaumur to Fahrenheit—multiply by 9, divide by 4, add 32. See *Temperature Conversions.*

THIMBLE—Another name for a ferrule. A short piece of tubing used for preventing wooden file handles from splitting. Also a short piece of tube used at the end of boiler tubing, for making it tight in the tube sheet.

THORIUM—A metal used in making incandescent mantles and in similar places.

THREAD GAGE—A gage of thin flat steel with a 60 degree point at one end and a corresponding notch at the other end; also a smaller V notch on the side. Used in grinding single point thread tools and in setting them square with the work. A thread gage is also a tool with a series of notches for measuring the pitch of screw threads. Usually made with leaves or blades, each measuring a given pitch of thread. Sometimes made in circular form with portions of the edge cut to measure different pitches. See *Gages.*

THREAD MEASUREMENT, ACME AND WORM THREADS—Instead of using wires which touch the 29-degree Acme or worm thread at the pitch line, it has been common practice to use wires which come flush with the top of the threads. The National Screw Thread Commission now recommends use of "best wires" for 29-degree Acme threads, but makes no recommendations for 29-degree worm threads.

THREAD MEASUREMENTS, BEST WIRE—The "best wire" to use in measuring screw threads, as recommended by the Bureau of Standards, is one that touches the sides of the thread at or near the pitch diameter. This is because the resulting pitch diameter is least affected by an error in the included angle of the screw thread. This means that there is a "best wire" for each pitch of screw thread.

THREAD, WHITWORTH—The standard form of screw thread for Great Britain until the adoption of the Unified Screw Thread in 1948, known as the UN. The old thread was designed by Sir Joseph Whitworth and had a 55-degree angle with rounded tops and bottoms. It now has a 60-degree angle. It is a very strong thread and the rounded bottom is now part of the UN thread. See *Screw Threads, Unified.*

THREAD, WORM—A screw thread with a 29-degree included angle. It is deeper than the Acme thread, being 0.6866 of the pitch instead of 0.5 as with the Acme. It is used in connection with worm gears.

THREADING DIE HEADS, CHASERS FOR—Chasers are made both with the teeth radial and tangent to the blank being threaded. See *Die Chasers* and *Die Heads.*

THREE-SQUARE—A shop term for a three-cornered piece of steel, such as a triangular file.

THREE-WIRE METHOD OF MEASURING SCREW THREADS—See *Screw Threads, Measuring with Wires.*

THROUGH FEED—In centerless grinding where the work is fed continuously between the wheels parallel to the wheel spindles. This may refer to the grinding of long rods or to short pieces which are fed continuously end-to-end as though they were in one piece.

THROW—See *Crank Throw.*

THRURAY—See *Supersonic Thruray.*

THURY'S SWISS SCREW THREAD—See *Screw Threads, Thury's Watch.*

THRUST BEARING—Any bearing which resists thrust or end pressure. See *Bearing*.

THUMB NUT—A nut operated by thumb and and finger. See *Screw Heads*.

THUMB SCREW—A screw with a flattened or roughened head to be turned with thumb and finger. See *Screw Heads*.

TIERING—The stacking of material loaded on pallets or other work holding platforms. This stacking saves a large amount of floor space and is easily done with modern lift trucks used in shops and warehouses.

TIGHTENING PULLEY—A pulley which runs against the slack side of a belt to increase its contact with the driving and driven pulleys. Same as an idler.

TILT HAMMER—A power hammer with an arm or helve, which is raised by a cam or trip and let fall on the work. Is entirely out of date except in extreme cases, or on special work. See *Hammer, Power*.

TIN—A soft and malleable metal used largely as an alloy. Sp. gr. 7.298. Melts at 450 deg. F.

TIN BASE ALLOYS—Alloys in which tin is the principal metal used, as in the various babbitt and bearing alloys. See *Babbitt*.

TIN PLATE—Sheets of iron or steel, usually the latter, coated with pure tin, ordinarily used in making cans or other containers which are to be used for a long time. It comes in sheets 20 x 28 inches and thicknesses which approximate U. S. Standard gages from No. 28 to 25. Plate thickness is indicated by the number of X's and thicknesses of the tin coating by the number of A's. Sheets vary from 0.62 to 0.895 pounds per square foot, depending on the thickness of both the sheet and the tin coating.

TIN SHEETS—Thin sheet steel or iron coated with tin as a protection against rust. Also the operation of coating a surface with tin or solder, as in soldering. See *Solder*.

TIT—A small projection of almost any shape. Sometimes it results from a cutting tool not completing its job. In others it is an intentional projection to guide or hold a mating part. Sometimes called a "teat" or boss, the latter especially in larger sizes. In Great Britain it might be called a gudgeon.

TITANIUM—A metal found in ilmenite ore, which consists essentially of iron oxide and titanium oxide. It is plentiful in many parts of the country and Canada and seems likely to become one of our most valuable and commonly used alloys. On the basis of strength, its weight is less than either aluminum or stainless steel, some alloys developing a tensile strength of 190,000 pounds. Its corrosion resistance equals platinum and is better than either nickel or stainless steel. Its resistance to heat while retaining its strength makes it desirable for blades of gas turbines and similar uses. Its present high cost is expected to be materially reduced.

TOE DOG—In some shops, a dog or projection, such as used on planer tables to control the length of stroke of the table. In others it is a clamp which may exert presure downward and sideways at the same time, for holding work against stops.

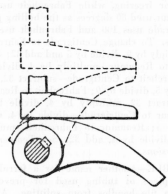

Toe and wiper, or lifter.

TOE AND WIPER MOTION—A device with a curved wiper in contact with a flat surface which is lifted to operate valves or other mechanisms. It was used largely on marine type vertical engines for operating the valve mechanism.

TOGGLE—A combination of levers which multiply the pressure end to secure greater force at the expense of greater movement. Many cutting pliers have jaws which work on a toggle. To calculate the advantage gained, divide the movement of the jaws into the movement at the point on the handles where pressure is applied. If the handle movement is 2 inches and the jaw movement only ⅛ inch, the power application is 16 to 1.

TOGGLE BOLT—A bolt with a lever in its head that can be pushed through a small hole in a wall. Then the lever falls at right angles and prevents the bolt being withdrawn. Used in fastening machinery or fixtures to a wall.

TOLERANCE—The difference between minimum limits. See under *Fits of Metal Parts.* Various classes of fits require different tolerances. The table gives standard tolerances for five kinds of fits. See table on page 469.

TOLERANCES AND ALLOWANCES—Basic Hole and Basic Shaft Systems: Choice between two systems. A cylindrical fit shall be specified in such a manner that it will be identified as belonging to either the basic hole system or the basic shaft system. The decision whether a fit shall be specified in the basic hole system or basic shaft system must be made after due consideration of a number of factors concerning the design of the product to which the part belongs and the methods by which the part is to be manufactured.

Tolerances and Allowances*

0.0001	0.0006	0.0025	**0.0100**
0.00015	0.0008	0.0030	0.0120
0.0002	**0.0010**	0.0040	0.0150
0.00025	0.0012	**0.0050**	**0.0200**
0.0003	0.0015	0.0060	0.0250
0.0004	**0.0020**	0.0080	**0.0300**
0.0005			

All dimensions are given in inches.
* The values indicated in heavy type are the preferred values.

TOLERANCE, BI-LATERAL—A method of stating the tolerance, or permissible variation, both above and below the basic size. Frequently called the "plus or minus tolerance." Probably more widely used than the uni-lateral tolerance, but can be more confusing unless thoroughly understood. Standard gages cannot be used because either mating part can be larger or smaller than basic. An upper limit shaft will not enter a lower limit hole unless the allowance or clearance is more than the total tolerance.

TOLERANCES, COMMERCIAL—Commercial tolerances vary with material made by different firms. Tolerances on drill rod and cold drawn seamless tubing are:

Drill Rod—Commercial tolerance on ground drill rod is plus or minus 0.0005 inch in practically all sizes up to 1 inch. On special order this tolerance can be about cut in half. On cold drawn drill rod the tolerance is generally plus or minus 0.001 inch. (Anchor Drawn Steel Company.)

Cold Drawn Seamless Tubing—Tolerances vary with the size of the tube and with the finish. On smaller tubes the O. D. tolerance is all plus and the I. D. all minus. Wall tolerance is given in percentages. This refers to round tubes. Greater tolerances are usually found in rectangular tubes.

TOLERANCES, FORGING—See *Forging.*

TOLERANCE, UNILATERAL—In the unilateral system, the tolerance of mating parts is plus for the holes and minus for the plugs or shafts. A standard plug gage will be a minimum for the hole and a standard ring gage a maximum for the shaft, except in force or shrink fits.

TOLERANCING—The setting of tolerances. The term is used in England more than in this country.

TONGS—Long handled pliers used by blacksmiths and in similar work, such as in dipping tools that have been heated into the quenching bath.

TONGS, CHAIN—A type of pipe wrench in which a chain around the pipe holds it in contact with sharp teeth on the wrench itself and grips the pipe firmly.

TONG HOLD—A projection left on a forging, outside the contour of the piece being made, by which it can be gripped by a pair of tongs.

TONGUE DRIVE—Applied to drills and reamers with a taper shank and a tongue or tang at the end which fits a slot in the machine spindle or an adapter. See *Drills and Reamers.*

TONGUES FOR T-SLOTS—See *T-Slots, Tongues for.*

TOOL ANGLES—These include tool-holder angle, shank angle, back-rake angle, side-rake angle, relief angle, side-relief angle, end-relief angle, clearance angle, side-cutting edge angle, edge-cutting angle, nose angle, working angles, setting angle, entering angle, true-rake angle, cutting angle, lip angle, and working relief angle. See *Single Point Tools* and their illustrations.

TOOL BIT—This usually refers to small pieces of tool steel or of carbide, used as the cutting points in lathe and similar tools. With tool steel or high speed steel, the bit is usually

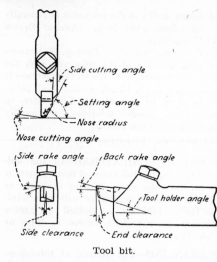

Tool bit.

square and is clamped in a holder which fits in the tool post of the machine. Carbide tips are usually brazed to the shanks of high speed steels. A later tendency is to use rods of carbide materials clamped in a holder, much as with high speed steel. These bits are frequently round and are held nearly vertically so as to cut on the end. By turning them slightly new grinding surfaces are presented, which obviates the necessity of frequent grindings. Square and triangular shapes are also used.

TOOL HOLDER—A sort of tool shank which supports small cutting tools, known as tool bits, and presents them to the work to be cut. Illus. page 473. See *Tool Bit.*

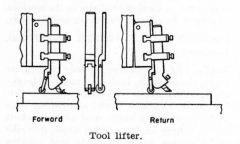

Forward　　　　Return

Tool lifter.

TOOL LIFTER—Device for lifting the tool in a planer, shaper or any reciprocating machine on the return stroke. They are either operated by mechanical connections or by air. They save the cutting edge of the tool from dragging on the work and impairing its keen-ness. The tool lifter shown has a roller, but this is not common practice.

TOOL MASTER—A tool used to locate and coordinate holes and fixed points in production tooling, for the purpose of effecting interchangeability of two or more production parts and eliminating additional layouts and set-ups in the manufacture of duplicate tools. (North American Aircraft Co.) Other aircraft companies use the following names: *Consolidated*—master gage or tooling sample; *Vultee*—master tool; *Douglas*—master plaster, pattern template, master tooling part, tooling master, tool master plaster, pattern and master plaster pattern; *Lockheed*—master tooling gage, master model and master model part; *Northrop*—master jig and master sample part; *Ryan*—tooling master and contour master.

TOOL POSTS—Devices for holding single point tools in a machine tool for cutting metal. The single screw tool post, with a rocker under the tool for adjusting the height of the tool point in a lathe, was the most common. Tool posts with a solid serrated base are used on small shapers and planers. A plate between the point of the screw and the cutting tool has advantages. Open-side tool posts have some advantages. On turret lathes or on engine lathes with a turret tool head, the four sided open tool post is most convenient. Planers and shapers use a strap-and-stud type of tool holder, with two straps and a serrated base on the clapper box, which relieves the cutting edge of the tool on the back stroke. Solid bases permit accurate setting of cutting angles. See pages 470, 471, 473.

TOOL SHANK—The body of a tool, which may have a cutting edge as part of the shank or have separate cutting tools clamped on to, or inserted in, the shank itself.

TOOL STEEL—A steel which contains from 0.5 to 1.3 per cent carbon and which can be hardened for use in cutting tools by proper heating and quenching. The carbon content was formerly given in "points' or decimals of the percentage. This would make the carbon read 50 to 130 points.

TOOLS, BORING—Tools designed especially for boring holes.

TOOLS, DIAMOND—Pieces of bort, which are very hard but are not gem diamonds, are set in a steel holder and used for special turning and boring. They are used largely in

Tolerances of Holes for Various Classes of Fits

Class	Nominal Diameters	Up to ½″	9/16″–1″	1 1/16″–2″	2 1/16″–3″	3 1/16″–4″	4 1/16″–5″
		Tolerances in Standard Holes*					
A	High Limit.....	0.0002	0.0005	0.0007	0.0010	0.0010	0.0010
	Low Limit.....	0.0002	0.0002	0.0002	0.0005	0.0005	0.0005
	Tolerance......	0.0004	0.0007	0.0009	0.0015	0.0015	0.0015
B	High Limit.....	0.0005	0.0007	0.0010	0.0012	0.0015	0.0017
	Low Limit.....	0.0005	0.0005	0.0005	0.0007	0.0007	0.0007
	Tolerance......	0.0010	0.0012	0.0015	0.0019	0.0022	0.0024
		Allowances for Forced Fits					
F	High Limit.....	0.0010	0.0020	0.0040	0.0060	0.0080	0.0100
	Low Limit.....	0.0005	0.0015	0.0030	0.0045	0.0060	0.0080
	Tolerance......	0.0005	0.0005	0.0010	0.0015	0.0020	0.0020
		Allowances for Driving Fits					
D	High Limit.....	0.0005	0.0010	0.0015	0.0025	0.0030	0.0035
	Low Limit.....	0.0002	0.0007	0.0010	0.0015	0.0020	0.0025
	Tolerance......	0.0003	0.0003	0.0005	0.0010	0.0010	0.0010
		Allowances for Push Fits					
P	High Limit.....	0.0002	0.0002	0.0002	0.0005	0.0005	0.0005
	Low Limit.....	0.0007	0.0007	0.0007	0.0010	0.0010	0.0010
	Tolerance......	0.0005	0.0005	0.0005	0.0005	0.0005	0.0005
		Allowances for Running Fits†					
X	High Limit.....	0.0010	0.0012	0.0017	0.0020	0.0025	0.0030
	Low Limit.....	0.0020	0.0027	0.0035	0.0042	0.0050	0.0057
	Tolerance......	0.0010	0.0015	0.0018	0.0022	0.0025	0.0027
Y	High Limit.....	0.0007	0.0010	0.0012	0.0015	0.0020	0.0022
	Low Limit.....	0.0012	0.0020	0.0025	0.0030	0.0035	0.0040
	Tolerance......	0.0005	0.0010	0.0013	0.0015	0.0015	0.0018
Z	High Limit.....	0.0005	0.0007	0.0007	0.0010	0.0010	0.0012
	Low Limit.....	0.0007	0.0012	0.0015	0.0020	0.0022	0.0025
	Tolerance......	0.0002	0.0005	0.0008	0.0010	0.0012	0.0013

Diamonds for Dressing Abrasive Wheels

Wheel Diameter and Face	Average Carat Weight	Wheel Diameter and Face	Average Carat Weight
6 x ½ in.	0.300	18 x 2 in.	1.750
8 x 1 ″	0.600	20 x 2 ″	2.000
10 x 1 ″	0.750	24 x 2 ″	2.250
12 x 1 ″	1.000	24 x 3 ″	2.500
14 x 1½ ″	1.250	24 x 4 ″	3.000
18 x 1½ ″	1.500	26 x 4 ″	3.500

turning hard rubber and plastics, and in final dressing of abrasive wheels. The sizes of diamonds to be used are important. See *Diamonds*.

TOOLS, FORGED—Tools for the lathes or other machine tools which have the cutting points forged from the shank. This was common practice when only carbon steel tools were used and in the beginning of high speed tools. Now the use of tool holders and bits of harder material is general practice. See *Tool Bit*.

TOOLS, SINGLE-POINT — See *Single-Point Tools.*

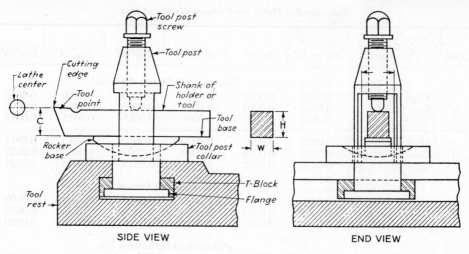

SIDE VIEW　　　　　　　　　　　　　END VIEW

Single-screw tool post with rocker base.

TOOLS, TURNING—Tools used in lathes of various kinds of turning the outside of bars or other work. The various part names have been standardized, as shown on page 473.

TOOTHED WHEELS—See *Gearing.*

TORCH CUTTING—See *Flame Cutting.*

TOREEFY—A little used term for driving off moisture by excessive heat.

TORQUE—A force which tends to cause torsion or to produce rotary motion. Fluid flywheels now common on automobiles are torque converters, as they convert torque, or twisting, at one speed to turning motion at other speeds.

TORQUE CONVERTER—A device, usually hydraulic, for applying power developed by a motor to the driven member at varying speeds. A variable speed device, but not merely a

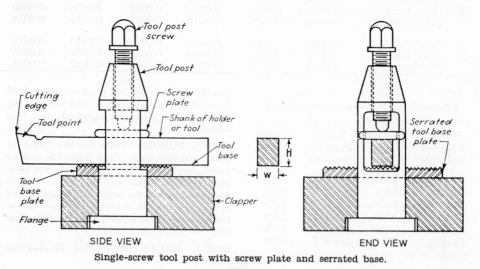

SIDE VIEW　　　　　　　　　　　　　END VIEW

Single-screw tool post with screw plate and serrated base.

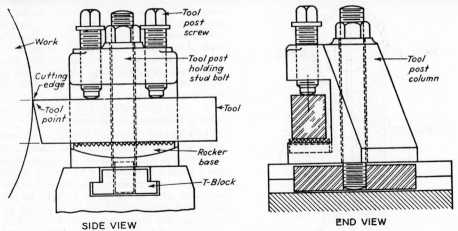

Open-side tool post with serrated rocker base.

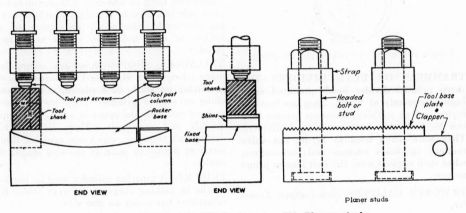

(L) Four-way open-side tool post.   (R) Planer studs.

speed reducer. A simple form of torque converter is shown. This is frequently called a "fluid clutch." See illustration on page 472.

TORSION—Twisting of any material places it in torsion. Most metals will stand a certain amount of torsion and return to their original shape. This quality is used in some instruments and devices, such as door closing springs.

TOTE BOX—Any box or pan used to carry, or tote, parts from one department to another. They are made in various sizes and shapes. When made with straight sides they can be stacked easily, especially when provided with

pins which locate them and insure proper stacking.

TRACTORS, SHOP—Power driven machines for moving material. Usually powered by either electric or gasoline motors. Nicknamed bugs, jitneys, trucks or locomotives. They sometimes tow wheeled trucks, or they may carry flat trays or pallets on forks which project in front of the machine.

TRAIN OF GEARS—See *Gear Train*.

TRAIN OF ROLLS—In rolling mill practice, any series of rolls through which rails or bar or sheet steel pass to be given the desired form or shape.

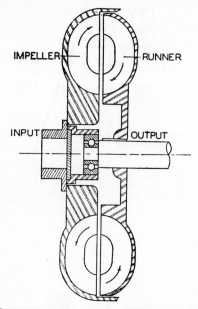

Torque converter—traction-type coupling.

TRAMMELS, OR BEAM DIVIDERS—Two sharp pointed divider heads mounted on a beam, frequently of wood. They are used in laying out, or scribing, distances greater than can be had with ordinary hinged dividers. They were much used in laying out valve motions on steam engines and locomotives, when such engines were the best known prime movers.

TRANSFER CALIPERS—See *Caliper, Transfer.*

TRANSITION FITS—See under *Fits, Various Types and Systems.*

TRANSVERSE—The same as crosswise. Opposite to lengthwise or longitudinal.

TRAPEZOID—A four-sided figure in which two of the sides are parallel to each other.

TRAVEL—The amount of motion, or length of stroke, of a reciprocating body, such as a shaper ram. The same term can be used in connection with a rotating motion which travels less than a full revolution, such as "a 90-degree travel."

TREPANNING—Boring or cutting holes by removing the center or core in one piece. The tool is similar to the hollow mill used in screw machine and similar work. A typical trepan-ning tool is the edge hole saw shown on page 347. While generally used on comparatively short holes, such as in boring the ends of locomotive connecting rods, the method has been used in removing the core from reinforcing rings for large artillery guns in which the core was several feet in length. In this case the teeth are on the end of a long tube, forcibly supplied with coolant. The work is supported on the outside.

TREPANNING TOOL—A tool which cuts holes without destroying all the material in the center, as with a drilling. A common form has a guide which enters a previously drilled small hole, and cutters of the large diameter, removing what resembles a washer. In railroad work the ends of connecting rods are bored in this way, saving all the metal removed except for the pilot hole. There is also a type of trepanning tool which is practically a tube with teeth on one end. This requires no pilot hole but must be rigidly held while starting the work. Similar in appearance to a hollow or edge hole saw, except made for metal.

TRIANGLES, SHOP—These are accurately made triangles of 30, 45 and 60 degrees used in setting up work on a planer, milling machine or surface grinder. They are of close grained cast iron and assist in setting work up quickly and accurately. They differ from draftsman's triangles, which are made of thin metal or plastic to assist in drawing standard angles.

TRIBLET—A tapering cylinder used by blacksmiths in making rings of different sizes. It sometimes has a slot on one side.

TRIGGER STOP—A design of stop finger or lever which moves out of the way after it has performed its duty. Not a fixed stop.

TRIGONOMETRY—A branch of mathematics which deals with the relation between sides and angles of triangles and their application to other figures in which triangles are involved, as in polygons with varying numbers of sides. It is used in laying out angular work, in spacing holes accurately and in similar work. One common application is in connection with the *sine bar*, which is now commonly used by tool makers and others. See *Sine Bar, Angle Constants,* and *Shop Trigonometry.*

TRIMMING ROUND SHELLS—Ends of drawn shells are trimmed either by flange trim or pinch trim methods. See *Punch Press Dies, Edge Trimming.*

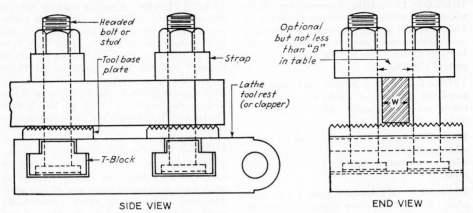

SIDE VIEW   END VIEW

Strap and stud clamp type of tool post with serrated base.

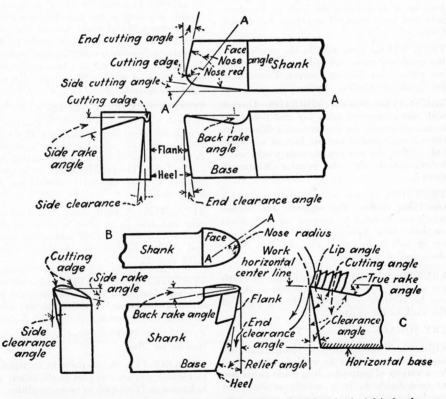

Turning tools: (A) A ground, straight cutting-edge, right-hand, straight-shank, single-point tool, with nomenclature. (B) A forged and ground, curved cutting-edge, right-hand, straight-shank, single-point tool, with nomenclature. (C) Section through A-A of Figs. A and B.

473

TRIPLE-ACTION DIE—A punch press die in which three different movements are obtained. This is usually done by having the part which moves first contact another movable part and force its action. This in turn actuates a third part of the die.

TRIPOLI—A white, porous rock which is powdered and used as a mild abrasive in polishing the softer metals. Also called rottenstone.

TRIPPER—Any device which trips a lever or other part to release or make possible some other movement, as the trip lever on a punch press.

TROLL PLATE—Another name for a scroll plate, as used in some types of universal chucks. It has spiral grooves or projections which mesh into corresponding or mating projections or grooves on the back of the chuck jaws, and move them all in unison. See *Chuck, Universal.*

TRUE RAKE—True rake is the resultant of the combined axial and radial rakes of a miling cutter. See *Milling Cutters, Terms Used for Teeth and Cutting Angles.*

TRUNCATED SCREW THREADS—Threads with metal removed from top and bottom to insure clearance. In the truncated Whitworth threads the rounded top and bottom was omitted so that the flat top threads would enter holes tapped with the regular Whitworth thread.

TRUNNION—A pin or projection on which something moves. The supports for cannon which are elevated by turning on projections on their sides. Sometimes used to describe a pin or shaft in the end of a wood rollar. Sometimes called a gudgeon.

TRUNNION FIXTURE—Any fixture in which the work is supported on trunnions so that it can be rotated to present different parts of the work to the machine.

TRY SQUARE—See *Square, Try.*

TUBING, MECHANICAL — Mechanical tubing is either seamless or welded tubing used for a variety of purposes. It is made either hot or cold finished. It is usually available in standard analyses, the maximum carbon content being about 0.25 per cent. Permissible variations in diameter and wall thickness of cold finish round tubing are shown on next page.

TUKON TESTER—A testing machine using a diamond point which makes very small indentations in the piece being tested owing to the light pressure used. It is made for both light load testing, from 10 grams, known as "micro-testing," and for heavy loads up to 50,000 grams, known as "macro-testing." It is the same type machine as the well known Rockwell testing machine. Built by the Wilson Mechanical Instrument Co. See also *Knoop Indenter.*

TUMBLE JIG—See *Jig, Tumble.*

TUMBLER OR TUMBLING BARREL—A barrel which rotates and throws castings or other work together to remove scale and sand. Also used for burring the edges of sheet metal work. Frequently the shaft runs through the barrels at an angle which gives an end motion in addition to rotary. Various abrasives and liquids are used in the barrels depending on the kind and size of work. Speeds vary greatly with the work and the result desired. When properly engineered, tumbling operations can appreciably reduce the cost of manufacture in many lines of work. These are also called rumbling barrels.

TUMBLER GEAR—A gear which can be put in mesh with either of two or more gears in a gear train. Used largely in changing the ratio between the two sets of gears or in reversing the motion, as in screw thread cutting in an engine lathe. The tumbler gears are frequently concealed, only the lever controlling them being visible.

TUNGSTEN—A hard metal found in other ores and used as an alloy in many steels. It is also used for electrical contacts in ignition and similar devices. Sp. gr. 19.6. Melts at 6,100 deg. F.

TUNGSTEN-ARGON WELD — A method of welding aluminum, using a tungsten arc in an argon atmosphere. It requires no flux and no cleaning of the weld.

TUNGSTEN STEELS—Steels containing tungsten as an alloy.

TUNKING FIT—When parts fit so tightly as to require tapping one part or the other. This is known as "tunking" in some localities.

TURBO-HEARTH STEEL—See *Steel, Turbo-Hearth.*

TURKS HEAD—A trade name for an adjustable draw plate used in drawing wires or rods

Mechanical Tubing

Group	Size O.D., in.	Permissible Variation from:					
		Outside Diam. in.		Inside Diam., in.		Wall Thickness, %	
		Over	Under	Over	Under	Over	Under
1	⅜ to ½ excl. (a) (b)	0.004	0				
2	½ to 1½ excel. (a) (b) (c)	0.005	0	0	0.005	10	10
3	1½ to 3½ excl. (a) (b) (c)	0.010	0	0	0.010	10	10
4	3½ to 5½ excl. (a) (b) (c)	0.015	0	0.005	0.015	10	10
5	5½ to 8 excl (c) when wall is less than 5% of O.D.	0.030	0.030	0.035	0.035	10	10
6	5½ to 8 excl. when wall is from 5% to 7.5% of O.D.	0.020	0.020	0.025	0.025	10	10
7	5½ to 8 excl. (a) when wall is over 7.5% of O.D.	0.030	0	0.015	0.030	10	10
8	8 to 10¾ incl. (c) when wall is less than 5% of O.D.	0.045	0.045	0.050	0.050	10	10
9	8 to 10¾ incl. when wall is from 5% to 7.5% of O.D.	0.035	0.035	0.040	0.040	10	10
10	8 to 10¾ incl. (a) when wall is over 7.5% of O.D.	0.045	0	0.015	0.040	10	10

of shapes other than round. The draw plates include tool steel rollers which work like a rolling mill on a small scale. Four rolls are used, two in a horizontal position and two vertical. All or part of the rolls may have adjusting screws.

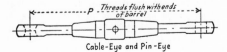
Cable-Eye and Pin-Eye

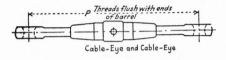
Cable-Eye and Cable-Eye

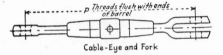
Cable-Eye and Fork

Turnbuckles.

TURNBUCKLE—A special form of threaded piece, or nut, used in tightening a rod or bar between two points. It is frequently an open link with a thread in each end, one right and the other left handed. It may have a thread in only one end, the other part of the rod turning but having no shortening movement. A common method of drawing two parts together.

TURN-MILLING—A name denoting the finishing of round surfaces by milling instead of turning. This is done by revolving the work under or against milling cutters instead of against single point tools. Either end milling cutters or peripheral toothed cutters may be used.

TURRET LATHE—Any lathe in which several tools are held in a turret, which may be horizontal or vertical. Small turret lathes are frequently called screw machines. Some are made with automatic feeds and so become semi-automatic lathes. See *Lathe, Turret*.

TWEEZERS—Small pliers in which the gripping points are pressed together by the thumb and finger direct instead of the jaws being hinged as in larger pliers operated by pressure of hand and fingers.

TWELVE-PITCH SCREW THREADS—A series of screw threads of 12 threads per inch, from ½ inch to 6 inches in diameter. Largely used in boiler practice from 1 to 1¾ inches in the retapping of stud holes in increments of 1/16 inch. Also used in machine construction for thin walled nuts and sleeves. See *Screw Threads*.

TWO-WIRE METHOD OF MEASURING SCREW THREADS—See *Screw Threads, Measuring with Wires*.

TYPE METAL—A lead, antimony and tin alloy used in printing type. It expands in cooling and fills the type mold. It is also used to hold bars in cored holes in castings and so save machine fits. A common mixture is 5 parts lead, 2 parts antimony and 1 part tin.

TUYERE—A grate or nozzle for directing the blast of air from the fan or blower in a forge. The coal or charcoal is placed over the tuyere so the fire will be fanned by the blast.

U

U. S. S. THREAD—Name formerly used for what is now the American National Standard screw thread. See *Screw Thread, American National*.

U-BOLT—A rod bent into a U shape and threaded on both ends. The ends either go through a flat plate or into some part of a machine, being held by nuts screwed on each threaded end of the bolt. See *Bolts*.

ULTRASONIC PROCESS OF METAL RE-MOVAL—This does not use electric current directly. The cutting or grinding tool is vibrated from 16,000 to 30,000 cycles per second through not more than a few thousandths of an inch. An abrasive, usually 280 grit boron, is carried in water to the tool and the work. Stresses are low. There is no local heating or cracking, pitting or coloring of the work.

UNBALANCED—Either a lever whose support is not in the center, or a rotating body in which the weight is not equally distributed around its axis. With the lever, the heavy end will go down, and with the rotating body, the heavy side will tend to fly away from the center and cause vibration.

UNDERCUT—Any surface cut below the normal surface. In the case of threaded parts, to undercut frequently allows the die to run over into the undercut and leave a full thread the full length of the large portion. Sometimes referred to as a "neck," as in reamers and other tools.

UNDULATED—A surface which is wavy instead of flat. Not generally used to describe corrugations but for unintentional waves in the surface.

UNGEAR—A seldom used term for disengaging gears.

UNGULA—A section of any round body, such as a cone, which is cut by a line at an angle with its base.

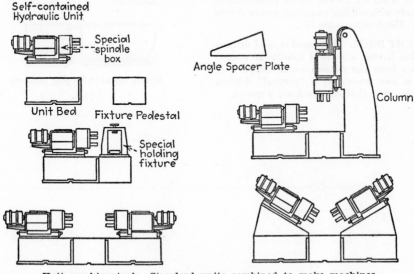

Unit machine tools. Standard units combined to make machines for special purposes.

UNIFIED SCREW THREAD — See *Screw Threads, Unified.*

UNILATERAL TOLERANCE—See *Tolerance, Unilateral.*

UNION—A term used in many kinds of piping for a type of connection between two pieces of pipe, usually in a straight line. It differs from a nipple in that it can be uncoupled without disturbing the pipe line, by loosening the nut on the union and separating the two halves.

UNIT ASSEMBLY—A self contained assembly which is considered as a single unit for replacement. It need not be made up of interchangeable parts, but the unit must interchange with a similar unit on the machine for which it is made. Automobile carburetors or fuel pumps may be interchanged on many cars but their parts may not interchange. Same as interchange assembly.

UNIT MACHINE TOOLS — Machine tools made up from unit, power driven heads, mounted on bases designed for the special work they are to perform. Those shown are made up from self-contained drilling heads, usually with several spindles, mounted on beds to suit the work to be done. With standard bases, columns and other parts, a great variety of arrangements can be made. While only drilling heads are shown, similar combinations are made with milling and other power driven heads. Illustration page 477.

UPRIGHT DRILL—The usual type of drilling machine having a vertical spindle at a fixed distance from the column which supports it. This is now known as a "vertical" drilling machine. See *Drilling Machine, Vertical.*

UPSET—To enlarge a rod or blank by end pressure, forcing the metal to expand sideways. Bolt heads are formed by upsetting the end into a die which gives it the desired shape. This is usually done hot.

UPSET FORGINGS — Forgings which are made by upsetting, or enlarging, the end of bar stock. This is now common practice in machine forging. See *Forgings, Upset.*

UPSIDE-DOWN DRILLING — See *Drilling, Upside-Down.*

UREA RESINS—As with most of the synthetic plastics, urea resins start with coal, air and water. Air and water are combined to make ammonia and carbon dioxide is added to make urea. Carbon monoxide, water and hydrogen make menthanol, which is changed to formaldehyde. Formaldehyde and urea make the resin used in molding.

Simple upset between flat dies

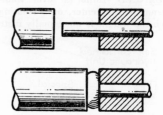

Simple upset in forging machine
Upset.

V

V's—Guiding strips or ways, raised above a machine bed to guide movable parts of the machine.

V-BELT—See *Belt, V.*

V-BLOCKS—Blocks containing one or more V-shaped openings for holding round bars or other similar objects. The block shown also will hold a ball in the center of the Vs, as shown by dotted lines. The dowel pins and holes permit other holding blocks to be located accurately.

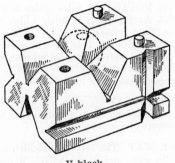

V-block.

V GAGES—See *Gage, V.*

V-HOOK—A term used in connection with an old type of valve motion used on either stationary or locomotive steam engines. Sometimes known as a "gab" hook. It was used to reverse the motion of the engine.

V-THREAD—See *Screw Threads, V.*

VACUUM—Absence of pressure, or reduced pressure, as in the nozzle of a vacuum cleaner. Pumps which lift water withdraw part of the air pressure from the top of the water and allow the pressure of the atmosphere, 14.7 pounds at sea level, to force the water up into the pipe and pump. This air pressure is approximately equal to a column of water 34 feet high, which is the maximum *lift* that can be obtained by vacuum. In practice, the lift is less than this, as there is no perfect vacuum.

VACUUM CHUCK—See *Chuck, Vacuum.*

VACUUM FORMING—A comparatively new method of forming by exhausting the air in the cavity of a die and drawing the material down into it. It is naturally confined to plastics and similar materials, but has been found very satisfactory in forming many intricate shapes.

VACUUM PUMP—See *Pump, Vacuum.*

VALVE—Any device which controls the flow or air, gas, water, steam or other liquid or gaseous substance. It may either allow entrance to a chamber or cylinder, or control the flow from it. Common valve types are: globe, gate, pop or safety, piston, flap, ball, rotary, and poppet, sometimes called mushroom valves, from their shape. Valves are usually named for the type of work they perform. Cocks, frequently called "plug cocks," are really rotary valves. The British also use this terms for electronic tubes, which control the flow of radio waves.

VALVE, BALL— A valve in which a ball forms the seating member, as in a ball-check valve.

VALVE, BY-PASS—A valve which controls passage of gas, water or steam around the regular control valve. A by-pass allows flow in other than regular channels.

VALVE, CHECK—A valve which permits the flow of liquid or gas in one direction only.

VALVE, GATE—A valve in which the seat slides across the opening through the valve, like a gate. When the valve is open, it gives a straight passage of the water or other liquid through the valve. The valve usually has a wedging action which forces the seat against the valve body surrounding the openings.

VALVE, GLOBE—A valve having a globular body. The passage enters one end, follows the rounded bottom of the body, goes up through a partition in line with the two ends and out at the other end. The valve seat is horizontal so that the fluid turns two right angles in passing from one end to the other. In the gate valve it passes straight through the valve. See *Valve, Gate.*

VALVE, GRIDIRON—A valve in which the gas or fluid passes through numerous openings, instead of only one, as in the slide valve. It enables the use of a narrower opening, but there must be more of them to give the same area for passage. In steam engines, the gridiron valve was used to enable the valves to be placed cross-wise of the cylinder.

VALVE MOTIONS—Mechanisms which actuate valves controlling admission of steam, air or gas into motors of any kind. In both steam locomotives and stationary engines some of the valve motions were of intricate design. The most common, however, were the old link motion, the Wahlschaerts, and a few others for locomotives. In stationary engines, the link motion and the Corliss valve motion were commonly used. With internal combustion engines, projections on a cam shaft actuate poppet valves in much the same way in all engines, although the location of the cam shaft varies.

VALVE, NEEDLE—A valve with a needle pointed spindle or stem, for accurate control of such liquids as gasoline or fuel oil, as in diesel engine injection units. The point may be a straight cone or a carefully designed curve.

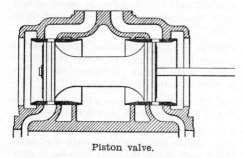

Piston valve.

VALVE, PISTON—Really, a slide valve. Although it is in the form of a piston it slides back and forth and controls the ingress and exhaust of steam in the same way as a slide valve, with its flat seat. A piston valve is more easily balanced against the pressure of the steam between the valve and the seat and gained favor for high pressure steam on that account. But many balanced flat slide valves have been used.

VALVE, POP—Another name for a safety valve. Any valve which "pops" open to relieve pressure.

VALVE, POPPET — A round valve with a large head and a guiding stem, as in nearly all internal combustion engines. The head is surfaced to make a tight seat when it is closed. Steam engines also have been built with valves of this type, but the slide or piston type of valve has been more commonly used.

VALVE, REDUCING—A valve which automatically maintains a lower pressure in the receiving chamber or boiler. This is sometimes done with a spring loaded valve or by a special piston valve, with the small diameter representing the higher pressure and the large diameter the desired lower pressure. The lower pressure on the larger diameter tries to close the valve when the secondary pressure rises.

VALVE, ROTARY—A valve which is a rotating disk having ports through which steam, gas or fluid passes into the ports which lead to the cylinder. It is sometimes confused with a sleeve valve, some of which turn to some extent around a cylinder barrel to bring the proper openings in line. See *Valve, Sleeve.*

VALVE, SAFETY—A valve on any pressure carrying container which will open and relieve the pressure at a safe point.

VALVE SEAT—The surface on which a valve rests. In slide and piston valves, it contains ports through which steam, gas or air goes to the cylinder. In most valves, the passages are closed when the valve rests on the seat.

VALVE, SLEEVE—A valve in the form of a sleeve which moves lengthwise on the inside or outside of a cylinder and admits steam or gas through openings, or ports, when they are in proper position. In some cases, the piston moves inside the inner sleeve, where two are employed, as in the Knight type of internal combustion engine.

VALVE, SLIDE—A type of valve largely used in steam engines and early locomotives, and to some extent in air-brake mechanisms and other applications. It has a flat sliding surface in contact with the valve seat of the steam chest, as shown. As it moves back and forth it admits steam to the cylinder ports at the end of the valve, while the exhaust steam flows into the cavity in the center and out the exhaust stack.

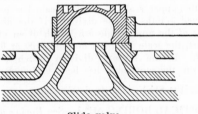

Slide valve.

VALVE, SNIFTING—A relief valve attached to the steam chest and constructed so as to admit air when the engine is running with the throttle closed. Also called *Drifting Valve*.

VANADIUM — A metal used largely as an alloy. It refines the grain of steel and was originally used largely as a cleanser. Sp. gr. 6.02. Melts at 3,236 deg. F.

VANADIUM STEEL—Steel in which vanadium is used as an alloy.

VAPOR—The term is usually applied to any substance lighter than air, as gases arising from gasoline, alcohol or other liquids. Many vapors are inflammable if not explosive.

VAPOR BLAST—See *Liquid Honing*.

VAPORIZER—A device which breaks liquids into fine sprays, which may not always be vapors in the exact sense of the term. Used in spraying perfumery, water, paints or fire extinguishing materials.

VARIABLE SPEED CONTROLS — Devices for varying speed ratios between the driving and driven members of any mechanism. They employ belting, friction devices and hydraulic mechanisms.

VARIABLE SPEED DRIVES — Methods of securing changes of speed without use of a step pulley, and usually giving almost any small increment of change instead of the fixed variations of the step pulley. One of the first methods was the disk friction drive, where a leather faced driven pulley moved across the face of a large driving disk. With the small pulley in the center no motion takes place but there is an ever increasing speed as the small wheel moves toward the large diameter of the driving disk. Moved in the other direction the variation is reversed. Early milling machines used this for feeding the table.

Another early device was the Evans drive, consisting of two long tapered pulleys or drums on parallel shafts, with an endless belt pinched between the two drums. Moving the belt along the pulleys varied the speed gradually as it changed the diameters of the driving and driven pulleys. The Reeves friction pulleys have been and are widely used. Here the pulleys are made in halves with conical faces. The belt has cross cleats which bear at the ends and contact varying diameters as the pulleys are moved with relation to each other. Variable speed motors make many other methods unnecessary. See *Pulley, Variable Speed* and *Evans Drive*.

VARIABLE SPEED GEARS—Mechanisms for varying the speed of driven parts. Some vary the speed by definite steps, as with gearing; others by continuous variations. Both friction and hydraulic devices are employed.

VARIABLE SPEED PULLEYS—See *Pulley, Variable Speed*.

VARI-PITCH SHEAVES—Sheaves or pulleys for V-shaped belts which can be moved endwise on a shaft to permit the belt to contact different diameters. This puts the contact

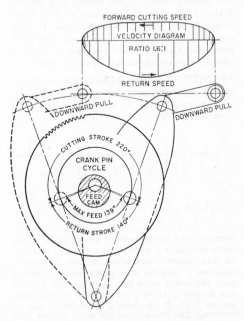

Power cam diagram showing velocity on cut and return speeds.

surfaces on different diameters and gives the effect of using pulleys of different diameters.

VELOCITY DIAGRAM—A diagram used to show variations in the velocity of moving parts such as the ram of a shaper. The variation is to secure a more rapid travel on the return or non-cutting stroke, and is obtained by various devices. The device shown is used by the Cincinnati Shaper Co. and gives a return speed 1.6 times as fast as the cutting stroke. Eccentric gears are used in some mechanisms to secure variations in speed. Illustration page 481.

VENT—An opening made to permit escape of steam, gas or air, frequently to prevent accumulation of too much pressure. Small holes are made in sand molds to permit escape of gases when the hot metal is poured into the mold. When the vent is mechanically controlled it becomes a safety valve.

VERGE—The spindle of the balance wheel of a watch or other timepiece.

VERMICULITE—A mineral weighing but 6 to 8 pounds per cubic foot after it has been exposed to heat and expanded. Its melting point is about 2,500 deg. F. Good for fire-proofing and sound-proofing. Used mostly as a plaster. Makes a strong wall but when used as floors wears better with a concrete top. Is strip mined in Colorado, Georgia, Tennessee, Wyoming, the Carolinas and elsewhere. Used in plaster, it costs about the same as sand.

VERNIER—A method of measurement by dividing known distances or spaces. It is credited to Pierre Vernier in about 1630. The usual method is to have 10 parts on one scale equal

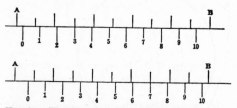

Vernier. The lower scale of 10 divisions is the same length as 9 divisions of the upper scale. In the upper illustration where division 3 matches a line on the upper scale, it shows that the lower scale has been moved 3/10 of one division. In the lower scale it has been moved 7/10. It provides a convenient way of securing fine measurements with marks that are easily read.

9 parts on the other, or upper scale, as shown in the two examples. When the third division of the lower scale matches the same division of the upper scale, the lower scale has been moved 3/10ths of one division. If the divisions of the upper scale are 1/10th of an inch apart, the scale has been moved 3/100 or 0.03 inch. If the seventh division matches, as shown, the movement has been 0.07 inch.

VERSED SINE—See *Angle Constants.*

VERTICAL BORING MILL—See *Boring and Turning Mill.*

VIBRATE—To move back and forth, like a clock pendulum, or a piece of spring steel held at one end and struck at the other end.

VIBRATOOL—An electric vibrator carrying a small, sharp pointed tool, used by engravers in engraving metals of various kinds. It cuts by vibration contact rather than by rotation.

VICKERS DIAMOND PYRAMID HARDNESS TEST—This is similar to the Brinell test, except that it uses a diamond, cut and polished to the shape of a square based diamond. This gives a square impression which can be easily read across the corners. The numbers compare with Brinell up to about 300, after which the Brinell reading falls below the Vickers, due to the flattening of the steel ball used.

VIEWING—British term for inspection. The inspection department is known as the viewing room.

VINILYTE RESINS—Used in plastics in a variety of forms and for many purposes. Resist acids and alkalis. Made under many trade names.

VISCOSITY—The internal friction of an oil or other liquid. It is measured in the U. S. by Saybolt Universal seconds. This is the number of seconds taken for 60 milli-liters of oil to flow through the Saybolt viscometer at 100 to 130 deg. F. for lighter oils and at 210 deg. F. for heavy oils. Sixty milli-liters is a trifle less than two ounces.

VISE—A device for clamping and holding work of any kind. They vary from small pin vises to be held in the hand to heavy bench vises for chipping. Special vises are made for use on machine tools of various kinds.

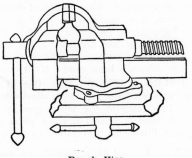

Bench Vise.

VISE, ANGLE—A work holding device in which the work can be tilted to any desired angle. Many tilt in one direction only. Some have a swivel base which permits the vise and its work to be turned to the desired angle.

VISE, DRILL—A vise for use in drilling, usually on a drilling machine table.

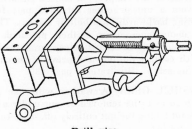

Drill vise.

VISE, HAND—A small vise to be held in the hand for small work that cannot be held conveniently in the hand itself.

VISE, JIG—A drilling vise with arms or projections which carry drill bushings so that duplicate pieces can be made without special jigs for them.

VISE, PIN—A small hand vise with a hole through the handle, for holding small wire rods firmly while they are being worked on.

Pin vise.

VISE, SWIVEL BASE—A work holding vise mounted on a base on which the work can be turned to any desired angle. Swivel bases are graduated in degrees for accurate work. By providing an adjusting screw with an indexing head, precise movements of the work can be secured.

VISE, UNIVERSAL—A vise with a swiveling base and graduated adjustments for various angles. Largely used by tool makers and in experimental work, in drilling and milling.

VITALLIUM—A high temperature alloy composed largely of cobalt and chromium. Devised for use in gas turbine blades and similar places.

VITRIFIED GRINDING WHEELS—Abrasive wheels in which the abrasive or cutting material is held in a vitrified bond. Such a bond is used for the majority of grinding wheels, as it is not affected by acids, oils, water or temperature.

VITRIOL—A name sometimes given to sulphuric acid.

VIXEN FILE—See *File, Vixen.*

VOLATILE—Easily dissipated. Many liquids, such as gasoline, evaporate rapidly if exposed to air and are said to be volatile.

VOLT—The unit of electrical pressure. This is based on the former theory that the flow of electricity could be compared to the flow of water in pipes. Although later theories indicate this is not a correct comparison, it serves to convey the idea and is accepted in most circles.

VOLT-METER—A device for measuring the electrical pressure being transmitted.

VOLUTE SPRING—The same as a spiral or clock spring. See *Spring, Volute.*

VULCANITE GRINDING WHEELS—Abrasive grinding wheels in which the bonding material holding the grains together resembles hard rubber.

VULCANIZED FIBER—Wood pulp, cloth or paper impregnated with a vulcanizing medium and vulcanized by heat. It is made in many forms.

VULCANIZED RUBBER — Latex, or crude rubber, mixed with a small amount of sulphur and heated to about 280 deg. F.

W

WABBLE—Also spelled wobble. A combination of rotary and endwise motions. A disk which has an endwise motion when revolved on a shaft is said to wabble. A wabble plate engine uses a disk of this kind instead of a crank. These have been tried for many years in various forms but few or none are in practical use. A later type is known as a "cam" engine, as they use a disk having a cam action instead of the wabble plate. See *Swash Plate*.

WALKING BEAM—A beam or lever, pivoted at or near the center, for transmitting motion by rods at each end. They were largely used by paddle wheel steamboats and other mechanisms.

WALL—The material in a tube or the enclosing material in any hollow piece. The piston of an engine travels against the cylinder "wall." The thickness of metal in a pipe is the "wall thickness."

WALL DRILL—A drilling machine fastened to a wall. Some were made with a swinging arm similar to the radial type. Practically obsolete now.

WALL PLANER—A planer with a tool head traveling on ways fastened to a wall. They have not been used for many years and were really shapers rather than planers. The work was fastened to the floor.

WALLOWER—A name sometimes given to a gear made with pins between two flanges or disks, or a lantern gear wheel.

WANDER—A term used in connection with drills and other cutting tools which cut out of line with the spindle. The drill point may strike small projections on the surface of the metal and be forced to wander out of line.

WARDING FILE—See under *File Names*.

WARP—To change shape from the original or intended shape. Metal which has been heated and cooled suddenly may "warp" out of shape. Cold rolled steel "warps" when the hard outer skin is removed from only one side of a bar.

WASHBURN & MOEN GAGE—One of the older gages used for measuring diameters of wires. This company was taken over by the Amercan Steel & Wire Co. many years ago. See *Gage, Wire*.

WASHER—A thin piece, usually of metal, circular in shape, to go over a bolt and between the nut and the surface beneath it. This is a plain washer. There are also many types of lock washers designed to prevent the nut from becoming loose when subjected to vibration.

WASHER CUTTER—A tool for cutting flat rings or annular disks of leather, rubber or other material for pipe and other similar joints.

WASHER, LOCK—A washer which acts to prevent a nut or other threaded part from turning backwards on a bolt or screw. There are many types, many of them patented, but most depend on sharp edges or serrations which contact the nut and prevent movement on the screw. Illustrations page 485.

WASHER, OPEN—A washer with one side open so as to be removed or put under a nut without taking the nut entirely off. Also called a C washer.

WASHER, SLIP—A washer with an opening large enough to slip the washer over a bolt, and under the bolt head. Also called a C washer because of its resemblance to the letter C. They do not afford nearly as good a bearing for the nut as a solid washer but save time in many cases.

WASTE—Usually a tangled mass of threads or other forms of fabric used in cleaning machinery of oil and dirt. Usually comes in bales as refuse from some textile mills although some is produced just as waste. The use of cleaning cloths replaces waste in many places, these cloths being secured as cheaply as possible.

WATCH AND INSTRUMENT THREADS—See *Screw Threads, Watch and Instrument*.

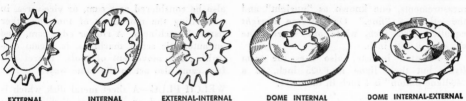

| EXTERNAL | INTERNAL | EXTERNAL-INTERNAL | DOME INTERNAL | DOME INTERNAL-EXTERNAL |

INTERNAL AND EXTERNAL TEETH—Teeth embed in face of work and bolt. External-tooth type is more generally used; internal-tooth type is used where smooth outer edge is desired and for other specific applications

WIDE BEARING—For use in place of flat washers but with added feature of automatic compensation for wear or developed looseness. Particularly suitable for use on materials subject to shrinkage, also for wide clearance holes. Tempered surface acts as thrust bearing

KANTLINK—Non-entangling spring lock washer suitable for applications similar to Knolink type. Angle-cut ends tend to embed more deeply and engage nut face and bolted surface

KNOLINK—Non-entangling spring lock washer suitable for general use and application on all types of automotive, farm implement, electrical, stove or industrial equipment

WOOD SPRING—For such as wood, rubber, plastics, fiber compositions or soft thin sheet metal. Anchor end embeds in surface and turned-up end engages nut, screw or bolt face

RIBBED TYPE "C"—Rib on inner periphery under compression wedges itself into the bolt thread and nut chamfer while introducing reactive pressure and tension in its assembly

HY-PRESSURE HY-CROME—Has superior strength and provides superior reactive values for each bolt size

POSITIVE TYPE "D"—Barbs on ends under compression embed themselves in face of nut, screw or bolt, and bolted surface, providing resistance to back turning

NONLINE POSITIVE—Non-entangling spring lock washer combining features of Kantlink and Positive types for use when these special features are needed

SPRINGLOX—Permits use of thinner, more resilient steel sections while providing reactive tension. Also, does not dig in or serrate bolted surface; for aeronautical purposes

ROUND EDGE HY-CROME—Special alloy-steel spring washer made to specification for each bolt size. Rounded edges avoid heat cracks. For high-quality products

LOCK WASHERS.

WATCH JEWEL—A hard stone used as a pivot bearing in watches or other instruments to reduce friction and wear. Usually made of ruby, sapphire or garnet, or of synthetic stones.

WATCH SCREW THREADS—See *Screw Threads, Watch.*

WATCH SIZES—Watch size is measured across the center of the shortest portion of the pillar plate. A 10-ligne Swiss movement is 10/12 of a *Paris* inch or 0.888 U. S. inch. American watches are measured by a system originated by Aaron L. Dennison, of the Waltham Watch Co., in 1850. The base size is Zero or 0 and is 35/30 of a U. S. inch. Larger sizes take full numbers, such as 1, 2, 3. Smaller sizes are designated by 2/0 to 6/0, each varying by 1/30 inch. A 12-size pocket watch would be 35/30 plus 12/30, or 47/30, or 1.566 inch.

WATCH, STOP—A watch that can be started and stopped at the beginning and end of an operation or other period.

WATCHMAKERS' MEASUREMENTS—Among measurements used by watchmakers are:

One douzieme—0.0074 inch, or 1/12 of a ligne;

One ligne—0.0888 inch, or 2.256 millimeters. The Elgin Watch Co., had two angular measurements, one known as "upright" and the other as "fine." One degree *upright* equalled 0.002 inch, while one degree *fine* equalled 0.0004 inch.

The button industry also uses the term *ligne,* but their ligne is 0.025 inch, so a "40-ligne button" is 1 inch in diameter.

WATER ANNEAL—See *Annealing, Water.*

WATER GLASS— A soluble silicate of sodium, also called soluble glass. A viscous liquid used for filling the porosity of many materials. It fills the pores in egg shells and preserves the eggs.

WATER RAM—See *Hydraulic Ram.*

WATT—The unit of electrical power. Volts, or pressure, multiplied by amperes, or quantity, equals watts; 746 watts equal one mechanical horse power.

WAVE BANDS—See *Light Wave Bands.*

WAYS—In machinery, the guides which keep moving parts in line. On machine tools the ways are usually inverted V's, although this is not necessary. Some use one V way and one flat way.

WAY DRILLING MACHINE—See *Drilling Machine, Way.*

WEAR LIMIT—The maximum amount which a part should be permitted to wear before being repaired or replaced. Wear limits are usually set by the designers or engineers to prevent failures of mechanism from too great wear. Motive power of railways and of important machines have wear limits set to show when they should be overhauled.

WEAR RESISTING STEELS—Steels especially designed to present hard wearing surfaces.

WEB—A thin section of a casting or forging which connects other portions. In an I-beam, the web connects the top and bottom, or the heads of the beam. The term is also used in some other connections of a similar nature.

WEB BELT—See *Belt, Web.*

WEDGE—In its simplest form a wedge is a flat piece which is thicker at one end than the other. A cold chisel point is a wedge which forces metal chips away from the body of metal by its wedge action. Wedges are also driven between two members to force them apart, or to raise heavy weights. A wedge may

also be considered as a cam, or vice-versa, in controlling the movement of tools or other parts of machinery. A rim or edge cam, used on automatic screw machines, is a cam controlling the movement of tools. Barrel and face cams also act in the same way.

WELCH PLUG—A sheet metal disk which is slightly cupped or dished, so that, when in place, a blow in the center expands it into the recessed hole. It is seated on a shelf or projection left by a counter bore. Largely used in automobile engine work for closing holes to which no connecting piece is attached.

WELD—A joint made by fusing two metal parts together. As generally used, the metals themselves are united by heat and pressure. In gas and electric welding other metals are used, as in soldering. There welding rods are selected both for their strength and their ability to unite the two parts by fusing between them. In resistance welding, formerly called incandescent welding, an electric current heats the adjoining surfaces which fuse together under pressure.

WELD, BUTT—Welding two pieces end to end without overlap.

WELD, LAP—Welding two pieces with one lapping over the other. The overlapping ends are usually beveled.

WELD METAL—Metal used in joining two parts by the welding process. In electric and gas welding these are usually known as weld rods, being prepared to give good welds of different materials.

WELDED ARC JOINTS, TYPES OF—Sixteen of the methods used in making welded joints with the electric arc are described and illustrated on page 488.

WELDERY—A department of shop in which autogenous welding is done. This includes oxy-acetylene and electric welding, of both the arc and resistance type. The latter includes spot welding, shot welding and seam welding by any modern method.

WELDING, ARC—The fusion of metals by an electric arc drawn between the metal and an electrode. With a carbon electrode, the weld is made by melting suitable metal wire or rod between the carbon and the metal to be welded. With a metallic electrode, the electrode itself is melted and welds to the metal to be welded.

WELDING, COLD PRESSURE—A method developed by the General Electric Co. of England of welding non-ferrous metals by pressure at room temperature, and used on aluminum, duralimin, copper, lead, nickel, silver and zinc. The surfaces must be free from any film of oxide. The metal is made to flow away from the welding point, as two surfaces of a special plier shaped tool force the parts together. The pressure can be steady or by impact. Straight welds, ring welds and continuous seam welding have been done.

WELDING, FLASH—The joining of metals by welding, by forcing contact between the metals and applying electric current. This draws an arc between the opposing edges and makes a flash. It differs from arc welding, which draws the arc between an electrode and the work.

WELDING, OXIDIZING FLAME—A flame with an excess of oxygen, which produces a very blue flame. Not good for brazing or welding and is to be avoided.

WELDING POSITIONER—A table or frame for holding, in any desired position, work to be welded.

WELDING, PROJECTION—A method in which parts to be joined have slight projections from the normal surface, which contact each other and weld more easily than where the entire surface is joined by welding.

WELDING, REDUCING FLAME—A low temperature flame with the air in excess of the oxygen. Good for brazing, but not for welding.

WELDING RODS—Rods used in welding by torch or electric arc. The composition is

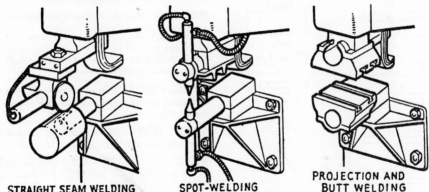

STRAIGHT SEAM WELDING   SPOT-WELDING   PROJECTION AND BUTT WELDING

Welding. Showing how, with a few minor changes, a standard welder can handle a variety of jobs.

WELDING, FUSION—The union of two pieces of metal by heat and pressure, but without hammering. Resistance or incandescent welding is fusion welding.

WELDING MACHINES—Mechanisms in which electric welds of different kinds are made—three types are shown above.

WELDING, NEUTRAL FLAME—In oxy-acetylene welding, an equal amount of each gas. In oxy-hydrogen welding, the volume of hydrogen should be about twice that of the oxygen. A neutral flame is considered best for all welding.

varied to suit the requirements of different welds.

WELDING SCREW—See *Screw, Welding.*

WELDING, SEAM—Welding two edges together in the same plane, as in illustration.

WELDING, SHIELDED ARC—Enveloping the arc with an inert gas, such as helium, which prevents contact with the air. This prevents oxidization of the metal at the weld. Welds made with a shielded arc are much stronger than those made wthout it.

487

WELDING, SHOT—An electric process, patented by the Budd Co., whereby a welding current is "shot" through the sheets in contact at frequent intervals, which can be varied, welding the sheets at these points. It can be a practically continuous seam. It is generally confined to thin metal sheets.

WELDING, SKIP—Welding small portions of a seam and skipping to another point some distance away. This distributes the heat and lessens the distortion due to continuous welding. After the early welds cool the vacant spots are welded.

WELDING, SPOT—Electric welding by current passed through the parts between the contact points when pressure is applied. It is largely used to replace riveting, as each spot is practically a rivet.

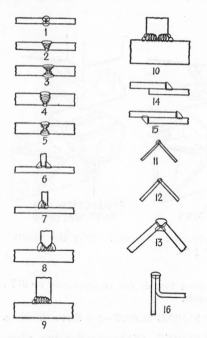

Types of welding joints—butt, corner, lap, and edge joints.

WELDING, STEP-BACK METHOD—A method of welding small portions of a seam instead of making a continuous weld. This distributes the distortion due to heating excessively in one spot. The welds may be made in regular sequence, or in irregular spots. It is practically the same as skip-welding.

WELDING, TYPES OF JOINTS FOR ARC WELDING—Sixteen types of arc welded joints —the practice of a well known concern—are described and illustrated.

WELDMENT—A welded joint or structure.

WELL CASING—Pipe used for lining drilled holes (wells) through which oil or water comes to the surface of the ground. Well casing varies from 4¾ to 24½ inches outside diameter. Over 5¾ inches it uses the standard pipe taper of ¾ inch per foot, with 8 threads per inch. Smaller sizes use ⅜ inch taper per foot, with 10 threads per inch. Threads are of National form but are sometimes rounded top and bottom.

WELT—A strip of metal laid over two pieces that are butted together. It secures an even surface on the pieces to be joined, but requires two rows of rivets, or two welded surfaces, instead of one as in the lap joint.

WET FIRE—See *Reducing Atmosphere.*

WHEEL—A circular device of any material revolving around an axle in its center. It may be solid or have spokes between the hub and rim.

WHEEL CENTER—In railroad terms, the cast or forged wheel which has the tire shrunk on the outside.

WHEEL HUB—The central part of a wheel which fits on the axle.

WHEEL HUB LINER—A flat ring or surface which goes between the hub of a locomotive driving wheel and the side of the driving box or axle bearing.

WHEEL LATHE—A lathe designed for turning locomotive driving or truck wheels. See *Lathe, Wheel.*

WHEEL TREAD—The part of a wheel which bears on the rail or roadway. In locomotives, the tread is tapered or coned, to partially compensate for the distance traveled in going around a curve.

WHEELABRATING — A trade name for a method of cleaning forgings or castings by abrasives which are thrown in contact with the work by centrifugal force instead of by an air blast.

WHET—To sharpen or to remove the fine feather edge from tools after they have been ground. While usually applied to the use of fine oil stones on fine cutting tools, the term is also applied to coarser abrasive hand stones used by farmers in sharpening sickles and scythes. Both the coarse stones and the fine oilstones are sometimes known as "whetstones" in some localities.

WHETSTONE—A type of sand stone or "stick" for sharpening tools. The term is usually applied to those used in sharpening or "whetting" scythes and sickles.

WHITE BRASS—A name sometimes given to bearing metals that do not actually belong in the list of brass products. An S. A. E. specification is 65 parts tin, 28 to 30 parts zinc and the rest copper.

WHITE GOLD—A jeweler's substitute for platinum. A common alloy is 25 to 50 per cent nickel, the rest gold.

WHITE IRON—An iron with a little graphitic carbon mixed with pig iron. It is very hard.

WHITE METALS—A general designation for lead, antimony and tin alloys used for bearings and similar purposes. The same term is applied to low melting alloys for toys and similar products.

WHITE ZINC—A snow white pigment also known as China white. It is an oxide of zinc.

WHITING—Pure white chalk. It is sometimes used as a thin paste and painted over such parts as locomotive connecting rods that have been in service. If cracks exist they usually contain oil which seeps out through the chalk and shows the location of the crack. It is also used in making putty.

WHITWORTH THREAD—See *Thread, Whitworth.*

WICK FEED—The use of a wick of textile material to feed oil to a bearing by capillary attraction. It feeds the oil from below a bearing just as the wick of a lamp feeds oil to the burner. See *Oiling Devices.*

WIDGETS—A name coined by Hanson-Van Winkle and Manning to cover accessories used in the plating and polishing industry. These include such items as aprons, gloves, glue and other things used in this work.

WIGGLER—A shop name for a type of center indicator which has a small pointer or rod that "wiggles" unless the work is correctly centered. See *Indicator.*

WINCH—A device for putting tension on a rope to lift or drag heavy objects. The rope is wrapped around a drum several times to secure the necessary friction but is not usually fastened to the drum, the loose end being pulled out of the way by hand. The drum may be turned by hand or power, usually the latter. It is practically a "capstan," such as is used on board ship for handling the anchor.

WIND—To wrap a wire or rope around a shaft or spool, as in winding a coil spring. The same as "wrap" when used in that way. The term is also used to describe a piece of material that is not straight or flat.

WINDING ENGINE—In mining practice, the engine or motor which hoists the cage from the mine.

WINDLASS—A drum on which the rope or cable is wound, in a hoist of any kind.

WING NUT—A nut with wings or ears for tightening with fingers.

WIPED JOINT—A lead joint in which molten solder is poured on the joint and wiped around it while still hot, by a cloth pad held in the hand. It is a delicate operation, as the temperature must be carefully controlled.

WIPER—Any piece which passes over, or "wipes" across another part. Many machines have felt wipers which clean the bearing surfaces ahead of a moving part. The term is sometimes used in connection with a cam in which the "toe," or high part of the cam, wipes or contacts a stationary piece.

WIPING DIE PLATE—See *Die, Wiping Plate.*

WIRE AND SHEET METAL GAGES—See *Gages, Wire* and *Sheet.*

WIRE CUTTER—Hand tool resembling pliers but having sharp edges for cutting wires. Also used as pliers.

WIRE CUTTER, PARROT BILL—A design of wire cutter in which the cutting edges are at an angle with points of the blades.

WIRE DRAWING—This may refer to the drawing, or pulling, of wire through dies to gives it the desired diameter. The term is also used in connection with steam engines when the valve is nearly closed. In such cases, it is said to be "wire drawn."

WIRE EDGE—Any sharp edge formed on metal corners. Practically another name for a "fin."

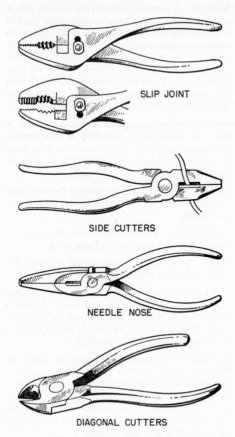

SLIP JOINT

SIDE CUTTERS

NEEDLE NOSE

DIAGONAL CUTTERS

Wire cutters (side cutters).

WIRE GAGE, BIRMINGHAM—A wire gage which is standard in Great Britain for *soft* iron and steel wire. It is known as the English Standard. It is also called Stubs' Iron Wire Gage, and should not be confused with Stubs' *Steel* Wire Gage, in which the sizes are different. Consult the *Tables of Wire Gages,* under *Gages, Wire.*

WIRE GAGES USED IN THE UNITED STATES—See *Gages, Wire* and *Sheet.*

WIRE MEASUREMENT METHODS — Methods involving use of proper diameter wires for measuring pitch diameters of either gearing or screw threads. See *Screw Threads, Measuring with Wire,* and *Gears, Measuring with Wires.*

WIRE TYPE PLUG GAGE—See *Gages, Wire Type Plug.*

WIRE WOUND GRINDING WHEELS—See *Grinding Wheels, Wire Wound.*

WIRES, GEAR MEASURING—Hardened and ground steel wires made in standard diameters for use in checking accuracy of gear teeth. They are made in four sizes: .192, .1728, .168, and .144, for measuring the teeth of gears of different kinds and sizes. See *Gears, Measuring with Wires.*

WIRES, SCREW THREAD — Wires ground accurately to size for measuring screw threads of different pitches and types. See *Measure of different pitches and types. See Screw Threads, Measuring with Wires.*

WIRING DIES—Dies which curl the edge of a metal vessel around a wire. See *Dies, Curling.*

WISHBONE—Any structural piece which resembles the wishbone of a fowl, such as found in many mechanical designs. An example is the forked member formerly used in automobile front end suspensions in connection with the coil springs.

WITNESS MARK—A term used both by surveyors and shop men. It is any mark from which other measurements are made. The surveyor drives a stake or more permanent marker into the ground to show points on property. The shop man makes a punch mark, or circle from which other measurements are taken. Both are witness marks.

WOLFRAM—The original name for tungsten. Recent action by metallurgists adopted tungsten as the correct name. See *Tungsten.*

WOOD SCREW—See *Screw, Wood.*

WOOD TURNING—The shaping of wood in cylindrical shapes, by turning in a lathe, as in pattern making.

WOODRUFF KEY—See *Key, Woodruff.*

WOODRUFF KEYSEAT CUTTER—See under *Milling Cutters, Classification,* page 275.

WOOL, STEEL—Finely shaved steel for use as an abrasive, usually on woodwork.

WORK BENCH—A bench for performing hand operations or for assembling or inspecting work. It usually has a vise and is normally from 33 to 35 inches in height. Now largely made of metal with the top of wood or of metal covered with linoleum or formica.

WORK HARDEN—Some metals acquire added hardness from contact with cutting or forming tools, which is called "work-hardening." In some cases, it is due to a peening action, in others from the pressure of the tool which forces the grains of the metal into closer contact and makes it harder. This work hardening effect sometimes makes it necessary to anneal the metal being worked on between operations. This is particularly true in deep drawing of sheet metal.

WORKING DRAWING—A drawing made to be used in the shop by those working on the part to be made. These drawings vary in different shops. In some they only contain the actual dimensions of the portions affected by that particular operation. In others they show all the dimensions of the finished part. These are usually either blueprints or some type of photographic reproductions. In some shops no drawings are used, but each workman has a sample piece which he is supposed to duplicate, either by measurement or with gages furnished by the shop.

WORKING RANGES OF MACHINE TOOLS—Capacities of different machine tools, as standardized by the National Machine Tool Builders Association, in cooperation with the Society of Automotive Engineers, the Metal Cutting Institute and the American Society of

Mechanical Engineers. The object is to have machines built by different builders have similar capacities for similar designations as to number or size.

WORM—A threaded shaft or bar which meshes with or works in a worm wheel, or gear with teeth cut at the proper angle to fit the theads of the worm wheel. See *Gears, Worm.*

WORM AND WORM GEARING—See *Gears, Worm.*

WORM, ELEMENTS OF—Worms are used in so many types of mechanisms that it is essential to know the names of the different elements, which are illustrated. The difference between the axial pitch and the normal circular pitch should be noted. See *Gearing.*

WORM GEAR—Usually a gear with a concave face to fit the worm which drives it. Sometimes has a flat face with shallow gashes for the threads.

WORM THREAD—A screw thread with a 29-degree angle. It is deeper than the Acme thread, being 0.6866 of the pitch instead of 0.5 as with the Acme. It is used in connection with worm gears.

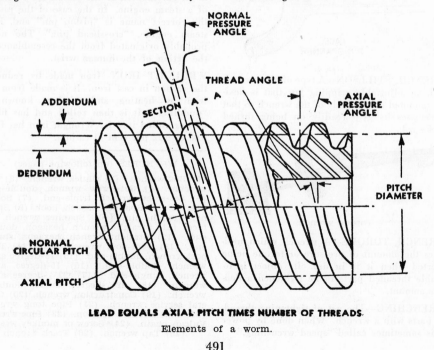

LEAD EQUALS AXIAL PITCH TIMES NUMBER OF THREADS.

Elements of a worm.

WORM WHEELS—Worm wheels can be cut with either a single cutter or a hob, the latter being the better. Frequently a single cutter is used to rough out, or *gash*, the teeth, which are then finished by a hob, as shown. In other cases the hob is tapered on the end and is fed tangentially, beginning with the tapered end, until it is at full depth. In still other cases, the hob is straight and is fed radially into the wheel until it reaches the proper depth.

WRENCH—A tool for turning threaded parts. There are many types, some of which are shown on the following 3 pages.

WRENCH, SPANNER—See illustration.

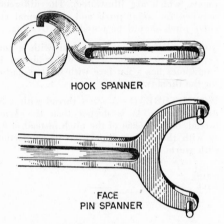

HOOK SPANNER

FACE
PIN SPANNER

WRENCH, STILLSON—A type of pipe wrench with an adjustable gripping jaw that is flexibly mounted on the body of the wrench so that it releases its grip readily on being turned backward.

Torque wrench.

WRENCH, TORQUE—A wrench which indicates the amount of pressure or torque being exerted when it is in use. Its object is to enable threaded parts to be tightened a definite amount.

WRENCHING—The act of tightening threaded parts with a wrench. When done by power it is sometimes called "speed wrenching."

WRENCHING NUT—See *Nut, Wrenching.*

WRING—To twist together, as in plug gages and rings. It frequently happens that the hole and the shaft are so nearly the same size that they cannot be put together except by twisting or "wringing." This is known as a wringing fit.

WRINGING GAGE BLOCKS—Putting the surfaces together so as to exclude air between them. Wipe the gage dry and clean. Then apply a very thin film of oil and grasp gages between thumb and forefinger of each hand. Touch the ends of the gages together. Slide one gage forward over the other in a smooth, parallel motion, exerting a slight pressure while moving gages together. When wrung together properly they will stick together as though they were fastened.

WRINKLE PAINTS—Paints for cast surfaces which do not dry in a smooth surface but present numerous tiny wrinkles which hide little defects in the surfaces of the casting. They serve the same purpose as the "crackle" finish used many years ago.

WRIST PIN—Any pin on which a bearing makes a partial turn, as the pin in the piston of an automobile, or the pin in the crosshead of a steam engine. In the case of the piston, the correct name is "piston pin" and, in a steam engine, "crosshead pin." The name probably originated from the resemblance to the action of the human wrist.

WROUGHT IRON—Iron made by reducing the carbon in cast iron. It is made from pig iron by heating and stirring, known as "puddling." It is then rolled and has fibers of slag rolled into it. Wrought iron has from 0.08 to 0.12 per cent of carbon.

WRENCHES (on following pages).

(1) Box wrench. (2) Chuck wrench. (3) Key wrench. (4) Set-screw wrench, double-end. (5) Set-screw wrench, triple-end. (7) Socket wrench. (8) Spanner wrench, hook. (9) Spanner wrench, pin. (10) Spanner wrench, pin face. (11) Straight wrench, hexagon, double-end. (12) Straight wrench, hexagon, single-end. (13) Tool-post wrench, box. (14) Tool-post wrench, double-end. (15) 15-degree angle wrench, double-end. (16) 15-degree angle wrench, single-end. (17) 22½-degree angle wrench. (18) 22½-degree angle, double-S wrench. (19) Construction wrench. (20) General service wrench. (21) Pipe tong wrench. (22) Pipe wrench, Stillson. (23) Pipe wrench, Vulcan chain. (24) Screw or monkey wrench. (25) Tap wrench. (26) Track wrench.

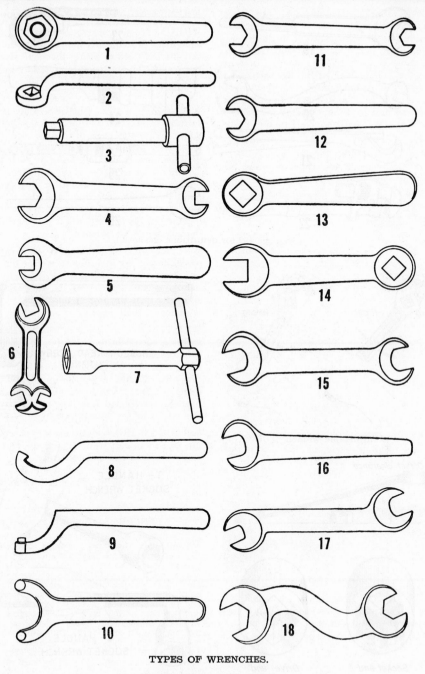

TYPES OF WRENCHES.

(Continued on next page.)

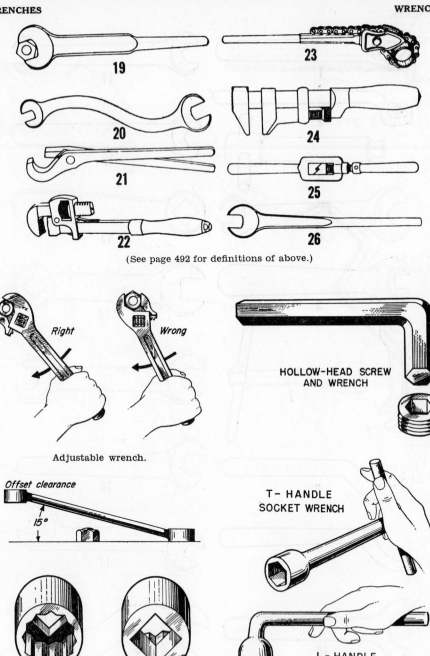

19

23

20

24

21

25

22

26

(See page 492 for definitions of above.)

Right   *Wrong*

Adjustable wrench.

HOLLOW-HEAD SCREW
AND WRENCH

Offset clearance

15°

T- HANDLE
SOCKET WRENCH

Socket end   *Drive end*

SOCKET

L- HANDLE
SOCKET WRENCH

(See next page)

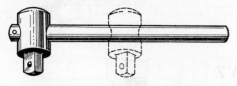

SLIDING OFFSET HANDLE

UNIVERSAL JOINT

SPEED
HANDLE

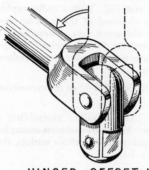

HINGED OFFSET HANDLE

XYZ

X-FRAME — Any structural member in the form of a letter X. Many automobile frames are made in this form.

X-RAY DIFFRACTION—If a beam of X-ray is passed through a crystal the beam will be bent, or redirected, in a series of emergent rays whose separation and intensities are characteristic of the material. With a radiographic film a record is obtained of the location and intensity of the diffracted rays. These form a distinctive pattern or "finger print" of the substance, because no two substances produce identical patterns.

X-RAY SPECTROMETER—See *Spectrometer, X-ray.*

Y-COUPLING — Any coupling resembling a letter Y in shape. The most common examples are in pipe couplings having three outlets, the whole forming a letter Y.

YELLOW BRASS—See *Alloys.*

YELLOW METAL—Same as *Muntz Metal.*

YIELD POINT—The point at which a test speciment begins to yield or stretch. For most uses this represents the real strength of the metal, as further loading stretches or deforms the piece.

YOKE—A connecting piece between two other members of any machine. This connecting piece can be straight or curved to suit the design of the machine. Examples are found in many machine tools, such as the top member of a planer frame, between the side housings.

Z-BARS—Steel angles rolled with a cross-section in the shape of a letter Z.

ZERO, ABSOLUTE—A temperature 273 degrees Centigrade or 460 degrees Fahrenheit below the zero of either thermometer.

ZIGZAG RIVETING—Two or more rows of rivets which do not line up in both directions. The rivets in each succeeding row are opposite the spaces in the next row.

ZINC—A bluish white metal. It is used in electric batteries, but mostly as an alloy with copper, tin and lead. In slab form it is sometimes called spelter. Sp. gr. 7.1. Melts at 787 deg. F.

ZINC CASTINGS—Castings in which zinc is one of the alloys, usually in connection with aluminum and lead. Largely used in die-castings.

ZINC SHEET GAGES—See *Gage, Sheet Zinc.*

ZIRCONIUM—A silver white metal. Used as a de-oxidizing agent in steel and other metals and as an inhibitor in mercury boilers. Sp. gr. 6.4. Melts at about 3,000 deg. F. A comparatively new metal resembling silver, about 75 per cent as heavy as mild steel but more than twice as strong. It becomes stronger with work hardening, when it is much stronger than when annealed. It begins to scale at 900 to 1,000 deg. Fahrenheit., which weakens it. It is being developed by the U. S. Bureau of Mines and has been produced over 97 per cent pure. The impurity is a rare metal known as hafnium, which is very heavy and resembles platinum. Hafnium, like zirconium, is never found in a free state, although it is widely distributed in nature, but is always associated with zirconium. Although closely related to hafnium, zirconium is gaining much more rapidly in technical importance. It is mined in Australia, India and Brazil and is also found in Florida on the east coast. It is a good scavenger for oxygen, nitrogen and sulphur and is used in steel alloys, as well as in some bronzes, making an age-hardening alloy. Also used in enamels, porcelains and glass.